ILLINOIS IN THE ROARING

BY
BILL NUNES

Bill Nunes!

ISBN 0-9710718-9-6

© 2006

Special thanks to Bill Jacobus and Marillyn Watts of Belleville, Harold Zeigler of Granite City, Dan Oberle of Edwardsville, Arleigh Jones of Arcola and my wife, Lorna Nunes

Made in USA by Corley Printing of St. Louis (314) 739-3777 – Distributed by Partners (800) 336-3137

Other books by Bill Nunes (satisfaction guaranteed) still available include:

Sixty-Two Nationally Prominent East St. Louisans – 72 softbound pages, 45 pictures, Originally $9.95, sale price $5.00 plus $2.00 shipping   2001

Illinois Crime – 288 softbound pages about true crime, 600 pictures, 8.5 x 11   2003
Includes full-length, illustrated novel – ***Illinoistown***
Romance, gangsters, cold war intrigue, murder mystery set in 1950 Southern Illinois
Originally $20.95, sale price = $12.00 plus $2.00 shipping

Incredible Illinois – 2004 - An illustrated year-by-year history of the entire state - 296 softbound pages, 8.5 x 11, 700 pictures: covers history, geography, railroads, mines, legends, lore, landmarks, counties, towns, gangsters, KKK, labor violence, inventions, famous firsts, sports, media stars, writers, artists, and much more - originally $20.95, sale price $12.00 plus $2.00 shipping

Southern Illinois: An Illustrated History – Alton to Cairo – 10,000 copies sold, $20.95 – free shipping

Illinois Trivia Illustrated – 4,000 questions and answers, 600 pictures, $12.95 plus $2.00 shipping

Bill Nunes, 3029 Mark Trail, Glen Carbon, Illinois, 62034   (618) 288-5185   bnunesbook@aol.com

TABLE OF CONTENTS

INTRODUCTION

It is an odd twist of fate that I have come to write a number of books that contain material about law-breakers and gangsters. For I am very much a button-down straight arrow, like the church going Brad Logan character in my novel, *Illinoistown*. I don't drink, gamble, smoke or cuss, and have been married to the same woman for 45 years.

I detest those brutal Mafia, wiseguy, and goodfella-type movies and have never watched a single episode of *The Sopranos*. My wife and I saw the first *Godfather* movie, but disdained the sequels. Nor had I seen the Kevin Kostner and Sean Connery version of *The Untouchables* until I started to do research for this book.

I grew up in those halcyon pre-television days, and there were very clear-cut lines between good and evil back then. Hollywood and radio adhered to a strict production code where there was no such thing as an anti-hero, and criminals always ended up either in jail or dead at the end of the melodrama. Many of the old radio shows were morality plays about bad and good. Superman fought for truth, justice and the American way. Everyone knew that meant living a decent life by following the rules, obeying the laws and treating fellow human beings with respect.

Lamont Cranston opened my favorite radio show with the admonition: "The weed of crime bears bitter fruit – the Shadow knows . . ."

My parents never sat down and had heart-to-heart talks with me the way Jim Anderson did with his son Bud on *Father Knows Best*. It wasn't necessary. I went to church with my family and was inculcated three times a week with sermons about doing God's will and Sunday school lessons that taught the Golden Rule.

I was an avid moviegoer and learned even more about right from wrong on the silver screen. Gregory Peck taught me about religious intolerance in *Gentleman's Agreement*. I knew to avoid gangs after seeing Marlon Brando play that motorcycle creep in *The Wild One*. I realized African-Americans weren't getting a fair shake when Jim Crow reigned supreme in *To Kill A Mockingbird*.

Sure, I thought James Dean was "cool" in *Rebel Without A Cause*. But I also figured he was pretty stupid for rebelling and getting tanked merely because his father was henpecked. After all, he lived in a great neighborhood, attended a school that took kids to a planetarium for field trips, wore a cool sport coat to classes, had a great looking girl friend, and drove that classic dark Mercury coupe.

I was absolutely stunned when the cops didn't send that screwy Plato/Sal Mineo character to juvenile hall for shooting those puppies. It didn't take long for my adolescent brain to conclude that these well-dressed, spoiled, middle-class delinquents simply lacked a moral compass.

I am forced to deal with a certain amount of ambivalence when it comes to writing these books. There is a mercurial mixture of pride and melancholy. On one hand, my works simply relate facts and stories that have long been part of the historical past. To paraphrase the New Testament, "The truth will set you free." Yet I have qualms about the perception by some that this material lends a certain

glorification to those who break the law or commit murder. There are those who believe writing about true crime is like selling tickets to see the Romans slaughter the Christians. Okay, it's not as if I were producing a set of collectable cards about serial killers. But neither do I want anyone to admire or emulate the manner and behavior of these Neanderthal psychopaths from a distant era. It bothers me that these gangsters have become quasi-folk heroes.

It is my fervent hope that while readers will look upon these vignettes and my characters in the novel with great interest, they will come away with attitudes and lessons, much as I did when I listened to the heroic deeds of Sky King, Jack Armstrong, and the Lone Ranger.

Author Bill Nunes (wearing **Edwardsville** Tigers T-shirt) with daughter (Laurie) and son (Steve) circa 1982

The good guys in this book are the honest citizens, cops and politicians who fought tirelessly to put the bad guys away. Remember folks, the real hero was Mayor William Dever – **not** Big Bill Thompson; Melvin Purvis – **not** John Dillinger; Eliot Ness – **not** Al Capone.

Despite my extensive grounding in history, the novel is a work of fiction and some liberties have been taken with facts, time, and space regarding *Mike Kriegan And The Capone Wars*. This book is an attempt at self-education; I accept responsibility for any typos, historical inaccuracies or factual errors.

The decade of the Twenties is one that has been neglected by serious historians. They have been conditioned to believe it was a frivolous era in which little happened except economic excess which brought on the Depression. It is my firm belief that they are mistaken, and that this period in our history laid the groundwork for modern America.

Just as the Fifties quietly set the stage for the civil rights revolution of the Sixties, and Reaganomics set the stage for the surge of prosperity of the Nineties, the Twenties became the crucible for social, political and economic change in the Thirties. This raucous period saw a revolt against prevailing Victorian manners and morals. It became the battleground that saw a bitter struggle between the old order and the new.

This **Era of Wonderful Nonsense**, as Westbrook Pegler labeled it, started off with, and ended with, an economic recession. After the Great War, our country suffered a mild downturn in 1920. The stock market crashed in October of 1929, and this marked the beginning of the Great Depression. But sandwiched between were the **Ballyhoo Years**, one of the **wildest, craziest and most prosperous eras in our nation's history**. America was emerging from a long period of glacial fundamentalism, its Ice Age of Puritan orthodoxy. This became an era of frivolity, the age of daring liberated women, fast cars, intrepid aviators, sports heroes, frenzied music, glamorous movie stars, stock market millionaires, and big-time gangsters.

Women kicked up their heels and shrugged off a century of social restrictions. It is little wonder that this frivolous (yet significant) decade has come to be known as the **Roaring Twenties**.

Not a definitive history, this work, like all my others, has been written in a colloquial style without footnotes. In an effort to express my obligations I have listed books that I relied heavily on for certain sections of the non-fiction section in the first half of the book. It is my hope that this informal tome will help the memory of that decade come alive for my audience of readers. Get ready for a fun ride. **This is not a dull, eat-your-spinach history!**

Flapper with Galoshes (Harpers)

ROARING TWENTIES FAMOUS QUOTES

"**You can go farther with a kind word and a gun than with just a kind word.**" – Al Capone

"**Prohibition is better than no liquor at all.**" – Will Rogers

"**Men are God's trees; women are His flowers.**" - author unknown

"**All I ever did was sell beer and whiskey to some of our**

best people . . . some of the leading judges use the stuff." - Al Capone

H.L. Mencken (Library of Congress)

"**If you have the football and eleven guys are after you, if you're smart, you'll run.**" – Red Grange

"**The world would be a safer place if the human race remained in a perpetually drunken state.**" – H.L. Mencken

"**Here was a new generation . . . grown up to find all gods dead, all wars fought, all faiths in man shaken.**" - F. Scott Fitzgerald's *This Side of Paradise*

"**You're doomed! I've told that to at least 14 other men sitting on that stool and they're all dead.**" – Captain John Stege of the Chicago police to get stoolies holding out on him to talk

"**The very fact that the (Prohibition) law is difficult to enforce is the clearest proof of the need of its existence.**" – Congressman Wayne Wheeler

"**If a majority of the people in this country favor repeal of Prohibition, how do you explain the continued presence of a 'dry' Congress?**" – President Herbert Hoover

"**When motherhood becomes the fruit of a deep yearning, not the result of ignorance or accident, its children will become the foundation for a new race.**" – Margaret Sanger

"**Americans are cocksure but bewildered in a world they cannot understand which is new and constantly changing.**" – Historian Arthur M. Schlesinger

"**They tell me you are Wicked and I believe them.**" – Carl Sandburg in a poem about Chicago, his adopted city

"**I wrote, I read. I prowled Chicago's streets and byways . . . I found it then, and I find it now, one of the most vital, unformed, fascinating, horrible, brutal, civilized and beautiful cities in the world.**" – Edna Ferber

"**Let men who are rending the moral fiber of the Republic through contempt for the Prohibition law, because they think it restricts their personal liberty, remember that they breed contempt for all law.**" – President Harding

"Prohibition will be enforced if we stick to it long enough. Ten years is but little time with 100,000 years ahead." – Carrie Catt in 1930

"Day by day the great metropolitan newspapers of the country are dropping poison in the breakfast cups of millions of people." – Superintendent of the Anti Saloon League in reference to newspaper bias against Prohibition

"If you think I did it shoot me." – Al Capone as he handed a gun to the father of the slain prosecutor, William McSwiggin. The man thought Capone was responsible for his son's killing.

Body of William McSwiggin – Chicago Historical Society

"Stick to women; there's no future in bootlegging." – Vice lord Jim Colosimo's advice to Johnny Torrio

"I can whip this bird Capone with my bare fists." – Spike O'Donnell

"My life with Johnny has been one long, unclouded honeymoon." – Johnny Torrio's wife

"Plenty!" – Al Capone's response to *St. Louis Star* reporter Harry Brundige who asked in an interview how many reporters he had on his payroll

"No! The public has one idea of my husband and I have another. I will always love him." – Mae Capone's refusal to a publishing company's offer of $50,000 to write a biography of her life with husband Al at a time when she was broke after he died

"Nobody shot me." - Frank Gusenberg's reply to police when asked who had gunned him down in the St. Valentine's Day Massacre

"I'm wetter than the middle of the Atlantic Ocean." – Mayor Big Bill Thompson, confirming his anti-prohibition stance

"The only man who kills like that is Bugs Moran." - Capone, when asked who he thought was responsible for the St. Valentine's Day massacre in 1928

"The only man who kills like that is Al Capone." – Bugs Moran, when asked who he thought killed his men in the St. Valentine's Day massacre

"I'm going to give Al Capone the hot end of a poker and

preach him out of Chicago." – evangelist Billy Sunday

"I love jazz music because it's got guts and it don't make you slobber." – Al Capone

"We ain't open for business today." – Al Capone, when anyone called his second hand furniture store that he used as a front for illegal activities

"The Beast uses his muscle to peddle rot-gut alcohol and green beer." – Bugs Moran in an interview describing Capone with one of his pet names

"You are famous, like Babe Ruth. We can't help printing things about you, but I'll see the newspaper gives you a square deal." – Colonel Robert McCormick of the *Tribune* to Al Capone

"Many a poor family in Chicago thinks I'm Santa Claus." – Capone to reporters in an effort to bolster his image as a public benefactor

"Harness bulls, dicks, front-office men/ And the high goats upon the bench/ Ain't they all in cahoots?/ Ain't it fifty-fifty down the line?" – Carl Sandburg in a Chicago poem

"A streak of fire, a breath of flame/ Eluding all who reach and clutch;/ A gray ghost thrown into the game/ That rival hands may never touch . . ." - Immortal sportswriter Grantland Rice describing Red Grange on the gridiron

Humorist Will Rogers on stage

"I'm no Italian. I was born in Brooklyn." – Capone to reporters

"The worst crime a child can commit is to eat the raisins dad brought home for fermenting purposes." – humorist Will Rogers

"Judge, that's a beautiful diamond you're wearing. If it's snatched some night, promise me you won't go hunting me. I'm telling you now I'm innocent." – Bugs Moran to Judge Lyle

"We have a new disease in town, it's called Capone amnesia." – Dion O'Banion complaining about potential witnesses fearful about testifying against Capone

"It wouldn't be healthy to bring in a guilty verdict against these guys, Why, I'd have to carry a gun with me the rest of my life." – potential juror to a Chicago judge

"I'll get you for this!" - Schemer Drucci's last words as he grabbed a policeman named Dan Healy who had slapped him. Healy drilled him with four close shots.

Schemer Drucci

"They've hung every-thing on me but the Chicago fire." – Capone to a reporter

"Maybe the law about self-defense is a bit broader than the law books have it." – Al Capone, when reporters asked how he justified killing off his rivals

"To heck with the public. We're at the trough now and it's our turn to feed." – Paul Lundlin, Big Bill Thompson's campaign manager

"All right. I'll have the cops send over squad cars the night before the election and jug all the hoodlums and keep 'em in the cooler until the polls close." – Al Capone in response to Frank Loesch's plea for a safe and sane general election after the raucous "pineapple primary." Civic leader Loesch was a member of the Chicago Crime Commission.

"I'm going to shoot some pheasants." – Mike "Golf Bag" Hunt to a policeman who looked into his golf bag and found a shotgun

"The law does regulate morality." – Congressman Andrew J. Volstead

"Chicago washes her dirty feet in the Michigan sea, and her feet are forever dirty." - Artist Emanuel Carnevali

"Of course I didn't kill him. Why should I? I liked the kid." – Capone to a reporter asking him about Chicago prosecutor William McSwiggin

"That's *the* gun. It's got it over a sawed-off shotgun like the shotgun has it over the automatic." Capone to a reporter expressing his interest in the new Tommy gun

"I wouldn't do that to a yellow dog." - Capone's answer to Hymie Weiss who proposed a peace between the two if Capone would kill two of his own men that Weiss hated

"People don't understand that *I* settled it." – Capone to reporters while trying to take credit for settling a Chicago newspaper strike

"Your Honor, I ask that the epithet be stricken from the record." – Capone's lawyer in the 1930 case of "The People of the State of Illinois v. Alphonse Capone alias Scarface Al Brown," explaining that Capone was sensitive about his disfigurement

"I'm known all over the world as a millionaire gorilla." - Al Capone, lamenting his reputation to reporters

"I fix the price of beer in this town." – *Tribune* reporter Jake Lingle bragging about how payoff costs by the Capone mob were figured into the price of a barrel of beer

"Women have a special kind of sympathy for gangsters. If you don't understand why, consult with Dr. Freud." – Eleanor Patterson of the *Washington Herald*, after interviewing Capone

"I'm in the undertaking business." – Mobster Frankie Uale, aka Frankie Yale

"Just call me Snorky." – Capone to George Jessel, when introduced to one of the stars of *The Jazz Singer*

"I'm not going into the literary business." – Capone to reporters as he explained how he had turned down a two million dollar offer to write his memoirs

"Oh, they're only trying to scare me." - Capone to journalist Cornelius Vanderbilt Jr. shortly before his trial for tax evasion

"Bottles" Capone

"It's impossible to talk to Capone without conceding that he has that intangible attribute known as personality, or, as we say in the world of sport, color." – Writer Damon Runyon after interviewing Capone

"I would not wish to a dog or to a snake . . . to suffer what I have had to suffer for things that I am not guilty of." - Bartolomeo Vanzetti

"If it had not been for this thing I might have lived out my life among scorning men . . . an unknown, a failure.

4

This is our career, our triumph. The taking of our lives . . . . Never in our full life could we hope to do such work for tolerance, for justice, for man's understanding of man, as now we do by . . . the taking of our lives." – Nicola Sacco

"I got this wound while serving with the Lost Battalion during the Great War in France." – Capone, lying to his friends about how he got the scars on his neck and cheeks

Johnny Torrio

"Watch the morgue, they'll show up there." – Capone's answer to a bunch of reporters who wanted to know who tried to gun him down in front of the Hawthorne Inn in 1926

"The difference between guilt and innocence in any court is who gets to the judge first with the most." – Murray Humphreys, Capone's successor

"We've got to stop this Old World custom of greeting each other with a kiss. After all, we stick out like a sore thumb in restaurants." – Lucky Luciano after wiping out all the old line mafiosi and emerging as the new kingpin

"Let Johnny Torrio make the stuff. I'll steal what I want of it." – Dion O'Banion, talking about his intent to start what became known as Chicago's Beer War in the early 1920s

"Remember now, I want this man Capone in jail." – Treasury Secretary Andrew Mellon who was the head of the IRS and the Prohibition Bureau.

"Why don't you order a suit with some stripes on it?" – Capone associate Frankie Rio, as he watched his boss being fitted for two new linen suits, shortly after Capone's trial for tax evasion had begun

"I'm telling you, the fix is in." - Capone to his cellmate in Atlanta, mistakenly thinking he had paid off the right people to keep from going to Alcatraz

"FIFTY-THREE CRATES OF FURNITURE FROM ATLANTA RECEIVED IN GOOD CONDITION, INSTALLED NO BREAKAGE" – Coded telegram sent by the warden of Alcatraz to Attorney General Cummings letting him know that Capone and the others were behind bars at Alcatraz

"Betting on horses is a social good. It enables people who lead humdrum lives of poverty or hold grinding jobs working six days a week a little hope that good fortune will come their way." – Moe Annenberg, publisher of the Daily Racing Form

"You never get no back talk from a corpse." – Frank Capone

"Chicago ain't ready for reform." – Chicago alderman and tavern owner Paddy Bauler

"He was a good guy. The idea that he (Capone) founded a syndicate of evil is a lot of hornswoggle." – author Nelson Algren

"America is the first country in history to go to the poorhouse in an automobile." – Cowboy-philosopher Will Rogers commenting on the advent of the great Depression

FAMOUS PERSONALITIES OF THE TWENTIES

Fred Allen – Radio genius who comically feuded with Jack Benny on the air for years; invented new comedy by poking fun at his show's sponsors; became interested in comedy after finding a book on its history in his father's bookbinding shop and reading it; started out in vaudeville as a juggler and comedian; married Portland Hoffa who became his radio co-star; boisterous southern senator Claghorn was a memorable character on his comedy skits, many of which he wrote himself.

Amos n' Andy – By far the era's most popular radio show, broadcast six times a week; fifteen minute program about black people featured Charles Correll and Freeman Gosden, two Chicago white guys; the adventures of the pair who owned the Fresh-Air Taxicab company in Chicago entertained listeners with raucous and stereotypical humor; Amos was usually the innocent victim of Andy's madcap schemes and antics.

Little Orphan Annie

Little Orphan Annie – This serious strip about a redheaded orphan girl first began in 1924; cast included her mentor, Daddy Warbucks, her dog Sandy, and her protector, Punjab; drawn by Harold Gray of **Kankakee**

Roscoe "Fatty" Arbuckle – One of nine children, weighed 16 pounds at birth in 1887; one of the Keystone Kops, a funny, inept group of law enforcement officers in the movies; did some directing and formed partnership with Joseph Schenck; it was Arbuckle who discovered and signed Buster Keaton; at the peak of his career he was earning $5,000 a week; a wild, bacchanal party in San Francisco resulted in the death of actress Virginia Rappe; coroner concluded it was from peritonitis, caused by a ruptured bladder as a result of boisterous sex with the 350 pound Arbuckle; after three trials he beat the manslaughter rap, but the public never forgave him and his acting career was finished; did some directing under the pseudonym William Goodrich; he died in 1933 from a heart attack at age 46, at his pinnacle, second only to Charlie Chaplin as a comedy star; films include: *Gasoline Gus, Traveling Salesman, Dollar A Year Man, Brewster's Millions, Life of the Party*

Edwin Armstrong – Radio inventor who had a running feud with Marconi, inventor of the wireless; sold his patents to Westinghouse in 1920 for $335,000; **developed FM radio**; committed **suicide by taking a high dive off one of his radio towers**

Louis Armstrong (1900-1971) – One of the all-time great jazz musicians, he learned to play the coronet while in an orphanage; New Orleans Jazz musician who moved to Chicago at age twenty-two; played in Joe "King" Oliver's band; his "Heebie Jeebies" in 1926 was a big hit song; by 1927 had a band of his own – became known as **America's Goodwill Ambassador**

Artists of the Twenties – Edward Hopper, Max Ernst, Paul Klee, Vassily Kandinsky, Pierre Bonnard, Pablo Picasso, Max Beckmann, Georgia O'Keefe, Salvadore Dali, Kurt Schwitters, Henri Matisse, Joan Miro, Georges Braque,

Agnes Ayers with Rudolph Valentino

George Bellows, John Held Jr., and Thomas Hart Benton
Fred Astaire – Triangular-faced, diminutive hoofer who partnered with his sister Adele to enthrall audiences as a dance team. Their act broke up when she married Lord Charles Cavendish of British nobility and quit the stage. For films of the Thirties, he teamed with the incomparable Ginger Rogers. He and his sister enchanted London in 1923 when they performed the Oom-Pa Trot in "Stop Flirting" at the Shaftesbury Theater.

Lady Astor – Nancy Witcher Astor - American-born woman who became the **first female member of Parliament**. In one famous quarrel with Winston Churchill, she quipped: "If I were your wife I'd put poison in your tea." His reply: "If I were your husband I'd drink it."

Charles Atlas – Named "America's Most Perfectly Developed Man" in 1922 at a physical culture exhibition in Madison Square Garden; real name was Angelos Sicilano

Agnes Ayers – **Carbondale-born, Cobden reared** actress who starred with Rudolph Valentino in *The Sheik*. She made her screen debut with Essanay Studios in 1915 but disappeared from the screen with the advent of talkies. Died of a cerebral hemorrhage in 1940 at the age of 42. Agnes made about 40 movies in the 1920s including *The Son of The Sheik* in 1926 and *The Ten Commandments*.

B

Josephine Baker – The Black Venus; The Black Pearl; Famous Negress who lived in Boxcar Town on the **East St. Louis** riverfront at the time of the famous 1917 race riot that occurred there.

Josephine Baker of East St. Louis

Disillusioned by Jim Crowism, she migrated to Paris and became a **sensation as a dancer at the Folies Bergère**, wearing eye-popping skimpy outfits that left little to the imagination. Her most celebrated outfit was a banana skirt that she began wearing in 1926.

Frederick Banting – Invented insulin to help control diabetes

Tallulah Bankhead – Madcap daughter of an American senator, she was the first actress to have a predominantly female following.

James Barrie – Created the character Peter Pan, a boy who refused to grow into adulthood

John Barrymore – Part of America's most famous theatrical family, Lionel and Ethel were his siblings; heavy drinking ruined his career; known as the **Great Profile**; this matinee-idol starred in *Sherlock Holmes, Dr. Jekyll and Mr. Hyde, The Lotus Eater, Beau Brummel, The Beloved Rogue, Don Juan*

Bruce Barton – Wrote a best-selling book titled *The Man Nobody Knows*. He argued that Jesus was both a popular dinner guest and a businessman. As an executive, he argued, Jesus formed a nucleus of 12 salesmen who went out with an idea and conquered the world.

Clyde Beatty – Diminutive circus impresario and lion tamer born in 1903; appeared in several films in the 1930s and 1940s

Sidney Bechet – (1897-1959) Bechet was born in New Orleans and was the youngest of seven children. His father was a coronetist, but he decided to take up the clarinet at age eight. As a young teen he joined his older brother's band. At the age of twenty he left New Orleans and went to Chicago where he played with many of the leading jazz musicians of the day. He soon joined up with Duke Ellington's orchestra. In 1950 he bought a small estate in Paris and lived in France for the rest of his life.

Max Beckman – Abstract German artist popular in the 1920s. He was associated with the Blue Rider movement that disdained traditionalism. When Hitler came to power Beckman and others like him were labeled degenerates.

Wallace Beery – Lovable rogue character actor with a folksy drawl and a lumpy face; unhappy marriage to Gloria Swanson; starred in *Dynamite Smith, So Big, Robin Hood, The Pony Express, Casey at the Bat, Fireman Save my Child*; Best Actor award for *The Champ* (1931)

Noah Beery – Starred in *Careers* with Billie Dove; also in *The Brute* with Lina Basquette; brother of Wallace Beery

Irving Berlin – America's Minstrel; wrote 1500 songs including "White Christmas," "God Bless America," "Puttin' on the Ritz," "Blue Skies," "Cheek to Cheek," "There's No Business Like Show Business," "Easter Parade," "A Pretty Girl is Like a Melody," "Alexander's Ragtime Band"

Bix Beiderbecke (1903-1931) – Chicago musician born in Davenport, Iowa, and was a self-taught child prodigy. Some claimed **his ear for music was so good he could tell you the pitch of a belch**. He was the first white musician to be admired and copied by black musicians; greatest "white" trumpet player of the twenties; hair parted in the middle was called the Beiderbecke look

Blondie – This comic strip by Chic Young began in 1930 and started with a gold digger who pursued a rich, but naïve playboy, Dagwood Bumstead; it evolved into a family series

Bobbsey Twins – The adventures of these boy and girl twins were written around 1904 by Laura Lee Hope but the cute and lovable pair was still popular reading in the 1920s. The eight-year-old characters, Bert and Nan were actually created by Edward Stratemeyer. He merely used the pseudonym Laura Lee Hope in the belief that children's books would sell better if the public believed the author was a woman.

Betty Boop – Created by Myron Natwick, she made her debut in a Max Fleischer cartoon in 1930; sexy, curvy, short-skirted – known for her "Boop-oop-a-Doop" bit; popularity faded when censorship craze swept the country and she went from sex symbol to housewife; popularity revived in recent years with her image being seen on inexpensive products such as stickers, bookmarks and notepads

Clara Bow – Clara's mother **tried to slit her throat** when she learned her daughter wanted to be an actress. She changed her name from Juanita Hansen and landed a lead part in *The Secret Of The Submarine*; received 45,000 fan letters a month; hurt by thick Brooklyn accent when sound came along; **Hollywood's "It" Girl**; career launched when she sent her picture in

Clara Bow

and won a magazine contest looking for The Most Beautiful Girl in the World; married cowboy movie star Rex Bell in 1931; suffered mental breakdown from the stress of her

earlier career; died in a sanitarium 1965; movies include: *The Adventurous Sex, It, Eve's Lover, Daughters of Pleasure, Wings, Fascinating Youth, The Fleet's In, Dangerous Curves*; made an astounding 15 films in 1925; it was **Clara Bow who made curves on women popular again.**

William Boyd – Prematurely gray when he arrived in Hollywood in 1919; *The Volga Boatman* by Cecil B.

Fanny Brice

DeMille was his first starring role in 1926; other films include *Forty Winks, Triumph, Tarnish, The Midshipman, Eve's Leaves, Wolves of the Air, The Night Flyer*; took 1930s role of Hopalong Cassidy, a cowboy who limped from an old wound; made about 140 films

Fanny Brice – Born Fanny Barach; spotted by Flo Ziegfeld at a burlesque house; portrayed the seven year-old brat named Baby Snooks on radio

Nan Britton – Woman with whom President Harding had an affair while he was a senator and continuing in the White House; wrote all about it in a 1927 book titled *The President's Daughter;* dedicated it to all unwed mothers; Harding's marriage to his wife Florence King was childless; the baby's name was Elizabeth Ann; Florence Harding was spared the agony – she passed away a year after the president died; Will Hays, a former Postmaster General of Harding's cabinet and now the Hollywood censorship czar, vowed the book would never be made into a movie; it would take four decades for Hollywood to throw off the restrictions of the Hays Office

Earl Browder – Ran for president several times on the Communist Party ticket

Buster Brown – Historian Don Markstein says this comic strip first appeared in 1902 and the Brown Shoe Company of St. Louis introduced the shoe at the 1904 World's Fair at St. Louis; Buster's constant companion was his talking dog **Tige**, and the two were constantly getting in trouble; most strips ended with the pair being forced to sit in the corner as punishment and Buster promising not to repeat the offending deed again; Buster Brown haircuts, shoes and suits became part of the popular culture

William Jennings Bryan – Three-time presidential candidate on the Democratic ticket; called the Great Commoner; attended Illinois College in **Jacksonville**; known for his Cross of Gold speech when he supported the idea of bimetallism – gold and silver coinage; prosecuted John Scopes in the 1925 Monkey Trial in Dayton, Tennessee; died five days after trial was over

Frank Buchman – Lutheran minister who led a spirit of religious revival on the eastern college campuses in the 1920s. The plan was for people to meet in groups and confess to each other their problems and temptations. *Buchmanism* was once described as "an approach to religion through an exaggerated emotional appeal with undue emphasis on sex." Mae West and Richard Byrd were adherents. The never married Buchman, who often referred to himself as a "soul surgeon," died of a heart attack in 1951.

Edgar Cayce

Frank Buck – Jungle adventurer, lion tamer; films include *Bring 'Em Back Alive, Wild Cargo, Fang and Claw, Jungle Menace*; Frank Buck Zoo is located in New York

Richard Byrd – American aviator who became popular by being the **first person to fly over the South Pole**, planting the U.S. flag in 1929. He and co-pilot Floyd Bennett had earlier flown over the North Pole in a trimotor Fokker.

C

Eddie Cantor – Starred on Broadway and had his own radio show; starred in the 1928 musical *Making Whoopee* and popularized song of the same name; also in *Kid Boots*; Cantor came up with the phrase "**March of Dimes**" in the campaign against polio; wrote the song "Merrily We Roll Along;" nicknamed "Banjo Eyes"

Harry Carey – Director John Ford called him an Early Star of the Western Sky; classmate in college of future New York mayor Jimmy Walker; married actress Olive Fuller; also did some writing and directing; some of his more than 230 films include: *The Man From Texas, The Night Hawk, Desert Driven; Beyond the Border, The Man From Red Gulch, The 7th Bandit, Satan Town, Cavalier of the West*

Primo Carnera – A big lumbering heavyweight from Italy. Through a succession of fixed fights he managed to become the Champion of the World. He lost the title to Max Baer.

Enrico Caruso – Considered the greatest operatic tenor ever; the first recording star in history; operatic superstar for first two decades of twentieth century; **survived San Francisco quake of 1906** and vowed to never return to that city; many appearances with conductor Arturo Toscanini; made his first record for RCA in 1920; died at Naples in 1921

Irene Castle: Teamed with husband Vernon to make ballroom dancing popular before World War I; Vernon was killed in a World War I airplane training accident. She is credited with **starting the bobbed hair fashion when she cut it short after accidentally burning part of it**.

Willa Cather – Best-selling female novelist of the Twenties, wrote regional farm stories about immigrants living in the Midwest

Edgar Cayce – Home gardener, father of two, Sunday school teacher and spiritualist; he demonstrated an unusual ability to place himself into a self-induced sleep by lying down, closing his eyes, and going into a relaxed state of meditation. He did this on a daily basis and provided with the name and location of anyone in the world he would speak in a clear voice and give answers to any questions asked about that person. His answers were written down by a stenographer and they were categorized into "readings." He founded the Association for Research and Enlightenment in 1931 and his more than 14,000 readings are available for study at the organization's headquarters in Virginia Beach, Virginia.

By the time of his death in 1945 he had written numerous books on self-help and had millions of followers worldwide. Like a modern-day Nostrodamus, he is said to have foreseen the collapse of communism fifty years before it actually happened.

Lon Chaney – Born to deaf mute parents; known as the Man of a Thousand Faces; starred in *Hunchback of Notre Dame* and *Phantom of the Opera, The Monster, All the Brothers Were Valiant, Oliver Twist, Flesh and Blood*; died of lung cancer in 1930; son Lon Chaney Jr. was the Wolfman in 1940s horror films

Coco Chanel

Coco Chanel – French perfume maker who introduced Chanel No. 5 in 1922; it quickly became the world's best-known perfume

Charlie Chaplin – English-American comedian; married Paulette Goddard; starred in *The Kid, The Tramp, The Gold Rush, The Circus*, and later on, *The Great Dictator*; formed United Artists Studio together with D.W. Griffith, Mary Pickford and Douglas Fairbanks; **his unpopular pro Soviet stance sent him to Europe in exile after the war**; film critics have been unkind to Chaplin in recent years, attacking his archaic technique that did not evolve from the single character of the tramp clown; Jackie Cooper played the small boy in *The Kid*.

Ray Chapman – **Baseball's only fatality**; Giants shortstop was hit in skull by a pitch from Cleveland's Carl Mays in a 1920 game.

Maurice Chevalier – Popular Frenchman who was host of the Chase and Sanborn (coffee) Hour – a variety show

Cliquot Club Eskimos – Cliquot Club Ginger Ale decided to boost sales by sponsoring a band of nine men, most of them strumming banjoes while dressed in Alaskan outfits

Ty Cobb – Legendary (and possibly psychotic) Detroit player who stole home an astounding 36 times; known as The Georgia Peach; his .367 lifetime average remains the highest in baseball history; sharpened his spikes to intimidate infielders; known for hating blacks; became wealthy by buying stock in Coca Cola

Jack and Harry Cohn – Founded Columbia pictures in 1924

Vincent "Mad Dog" Coll – Given the nickname because of his reckless use of the gun; once accidentally killed a 5-year-old and several other children in a street shootout in Harlem; his brother killed by Dutch Schultz gang in retaliation for Coll welshing on a $10,000 loan; gunned down in a drug store while answering a decoy phone call

Glenna Collett – The Queen of Golf during the Twenties; suffered a famous upset in 1923 when she lost to Mrs. Caleb Fox, a 60-year-old grandmother

Floyd Collins – Spelunker who was exploring a cave in Cave City, Kentucky, and became trapped by a rock fall; this 1925 story made national daily headlines and the country held its collective breath as workers tried valiantly to rescue him; died after 18 days from exposure; his foot had to be amputated to remove the body

Ronald Colman – Actor who starred in *Dark Angel, Beau Geste, The White Sister, Romola*

Russ Colombo – Popular radio singer who died from a self-inflicted wound in the 1930s after carelessly handling an "unloaded" gun.

Charles Comiskey – The "Old Roman" played baseball back in the 1880s and gained the distinction of being the **first ballplayer to play off the first base bag.** He was the son of a rich contractor-politician and was one of the men who helped found the American League. His 1919 team was the best in either league, but they will forever be remembered in baseball lore as the Black Sox – the team that took money to "throw" the World Series. Comiskey is best remembered for being a rich tightwad and paying his players niggardly salaries. The White Sox, deprived of their star players who were banned for life from baseball, stumbled to oblivion in the 1920s. Comiskey died in 1931, a bitter recluse.

Joyce Compton – From 1925 to 1958 she appeared in an astounding 119 movies, many as a "dumb" blonde. She was a Wampas Baby. The Western Association of Motion Picture Advertisers annually picked the 13 most promising young actresses. She starred in Paramount's *The Wild Party* with Clara Bow and Frederick March.

Floyd Collins tragedy

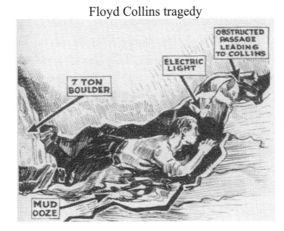

Jackie Coogan – A child star with his parents in vaudeville; spotted on stage by Charlie Chaplin who cast him in *The Kid*; lost his popularity after he grew up; mother and stepfather spent most of the money he earned in movies as child actor; California legislature passed Coogan Act to protect child stars, requiring trust funds to be established for them; **married Betty Grable** in 1937; she divorced him three years later and married Harry James; later starred as uncle Festus on television's The Addams Family

Calvin Coolidge – Republican president from 1923 to 1929 who said: "The business of America is business." A man of few words, he was sometimes referred to as "Silent Cal;" was vacationing in Vermont when told of President Harding's death; sworn in by his father; first came to prominence during the Boston police strike of 1919 when, as Governor, he told Samuel Gompers: "There is no right to strike against the public safety by anybody, anywhere, anytime." A reporter once told him he had made a bet with a colleague that he could get him to say more than two words. He answered tersely - "You lose."

Out of his Vermont bathroom window each morning, where he shaved, he watched a young woman walking up the hill towards the "deaf - and - dumb" school where she worked. When a friend asked Calvin if he knew who she was, he replied, "No, but someday I'm going to marry her. Grace Goodhue had several other suitors and the smart money had the taciturn Coolidge ranked dead last. But in the end Grace fell in love with him and even consented to marriage in 1905 despite vehement opposition from her mother.

Calvin Coolidge

When novelist Irving Stone wrote about Coolidge he called it "A Study in Inertia." He described Coolidge as a "living symbol of Yankee frugality." His mother died when he was twelve and his grandmother had a hand in his rearing. She once forbade him to dance, and for the rest of his life he thought that fun, joy, and sin were three letter synonyms. His hair was a carroty red, his features sharp, his skin pale with big freckles. His voice was a high, twangy, unmusical New England drawl.

Coolidge earned a degree from Amherst and became friends there with Dwight Morrow, the man whose daughter Charles Lindbergh would marry. Instead of practicing law he went into politics, becoming governor of Massachusetts. Thousands of gallons of ink were spilled in his praise after his utterance about the Boston police strike endangering public safety. That single incident drew him enough national fame to secure him the second spot on the 1920 Republican ticket with Harding.

9

As Vice-President, he served as an astute parliamentarian over the Senate. He and his wife accepted invitations to Washington dinners, although he usually sat in curdled silence. A sympathetic woman, sensing his uncomfortableness, asked him why he continued to dine out considering the circumstances. His famous reply: "**Got to eat somewhere!**"

Coolidge was vacationing in Vermont at the time the news of President Harding's death reached him. His father, using an old family bible, performed the swearing in ceremony of the new President by the light of a kerosene lamp.

In some ways Coolidge was similar to President Ronald Reagan. Like Jefferson, they both believed that the government that governs least governs best. Both men napped during White House afternoons. Unlike Reagan, who had a way with words, words with Calvin Coolidge were at a premium. An early biographer claimed that whenever Coolidge opened his mouth to speak, a moth flew out.

Biographer William Allen White lambasted Coolidge in *A Puritan in Babylon* for doing little to stop the stock market speculation of his era.

The Coolidge presidency ended with one final last famous quote. As Republicans were preparing to nominate him for a second full term, he astonished them by declaring, "I do not choose to run for President in 1928." Perhaps he foresaw a few suspicious cracks in the American economy and decided that he didn't want Depression-era shantytowns to be labeled Coolidgevilles.

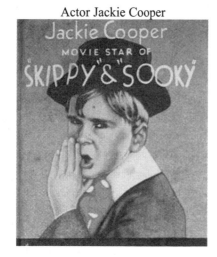

Actor Jackie Cooper

Gary Cooper – Worked as an extra in cowboy westerns for three years with Tom Mix and Richard Dix before being given the lead in *Arizona Bound* (made in Nevada); he once played a Cossack in a Rudolph Valentino film

Jackie Cooper – Child star of late Twenties known for his ability to pout and shed buckets of tears; director got him to cry by making him think that he was going to shoot his dog; only actor nominated as Best Actor or Actress under the age of 18 (*The Champ*); all others so nominated were for supporting roles; was in 15 episodes of *Our Gang*

Emil Coué – Frenchman who smoked about 40 cigarettes a day and wrote a best-seller titled: *Self-Mastery Through Conscious Auto-Suggestion*; "Every day, in every way, I'm getting better and better" was his mantra; one of the best super salesmen of his era, he proved to be quite good at healing hypochondriacs; ran into trouble when he claimed that women who wanted male babies could dictate in advance the sex of their newborn by repeating thirty times a day, "My child will be a boy."

Father Coughlin – Made a startling Detroit radio broadcast in October of 1930. He had been on station WJR for four years but this time he delved into politics instead of religion. He blamed the Depression on international bankers and warned that the Communists were trying to take over our country. Letters of support poured in and his popularity grew. At first he praised F.D.R's New Deal but later became its greatest critic. By 1934 his radio time alone cost $14,000 a week, but enough people sent in dollar bills that there was enough left over for him to invest in silver futures.

Next he took on corrupt labor unions and advocated that the government take over the role of collective bargaining for labor. He urged the abolition of private banking and advocated the formation of a central government bank. In time of war he called for the conscription of wealth as well as men. By 1936 his listeners numbered in the millions. He announced the formation of a new Union Party that would challenge Democrats and Republicans. He claimed to have support from those who adhered to the Townsend Plan. William Lemke was the candidate of the Union Party and Coughlin made the bold prediction that if his candidate didn't win at least nine million votes he would retire from the airwaves. Lemke garnered only about a million votes, and Coughlin receded into oblivion.

Noël Coward – British playwright and lyricist who wrote his first hit, "The Vortex," at the age of 24; considered one of the authentic voices of the Twenties.

Joan Crawford – Actress who created a sensation in *Our Dancing Daughters*, when her character of 'Dangerous Diana' tossed off her frock and Charlestoned to keep a party going. The Charleston was a difficult dance to master for it required performers, with bent knees in opposition, to kick out one leg at right angles while the other ankle twisted in reverse. Joan was also in *Tramp, Tramp, Tramp, West Point, Taxi Dancer, Twelve Miles Out,* and *Sally, Irene and Mary*; Crawford's irresistible vivacity made her a great star for three succeeding decades; F. Scott Fitzgerald called her the perfect example of a flapper; married Douglas Fairbanks Jr. in 1929; MGM disliked her name of Lucille and sponsored a contest to rename her; Norma Shearer was her bitter rival; she had affairs with Spencer Tracy and Clark Gable; divorced Doug Fairbanks Jr. and married Franchot Tone; won Best Actress for *Mildred Pierce* in 1945

Marie Curie

Madame Curie – This Polish-born, Paris-educated woman was the first person to receive two Nobel prizes. She is credited with the discovery of two elements – polonium and radium. Marie Sklodowska married Pierre Curie, a fellow atheist ten years her senior who was in charge of the physics and chemistry lab where she worked at Sorbonne University. They had two daughters, Irene and Eve.

During the course of Marie's research she invented the word "radioactivity." Both Pierre and Marie began to suffer pain, not realizing that the radioactive materials they were working with might have deadly consequences.

Pierre, accustomed to not paying attention to his surroundings, his mind preoccupied with scientific matters, was **run over and killed by a horse-drawn wagon**.

Marie was only 38 at the time of her husband's death and about a year later she began an affair with one of her husband's lab assistants, an act that caused a scandal because he was married.

Marie toured the United States in 1921 and was received by President Harding at the White House. Her physical health started to decline at this point, as she had to have several operations to remove cataracts from her eyes, cloudiness that had been caused by exposure to radiation. She died on July 4th, 1934, from a blood and bone marrow disorder. We now know that radiation exposure causes destruction of red blood cells.

D

Clarence Darrow – Famous Chicago criminal defense attorney who defended Leopold and Loeb in the infamous Bobby Franks murder case; also represented biology teacher John Scopes in the sensational "monkey trial" (Darwin claimed that humans were descended from apes) where William Jennings Bryan was the prosecutor

Marion Davies – Born Marion Douras in 1897 and reared in Brooklyn; actress and longtime friend of William Randolph Hearst; built a $1,750,000 mansion called Ocean House where 32 employees catered to her every whim; shareholder in some of Hearst's publishing enterprises; started dancing in Ziegfield Follies and acted on Broadway at a young age and did films for the Hearst movie company in New York before it moved to Hollywood; developed polio in 1942 and this accounted for an unstable walk

Marion Davies

that many attributed to her drinking habit; died of cancer in 1961; her film career spanned the teens, 1920s, 1930s and 1940s; her forte was comedy and she made about three movies a year during the Twenties; overcame a slight stutter to successfully make the transition from silent to sound films; was very well liked by most people who knew her; sold $1 million worth of her jewelry to help Hearst out of financial difficulties in the late 1930s; established two children's hospitals and a foundation to care for them after she was gone; Marion never married until after the death of

Hearst when she was 54 years old; Hearst's life was later used as the inspiration for the film *Citizen Kane*, a depiction of the American Dream gone sour

Eugene Debs – Pardoned in 1921 by President Harding; the socialist labor leader had been given a 10-year sentence in 1918 for violating provisions of the Espionage Act by speaking out against the war; allowed to run for president (while in jail) in 1920 when the Socialist Party nominated him; drew only 915,302 votes

Lee DeForest – The man generally credited with inventing radio though several others are nearly equally important; invented the three-element vacuum tube; greatly shocked when his invention was used for crass commercial advertising

Jack Dempsey – Heavyweight boxing champ (the Manassa Mauler); **charged with evading the draft** but was acquitted; married to Estelle Taylor, then to Hannah Williams who bore him two daughters; lost his title to Gene Tunney in a storied bout in 1927 that

Jack Dempsey

involved the famous "long count" by the referee. Dempsey knocked Tunney down but the referee gave Tunney five extra seconds before starting the count to ten because he had to direct Dempsey to a neutral corner. Fifty million listened to the "Fight of the Ages" and 100,000 attended the pugilistic fracas. Tunney retired as an undefeated champion in 1928 with a record of 60-1.

John Dewey – Progressive educator and philosopher at the University of Chicago and Columbia; called for reform in the nation's schools. He believed school curriculums should be more varied and interesting and that students should be taught skills that would prepare them for life in a democratic society; wrote *Democracy and Education*

Jack "Legs" Diamond – A busy triggerman in New York; served as a bodyguard for Arnold Rothstein; Kiki Roberts, a Ziegfeld Follies player, was his girlfriend; survived four assassination attempts, but was killed by the Dutch Schultz gang in 1931; wife Alice was the lone mourner at his funeral

George and Gladys Dick – Invented a cure for deadly **scarlet fever** by discovering the streptococcus germ that caused the disease and then developing an antitoxin injection

Marlene Dietrich – German actress who starred in *The Blue Angel* wearing a brief outfit that showed her garters

Dorothy Dix – Wrote a daily syndicated column giving advice to young women and housewives

Richard Dix – Handsome leading man and western star; unlike Tom Mix, easily made transition to talkies; starred in *Quicksands, Sinners in Heaven, The Ten Commandments* (1923), *Nothing But the Truth, Moran of the Marines, Shanghai Bound*

Jimmy Doolittle – In 1925 this navy lieutenant flew a Curtiss R3C-2 and broke the world record by attaining speeds of up to 233 miles per hour. He would achieve more fame in World War II for leading a raid of B-25 Mitchell's on a bombing raid of Tokyo in 1942.

Donald Douglas – Aircraft designer and founder of Douglas Aircraft out in California

Theodore Dreiser – Born in Indiana, worked in Chicago; he was one of those people (such as Vincent Van Gogh) who was never fully appreciated during his lifetime. His songwriter brother, Paul, earned more money by penning "My Gal Sal" and "On The Banks of the Wabash" – the state song of Indiana.

When *Sister Carrie* was published it sold a mere 456 copies, earning him the grand sum of $68.50. Dreiser was well known for his many affairs with younger women. His vivid portrayal of decadent urban life in America made him a hero in the Soviet Union. He foolishly **flirted with communism** and even visited that country where personal liberty was almost nonexistent. He despised and was jealous of Sinclair Lewis. He finally found success with *An American Tragedy*. *The Financier* and *The Titan* were both based on the life of Illinois utilities mogul, Charles Yerkes. Yerkes was the monopoly titan of Chicago's streetcar system.

H.L. Mencken once proclaimed Dreiser **America's greatest writer**. Dreiser is considered the father of naturalism and realism in American literature.

Marie Dressler – Born Marie Koerber in 1871, this large and frumpy woman learned that she could make people laugh at a young age; found her niche by performing vaudeville ditties; by 1892 she had moved on to Broadway and found more success on the

Marie Dressler

stage; became famous for playing Tillie Blobb, a boarding house drudge; starred in the first feature length comedy ever made (*Tillie's Punctured Romance* with Charlie Chaplin, 1914), produced by Mack Sennett; she wrote her memoirs in 1917, thinking her career was over because she was nearly 50; her career was revived in 1929 and she went on to make eight "talkie" movies with co-star, Polly Moran. Marie was sixty years old when she won Best Actress (*Min And Bill*) for playing a boarding house proprietress, opposite Wallace Beery. After that, MGM began billing her as the **World's Greatest Actress**. Marie made her last film in 1934 under the duress of a long bout with cancer.

Of all the films Dressler ever made, she is probably best remembered as *Tugboat Annie*, which was later made into a brief TV series.

Nancy Drew

Nancy Drew – Carolyn Keene created Nancy Drew in 1930. This teenage detective (sixteen years-old) could do anything – brave white-water rapids in a sinking canoe, explore dark caves, or cook a gourmet meal. She was a rich kid, the daughter of a lawyer who lived in River Heights. But she wasn't above getting her hands dirty and mixing with the masses. Nancy Drew solved many a mystery with pluck, determination and quick wits.

Philip Drinker – Invented the **Iron Lung**, a mechanical respirator for people unable to breathe on their own due to an accident or polio; person affected was placed in a long tube with only their head sticking out

Isadora Duncan – Famous dancer who was killed in Nice, France, when her long, flowing scarf tangled in the wheel of an open sports car, **breaking her neck**

Mary Duncan – Well-known New York actress, signed by Fox after starring for three years in the production of "The Shanghai Gesture."

Charles & Frank Duryea – Brothers from **Peoria** credited with building the first practical automobile in the U.S. in 1893 at Springfield, Mass. Frank Duryea won the first automobile race in America, an 1895 Thanksgiving Day race in **Chicago**, beating the German driver, Carl Benz. Benz had created the first motor vehicle in 1886.

E

Jeanne Eagels – Actress who introduced the Sadie Thompson role in *Rain* on Broadway in 1923

Amelia Earhart – Graduated from Hyde Park High School in **Chicago**; one of the first women to obtain a pilot's license, she became the **first woman to fly the Atlantic Ocean**. In 1929 she became the first person to solo round-trip across the U.S. from New York to Los Angeles, then back again to New York. She established a number of speed and altitude records before disappearing during an ill-fated attempt to fly around the world in 1937.

George Eastman – The man who made the word Kodak synonymous with cameras. He developed the trademark name by inventing the word. He knew he wanted a name that began with the letter K because it was his favorite letter of the alphabet. Then he decided if the trademark name began with a K, why not have it end with a K. Next he merely tried inserting various combinations of other letters until he came up with the name Kodak.

He established the Eastman Kodak Company at Rochester, New York, in 1892. More than anyone else, he was responsible for converting photography from a rich man's hobby into something used by everyone. He became a multi-millionaire and donated large sums of money to the Massachusetts Institute of Technology. He suffered from a debilitating spinal disease and **took his own life in 1932**.

Gertrude Ederle – A 20-year-old New Yorker who became the **first woman to swim the 22-mile English Channel**, beating the men's record in the process; given a ticker-tape parade down Broadway; Mayor Jimmy Walker compared her feat to Moses crossing the Red Sea; she had failed in an earlier attempt and this time completed the ex-hausting journey in a little less than 15 hours

Gertrude Ederle

Edward, Prince of Wales – British heir to the throne (Edward VIII) whose tastes in fashion had a huge effect on what American males wore; popularized the **Windsor knot** in men's ties; in the 1930s gave up the throne to marry Wallis Simpson, a divorced American

T. S. Eliot – St. Louis expatriate who wrote the most influential poem of the 1920s, *The Waste Land*; many thought it to be merely a piece of rhythmical grumbling that contained all of the fashionable 'd's – disgust, disen-chantment and disillusionment

Duke Ellington – He and his orchestra opened at the Cotton Club in Harlem in 1927; strange, in that it was a club for black performers attended by whites; composed the classic song, "Mood Indigo;" referred to jazz music as the "jungle sound"

Hiram Evans – Texas dentist who became the Imperial Wizard of the KKK

F

Max Factor – The **Father of the Cosmetics Industry**; prior to his inventing Pan-cake, Hollywood stars were made up in greasepaint, much like vaudeville stars. He was immortalized in Johnny Mercer's song, "Hooray For Hollywood."

Douglas Fairbanks – The swashbuckling hero of the silent screen, famous for dashing, athletic roles such as *The Black Pirate, The Mark of Zorro, Robin Hood, The Three Musketeers, The Thief of Baghdad*. He married Mary Pickford and they lived in a house called Pickfair.

William Faulkner – Southern writer who invented an unpronounceable and unspellable fictional county in Mississippi (Yoknapatawpha) in novels like *The Sound and the Fury*

Albert Fall – Harding's Secretary of the Interior who went to jail for his involvement in the Teapot Dome Scandal. He leased U.S. oil reserves in Teapot Dome, Wyoming, to oil businessmen in return for bribes. He was the **first cabinet officer in history to go to jail**.

Edna Ferber – Probably the most important female novelist of the Twenties with novels like *So Big* and *Showboat*

Ma Ferguson – Rough talking, tough-looking female governor of Texas in the Twenties

W.C. Fields – Comedic great; D.W. Griffith directed him in 1925's *Sally of the Sawdust*. Fields played a carnival juggler and Carol Dempster played his daughter. The two were paired again in 1926 in *That Royle Girl*, also directed by Griffith.

Louis Firpo – "Wild Bull of the Pampas;" Argentine heavyweight champ of South America; fought Jack Dempsey in an impressive bout; Dempsey knocked him down seven times, yet Firpo summoned the strength to knock Dempsey clear out of the ring; Dempsey climbed back into the ring and knocked Firpo out; artist George Bellows, of the Ashcan School of realism, painted the memorable scene of Dempsey being knocked out of the ring

F. Scott Fitzgerald – American writer best known for *The Great Gatsby*, a novel about a rich Long Island gangster who is unlucky at love. He lived in Paris at the height of his fame with his wife Zelda and daughter Scottie; Zelda's mind started to go around 1929 and she ended up in a mental institution; died in 1948 when a fire swept through the sanitarium; Fitzgerald died of a heart attack in 1940. It was Fitzgerald who described the 1920's as the "**greatest, gaudiest spree in history**."

F. Scott Fitzgerald

Alexander Fleming – In 1928 discovered anti-bacterial penicillin in mold

Henry Ford – Automobile maker whose technique of mass producing Model-T Fords made cars affordable for working-class Americans and revolutionized our culture. The Model-T had **three foot pedals**. The one on the left operated forward speeds, the center one was for reverse, and the one on the right was a brake that operated off the transmission. The four-cylinder Model-T was underpowered with a mere 20 horsepower. When the four-cylinder Model-A came out with standard 40 horsepower, old Model-Ts could be bought for $15.00. Ford scorned colors and produced his famous car only in black; he was widely criticized for his anti-Semitic views.

Ford started out paying his assembly line workers the standard wage of $2.00 a day. He soon discovered that sullen and disgruntled workers could hold up an assembly

13

line so he increased wages to $5.00 a day to keep employees happy.

John Ford – The Great Poet of the Western Saga; his first two reel westerns were done without a script, improvising action around a rough scenario worked out between the star and director; *The Iron Horse*, about the building of the first transcontinental railroad, was completed in 1924; *Three Bad Men* (1926) was a story about three chivalrous outlaws; made about 60 silent films

Henry Ford

Gallant Fox – Immortal racehorse of Twenties

Agnes Franey – One of the youngest movie stars of the era, she was signed at age 18 to a contract by Warner Brothers while she was playing in the Ziegfeld production, "Rio Rita."

Sigmund Freud – Vienna doctor who pioneered the study of psychology. Journalists simplified his theories into the basic message that sex was the prime force that motivated human behavior. His books were widely read and his theories were the topic of conversation at dinner parties.

G

Paul Galvin – the man who put radios in automobiles and the **founder of Motorola**. He came up with the name of his company by combining words for motion and radio. During World War II Motorola developed the two-way radio known as the **Walkie-Talkie**. In the 1960s Motorola paved the way by producing beepers and pagers. By 1995 Motorola was Chicago's number one company.

Mahatma Gandhi – Young nationalist leader of India who was released from prison by the British in 1924 after a campaign of civil disobedience

John Gilbert – The highest paid star in Hollywood during the 1920s. He received a salary of $10,000 a week as a result of his success in *The Big Parade*

Greta Garbo – The Sphinx; silent screen Swedish star who became a famous recluse in later life. She starred with John Gilbert in *Flesh and the Devil* and *Anna Karenina*. She was **Adolph Hitler's favorite movie star**.

Marcus Garvey – Jamaica-born African-American who launched a black Zionist "back to Africa" movement that failed. Most of America's 10 million Negroes, as bad as they had it in America, did not want to return to Liberia. Called the "Moses of the Negroes," he preached a message of black pride and self-sufficiency. A man of dark color, he was a racist and **considered light-skinned Negroes inferior**. Garvey wore a fancy uniform and gave himself the title, Provisional President of Africa. His movement collapsed when **he was convicted of mail fraud** for selling stocks in a dubious business scheme, the Black Star steamship line. Sentenced to five years at the penitentiary in Atlanta, Garvey was pardoned by President Coolidge

after two years and he was then deported to Jamaica.

Lou Gehrig – Yankee ballplayer known as the Iron Horse, playing in 2,130 consecutive games; batted cleanup after Ruth in the lineup; part of Murderer's Row, feared Yankee sluggers (Ruth, Bob Meusel, Tony Lazzeri); took himself out of the lineup in May of 1938 because of his ALS illness which came to be known as Lou Gehrig's disease

Floyd Gibbons – Famous Twenties reporter for the Chicago *Tribune* who wore a white patch over one eye

Hoot Gibson – 1892-1962 - Cowboy star, rodeo champion; earned nickname "Hoot" as a delivery boy for Owl Drug Company; was a wrangler for Universal; several bit parts in Harry Carey films; doughy face and snub nose enhanced the many comedic moments in his films; as a silent star he ranked second only to Tom Mix, earning $14,000 a week from Universal Studios. Out of work in the 1950s, he became a casino greeter at Las Vegas; films include: *Hit and Run, Stampede, The Silent Rider, King of the Rodeo, Flaming Frontier, Calgary Stampede, Chip of the Flying U*

Josh Gibson – Popular slugger in the Negro Leagues; is thought to have hit over 900 home runs in his career

Lou Gehrig

Lillian Gish – Her mother, Mary McConnell, married James Gish, a traveling salesman in Ohio. He was a drunkard and a poor breadwinner. Consequently, the family moved a lot because they couldn't pay the rent. Lillian had very little formal education.

Mary was friends with actresses who encouraged her and her daughters to do the same. Young Lillian started acting at the age of five. As a young performer, Lillian often had to lie about her age and dress older because of existing child labor laws. Whatever town they were in, mother sent the girls to some kind of church, which they liked. Any church was better than no church. Fortunately, sister Dorothy and Lillian were best friends.

James Gish deserted the family when they were living in New York. Mary and the two girls moved to **East St. Louis** to live with relatives. Lillian and Dorothy spent about three years of their life attending St. Henry's Catholic school and occasionally working for their mother at the Majestic Kandy Kitchen in East St. Louis. Lillian had thoughts about becoming a nun, but when she shined in a school play, the sisters convinced her to pursue acting as a career.

When Lillian and Dorothy saw their first movie at the Majestic Theater, they were astonished to see a childhood chum, Gladys Smith, on the screen.

When the Majestic Theater and adjacent Kandy Kitchen burned, the Gish family went back to New York where Gladys Smith introduced Lillian to D.W. Griffith who was making films there. Incidentally, Gladys' new screen name was now **Mary Pickford**. Sister Dorothy Gish became a film star in her own right, excelling at light comedy.

Lillian, who never married, is considered by many to be the premier actress of the silent era – **Queen of the Silent Screen**. MGM lost interest in her when Greta Garbo arrived on the scene. Lillian turned to the stage with the advent of talkies. Some of her movies include: *Birth of a Nation, Intolerance, Hearts of the World, Broken Blossoms, Orphans of the Storm, The Scarlet Letter, La Boheme*

Elinor Glyn – The sensational Edwardian English novelist was nearly 60 when she arrived in Hollywood; it was Glyn who taught Rudolph Valentino how to sensuously kiss the palm of a woman's hand rather than the back

Robert Goddard – Became interested in science in 1898 when he read H.G. Wells' *War of the Worlds*; fired the world's first liquid-fueled rocket in 1926; **"Father of Rocket Science"**

Rube Goldberg – Rube Goldberg created cartoon panels that featured wildly complicated devices for accomplishing simple and mundane tasks. The inspiration came from a college professor who taught him about analytical mechanics. The Reuben, a top award for cartooning, is named for him.

Rube Goldberg

Samuel Gompers – Labor leader and head of the American Federation of Labor, a union for skilled craft workers; William Greene replaced him after his death in 1924

Barney Google – Created in 1919 by Billy DeBeck; the strip was only moderately successful until Spark Plug the horse was added; 1923 Billy Rose song further popularized the character with the "goo-goo-googly eyes;" another character in the strip was named Snuffy Smith; Sparky became a popular nickname for kids in the 1920s.

Martha Graham – Student of the Denishawn School of Dance in L.A.; became one of most influential choreographers of 20th century

Red Grange – Grange, the son of a policeman, won 16 letters in four sports at Wheaton High School. Nicknamed the "Wheaton Iceman" (he worked at an ice factory) and the "Galloping Ghost," his exploits against favored Michigan in 1924 as a running back for the University of Illinois (four touchdowns in the first quarter, six in the game) made him the most famous college football player of his time. He had 402 yards running and 64 passing that day. His coach told him he could have had another touchdown if he'd cut right instead of left on another play. He scored 31 touchdowns in 20 games at Illinois; number 77 quit school after Thanksgiving and signed a professional contract in 1925 for $100,000 with the Bears.

Halas barnstormed the country with Grange playing ten games in 19 days, bringing in more than a million dollars at the gate.

Historian Paul Sann asserts that it was Grange who

enabled football to vault over boxing and horse racing as America's favorite during the Golden Age of Sports.

Zane Gray – Premier writer of western novels – *Riders of the Purple Sage*

D.W. Griffith – Famed silent screen movie director; was the **first director to use false eyelashes** in a 1916 film to make a starlet's eyes look bigger on screen

Mary "Texas" Guinan – Raised on a ranch in Waco, Texas; did a few musicals but her brassy voice took her into the nightclub business; owned numerous clubs and speakeasies in New York; greeted customers with "Hello, suckers;" invented the slogan, **"Never give a sucker an even break;"** painted the swastika, an ancient symbol of good luck, on her El Fey Club; this was long before Hitler turned it into a symbol of hate; the thrice-married **"Prohibition Queen"** died in 1933

Andy Gump – Interesting comic strip character notable for his lack of a chin; it was an Everyman comic strip that featured everyday, ordinary people; Sidney Smith's character became the first strip adapted into a radio program in 1931.

H

Walter Hagen – Great golfer and rival of Bobby Jones; won PGA championship in 1921; Gene Sarazen, another great, won two PGA championships in a row.

George Halas – Halas was a three-sport star at Crane High School in Chicago and was voted the **most valuable player for the victorious Illini in the 1919 Rose Bowl**. Halas did not invent football, but it was he who shaped and molded it into a billion dollar business enterprise. He played for and coached a team called the **Decatur Staleys**. In 1920 he joined with a dozen other football enthusiasts (including Jim Thorpe) in a meeting at a Hupmobile showroom in Canton, Ohio, and **helped form the National Football League**. In 1921 Halas bought the Decatur Staleys and moved them to Chicago where they played at Wrigley Field. His team was more rugged than the Cubs so he called them the Bears. His first team earned a net profit of seven dollars, but he changed the game in 1925 by signing Red Grange, the popular University of Illinois star.

Barney Google & Spark Plug

It was Halas who introduced the concept of training camp. It was Halas who forced a rule change that allowed passing anywhere behind the line of scrimmage. It was his Bears that created the concept of "man in motion." It was Halas who pushed for the first NFL rules book.

Hall-Mills Murder – The nation was shocked by the double murder of Reverend Edward Hall and a choir singer, Eleanor Mills in 1922. The bodies were found amidst scattered love letters in an orchard near their homes in New Jersey. The immediate suspects were Eleanor's husband, Hall's wife, and the KKK, who were rumored to have done it to punish them for their immorality. The police bungled the investigation and no one was prosecuted for the crime.

William Randolph Hearst, of the *Daily Mirror*, in an effort to increase circulation, launched a drive to reopen the case in 1926, claiming new evidence had been found.

Jane Gibson, who became known as the "pig woman" because she raised pigs, testified that Mrs. Hall's cousin killed them and that Mrs. Hall had been there to witness the act. The jury decided that the testimony lacked credibility and voted to acquit.

Dashiell Hammet – Writer who perfected the hard-boiled, tough guy detective; creator of Sam Spade; wrote *The Maltese Falcon*; had a love affair with female writer Lillian Hellman

W.C. Handy – "Father of the Blues;" wrote the immortal "St. Louis Blues"

Warren G. Harding – Republican president from Ohio who invented the word "normalcy" to describe America's desire to withdraw from the pressures of international politics and take care of things on the home front. His term, shortened by death (1921-1923) was marked by political scandals and corruption; in *The Strange Death of President*

Harding, Gaston Means proposed a theory that gained currency – Harding was poisoned by his wife because she found out about Nan Britton; Harding had been dogged from the days of his youth by **rumors that he had Negro blood** and was a "bad nigger" trying to pass for white.

In Harding's early career he was a schoolteacher but quit in midyear because the job was too taxing. He drifted to the town of Marion, Ohio, where he purchased the *Star*, a struggling newspaper.

He met his future wife, Florence Kling, at a skating rink. She was five years older than he and a divorcée to boot. Her father, Amos Kling, developed an immediate hatred for Harding and wouldn't speak to him – even after the marriage. Florence went to work at the newspaper office and became the guiding force behind its success.

When Harding began dabbling in politics, one of his speeches was heard by Harry Daugherty, a man of influence in the State Capitol. Daugherty thought Harding talked and looked presidential. Daugherty and Mrs. Harding now became the moving force behind his rise to prominence. Harding lost the race for governor, but later won election to the U.S. Senate. While in the Senate, he began a romantic liaison with a young girl, Nan Britton, who was barely age twenty-one. Harding's record in the U.S. Senate was quite undistinguished.

Frank and Joe Hardy

When the favorites for the 1920 Republican presidential nomination became hopelessly deadlocked, Harding was trotted out as a compromise "darkhorse" candidate and was handed the nomination. He soon lamented that he was "a man of limited talents from a small town. I don't seem to grasp that I am president."

The President's favorite pastime was playing poker with his buddies. It wasn't long until his associates, known as the Ohio Gang, began to defraud the government and enrich themselves. There were bribery and corruption scandals in the Veteran's Department, Attorney General's office, Interior Department, and Navy Department.

Hardy Boys – Edward Stratemeyer conceived the idea in 1926 for Frank and Joe Hardy, two teen boys who solved mysteries a la Nancy Drew. He created plot outlines and then hired ghostwriters such as Leslie McFarlane to complete the stories. Typical titles include: *Footprints Under the Window, The Tower Treasure, The Giant Rat of Sumatra,* and *Secret of the Island Treasure*

William S. Hart – Known as Two-gun Hart; a tall actor and popular movie cowboy during the teens, but popularity faded after 1925

Will Hays – Appointed to head film censorship office ($100,000 a year) by Motion Picture Producers and Directors of America after the Fatty Arbuckle scandal; devised strict morality code for filmmakers; Hays came up with a list of 117 names of people who were to be blacklisted for their questionable conduct in private life; Hays became the guardian of movie decency; morals clauses were inserted into all contracts; language was also

censored by the board and it was only after considerable debate that the word "damn" was left in *Gone With the Wind*.

Helen Hayes – The First Lady of the Stage; starred in *What Every Woman Knows* and *Coquette*; her illustrious career lasted into the 1960s and she had a Broadway theater named in her honor

William Randolph Hearst – (1863-1951) Born in San Francisco, he became a miner and a rancher; became owner of the *San Francisco Examiner* as a result of a gambling debt owed to his father; at his peak he owned 28 newspapers and 18 magazines; a member of the U.S. House of Representatives 1903-1907; Hearst had presidential ambitions that were never achieved; he opposed U.S. entry into World War I and helped to prevent the U.S. from joining the League of Nations; he was pro-Nazi in the 1930s and anti Communist in the 1940s; employed Ambrose Bierce, Jack London, Stephen Crane, Mark Twain, and Richard Harding Davis as reporters; **his sensational, jingoistic "yellow journalism" is thought by many to have launched the Spanish-American War** in 1898; his life inspired the 1941 Orson Welles film, *Citizen Kane*. Hearst teamed with Louis B. Mayer of MGM to intimidate movie theaters and prevent them from showing the film that many critics rate as the best film ever made.

Hearst lived with film star Marion Davies and they threw lavish parties at San Simeon; Hearst is thought by some to have accidentally shot and killed Thomas Ince while Ince was celebrating his birthday aboard Hearst's yacht; according to the story, **Hearst saw Marion Davies kissing Charlie Chaplin and took a shot at him**; the bullet missed but fatally struck Ince; as the story goes, Louella Parsons was on board at the time and witnessed the incident; Hearst bought her silence by giving her a Hollywood gossip column in his newspaper.

Ben Hecht

Hearst disliked minorities and railed against them at every opportunity. Some say his hatred of Mexicans can be traced to his losing 800,000 acres of timberland in Mexico to Pancho Villa. The Hearst castle, on 2,400 acres, took 28 years to build and it has 165 rooms

Ben Hecht – The man who immortalized Chicago journalism with the 1928 stage play, *The Front Page*. He was one of those storied newsmen who never let the facts get in the way of what he thought was a good story. After the success of his hit play he moved to Hollywood and became a screenwriter. His name is on the credits of such notable pictures as *Stagecoach*, *Gunga Din*, *Scarface* and *Wuthering Heights*.

Ernest Hemingway (1899-1961) – Hemingway was born in suburban Chicago and at an early age decided he wanted to be a reporter. After high school graduation he became a cub reporter for the *Kansas City Star*. During World War I he signed up to be an ambulance driver in Italy near the fighting front lines. He was wounded and given a medal by the Italian government. It was this experience that led him to write *A Farewell To Arms*. Hemingway came back to Chicago in 1920 but then left for Europe and established himself as a novelist, writing about expatriates and the "lost generation."

He became interested in bullfighting, deep-sea fishing and hunting big game in Africa. Married four times; he covered the Spanish Civil War in 1936 and **sympathized with the Communists**. He received the Nobel Prize for literature for *The Old Man and the Sea*; committed suicide at an Idaho cabin in 1961

John Hertz – Chicagoan whose name is synonymous with the car rental business. Hertz became part owner of a French car company and when they took in trades he decided to put them on the streets as taxis. He was successful because he charged lower rates than the other companies. It was Hertz who started the practice of having his drivers pick up anybody who flagged them down instead of relying solely on advance phone reservations. His profits remained low because of the many accidents his drivers had. Then he heard about a **University of Chicago study that said the color yellow was the color easiest to see**. He began the Yellow Cab Company in 1915. Another Hertz innovation was the **fare meter**. His next big idea was the concept of **renting cars**. He started the Hertz Drive-ur-Self company in 1924. He became involved in a taxi war with the Checker Cab Company in the mid-1920s. He sold his taxi business to Checker in 1928. Hertz became fascinated with horse racing and was one of the original investors in the Arlington track built in 1928.

Tommy Hitchcock – The man credited with popularizing **polo** as a sport in America; the game was invented by the British in India.

Hedda Hopper – Famous for her attention-grabbing hats; actress who later became a Hollywood gossip columnist

Herbert Hoover – An Iowa farm boy who earned an engineering degree from Stanford; Republican president who won the office by emphasizing America's prosperity. He said that America had come closer to eliminating poverty than humanity had ever reached before. His words were cruel irony after the stock market crash, heralding the beginning of a decade-long depression in the 1930s.

Hoover had a very distinguished record before becoming president – head of Belgian Relief in WW I, U.S. Food Administrator during WW I, Secretary of Commerce under Coolidge

Harry Houdini

Harry Houdini – Escape artist born Ehrich Weiss in 1874 in Wisconsin and learned the trade of a locksmith; started out be doing handcuff tricks; devoted his life to debunking spiritualists, fortune tellers and clairvoyants; died from peritonitis resulting from a burst appendix on Halloween in 1926; he was also a movie star and was the **first pilot to fly a plane in Australia**; his followers hold séances every Halloween to get in touch with him.

Rogers Hornsby – St. Louis Cardinal who batted over .400 three times and led the league with an astounding .424 batting average in 1924, the all-time record. Teammate Jim Bottomly once drove in 12 runs in a single game, also the record. Hornsby led the Cardinals to victory in the 1926 World Series against the mighty Ruth-led Yankees.

Four Horsemen – Named for the Four Horsemen of the Apocalypse – war, famine, pestilence and death – the legendary 1920s Notre Dame backfield consisted of Don Miller, Elmer Leyden, Jim Crowley, and Harry Stuhldreher

Edwin Hubble – Discovered at the Mt. Wilson observatory in Pasadena that clusters of stars were actually galaxies that were not part of the Milky Way; calculated the Andromeda galaxy to be 930,000 light years away; his ideas about an expanding universe led to **Big Bang theory**, the generally accepted notion for the origin of the universe among scientists.

Howard Hughes – (1905-1976) Houston-born aviator and film maker who became the **richest man in the world**; father died when he was only eighteen leaving him the Hughes Tool business that made equipment for drilling oil; father invented a drilling bit that he leased for as much as $30,000 per well; he and his Houston socialite wife Ella moved to Hollywood so he could pursue the movie business; first movie was a flop but the next one, *Two Arabian Nights*, won an Academy Award; his *Hell's Angels*, (starring bit actress Jean Harlow who became a star) a movie about World War I flyers, was the most expensive ($3.8 million) to date (1928); he bought 87 vintage airplanes to

1922 Franklin

make the aforementioned movie. The opening scenes of *The Aviator*, the recent film about Hughes, deal with his frustrations during the production of *Hell's Angels*. In one scene Hughes brags about owning the **world's largest private air force**.

Hughes divorced his wife in 1929 and began dating Katherine Hepburn; also dated Ginger Rogers, Ava Gardner, Lana Turner and Terry Moore; married and divorced actress Jean Peters; became owner of Trans-World Airlines in 1939; built the famous wooden "Spruce Goose" cargo plane in World War II; with a wingspan longer than a football field, it is still the **biggest airplane ever built**; his Hughes Aircraft pioneered many innovations in the aircraft industry; as an aviator Hughes survived numerous crashes and he held every speed record of consequence; bought controlling interest in RKO Pictures in 1948; discovered actress Jane Russell and **invented the half-cup bra for *The Outlaw***; built the Texas Theater in Dallas, the one Lee Harvey Oswald was in when he was arrested for the

shooting of JFK; became a notorious mentally unstable recluse with an aversion to germs in later life. Hughes was not seen publicly or photographed for the last twenty years of his life.

Samuel Insull (Newberry Library)

Langston Hughes – Notable Black poet, writer, discovered by Vachael Lindsay when Hughes left a sheaf of papers at his dinner table and then sheepishly fled; part of the Harlem Renaissance; *Weary Blues* was his first published book of poems; fell in with the radical Left and worked with Communist causes in 1930s

Samuel Insull – Insull started out in 1881 as Thomas Edison's private secretary. He helped Edison create the General Electric Company and then left for Illinois to become president of the Chicago Edison Company. Marshall Field loaned him the money to buy $250,000 worth of company stock. He established practices in the industry that soon became the standard all over the country. In 1907 he created Commonwealth Edison. Next, he bought all of the Chicago area electric streetcar systems. In 1919 he bought the foundering Peoples Gas Company.

Insull **built the first grid system** that allowed excess power to be transferred to other states. He formed holding companies that sold stock; in an eight-month period in 1929 more than doubled their value. Then came the stock market crash in October of 1929 and by 1932 Insull was busted. Insull was blamed by many who lost their shirts speculating on the Bull Market of the 1920s. He fled to Europe, but was extradited from Greece and put on trial. He was acquitted of all charges in 1934 and an annual pension of $21,000 was restored.

Izzy and Moe – Two New York prohibition agents who became nationally famous for their outlandish disguises and vaudevillian antics used in the performance of their duties. They disguised themselves as waiters, middle-aged women, gravediggers, football players and pickle salesmen to gain entrance to speak-easies. They ordered drinks and then arrested those who sold them liquor.

J

Bee Jackson – Said to be the finest solo Charleston dancer in America

Lonnie Johnson – (1899-1970) Pioneering blues and jazz guitarist and banjoist. Born in New Orleans but moved to St. Louis after most of his family died in the 1918 Spanish Flu epidemic. Lived in **East St. Louis** and worked in the factories when music gigs were hard to find. Left for **Chicago** and played with a variety of bands and musicians including Eddie Lang, Louis Armstrong, Duke Ellington, Johnny Dodds and Jimmy Noone. He produced records probably longer than any other blues man.

In 1954 Elvis Presley recorded a Lonnie Johnson cover

song for RCA, "Tomorrow Night," and performed it in a manner similar to his style.

Al Jolson – Born in St. Petersburg, Russia; popular singer-entertainer who starred in the first talking motion picture in 1927, *The Jazz Singer;* his most famous line: "You ain't heard nothing yet," heralded the beginning of "talkies;" Songs include "Mammy," "Toot, Toot Tootsie," "April Showers," "California Here I Come"

Bobby Jones – Amateur golfer who won 13 national championships between 1921 and 1930 with his deadly putter, "Calamity Jane"

Buck Jones – Born Charles Gebhart, he became a champion bronco buster; went into movies and turned into a B-western star with his horse, Silver; died in the infamous Cocoanut Grove fire at Boston in 1942; made over 160 films including: *Whispering Sage, Chain Lightning, Shadow Ranch, Hills of Peril, The War Horse, Black Jack, Blood Will Tell*

Golfer Bobby Jones

Mother Mary Jones – Fiery crusader for rights of the workingman, especially in the coal mines. After losing her husband and children to Yellow Fever, she worked as a Chicago seamstress but was attracted to the labor movement after listening to inspirational speeches at meetings of the Knights of Labor. As she became more active and traveled all over the country rallying strikers, Industrialists referred to her as **"the most dangerous woman in America."** She died in 1930 and is buried in the miner's cemetery at **Mount Olive**, Illinois.

K

Ruby Keeler – Canadian-born with the name Ethel Keeler; Broadway dancer who married Al Jolson in 1928; they divorced in 1940; films include: *42nd Street, Dames, Gold Diggers of 1933, Showgirl in Hollywood, Flirtation Walk, Dames*

KKK – This organization traced its roots back to the Civil War Era and Nathan Bedford Forrest. It died out after the Reconstruction period but was revived in 1915 by William J. Simmons and continued in the Twenties under the leadership of Hiram Evans. Thousands of men paid dues and became Kleagles or Goblins and the elite were called grand Cyclops, grand Dragons, or imperial Wizards. Local organizations were organized into Klaverns. The rules and principles of the Klan were set forth in a book called the Kloran. It had **50,000 members in Chicago**. It was strong enough in 1924 to defeat a resolution at the Democratic National Convention that would have condemned the organization by name. The KKK's national headquarters at this time were in Atlanta.

A silk outfit with complete Klan regalia and pointed hood

might cost anywhere from five to ten dollars. The fiery cross was said to be a symbol of purity and dedication.

The old Klan had focused on intimidating Negroes, but the new **Invisible Empire** broadened to target all minorities, especially Catholics and Jews. The Klan was pro-Bible, pro-religion and pro-patriotic; it was anti-immigrant, anti-prostitution, anti-intellectual, anti-Communist, anti-liberal, and strongly supported Prohibition laws. The Catholic Knights of Columbus was seen as the Klan's main adversary. Native white Protestant supremacy was their banner. The Klan claimed to represent Nordic old-stock (northwestern Europe) Americans. They reached their apex when 40,000 members marched down Pennsylvania Avenue in a 1920s Washington D.C. parade. After a series of scandals, Klan influence greatly diminished after 1928.

The Klan was especially popular in southern Illinois during the Twenties for a variety of reasons. Sociologists claim the Klan had appeal in places such as **Marion** and **Harrisburg** because they were "inhabited by relatively uncultivated and unprosperous native white Protestants."

Another theme advanced by sociologists is that the Klan was a "reactive movement of 'middling' white males seeking to recover racial privilege and reclaim control over rebellious wives and children."

The Klan sought to stem the tide of social change and conservative church groups such as Baptists and Methodists gave them support. In southern Illinois (especially Williamson County), they often clashed with corrupt law enforcement authorities that were perceived to be in league with the bootleggers. They also waged war on the Birger and Shelton gangs.

This populist moral crusade and sense of fraternity was

Buck Jones

attractive to numerous men and women seeking to strengthen traditional values that had come under attack in the freewheeling Twenties.

The Klan of the Twenties was seen to be the Second Klan. The first originated in Pulaski, Tennessee, after the Civil War in opposition to Reconstruction and newly won rights of Negroes as a result of the 13th, 14th, and 15th Amendments to the Constitution. Civil War General Nathan Bedford Forrest played a significant role in the formation of this movement. Their name is derived from the Greek *kuklos*, meaning circle of friends.

The Third Klan emerged at the end of the 1950s with the advent of the Civil Rights Movement.

In recent years Klan influence has waned, giving way to a new group called the Posse Comitatus, popular out west. This organization, founded at Portland in 1969, is anti-government, anti-Jew and pro-White Supremacy.

James Joyce – Author whose Paris-published book *Ulysses*, released in 1922, gained him notoriety both for its revolutionary style and its generous use of hitherto forbidden words. The book was called immoral and banned in many areas.

Krazy Kat – Begun by George Harriman as a cat and mouse (Ignatz) chase in the imaginary county of Kokonino; despite being a favorite of William Randolph Hearst, the strip had difficulty attaining a wide readership

The Katzenjammer Kids – According to archivist Don Markstein, this popular strip dates all the way back to 1897; some consider it, not Richard Outcault's *The Yellow Kid*, to be the first true newspaper comic; Rudolph Dirks created the strip that featured two mischievous German/American kids (Hans and Fritz) pulling pranks on their elders

Buster Keaton – The Great Stone Face; given the nickname "Buster" by Harry Houdini (who knew his parents) after he survived a fall down some stairs at six months; did 15 two-reelers for Fatty Arbuckle and then formed his own production company; made several hundred comedy films over a long career; did numerous dangerous and acrobatic feats without the use of doubles or stunt men; films include: *The Cameraman, The Navigator, The Balloonistic, Daydreams, Sherlock Junior, The Frozen North, Seven Chances, The Three Ages, Steamboat Bill Junior, The General* (his masterpiece)

Alvin "Shipwreck" Kelly – Spent 20,163 hours of his life sitting on top of flagpoles; he started the fad in 1924 when a Hollywood theater hired him to attract crowds; his pole sitting soon became an advertising tool

Joseph Kraft – The man who left Ontario, Canada, in 1904, moved to Chicago and made the word *cheese* a household word. Before Kraft came along, cheese was not a popular food item with American consumers because it was hard to preserve. Kraft learned to better preserve the cheese by placing it in glass jars or by wrapping it in tin foil. In 1916 he **invented a process of pasteurization** that increased its shelf life. He made his fortune during World War I when the government bought millions of pounds from him to feed the soldiers. He **invented Velveeta spread in 1924** and bought the Philadelphia Cream Cheese Company in 1927. In the 1930s he added Miracle Whip salad dressing (**invented in Salem, Illinois**) to the line of products.

Paul de Kruif – Published *Microbe Hunters* in 1926; it still remains the most popular book ever printed about microbiology/bacteriology

L

René Lacoste – French tennis player and fashion guru who introduced the short-sleeve **Polo shirt with a crocodile** emblem on the chest pocket; later became the logo for IZOD

Robert M. LaFollette – Wisconsin governor and U.S. Senator who ran for president on the Progressive ticket in 1924. He is considered one of the five greatest senators of all time. He did much to spread the gospel of reform throughout the nation. He opposed U.S. entry into World War I and he also opposed our joining the League of Nations.

Phar Lap – Australian "wonder horse" that won 37 of his 51 starts. He went to that great equine heaven in the sky in 1932 after winning the rich Aqua Caliente race in California, dying from a mysterious illness that many think was poison from American gangsters.

Ring Lardner – Chicagoan who went from baseball reporter to columnist to short story writer; penned numerous stories with sports themes; wrote "Golden Honeymoon;" his son also became a writer.

John Larson – A Berkeley, California, policeman who developed the first lie detector test in 1921; it used three pens moving on a strip of paper to record blood pressure, heart rate and breathing rate

Albert Lasker – the **"Father of Modern Advertising"** – the man who became the richest advertising mogul in America. The *enfant terrible* of advertising was taught the business by the prestigious Chicago firm of Lord and Thomas. Within 12 years he owned the firm. It was Lasker who first developed the notion that every product could be sold based on a claim that made it superior to rivals. He coined the phrase "Meter Miser" for efficient Frigidare refrigerators. His salesmanship led to the notion that the juice from Florida oranges could be sold as a healthy, delicious drink. His "Keep That Schoolgirl Complexion" helped make Palmolive the best selling bath soap for half a century. Kleenex became the "handkerchief you can throw away." Quaker Puffed Wheat became popular after he told consumers it was "shot from guns." He hooked American women on cigarettes with the catchy slogan, "Reach for a Lucky instead of a sweet." This is considered the **most successful slogan in advertising history**. It was a toothpaste company that sponsored the popular Amos 'n' Andy Show and Lasker scored again with a catchy tune: ♫ "You'll wonder where the yellow went, when you brush your teeth with Pepsodent."

Stan Laurel and Oliver Hardy – Comedic pair whose first film together was *Putting Pants on Phillip;* Hardy's famous chastisement to his squeaky-voiced, weepy-eyed partner in later years would be: "Well, here's another fine mess you've gotten us into."

Gertrude Lawrence – Actress and singer who recorded the hit song, "Someone to Watch Over Me" in 1926; starred in *Oh, Kay* on Broadway; starred in *Candlelight* in 1929 with Leslie Howard

T.E. Lawrence – In 1922 spent his own money to print eight copies of *The Seven Pillars of Wisdom* about his Middle-East exploits during the Great War; Lowell Thomas helped create the legend by producing a film and lecture titled *Lawrence of Arabia*

Leopold and Loeb – The nation was shocked to learn that a couple of suburban Chicago college students had murdered a neighbor lad named Bobby Franks, simply for the thrill of it and to see if they could commit the perfect crime. A lost pair of eyeglasses at the scene of the crime led to their immediate arrest and they quickly confessed.

Their parents hired famed defense lawyer Clarence Darrow to try and save them from hanging. Leopold's millionaire father was president of Fiber Can Company and Loeb's father was vice-president of Sears.

The pair had read and had become fixated on Friedrich Nietzsche's concept of the superior man who possessed an iron will and was unfettered by existing social or moral codes.

Darrow ignored an insanity plea and developed the "glandular defense." He claimed that due to abnormal pituitary, thymus and adrenal glands, the boys lacked normal emotional development and had impulses beyond their control.

The judge, because of their youth and lack of criminal past, gave them life in prison. A fellow prisoner murdered Loeb in 1936; Leopold was paroled in 1958 and died in Puerto Rico in 1971.

Sinclair Lewis: Author of *Main Street* and *Babbitt*; *Main Street* revealed the ugliness of the American small town, the cultural poverty of its life, the tyranny of its mass prejudices; of course the book overlooks the friendly sentiment and easy generosity of the Zeniths and Gopher Prairies of America; conservative George Babbitt was the arch-enemy of the enlightened; *Babbitt* reflected the dissatisfaction of the highbrows with the rule of America by the business man

Author Sinclair Lewis

Charles A. Lindbergh – Known as "Slim," "The Lone Eagle," and "Lucky Lindy." In 1927 he became the first person to fly nonstop from New York to Paris in his monoplane, the *Spirit of St. Louis*. Prior to his flight, six other people died trying to accomplish the feat. He used a periscope to see because his plane lacked a windshield; his only food was five sandwiches and **he had no radio, no parachute, and no fuel gauge**. His incentive was a $25,000 prize offered by a hotel mogul. While others were getting ready to claim the prize, Lindbergh fearlessly took off from Roosevelt Field on Long Island during a sleet storm. His rivals cautiously waited on the ground for a break in the weather.

After he landed in Paris, President Coolidge sent the cruiser *U.S.S. Memphis* to bring him back home. Most thought it should have been a battleship. He was promoted to Colonel and given a ticker-tape parade in New York that cost $16,000 to clean up. He became the most celebrated person of the era; a song and a dance were named for him; He later became an executive for TWA – The Lindbergh Line; married Anne Morrow, the daughter of the U.S. Ambassador to Mexico.

When World War II was on the horizon, Lindbergh became an isolationist and a member of the America First group. The president of Chicago-based Sears and Roebuck, Robert Wood, was also an America Firster, following the advice of George Washington in his farewell address.

Lindbergh was of Swedish descent, his grandfather having first arrived in America in 1860, settling in Minnesota. The original family name was Mansson. His father, who flew with Charles Jr. only once, wanted his son to be a lawyer but the young scion would have none of it. Lindy was interested in flying. After graduation from high school, "Slim" enrolled in a flying school in Lincoln, Nebraska. Within four years he had earned the respect of his colleagues as one of the best fliers in the country, earning extra money by barnstorming. After learning additional skills in the War Department's Air Service, he joined the Missouri National Guard. The senior Lindbergh died of a brain tumor in 1924 while his son was in the Army. Next the young man went to work for Robertson Aircraft, a company that won the government contract to fly mail between St. Louis and Chicago.

When he learned of the $25,000 prize being offered to the first person to solo the Atlantic, he sought sponsorship from the St. Louis *Globe-Democrat*. He practiced for the flight by learning how to stay awake 35 hours at a time.

Although some termed the prospect of soloing the Atlantic a suicide flight, Lindbergh already knew danger. On four separate occasions he had to parachute out of his plane when it ran out of gas or the controls froze. His silver mono-wing, dubbed "The Spirit of St. Louis," was made by the Ryan Aircraft Company of San Diego.

Lindbergh's son was kidnapped for ransom on March 1, 1932. The baby's body was found 72 hours later in a patch of woods near the New Jersey family home. Congress quickly responded with the Lindbergh Law that made it easier for federal agents to get involved in such crimes.

Richard Bruno Hauptmann, a carpenter who maintained innocence, was apprehended several years later and executed for the crime. The wood that was used to build a ladder to gain second story entrance matched the wood in Hauptmann's garage. He was also caught spending the ransom money and more of it was found squirreled away in the garage.

The Lindberghs raised another son and left for England in 1935, hoping to escape the excesses of the American press. Charles and Ann later toured India, Egypt, Germany, France and Italy.

Charles Lindbergh

Lindbergh visited Nazi Germany in 1936 at the invitation of Herman Göring, head of Hitler's Luftwaffe. Germany decorated him with the Order of the Eagle. He was given a tour of German military might and was duly impressed. He was convinced that the combined Allies could not defeat the German Wehrmacht.

Lindbergh returned to America in 1939 and told our leaders to steer clear of any impending conflict because Hitler was too strong and the ocean made us safe from attack. Lindbergh resigned his Army commission in 1941 after F.D.R. called him a Copperhead – synonymous with traitor. Sadly for Lindbergh, copies of his speeches were used by Germany, Italy and Japan for propaganda purposes. As the war came to an end, Lindbergh now devoted his energies to lambasting the U.N.

For further details see *Lindbergh* by Scott Berg, 1998.

Vachel Lindsay – (1879-1930) **Springfield** poet; *The Congo, Abraham Lincoln Walks at Midnight; General William Booth* (Salvation Army) *Enters Heaven*; witnessed the Springfield race riot; considered Springfield's second most famous son; **committed suicide by drinking Lysol** in his Springfield home near the governor's mansion

Walter Lippmann - Writer, author, and observer of the American scene; thought that all those intellectual Americans who dashed to Paris to be free to do what they pleased were spoiled, undisciplined, and ended up being disillusioned with their own rebellion; "What most distinguishes the generation who have approached maturity since the debacle of idealism at the end of the war is not their rebellion against the religion and the moral code of their parents, but their disillusionment with their own rebellion."

Jack London – This famous socialist author of *The Call of the Wild,* who died in 1916, was still popular in the 1920s with such books as *John Barleycorn: Alcoholic memories, The Iron Heel*, and *The Cruise of the Dazzler*

Anita Loos – Wrote *Gentleman Prefer Blondes*; Alice White played Dorothy in the Paramount film version; followed it up with *Gentlemen Marry Brunettes;* a child prodigy, Loos was supplying Biograph Studios with ingenious story ideas at age 15.

Anita Loos

Harold Lloyd – Bespectacled comedian who starred in such films as *Safety Last* in 1923 (where he dangles seven stories up from the hands of a large clock), *For Heaven's Sake, Girl Shy, Hot Water, Dogs of War*, and *The Freshman* in 1925; said to be the only actor who owned every film he made; **lost two fingers in a papier mâché bomb accident**

Guy Lombardo – Bandleader of the Royal Canadians who played extensively in Chicago during the 1920s; became famous for his rendition of **"Auld Lang Syne"** on New Year's Eve.

John Looney – Prohibition era mobster in **Rock Island**, Illinois. This figure was the inspiration for the Tom Hanks/ Paul Newman movie, *The Road to Perdition*. In the 2002 Hollywood version, the name Looney was changed to Rooney.

Born John O'Lowney in 1865 and reared in the Kerry Patch Irish section of **Ottawa** (Illinois), Looney began his career by practicing law, getting involved in local politics, starting a newspaper and dabbling in theater. His father was a drayman (wagon driver) for the Chicago, Rock Island & Pacific Railroad. His mother was a schoolteacher. For a while, John worked as a telegrapher for the Rock Island Railroad. In 1887 Looney took a similar job in **Rock Island**. He was admitted to the bar in 1889, thanks to a Rock Island attorney who loaned him his law books. In 1892 Looney married an **Ottawa** woman who ran a

John Looney

millinery (hat) shop, Nora O'Connor. Looney campaigned as a Democrat for a seat in the state legislature in 1900 but lost. Sadly, his wife Nora died of cancer in 1902. Looney had the odd habit of eating raw liver on toast nearly everyday.

Looney became involved in a storm drain construction fraud scheme and was indicted on charges of bribery, extortion, and libel in 1897. These charges were later dropped.

Looney built an impressive three-story mansion on Watch Tower Bluff and it became the scene of numerous all-night orgies. It had a **secret tunnel** that led from the main living quarters to the carriage house.

Looney soon became the vice lord in the tri-city area. He had his finger in prostitution, gambling, slot machines, dice games, drinking and the protection racket. He was in cahoots with Anthony Billburg, owner of a tavern with the **"longest bar in the world."** Instead of the usual cuspidors, the bar had a metal trough with running water.

He published the *Rock Island News* from 1900-1923 as a rival newspaper of the *Argus*. Looney's newspaper engaged in yellow journalism, printing sensational tabloid news to attract and hold readership. Looney's press was bombed in 1909. He had engaged in a running feud with the town mayor, Harry Schriver. In 1912 Looney's newspaper libeled Schriver and the angry mayor retaliated by having his men administer a beating to Looney who was not a physically imposing man, weighing a mere 130 pounds.

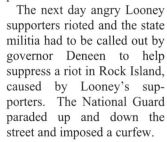

The next day angry Looney supporters rioted and the state militia had to be called out by governor Deneen to help suppress a riot in Rock Island, caused by Looney's supporters. The National Guard paraded up and down the street and imposed a curfew.

Looney subsequently fled to his ranch in New Mexico, and did not return to the tri-city area until 1917. By now other rival groups had gained access to the lucrative vice trade and Looney engaged in an all-out conflict with them. Former lieutenant Anthony Billburg was now an enemy.

With the advent of Prohibition, Looney re-established himself in the gambling, liquor and prostitution rackets. His son and bodyguard, Connor, was killed in 1922 when rivals opened fire on a car in which he was sitting in front of the Sherman Hotel in Rock Island. Several innocent bystanders were wounded in the ensuing battle. Anthony Billburg was given 20 years in jail for plotting the attack, while three of his associates were given 14 years.

Looney was charged with killing saloonkeeper William Gabel in 1925. Gabel grew tired of paying protection money to Looney's men and refused to pony up. A change of venue request was granted and the trial was held in Knox County at **Galesburg**. Looney was so hated that leading citizens of Rock Island amassed a fund of $75,000 to pay for his prosecution. Willis Graham of **Monmouth** was the presiding judge. After six ballots, Looney was found guilty and sent to **Joliet** prison for 14 years. He was released in 1934 at age 68 and kept out of trouble thereafter. Looney died at age 80 in El Paso, Texas, in 1947.

It took many years for the tri-city (later quad city) area to shake its bad image imposed by the machinations of the Looney Gang. Evangelist Billy Sunday visited Rock Island on several occasions and he fought valiant battles against Lucifer with his fiery preaching.

Looney's large stone mansion on 1635 Twentieth Street in Rock Island is still a popular tourist magnet.

The 2002 film, based on a graphic novel (glorified comic book) by Max Collins, is set in the 1930s and is largely fictional.

For further details, see *Rock Island: Yesterday, Today, and Tomorrow* by B.J. Elsner - 1988.

Frank Lowden – Governor of Illinois during the Wilson era; he was one of the favorites to secure the Republican presidential nomination in 1920 but he ultimately lost out to Warren Harding

Lum and Abner – Chester Lauck and Norris Goff attended an audition dressed as Amos and Andy wannabes; when they saw a horde of other potential acts dressed the same way, they ridded themselves of blackface and did an impromptu hillbilly act

Robert and Helen Lynd – Sociologists who published a study of a town in Middle America called *Middletown* (Muncie, Indiana)

Looney Mansion (**Rock Island** Hist. Society)

M

Man o' War – De mostest hoss; famous race horse of the early 1920s. He was nicknamed Big Red and he set numerous track records. He only lost once (by a half a length) in 21 career races. The next best horse of the era was named John P. Grier. Man o' War's grandson was Seabiscuit and he defeated Triple Crown winner War Admiral, his uncle, in a famous 1938 match race.

Ken Maynard – Maynard performed as a stunt rider with Buffalo Bill's Wild West show. He was once a rodeo champion. He entered the films in 1923 and became a major cowboy star. He was especially popular with children, doing tricks on his horse Tarzan. He made the transition to talkies and is generally regarded as **the first "singing cowboy."**

Colonel Robert R. McCormick – This bombastic man started his career as a Chicago alderman. McCormick was the owner of the *Chicago Tribune*, a newspaper that he shaped into one of the great franchises in America. He was a dour conservative of the isolationist mold. Like Big Bill Thompson, he was well known for his diatribes against England and feared that ties to that country might drag America into another world war. He was the last of the journalistic autocrats who believed that a newspaper's role was advocacy, not objectivity. His *Tribune* became a political bible throughout the Midwest. It was his grandfather, Joseph Medill, who brokered the nomination of Lincoln at the 1860 Republican National Convention in Chicago.

Bill McCoy – Florida rumrunner who was said to provide only the best liquor available – hence the term " **the real McCoy;**" others say it comes from a boxer named Kid McCoy; some claim it comes from a Scottish clan leader named MacKay. Lastly, there are those who say the expression comes from an oil drip cup for machines, devised by Elijah McCoy, a Negro, around 1872.

Actor Tim McCoy

Tim McCoy – 1891-1978 – Tim was born in Michigan but honed his riding and western skills on a Wyoming ranch. He started in Hollywood in 1923 as a technical advisor to filmmakers. He soon moved in front of the cameras in a career that lasted from 1926-1940. He reputedly had the **fastest draw in Hollywood**. He could sling hot lead in ¼ of a second. McCoy served as an officer in both world wars.

Graham McNamee – Radio's first sports announcer, working for station WEAF in New York. He did the play-by-play the first World Series carried by radio from the Polo Grounds

Maggie and Jiggs – George McManus created a strip in 1913 for King Features called "Bringing Up Father." It is about a wealthy Irishman (a bricklayer who won the Irish Sweepstakes) named Jiggs and his nagging, social-climbing wife, Maggie. Jigg's friend was a saloonkeeper named **Dinty Moore**, and that name later became attached to a brand of canned foods.

Marx Brothers – Harpo (curly blonde wig, played the harp), Groucho, Chico, Zeppo – starred on stage and in numerous zany movies, including *The Coconuts* in 1926 with songs by Irving Berlin; they also starred in George Kaufman's *Animal Crackers*; Zeppo was married to Barbara who later divorced him and married Frank Sinatra, his fourth wife (Nancy, Ava, Mia, Barbara)

John McCutcheon – Indiana-born political cartoonist; worked for the Chicago *Tribune* from 1903-1946; died in 1949 at **Lake Forest**, Illinois; The Dean of American Cartoonists; won the Pulitzer Prize in 1932 for a cartoon about bank failures

Fibber McGee and Molly – Jim Jordan and Marian Driscoll met and married in **Peoria**, Illinois; started out on a local radio show; NBC gave them their own show in 1935 and it lasted until 1957

Boob McNutt – Rube Goldberg's Sunday-only strip ran through all the Twenties and lasted until 1934. Boob's girlfriend was named Pearl, and he had a rival named Major Gumbo

Sister Aimee Semple McPherson – Famous female evangelist of the era who built a great temple in Los Angeles called the International Temple of the Four-Square Gospel. She married a minister when she was eighteen and after their marriage they did a stint of preaching in **Chicago** and then left for China to do missionary work. Husband Robert Semple died of the "eastern fever" in Hong Kong a month before the birth of their daughter. When Aimee came home she did some more missionary work in Chicago. She soon married again, this time to Robert McPherson, a grocery clerk. After the birth of a son, the marriage ended in bitter divorce.

Aimee took to the sawdust trail and soon discovered that by becoming a skillful showman she had a gift for winning converts. The **thrice wed, once-divorced evangelist** wore a stunning white robe and had colored lights shine on her golden hair as she delivered sermons. Her 5,000-seat Angelus Temple in Los Angeles was complete with an orchestra section and a radio station. Before Aimee's death she had baptized 40,000 people at the Temple.

Billy Mitchell

Her credibility was harmed when she disappeared for 32 days. At first it was thought she had been kidnapped, but when she reappeared unharmed, some thought the evidence suggested she had spent the time with a lover, her radio operator; her 13 hour trek across the desert to escape didn't wash with reporters; she wasn't sunburned or exhausted, and didn't even ask for a drink of water. Aimee said she was kidnapped by three people, two men and a woman named Rose, and taken to Mexico. The trio, she claimed, were planning to ask for a large sum of money in exchange for her return. Aimee's disappearance and return was one of the great stories of the decade.

The public, its passion for scandal inflamed, its appetite for scandalous detail whetted by months of speculation, demanded action. Sister Aimee was charged with obstruction of justice. Tongues wagged. One theory had it that Sister Aimee had disappeared for the purpose of having an abortion. Her 30,000 devoted followers raised a $250,000 "Fight-the-Devil" fund for her defense. At the trial, Sister Aimee testified that she had overheard her kidnappers plotting to capture Mary Pickford. Finally, on January 4, 1927, the district attorney moved to dismiss the case.

Aimee later married (her third) another radio man, Dave Hutton, whom she shortly divorced. Aimee was found dead from a possible overdose of sleeping pills in 1944. Unlike most evangelists of the day who preached hellfire and brimstone, Sister Aimee dispensed love and sunshine.

Margaret Mead – Anthropologist who published *Coming of Age in Samoa*, a 1928 classic study of the influence of culture on personality

Andrew Mellon – Pittsburgh aluminum mogul; considered second only to Alexander Hamilton as the nation's greatest Secretary of the Treasury; created annual budget plan for spending of federal money; Carnegie-Mellon school named for him

H. L. Mencken – Chief cynic and tomtom beater for the revolt of the highbrows; known as the decade's **Great Debunker**; influential acerbic writer for the *Baltimore Sun*; editor of "Smart Set" and "American Mercury" magazines; *The American Language* his major literary achievement; denounced Puritanism, prohibition, patriotism, censorship, the KKK and religious fundamentalism; the "American Mercury" appealed to the intellectual left wing; when he covered the Scopes trial in Dayton, Tennessee, he condescendingly described the natives as yokels, peasants and hillbillies. Mencken scoffed at patriotism, Christianity and morality. It was the acerbic Mencken who coined the term "**boobus Americanus**" to describe provincial, narrow minded U.S. citizens.

Adolph Menjou – Suave and sophisticated film star known for his moustache

Marilyn Miller – Ziegfeld Follies star; Broadway musical star of the Twenties who appeared in three early talkies; married Jack Pickford in 1922, making her the sister-in-law of Mary Pickford; both June Haver (*Look For The Silver Lining*) and Judy Garland portrayed her in films

Florence Mills – Negress who was the beautiful star of several colored revues and sang "I Can't Give You Anything But Love"

William "Billy" Mitchell – Early proponent of air power; demonstrated that an airplane could destroy a battleship by

Tom Mix

sinking the German warship (Ostfriesland) with eight Martin bombers off the Virginia Capes in the Atlantic Ocean (1921); when the navy dirigible *Shenandoah* crashed in 1925, he blamed it on careless actions of superiors; his constant carping led to his court martial; his dream of an independent air force was realized after World War II.

Tom Mix – Cowboy star who had a famous horse named Tony; was a bar-tender and sheriff in Oklahoma; starred with Billie Dove in *Lucky Horseshoes*. King of the Saddle Sagas in 1920s; also in *Tom Mix in Arabia*, *Dick Turpin* (Turpin was a famous English outlaw), *The Best Bad Man, No Man's Gold, Horseman of the Plains*; one of the few cowboy stars who did his own tricks; killed in 1940 car accident

Harriet Monroe – Chicago poet and editor of *Poetry Magazine* who sued the *New York World* for publishing her poem about the 1893 Columbian Exposition (*Columbian Ode*) without giving her credit. Her judgment for $5,000 was the ***first successful suit for copyright infringement in America***. Eastern critics called her magazine "Poetry in Porkopolis." She published works of such noted versesmiths as Vachel Lindsay, Carl Sandburg and Joyce Kilmer.

Colleen Moore – Starred in the 1926 silent movie *Ella Cinders*, based on a popular contemporary comic strip. The title character's name is a play on the word Cinderella. The movie was about a small town girl who won a trip to Hollywood.

Helen Morgan – Torch singer whose trademark was sitting on an upright piano and sobbing about jilted lovers in song; "Can't Help Lovin' Dat Man" and "Why Was I Born?" (from *Showboat*) were her trademark songs; people flocked to her nightclub for her "blues in the night" routine

Helen Morgan (Culver Pictures)

Moon Mullins – Cartoon character created by Frank Willard of **Anna**; Moon, short for Moonshine, was a cigar-smoking, would-be boxer tough guy; Moon resided in Emmy Schmaltz's boarding house; Moon's kid brother was named Kayo; a Milton Bradley Moon Mullins board game came out in 1927.

Arthur Murray – He started out teaching people how to perform the popular dances of the era. He began selling mail order courses with a sixteen-lesson course on dancing. His studios soon dotted the entire national landscape.

Mutt and Jeff – The first successful comic strip to appear as a strip series of panels running left to right; first appeared in 1907 with Bud Fisher being the creator; the two main characters first met in a mental institution; Mutt had a proclivity for playing the horses, Jeff always doing crazy things; today, "Mutt and Jeff" are slang for a tall person being paired with a short one

N

Alla Nazimova – Hollywood sex goddess who invested her life savings to produce *Salome*

Reinhold Niebuhr – Iconoclast pastor, writer, and theologian reared in **Lincoln**, Illinois. He was critical of Protestant churches that were passive and did not preach the social gospel. His *Leaves From The Notebook of a Tamed Cynic* reflects his life in the 1920s. Niebuhr was highly critical of Henry Ford and accused him of trying to buy his way into heaven with his philanthropy.

O

Georgia O'Keefe – Female artist famous for her paintings of large flowers and desert scenes from the Southwest

Joe "King" Oliver – 1885-1938) Oliver was born in Louisiana and went to live in New Orleans as a young boy.

Harriet Monroe

When he was yet a teen he began playing coronet in the high school marching band and then graduated to the cabarets in that town. Oliver left for Chicago in 1918. He had already earned the nickname "King" from his many fans. Leading his Creole Jazz Band, he played the Chicago scene before moving on to New York City.

Eugene O'Neill – Great American dramatist; *Emperor Jones; The Hairy Ape, Anna Christie, Desire Under the Elms, Strange Interlude;* four-time Pulitzer Prize winner; famous for depressing plays about murder, suicide, insanity and death

P

Ruth Page – Chicago ballet dancer and choreographer, a pioneer of ballet in America. She performed at the emperor Hirohito's coronation in 1928. She established the Ruth Page Foundation School of Dance.

Mitchell Palmer – Attorney General under President Wilson; arrested radicals, illegals and communists all over America, reflecting a fear of the Red Menace brought about by the Russian Revolution; many "reds" were shipped back to Russia on a ship called the *Buford*, nicknamed the *Soviet Ark*; S.O.S. was his motto – ship or shoot. **Palmer Raids led to the formation of the ACLU.**

George Papanicolaou – Invented the **pap-smear test** to enable doctors to discover uterine cancer

Dorothy Parker – Writer who belonged to the Algonquin Round Table, an eclectic group of writers who regularly met for lunch at a large round table at New York's Algonquin Hotel (Robert Benchley, Edna Ferber, Robert Sherwood, George S. Kaufman, etc.); the group included almost anybody who could hold his own in invective and come up with a memorable wisecrack every half hour or so; Parker's famous witticism: "**Men seldom make passes at girls who wear glasses.**"

Louella Parsons – Born Louella Dettinger in **Freeport**, Illinois, became drama editor for the **Dixon**, Illinois, *Morning Star*; husband died in 1914 and she began writing her first Hollywood gossip column for the *Chicago Record-Herald*; contracted TB and moved to California for her health; became a columnist for the Hearst chain, eventually appearing in 400 newspapers; wrote last column 1965, died 1972

Minnie Pearl – The Grand Ol' Opery started broadcasting in Nashville in 1925; one of its early stars was Minnie Pearl, the comedienne who told folksy stories about life in Grinders Switch, Tennessee; famous for her hats that still had a price tag hanging from the brim

Henry Perky – This cheerful, dyspeptic man from Denver tried to cure his own indigestion by developing a kind of wheat pudding that was easily digestible. He next invented a machine that converted the wheat into stringy filaments and then folded them into small biscuits. Unfortunately, these biscuits had a short shelf life and turned moldy if not eaten quickly.

One day Perky was visited by Dr. Kellogg who suggested that the problem could be solved by toasting the **shredded wheat biscuits**. Then Dr. Kellogg tried to buy the rights to the cereal but the deal fell through by a disagreement of the smallest of margins.

The new cereal did not go over well at first. People said it was like eating a whisk broom. But Perky soon became a millionaire through clever advertising and public tours of his new factory at Niagara Falls in New York.

Mary Pickford – Original name was Gladys Smith; gained experience working on stage as a child actor; hired by D.W/ Griffith to make movies in New York; convinced Griffith to hire Dorothy and Lillian Gish, her childhood friends; married Douglas Fairbanks. Early silent films stressed the girl-next-door look and Mary Pickford was the embodiment of that image. She made a fortune by hanging on to her pigtails and millions of women followed the fashion trend. Like Shirley Temple, the public never accepted Mary in mature adult roles; known as "**America's Sweetheart**"

Pope Pius XI – Elected Pope by the Cardinals in Rome in 1922; was an outspoken critic of Nazism and Fascism

Popeye – Elzie Segar of **Chester**, Illinois, had been drawing a *Thimble Theater* strip for King Features since 1919. It featured characters Castor Oyl and Ham Gravy. In a 1929 strip they encountered a sailor on a sea voyage. Popeye was a one-eyed sailor with a nautical outfit, a corncob pipe and a tattoo on his massive forearm. Popeye soon replaced Castor Oyl as the main character and became the love interest of Castor's

Popeye

sister, Olive Oyl.

Emily Post – Writer, interior decorator, novelist, and author of America's first book on etiquette in 1921

Charles Post – Before the inventor of flaked cereal came along, a typical breakfast consisted of biscuits, fried salt pork, fried mush and sorghum molasses. In ill health, Post left his Texas ranch and went to Battle Creek, Michigan, to get well at a Seventh Day Adventist sanitarium run by Dr. John Kellogg. He stayed in that town and became a wealthy man by inventing Postum and Grape Nuts cereal.

Post once **tried to produce rainfall by the simultaneous detonation of 150 sticks of dynamite, hoisted by twenty kites above his Texas ranch**.

Dr. Kellogg's brother invented toasted corn flakes and a bitter feud developed between Post and Kellogg who became the Cereal Kings of America; Battle Creek, Michigan, became synonymous with breakfast cereals.

When this author was a youngster in the late 1940s, his favorite cereals were Kellogg's Pep, Kellogg's Corn Soya, and Post's Grape Nuts Flakes.

Kathryn Ray and Earl Carroll

Ezra Pound – Iconoclast poet and critic; concluded that World War I proved Western Civilization was a failure; accused of treason for making Fascist propaganda radio broadcasts for Mussolini during World War II; spent last years of life in a mental institution

Q

Ellery Queen – Mystery writer who gave the detective story a chrome-plated elegance in *The Roman Hat Mystery*

R

Kathryn Ray – Born in 1903 and reared in **East St. Louis**; attended Franklin School. While still in her teens she heard the call of the bright lights of Broadway and left for New York. She tried out for and was accepted into the Ziegfield Follies. She appeared as a dancer in Earl Carroll's "The Vanities." The Gotham sensation soon became known as the "**Modern Venus**." In one show she **appeared nude while sitting on a giant pendulum that swung from one side of the stage to the other**. As Carroll termed it: "The exaltation of the American girl – sans costume, sans silk manufacturer, sans shoemaker – the whole effect being placed on the hairdresser, the pearl manufacturer and the heaven-sent smile."

Mayor Hylan of New York said it was vulgar and called for censorship. Kathryn said it was about the same as seeing a nude statue in an art gallery.

Virginia Ray – Virginia was born in 1902 at **Pulaski**, Illinois, in a log cabin. She soon moved with her parents, Mr. and Mrs. W.F. Whitaker, to **East St. Louis**. From the age of three she was able to perform the popular dances of her day, which she learned from a Negro "mammy."

Virginia left East St. Louis and traveled to New York in the winter of 1920. She went to the office of Flo Ziegfield and demanded an audience. She was hired on the spot. When Virginia came out of Ziegfield's office, there were more than 50 girls waiting for an audition.

Miss Ray knew a host of stars from stage and screen because many were her sidekicks in the chorus line. She also knew actors Ben Lyon, Malcom St. Clair, and director Allan Dwan. **She met Rudolph Valentino** at Club Lido four days before he died, where she was dining with future husband (1926) Thomas Purcell. Valentino signed Purcell's ukulele, the 138th signature on the instrument, and it was the last autograph he ever signed.

In 1925 Ray went to Palm Beach, Florida, and worked at minor roles in the movies. She appeared with Olive Borden, Neil Hamilton, and Marie Dressler in *The Joy Girl*, a Fox production. She first served in the movies as an extra in 1921.

Virginia subscribed to the East St. Louis *Journal* and frequently came back to visit the city, which she claimed was second only to New York as her favorite city.

Virginia had several narrow escapes in train wrecks. Leaving East St. Louis in 1925, she was riding on a limited that was involved in an accident that killed several passengers. Another time she had just left an Illinois Central car and gone into another when the first crashed over a bridge. On a third occasion, while en route to Chicago from New York, a wreck occurred near Pittsburgh in which four Pullman cars derailed, turned over, and killed 11 people.

Virginia admitted she was lucky. During the Sacco-Vanzetti riots in New York, she was waiting for a subway that was late. She decided instead to take the "elevated." The subway was wrecked by a bomb a few minutes later.

Virginia said that people often mistook her for Kathryn Ray, also a Follies and Vanities girl from East St. Louis, and admitted that sometimes their mail got crossed.

Tex Rickard – Legendary boxing promoter; glamorized boxing to the point where it was seen to be a big social event for the rich and famous

Grantland Rice – Sports columnist and broadcaster. It was said he reported sporting events like he was describing the Trojan War

Irene Rich – Silent star whose career faded with the advent of sound; one of the few who then switched to radio with the NBC Irene Rich Dramas, co-starring Gale Gordon

Eddie Rickenbacker – Race car driver; helped create Indianapolis Speedway; America's Air Ace of Aces during World War I, president of Eastern Airlines; produced the Rickenbacker auto for seven years;

Rin Tin Tin – Born 1917, died 1932; made more than 40

Rin Tin Tin

films; earned $15,000 a week in his prime; no other dog has ever matched his athleticism and skill at tricks

Robert Ripley – Author of the "Ripley's Believe it or Not" newspaper feature

Paul Robeson – Most famous black actor and baritone of the era; threatened by KKK for portraying a black man married to a white woman in a Eugene O'Neill play, *The Emperor Jones*

Bill "Bojangles" Robinson – Performed at places like the

Paul Robeson and Edith Day in Showboat

Saratoga Club, the Savoy, the Cotton Club, and Connie's in Harlem; considered the outstanding dancer of his era; appeared in several Shirley Temple movies in the 1930s

Knute Rockne – Famous Norwegian Notre Dame coach who turned that school into a football powerhouse; **killed in a plane crash** in the 1931 while flying to California to be a technical advisor on a sports movie

Norman Rockwell – Illustrator for the cover of The Saturday Evening Post; his lifework was an ode to ordinary Americans who were decent, God-fearing, hard-working, patriotic citizens

Buck Rogers – Became the first science fiction comic strip in 1929; it was about a contemporary American who awoke from a deep sleep after five centuries

Charles "Buddy" Rogers – Musician and film star; married Mary Pickford in 1937; Clark Gable predicted it wouldn't last because he was 11 years younger than her; it lasted 42 years; films include: *Wings, Varsity, Illusion, Halfway to Heaven; Young Eagles; My Best Girl*

Will Rogers - Oklahoma comedian and columnist noted for his humorous stories; got his start in the Ziegfeld Follies; He often made Congress and the government the butt of his jokes. He claimed the congressmen were making life difficult for comedians because everything they did was a joke. Will Rogers was **killed with his friend Wiley Post in a 1935 Alaskan plane crash**; had previously referred to flying togs as a "one-piece suicide suit." He is remembered for saying, "I never met a man I didn't like."

Franklin D. Roosevelt – A descendant of an old Dutch patroon; married Eleanor, a distant relative; was Assistant Secretary of the Navy in World War I; ran for Vice-president with James Cox in the 1920 loss to Harding; contracted polio shortly after the election; captured the governorship of New York in 1928; elected president in 1932 after promising the "forgotten man" a New Deal

Herman Rorschack – Developer of the inkblot personality test

Julius Rosenwald – He became partners with Richard Sears in 1895 with an investment of about $37,000 that was parlayed into a fortune of nearly $150 million. It was Rosenwald who convinced Sears to put out a catalog that was bigger than Montgomery Ward's and especially appealed to farmers. Sears died in 1914 but Rosenwald saw to it that the company prospered. He stunned the rich Captains of Industry by introducing profit-sharing to his employees in 1916. Numerous Sears employees retired well off due to their stock in the company.

Rosenwald (from **Springfield**) quickly became a life-long philanthropist. He gave millions to Booker T. Washington's Tuskegee Institute. He donated $5 million to help start the Museum of Science and Industry. Before his death in 1932 he turned the Sears Company over to Robert Wood. It was Wood who started the first retail store for the company in 1925.

Barney Ross – Chicagoan who became the lightweight boxing champion when he bested Tony Canzoneri and later defeated Jimmy McLarnin to take the welterweight crown.

Baby Rose Marie – One of radio's first child stars; started singing at the age of three; started her own radio show on NBC, lasting until 1938; as an adult played Sally Rogers on the Dick Van Dyke Show

Helena Rubinstein – Along with Elizabeth Arden and Max Factor, they were the top names in the cosmetics industry.

Jack Ruby – Born Jack Rubenstein in 1911 to Polish immigrants of Jewish extraction. When his parents separated he was placed in a foster home. He quit school at the age of sixteen and began running the streets on Chicago's west side. He worked as an errand boy running notes and messages for Al Capone for a dollar per delivery. He was in the Army Air Corps during World War II and served honorably. In 1947 he moved to Dallas and began running a nightclub. At the time of Kennedy's assassination in 1963 he owned a strip joint called the Carousel Club.

As Lee Harvey Oswald, JFK's assassin, was being led from the Dallas City Jail, he was shot and killed by Jack Ruby. It is not known for sure whether Ruby acted to "wipe the smirk off Oswald's face," or if he was acting under orders from the Chicago mafia.

Charles "Pee Wee" Russell – jazz clarinetist who performed in Chicago; was once a student at **Alton's Western Military Academy**; greatly influenced Benny Goodman

Babe Ruth

George Herman "Babe" Ruth – The Bambino, the Sultan of Swat, the most popular athlete in an era known as The Golden Age of Sports, his popularity saving baseball from the Black Sox scandal. Not a traditional hero and called the Bad Boy of Baseball, he smoked, drank, gambled, overate, and stayed out late with flappers.

Ruth started out as a pitcher for the Red Sox, but his hitting prowess earned him a job as an outfielder. He was sold to the Yankees in 1920 for $125,000. He drew so many fans that the team had to quit the Polo Grounds and build a new Yankee Stadium – the House That Ruth Built. In 1927 he accomplished the astounding feat of hitting 60 home runs in a single season, a record that stood until 1961 when it was broken by Roger Maris, a fellow New York Yankee. Ruth died in 1948 from cancer.

S

Sacco and Vanzetti (Brown Brothers)

Sacco and Vanzetti – Two Italian immigrants were convicted of killing a guard in 1920 while committing a payroll robbery in Massachusetts. Despite the fact that the pair were found in a car connected to the crime and were carrying a weapon of the same caliber involved in the killing, supporters claimed they were victims of the Red Scare because of their anarchist beliefs. Robert Benchley and Dorothy Parker championed the pair's cause. John Dos Pasos and Edna St. Vincent Millet leapt to their typewriters and churned out prose about the unfairness of their conviction.

Sacco cried out "Long live anarchy!" in Italian as he was seated in the electric chair. They were executed in 1927 and pardoned posthumously in the 1980s by Governor Michael Dukakis who claimed the two were victims of a prejudicial press and a biased judge Thayer.

A few months after the execution, a bomb blew off the front porch of Judge Thayer's house.

Carl Sandburg – Noted poet and Lincoln historian who lived at 4646 North Hermitage in Chicago and later moved to Maywood and then to Elmhurst.

Abe Saperstein – This plump, curly haired Jewish man **founded the Harlem Globetrotters** in 1927. He grew up on the west side of Chicago and quickly became addicted to sports. In 1926 he was hired to coach a team in a Negro basketball league. He bought the team a year later and took them on a road tour. Their first game ever was played against a group of local hot shots in **Hinckley, Illinois**. They barely earned enough to pay for their meals and hotel rooms. That's when Saperstein figured he needed something more; he decided to make it entertaining with fancy passing, dribbling, combined with fantastic shots. They practiced while Saperstein played a recording of "Beer Barrel Polka." They even worked in football and baseball routines. Crowds howled with laughter at their vaudeville-like comedy routine with the referees. In 1950 they played a game in Berlin, Germany, before a crowd of 75,000. It is still **the largest crowd ever to see a basketball game.**

Al "Fuzzy" St. John – Appeared in nearly 300 films; appeared in dozens of Mack Sennett Keystone comedies; after the advent of talkies, became a bewhiskered comedic sidekick in B westerns with Buster Crabbe and Lash LaRue, using the character name Fuzzy Q. Jones

Margaret Sanger – Leading advocate of birth control advice centers for women; became head of Planned Parenthood. Margaret had nine siblings and all were left to fend for themselves when her mother died at an early age from T.B.

William Scholl – When William was thirteen he was apprenticed to a cobbler and learned the shoe business. Around the turn of the century he went to Chicago and worked as a shoe salesman. This was an era when many shoe manufacturers didn't distinguish the left foot from the right – shoes were interchangeable. He earned a degree from Illinois Medical College (Loyola) and went into the business of making products to relieve the symptoms of corns, bunions, hammertoe and fallen arches. He made a fortune because he virtually had no competition. He never married and worked seven days a week in his room at the Illinois Athletic Club.

Oodles Candy Bar

Dutch Schultz – Born Arthur Flegenheimer, known to everyone as the Dutchman; got mixed up in the bootlegging business and engaged in New York beer wars with Vincent "Mad Dog" Coll and Legs Diamond; gunned down at a bar in New Jersey in 1935

Howard Scott – Inventor of the word *technocracy*. According to his concept, technology and machinery had advanced to the point where men, with the proper mental approach, only needed to work a mere sixteen hours a week and could retire at age forty-five. Scott became the high priest of a movement that, in the beginning of a depression, promised a salary of 20,000 a year. Americans by the thousands paid a $6 membership fee and enlisted in his crusade. What these lemmings failed to ask was how this easy-living society was to come about and what would sustain it?

Scott toured the country, giving lectures and spouting platitudes. He even came up with a unique military salute for his followers and a standard uniform that consisted of a gray suit, gray shirt, gray socks, blue tie, and cordovan shoes of reddish cowhide. Scott soon adopted the presumptuous title, The Chief.

When World War II broke out, Scott decided that it would be easier to fight the Axis if North America joined with Central America and the Caribbean in the United Technate State of North America.

After World War II technocracy receded into oblivion with a formal burial.

Mack Sennett – Maker of numerous comedy films with his Keystone Company; found his actors from vaudeville, burlesque and circuses; his stars included Charlie Chaplin, Roscoe Arbuckle, Al St. John, Ben Turpin, Wallace Beery; built a tall tower in the middle of his studio so that he could see everything going on at any given moment.

Norma Shearer: (1902-1983) "The First Lady of MGM;" Canadian-born, she won a beauty contest at age 14; rejected for Ziegfield Follies but Irving Thalberg saw her in minor movie roles and gave her a five year contract with MGM; won five Oscar nominations; won Academy Award for Best Actress in 1930 for *The Divorcée*; married Irving Thalberg and had two children but was more interested in her career than rearing children; her sister Athole married producer Howard Hawks; David Selznick offered her the role of Scarlet in *Gone With The Wind* but public outcry against it killed the deal; in 1942 married ski instructor Nelson Arrouge who was twenty years her junior; he signed a pre-nuptial waiving community property rights

Igor Sikorsky – Russian-born American who designed fixed wing aircraft in the Twenties and then made the **first working helicopter** in the 1930s

Upton Sinclair – Muckraking Chicago journalist who wrote *The Jungle*, describing deplorable and unsanitary conditions at the Union Stockyards. He crusaded for socialist reforms in his more than 80 books. Ran for governor of California on the Democratic ticket in 1934 but was defeated by Hearst money and newspaper opposition.

Skippy – A King Features comic strip started in 1928; plot is about a sardonic ten-year-old boy who observes the passing scene and the world made for him by adults

Alfred E. Smith – Catholic youth from the lower East Side who became Mayor of New York; ran for president in 1928 but was defeated by a nasty "whispering campaign" (because of his religion) and Republican prosperity – a chicken in every pot, a car in every garage; "Sidewalks of New York," an 1894 song, was his campaign trademark; Franklin Roosevelt called him the "Happy Warrior;" ran as a wet – an opponent of Prohibition; legions in the Midwest distrusted his Tammany Hall political machine connection; greatly upset when Franklin Roosevelt took the nomination from him in 1932

Execution of Ruth Snyder

Bessie Smith – **Empress of the Blues**; made 160 records but was largely unknown to white audiences in the Twenties; killed in an auto wreck in 1937

Ruth Snyder - Female executed at Sing Sing prison in New York; reporter for the *N.Y. Daily News* violated prison rules by snapping her picture with a camera secretly strapped to his leg;

the published photo and story was a sensation; she and her lover, a corset salesman named Judd Gray (also executed) murdered her husband with a sash weight; claimed that a burglar did it at first, but she later confessed when her story didn't add up and investigators discovered she had recently taken out large insurance policies on her husband; each blamed the other for the crime at the trial

Stanley brothers – Invented a steam driven car. Contrary to popular notion, **no Stanley Steamer ever blew up**; popularity faded because it took 20 minutes to build up a full head of steam in the boiler. The water compartment held 45 gallons.

Stanley Steamer

There were no tricky gears to try and shift, no jumpy clutch to catapult you out of your seat. This car operated with just a throttle, brake and reverse pedal. Instead of a cranky-sounding electric horn, it had a deep-throated whistle. In place of dirty exhaust fumes, there was only a hissing cloud of white vapor.

Harold Stearns – Editor of a highly controversial book, *Civilization In The United States*. Various writers penned chapters on certain aspects of American life in the 1920s such as "Poetry," "Education," "Family," "Radicalism," and "Politics." Arthur M. Schlesinger criticized the book because it left out rural life and agriculture.

Gertrude Stein – Born in Pennsylvania in 1874 but grew up in Oakland, Calif.; attended Radcliff College in 1893 where William James was one of her professors; artists and writers flocked to her popular salon in Paris at 27 Rue de Fleurus, where she lived with her brother Leo; she was an art collector and covered her walls with paintings by the likes of Cezanne, Renoir and Picasso (who painted her portrait). Gertrude had a relationship with Alice B. Toklas for 37 years; was a prolific writer but her abstract "cubist" style was not well received by the public; did a speaking tour of America in 1934 and was well received; of Jewish extraction, Gertie was nearly captured and sent to a prison camp by the Germans in World War II; best known for coining the phrase "The Lost Generation" to describe the disillusioned intelligencia in the aftermath of World War I. She also authored the famous quote, "A rose is a rose is a rose." (Not sure I can explain why that is famous.)

Louis Sullivan – Chicago architect famous for the dictum, "form follows function;" mentor of Frank Lloyd Wright and assigned him the task of designing family dwellings for the firm, leading to Wright's famed Prairie Style of architecture; died broke and bitter from alcoholism in 1924; **Father of Modern Architecture**

Billy Sunday – Former baseball player and stolen base record holder until the mark was broken by Ty Cobb; when prohibition went into effect, Billy Sunday presided over mock funeral services for John Barleycorn in Norfolk, Virginia. The most famous evangelist of the Twenties, sometimes pounding out fundamentalist sermons to crowds as large as 100,000.

Gloria Swanson – Chicago-born actress known for collecting husbands and lovers; tried royalty with her third husband, Marquis de la Falaise, in one of Hollywood's most celebrated marriages; started as a Keystone comedienne working with Mack Sennett; signed contract in 1919 with D.W. Griffith and he turned her into a star; movies include: *Sadie Thompson, The Untamed, Stage Struck, Bluebeard's Eighth Wife, Wages of Virtue, Lady Manhandled, Zaza*; made successful switch to the talkies; memorable as Norma Desmond in *Sunset Boulevard*, 1950

Tom Swift – Author Victor Appleton created this spirited, precocious young lad who had a knack for scientific creations. The series of Tom Swift books covered four generations from 1910 to 1941. Many of these inventions talked about in the books ultimately became reality. Unfortunately, the electric rifle has yet to be invented. Tom Swift books are in greater demand on E-Bay than Hardy Boys books.

T

Tailspin Tommy – Glenn Chaffin and Hal Forrest created this character shortly after Lindbergh soloed the Atlantic. Tailspin Tommy made its debut in 1928. Tommy Tomkins was a youngster with a keen interest in aviation. He began working at a job in Texas fixing planes and later began to fly them. Betty Lou Barnes was his romantic interest. In 1934 Tommy became the first comic strip made into a movie serial, a 12-parter.

Tailspin Tommy

Marion Talley – Star singer for the Metropolitan opera

Norma Talmadge – Poverty-stricken childhood; became a New York model; signed to movie contract in NY by Vitagraph; left for California in 1915; signed by D.W. Griffith; career helped by her marriage to film executive Joseph Schenck; films include: *The Eternal Flame, Ashes of Vengeance, Kiki, New York Nights, Camille, The Lady*; career was killed off by talking pictures; married George Jessel in 1930s and appeared regularly on his radio program

Irving Thalberg

Irving Thalberg – Irving Thalberg: (1899-1936) Called the "Boy Wonder," became

head of MGM movie production while in his early twenties; forced to leave high school because of rheumatic fever; read voraciously during his convalescence, giving him ideas for movie plots in later life; invented the star system for movie studios; oversaw the production of about 50 movies every year; he was a born leader and decision maker; MGM was one of the last studios to switch to talkies because Thalberg thought they were a passing fad; frequently pestered Louis B. Mayer for a larger salary; modest, he refused to allow his name to be shown on the credits of his films; revived the fading career of the Marx brothers; saw Clark Gable in a minor film role and decided he had star quality; married actress Norma Shearer and they had two children; sickly as a child and sickly as an adult with a weak heart; was good friends with William Randolph Hearst and was a frequent guest at the Hearst castle, San Simeon; died in California after contracting pneumonia; after Thalberg's death, his name appeared on screen for the first time at the beginning of *The Good Earth*; Thalberg Award created by Motion Picture Academy for achievement in movie production; Thalberg was also responsible for *Ben Hur, Broadway Melody, Flesh and the Devil* and *The Merry Widow*.

William Hale Thompson – This three-time Republican mayor of Chicago called himself "Big Bill the Builder." It was Thompson who started the **Michigan Avenue Bridge** project and he built **Navy Pier**. He failed in a bid for a U.S. Senate seat in 1924 and actually toyed with the idea of seeking the presidency in 1928. He did win a third term as mayor in 1927 with the help of a half a million dollars donated to his campaign chest by Al Capone. Thompson was both corrupt and arrogant. Author Richard Ciccone claims that without bombastic Big Bill, the machine gun and Chicago would never have been synonymous.

Bill Tilden – A slim 165 pound six footer, the most famous name in tennis during this era; won seven American Amateur Tennis Championships; in 1925 won 57 games in a row; if a linesman missed a call in his favor, he purposely ruined his next shot to even things up through a show of sportsmanship; in later years he served prison time for molesting young boys

Bill Tilden

Tillie the Toiler – This Russ Westover comic strip first appeared in 1921. Tillie Jones was a working girl who toiled for a dress manufacturer and occasionally did some modeling; Marion Davies played the title role in MGM's 1927 *Tillie The Toiler*

Dave Tough – **Oak Park**, Illinois, drummer who patterned his style after Baby Dodds. Developed his own style and went on to become one of the most noted jazz drummers, performing with Ray Noble and Tommy Dorsey

Sophie Tucker (1884-1966) - The Last of the Red Hot Mamas; Born Sophie Abuza in Russia, her family migrated to Hartford, Connecticut, and bought a restaurant. She eloped at age 16 with Louis Tuck and divorced him after a son was born. She left her son for her parents to rear and fled to New York to try her hand in the acting business.

Flapper girl

She started out wearing blackface in vaudeville because producers and directors said she was too big and ugly to appear otherwise. She landed a job with Ziegfield Follies and was so popular she launched a career on her own. She sold herself as an overweight, bawdy, over-sexed, independent woman. She made about eight Hollywood films but discovered screen roles to be too confining. During the Thirties she went abroad and became very popular in England. Her favorite songs with audiences were "I'm Living Alone and Liking It," and "I Don't Want To Be Thin." She was noted for singing maudlin tunes and telling off-color jokes.

Gene Tunney – Tunney got his start in boxing while he was in the service during World War I. He became the light heavyweight champ of the American Expeditionary Force. While in the service, Tunney heard about a boxer back home who was acquiring fame. Jack Dempsey was about to fight Jess Willard for the heavyweight title.

Tunney had been a hard hitter but he hurt his hands while boxing in the service. He was forced to change his style to the skill of sparring and defense. When Dempsey fought Carpentier, the European champ, Tunney was on the card in a preliminary bout which enabled him to get a good look at Dempsey's style. The **Manassa Mauler** murdered "The Orchid Man" of France.

Tunney made a habit of going to most of Dempsey's fights and came away with a strategy to defeat him. He had seen Firpo, the "Wild Bull of the Pampas," nearly defeat Dempsey when he knocked him through the ropes. Sportswriters on the first row pushed Dempsey back into the ring, saving him from defeat. In all the confusion, the referee forgot to disqualify Dempsey for this illegal action.

Tunney concluded that he could not outpunch "**Man Killer,**" but he could outbox him. His plan was to surprise Dempsey with a hard punch in the first round, putting him in a daze, and outboxing him on points the rest of the way. To toughen his damaged hands, he worked as a lumberjack for a solid year, swinging

Tillie The Toiler

an axe.

When Tunney finally won enough bouts to get a shot at the title, Dempsey was rated the heavy favorite. Dempsey had that killer instinct while Tunney was seen as a finesse fighter. During the war Tunney had gotten hooked on reading Shakespeare and when he mentioned that in an interview, the press ran with it – the killer verses the bookworm.

Their first fight took place in Philadelphia. Tunney's strategy worked. He stunned Dempsey in the first with a blow high on the cheek. After that he concentrated on outboxing him by foiling his rushes and landing enough blows to win each round. Another thing that worked in Tunney's favor was a slight drizzle that made the mat wet and made it difficult for a hard puncher to set his feet and land his blows.

The rematch took place in Chicago and it is remembered in history as the "long count" fight. The disputed event took place in the seventh round with Tunney, now labeled the "**Fighting Marine**," ahead on points by side-stepping and parrying jabs, and beating Dempsey to the punch. Suddenly, Dempsey landed a hard punch squarely on Tunney's jaw, and he went down, landing on the seat of his pants. Dempsey hovered over Tunney, planning to finish him off as he staggered to his feet. However, a new rule had gone into effect that required a boxer to go to a neutral corner before the referee would begin his count. This gave Tunney four revitalizing seconds and he was up on his feet at the count of nine. Tunney went on to win the fight and barroom kibitzers have debated the question ever since.

Fight fans thirsted for a rematch, especially due to the controversy. Tex Ricard was eager to promote it. But Dempsey declined due to a fear by physicians that he might lose sight in one of his eyes.

Tunney always claimed that his head was clear when the referee reached the count of two and that he could have gotten to his feet without the four extra seconds.

Tunney went on to become the head of a construction company, president of a bank, and CEO of Eversharp Inc., maker of executive pencils and pens. In World War II he served as fitness director of the Navy.

Ben Turpin

For more info on this topic see Isabel Leighton's *The Aspirin Age*, 1949.

Ben Turpin – Cross-eyed comic actor of the Twenties; had a large and very expressive Adam's apple; **insured his eyes with Lloyds of London to make sure they didn't become uncrossed**; began his career with Essanay in Chicago; died in 1940

King Tut – Boy king of ancient Egypt; his excavated tomb was opened by Lord Carnarvon at Luxor in 1922-23 and despite a famous curse that resulted in death for many associated with the project, it produced a craze that affected fashions and architecture called Egyptianism. The tomb of the pharaoh Tutankhamen yielded many treasures and objects of beauty and interest, as well as the king's mummy in a gold sarcophagus. Carnarvon died five months later from a mosquito bite and pneumonia.

V

Rudy Vallee

Rudy Vallee – Born Hubert Vallee in 1901, he changed his name to Rudy after the famous saxophonist Rudy Wiedoft. Singer whose 1929 radio program was sponsored by Fleishman's yeast; had his own orchestra; noted for amplifying his voice with a megaphone; theme song was "My Time is Your Time"

Rudolph Valentino – Born Rudolpho Alfonzo di Valentina; migrated from Italy in 1913 to seek a career in the U.S.; worked as a gardener and bus boy in New York before landing a job as a dancer in a touring musical; obtained several bit roles in movies until he hit it big after he successfully tested for the lead in 1921's *Four Horsemen of the Apocalypse*; the Great Lover divorced actress Jean Acker in 1922; married Natacha Rambova; they separated and Valentino became an item with Polish star Pola Negri; made *The Sheik* and *Blood and Sand* (bullfighting) in 1922.

A Chicago *Tribune* reporter found some pink talcum powder in Valentino's sink and wrote a piece about his being effeminate. Valentino, deeply offended, challenged him to a duel. He became seriously ill in 1926 with inflamed appendix, an ulcer, and peritonitis, causing his sudden death at age 29. More than 30,000 people showed up to view the body lying in state and there was a near riot with 75 people being injured. Several of his female fans committed suicide. Pola Negri was hysterical at the funeral.

H.L. Mencken once said that **Valentino was catnip to women**. Tin Pan Alley wrote a song for him, "There's a New Star in Heaven Tonight."

Thorstein Veblen – (1857-1929) Theoretician, economist, social commentator, writer, and societal critic; wrote *The Theory of the Leisure Class* and coined the phrase "conspicuous consumption"

W

Jimmy Walker – Notorious Irish playboy Mayor of New York City who picked his wife and girl friends from chorus lines; called the "Night Mayor;" also known as the "Late Mayor" because he seldom got to city hall before noon; his reputation became tarnished when criminal investigations discovered that he had used his name and influence to enrich himself in shady investment deals; he resigned from office in 1932 and fled to Europe; he divorced showgirl

Janet Allen and married showgirl Betty Compton in Cannes, France

Lila and Dewitt Wallace – Founders of *Reader's Digest* which printed condensed versions of articles from other sources; the magazine focused on articles that were upbeat and positive; politically conservative up to the present

Fanny Ward – Sixty plus actress who **added the word "facelift" to our vocabulary when she decided she wanted to look like a little girl again**

Muddy Waters – Came to Chicago from Mississippi as part of the Great Migration in World War I; he gained his nickname from childhood chums because he was always playing in the mud. He is credited with **inventing Chicago Blues**. It differed from the languid, lamenting blues that originated in New Orleans in that it had a hard rhythm accentuated by a slow, deep beat.

Johnny Weissmuller

Johnny Weissmuller – Chicagoan who started swimming at Oak Street beach **to overcome childhood polio**; won Olympic gold medals in 1924 and '28; it was Weissmuller who was credited with making swimming a popular sport; set 67 world records; never lost a swimming match; chosen to portray Tarzan in the movies. He did all of his own stunts and once dropped from a tree to the back of a rhinoceros, which he rode for a considerable distance.

H.G. Wells – British writer whose *Outline of History* was the best-selling non-fiction book in 1921 and 1922

Mae West – Actress who was a child star in vaudeville; did not act in silent films; starred in a scandalous New York play titled *Sex*. The production was closed by authorities, and she served ten days in jail for participating in an indecent show; authorities also closed her production of *Pleasure Man*; lifejackets today are called "Mae Wests"

Edith Wharton – (1862-1937) New York-born novelist who wrote over 40 books including *The House of Mirth* and *Ethan Fromme*. Her women were often depicted as victims of cruel social conventions. She did not attend school and educated herself by reading books from her father's library. She was in her mid-thirties before her first book was published. Her marriage to Edward Wharton was an unhappy one, ending in divorce in 1913. Edith's characters often dealt with the problem of divorce and in her novels she attempted to sort out her own feelings about the subject. She moved to Paris permanently around 1908 and had a passionate affair with a journalist for the *London Times*. Edith was fiercely dedicated to the Allied cause in World War I and strongly urged America to enter the war effort. She received the Pulitzer Prize in 1921 for *The Age of Innocence*.

George Whipple – Scientist who discovered in 1925 that lack of iron in the diet was the cause of pernicious anemia, a serious illness back then. (Be sure to eat plenty of liver.)

Pearl White – Born to a poor family in the Missouri Ozarks; battled her way through episode after episode of countless serials fighting rustlers, gamblers, bandits and smugglers; provided post-war America with an athletic heroine; she was a screen idol to millions of young women; the end of each serial always left her in a life-threatening predicament such as being tied to the railroad tracks while a roaring train was rushing toward her; she insisted on doing all of her own stunts which nearly led to her death on several occasions; was good friends with Texas Guinan; she spent her last years in Paris a very rich woman

Paul Whiteman – The "King of Jazz" - orchestra leader most responsible for making jazz cross-cultural by introducing it to white audiences; always wore a white tuxedo; Bing Crosby was an unknown singer with his band in 1929; it was Whiteman who championed syncopated rhythm. Whiteman was an early flop when his orchestra played at the large ballrooms in Chicago. It took people a while to figure out his music was more for listening than dancing.

George Wickersham – Appointed by Hoover to head a commission to study the effectiveness of Prohibition; the oxymoronic conclusion was that it wasn't working very well but that it ought to be continued.

Hazel Wightman – The "**Queen Mother of Tennis**;" winner of four U.S. singles championships; tutored numerous American women tennis players; Wightman Cup named in her honor

Thorton Wilder – Wrote the best-selling novel of 1925, *The Bridge of San Luis Rey;* wrote the play *Our Town* in 1938

Helen Wills – Little Miss Poker Face; famous female tennis player of the Twenties – made tennis popular for girls of all classes, not just the privileged social elite; won eight Wimbledon singles titles; female tennis players back then wore knee-length skirts in competition; she rebelled against the idea that women were delicate and dainty

Winnie Winkle

Winnie Winkle – First appeared as a comic strip in 1920, created by Martin Branner; another working girl, she also had an adopted kid brother named Perry; in 1937 she married an engineer named Will Wright who was killed in World War II and left her to raise twins

Walter Winchell – Columnist and news broadcaster; started off writing gossip and backstage news about famous entertainers – "Fanny Brice is betting on the ponies today at Belmont;" his radio broadcasts opened with "Good evening Mr. and Mrs. America and all the ships at sea;" invented words and phrases that became known as Winchellese – *Chicagorilla* (gangster from Chicago), *Phfft* (broken, ended, spoiled), *renovated* (divorced)

Frank Lloyd Wright – Chicago architect whose **prairie-style architecture** blended function and environment; his Imperial Hotel in Tokyo was one of the few buildings to withstand the 1923 earthquake. Wright had three wives, a mysteriously murdered mistress, and fathered seven children.

William Wrigley – The man came to Chicago as a baking powder salesman. As an **added incentive he gave away a pack of chewing gum** for each box of powder sold. He soon discovered that there was more money to be made from selling gum than baking powder. Wrigley once filed charges against a fan that caught a foul ball and tried to keep it. He bought the Cub franchise in 1916 from the Taft family of Cincinnati – not due to his rabid interest as a fan, but because he thought such a team should be owned locally. He built Wrigley Field and in 1924 he built the terra cotta Wrigley Building that soon became a Chicago landmark. It was his son, P.K. Wrigley, who took down the advertising and planted ivy against the outfield walls of Wrigley Field.

Ed Wynn – (1886-1966) Rubbery faced character actor; a slight lisp and memorable giggle was his trademark; born in Philadelphia with the name Edwin Leopold, he changed it to Ed Wynn because his family was ashamed he was a vaudeville actor; was a regular on the Rudy Vallee Show, better known as The Fleishman Hour; on radio he was best known as The Fire Chief; had numerous roles in Disney comedy films of the 1960s; when his comedy became outdated, he turned to serious character acting; **offered the title role in The Wizard of Oz in 1939** but turned it down because he thought the part was too small

Z

Flo(renz) Ziegfield – Showman who was said to know the subtle difference between desire and lust; married to showgirl Billie Burke but had many affairs, including one with Marilyn Miller; was **inspired to go into show business after seeing a Buffalo Bill Wild West Show in Chicago**; Eugene Sandow, the strong man with the washboard stomach and back, was his first featured performer; Anna Held was his first female star and his first wife; his first Follies were in New York in 1907; other stars included Lillian Lorraine, the Dolly sisters, Eddie Cantor, Will Rogers (the Cherokee Kid), W.C. Fields, Jessie Reed, Olive Thomas, Imogene Wilson, Marilyn Miller (married Jack Pickford at Pickfair, the

Actress Billy Dove, former Ziegfield girl

second marriage for both), Helen Morgan, Paulette Goddard, Irene Dunne, Ruth Etting, Gilda Gray (originator of "the shimmy"), Marion Davies, Gypsy Rose Lee, and Gladys Glad; he died in 1932 at age 63; one of his most bitter enemies was George M. Cohan.

WORDS AND PHRASES PECULIAR TO THE 1920s

ASSIFIDITY BAG – Cloth bag filled with garlic and other herbs and worn around the neck. Designed to ward off colds and flu.

AH-OOGA HORN – Many cars of the Twenties, such as the Maxwell, had a motor-driven electric horn that derived its unique tone from an armature that revolved and tickled an oscillating diaphragm. These horns were popular with teenagers in the 1950s.

1922 Dodge wooden station wagon

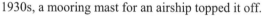

AIRSHIPS – Passenger travel by dirigibles was popular in the Twenties. The R-34 and the Graf Zeppelin were noted ships. When the Empire State Building was constructed in the 1930s, a mooring mast for an airship topped it off.

ALKY – Short for alcohol

ALKY COOKING – Alky cooking was an oft-used expression for those who engaged in the new cottage industry of making home brew.

THE AMERICAN MERCURY – Started in 1924 by H.L. Mencken and George Nathan; this magazine was the "lost" generation's Bible as it lambasted religion, democracy (the bilge of idealism) and the "stupidity of the gaping primates" who, in Mencken's view, constituted 95% of the population.

ANESTHETICS – The two in vogue at the time were ether and chloroform; when this author had his tonsils removed in 1945 the doctor used awful-smelling ether

APOPLEXY – Old fashioned expression for a stroke

APOTHECARY – Old fashioned name for a drug store

APPLESAUCE – That's baloney; that's bunk; that's applesauce

ARCTICS – Another term for galoshes and gaiters

ART DECO – Stems from an art exposition held in Paris in 1925; it became a popular design style characterized by bold lines, geometric and zigzag forms, and the use of new materials such as plastic. Clothing, architecture, household items such as ashtrays, graphic design, and art were affected.

ARTIFICIAL SILK – What rayon was called when it first came out; flesh-colored rayon hose was popular during the era. Silk stockings were still worn, but at 75 cents a pair, cost twice as much as rayon.

34

ASHCAN SCHOOL – A small group of artists (including John Sloan and George Bellows) who painted ordinary, everyday scenes and objects such as ash cans.

ASSEMBLED CAR – Small auto companies built their cars by using parts manufactured by other concerns. Though often criticized, the companies that made these parts maintained high standards. For example: Timken roller bearings, Bendix brakes, Continental engines, Delco electrical systems, and Harrison radiators

AUTOGIRO – Had the body of an airplane and helicopter rotors above the cockpit; never caught on with the public because it could not hover and needed to taxi a short distance before it could take off. Unlike a helicopter, no tail rotor was

Autogiro

needed to counteract torque from the main blades because they were freewheeling – unpowered. Another difference is that the angle of the rotor blades on an autogiro is fixed whereas they are adjustable on a helicopter. An autogiro was used in the wedding scene in the Clark Gable/Claudette Colbert vehicle, *It Happened One Night*

BAGMAN – This term was applied to the man who carried around money and made bribe payoffs. Jake Guzik was Capone's bagman. The Mafia liked to use women in that capacity and Virginia Hill in the 1950s was a noted "baglady."

BANANA OIL – That's banana oil; that's bunk; that's a lot of hooey

BANJO OPERAS – Name given to minstrel shows, one of America's first unique art forms. White actors in black face did comedy routines, told ethnic jokes, and performed lively high-stepping dance routines.

BARNSTORMING – Ex-World War I pilots, who came to be known as "gypsies," flew Curtiss JN-4 "Jennies" around the country to local fairs and performed exhibitions of daring stunt flying skills such as barrel rolls and loop-the-loops. In those jaunty days of flying by the seat of one's pants, circus performers were added to the entertainment with aerobatics and "wing walking." Members of the crowd were offered joyrides for $5. It was called barnstorming because the planes were parked in barns at night.

BARREL HOOP – Young children would take an old metal barrel hoop and roll it down a path or sidewalk, keeping it rolling by stroking the top with their hand or a stick

BATHTUB GIN – Ethanol flavored with oil of juniper; this potent mixture that withered the esophagus was often brewed at home in bathtubs.

BEE'S KNEES – Used to describe someone with outstanding qualities as in "she's bee's knees" (cute)

BELLY GUN – A small Colt .38 snub-nosed weapon carried inside the trouser waistband

BERRIES – Anything good or wonderful

BLACK AND TANS – Southside Chicago nightclubs that were predominantly black but were often frequented by slumming whites

BLEACHERS – Less expensive seats at baseball games consisted of unpainted and unprotected sun-bleached boards.

BLIND PIG – Similar to a speakeasy; so named because the storefront often had a blank façade; sometimes it was a type of speak-easy that was hidden behind a legitimate business such as a grocery store. The term originated from those who bought moonshine by handing money through a slot in the wall and the white lightning was handed back through the slot without the buyer seeing the seller.

BLOTTO – A highbrow description for a state of drunkenness; the highbrow term for a drunk is dipsomaniac.

BOBBED HAIR – Liberated young women of the 1920s openly smoked cigarettes for the first time in history and wore their hair cut short, similar to the bobbed tail of a horse.

BOILED AS AN OWL – An expression that described people who got drunk on home brew. Potted, piped, or squiffy were other colorful expressions that were used.

BREACH OF PROMISE – A legal term that allowed women to sue men who promised to marry them and then backed out. Georgia Jay won $20,000 in a lawsuit against Homer Rodeheaver, evangelist Billy Sunday's song leader.

BRICKBAT – A broken chunk of brick, often used as a weapon

BROGAN – Old term for a heavy work shoe that reached up to the ankles

(Courtesy Sears & Roebuck)

27H8015
Fancy
Knitted
Sport
Blouse
$1⁹⁸

Women's
and
Misses'
Sizes

27H8215
All Wool
Fancy
Tweed
Knickers
$2⁹⁸

BRONX CHEER – A slang expression for razzing somebody or giving him or her the raspberry. The most frequent display of this was to stick out one's tongue and blow, causing a semi-obscene noise.

BUCKWHEATS – When the order went out to kill someone it was usually over quickly. Buckwheats meant that the intended victim was supposed to suffer.

BULL MARKET – Shortly after the Great War (World War I) there was a recession in 1919. But recovery came quickly and it was the 1920s that, for the first time in history, saw wages rise high enough to produce a middle class. For the first time since the Stock Market was created in 1790 average Americans could afford to invest in stocks. Margin (down payment) requirements back then were only 10 percent and this led to wild speculation and a huge demand for stocks that, in turn, led to an artificial "bubble" known at Broad and Wall streets as a "bull market." The reasons for the crash were complex, but crash it did in October of 1929, ending the Bull Market and leading to the Great Depression. A market with generally declining stock prices and profits is referred to as a Bear Market.

"Duster" coat

BUM'S RUSH – To give someone the bum's rush means that you try to avoid the person or give him the brush off. Also used when you practically shove someone out the door to get rid of him.

BUNKY – Nickname often given to young boys after a character in a cartoon comic strip – The Yellow Kid

BUNNY HUG – A popular dance used when the orchestra was playing slower blues music.

BUNION DERBY – Nickname given to marathon running which became a fad in the Twenties.

CABARET – A nightclub that was usually a little more upscale than a speakeasy

CACKLEBERRIES – Eggs from the hen house

CAGERS – Basketball players

CAKE EATER'S SUIT – Popular suit style for young men who went to dances where slivers of cake were served, hence the name; the suit was narrow shouldered and wide trousered.

CAMIKNICKERS – A woman's foundation garment made of cotton or silk, which was a camisole on top and pants on the bottom, with buttons at the crotch; the bandeaux or brassiere eventually replaced the camisole; Tallulah Bankhead was the first to wear a camiknicker on stage in *Garden of Eden*

CARBUNCLE – A painful irritation of the skin and deeper tissues with a discharge of pus combined with necrosis and sloughing of dead tissue

CARTRIDGE CLOTH COAT – A three-button overcoat, popular in early Twenties, made from cloth used to hold WWI cartridges together

CATARRH – A sinus cold with a runny nose

CAT'S MEOW – Something that is sharp or outstanding

CAT'S WHISKER – On old time radios known as crystal sets, there was a wire which extended up through the box, and you would move the "cat's whisker," to tune in a particular station; the metal frame of one's bed could be used as an antenna; these cheap sets had no amplification and required headphones for listening.

CHAMBER POT – A container kept in the bedroom in homes that didn't have indoor toilets

CHARLESTON SHOE – This tricky dance influenced shoe styles. It demanded a securely fastened shoe with a low heel and closed toe. A single-bar pump with a pointed toe, high-waisted heel, and one tiny covered button was the most common style.

CHEATERS – Eyeglasses

CHESTERFIELD – A long semi-fitted man's overcoat with a velvet collar

CHICAGO AMNESIA - Witnesses who were supposed to testify against a Capone man were often threatened with death, causing the witness to take the stand and suddenly develop a startling loss of memory.

CHINEESE CHECKERS – A game with marbles introduced to the world in 1928 as Hop Sing Checkers

CHIPPIE – A female with a reputation for having loose morals; sometimes referred to as a floozy or a trollop

CHIROPODIST – Foot doctor

CHOPPER – Slang expression for a Tommy gun because it literally could chop off a limb

CHUCK-A-LUCK – A gambling game in which gamblers bet on the possible combinations of three thrown dice

CIGARETTE CASE – A flat sterling silver case, often ini-tialized, that was made to hold about a half a pack of cigarettes; very popular with men or women of means

CIGARETTE HOLDERS – Used by men and women to avoid getting nicotine stains on their fingers. It was considered stylish to use them and even President F.D.R used a cigarette holder.

COLLEGIATE LOOK – Ankle-length raccoon coats, crushed crown felt hats, diamond design pullover sweaters, college pennants, argyle golf socks, knickers, and a ukulele under the arm, were *de rigueur* for this male ensemble.

According to fashion artist Tom Tierney, females typically wore raccoon coats, a hip-length strand of pearls, unbuckled galoshes, geometrically patterned sweaters, a straight-cut skirt, and rolled their silk stockings below rouged knees.

CLOCHE HAT – A roundish skull hat for women that hugged the head and was usually worn at eyebrow level;

often called a Bob Hat.

CLOCK – An ornamental design on the ankle or sides of women's stockings.

C-NOTE – A 100-dollar bill, because the letter C in Roman numerals stands for 100

COFFIN VAR-NISH – This was a slang expression for bootleg alcohol; sometimes referred to as tarantula juice and horse liniment

COLORS – Popular colors of the 1920s included Afghan red, Kasha beige, gobelin blue, Lucerne blue, Mother Goose sand, Japonica red, Castilian red, café crème, Monet blue, gooseberry light green, almond green, oakwood brown, pearl gray, Prussian blue, Nile green, Versailles violet, Florentine cream, Alice blue.

COMICS – The most popular were Gasoline Alley, Thimble Theater (Popeye), Wash Tubbs, Little Orphan Annie, Winnie Winkle, Barney Google, Tillie the Toiler, Moon Mullins, Rube Goldberg, Mutt and Jeff, Katzenjammer Kids, Andy Gump

COMMODE – Toilet

COMPANIONATE MARRIAGE – Living with one partner in an experimental way, probably with the ultimate purpose of getting married

CONSUMPTION – An old fashioned term for tuberculosis or TB

CONTRACT – Gangster speak for a murder assignment

COOPERAGE – A company that made wooden barrels

CORK BALL – A popular game played by patrons of taverns. The ball consisted of a cork or stopper from the bunghole of a beer barrel. The bat was a sawed off broomstick.

CRAPS GAME – Gambling with dice

CROAKER - Physician

CROSSWORD PUZZLES – Simon and Schuster published the first crossword puzzle book in 1924 and it quickly became a fad. The craze also stimulated sales in Roget's Thesaurus, which many people weren't sure whether it was a prehistoric animal or a disease. Yo-yos and roller skates also became popular at this time

CROUP – Old fashioned term for a deep cough; often treated with a spoonful of sugar and coal oil.

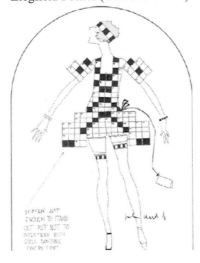

Crossword Puzzle dress for Ziegfeld Follies (Culver Pictures)

CRUSHER – Men's casual hat, rounded on top with a button in the middle, turned up brim; usually made of cotton poplin

CURLEY MOP – A variety of hairstyle popular with women in the Twenties. It required a "perm" and resulted in a bouffant tangle of curls not too different from Afros that blacks wore in the 1970s.

CURTSY – Young girls, when introduced to elders, were taught to show respect by holding the hem of their dress between their thumb and forefinger, while slightly bending their knees and briefly lowering their head.

CUSPIDOR – Sometimes referred to as spittoons. These were brass containers found in the lobby of banks and hotels and at bars. They were repositories for waste from men who chewed tobacco.

DAGO –A corruption of the common last name Diego and disparagingly used to describe people from Spain or Italy

DANCE MARATHONS – These were popular 1920s contests designed to test endurance that couples entered. *They Shoot Horses Don't They?* is a Hollywood film about dance marathons. The craze mostly died out in the 1930s.

DANDY – A fancy dressing male

DEAD MAN'S EYES – It was widely believed by mobsters that the last thing a murder victim saw was firmly implanted on his retinas when he died. Not taking any chances, killers often shot out both eyes of his victim to prevent the coroner from obtaining incriminating evidence.

DEAD RABBIT – Rabbit was slang for ruffian back then, and a "dead rabbit" was a super tough ruffian

DEAD SOLDIER – An empty beer bottle

DEBUTANTE – A young woman making her formal entrance into society; a lavish coming-out-party was often given for the occasion.

DETACHABLE COLLAR – Men shirts in the early Twenties had detachable collars. The separate collars could either be stiff or soft, and some, called "rubber collars," were made of celluloid.

DIME-A-DANCE HOSTESS – Ballroom dancing became very popular toward the end of the decade, and many of them featured girls who would dance with a man for a fee of ten cents

DIP – A bold and brazen dance move where the man bent his partner backward until her head touched the floor, at which point the woman would provocatively kick up one leg.

DIRTY DOZEN – Gangster slang for a jury

DISH – Slang for a female; That Mexican dish was a real looker.

DOGGONE – A puritanical euphemism for damn; it's a doggone shame

DOGS – A person's feet; my dogs are tired

DOUBLE SAWSKY – Two sawbucks equal twenty dollars

DRAMSHOP – A saloon, sometimes called a tippling house

DRUGSTORE COWBOY – Fashionably dressed idler who hangs around public places trying to pick up girls

DRUMMER – Salesman: he was a shoe drummer

DUMB DORA – A stupid girl

DUSTER – Lightweight overcoat, usually not waterproof, used when driving an open car to keep dust off the rest of one's clothes; often worn with goggles and a flat golf-style hat

DYSPEPSIA – Digestive or stomach problems

EARS LOWERED – A colloquial expression to describe a man getting a haircut – getting your ears lowered

EIGHTY-EIGHT – A piano was referred to as an 88 because it has that many keys.

Dance Marathon (Library of Congress)

EMPRESS EUGÉNIE (U-SHAY-NEE) HAT – Woman's hat that made a comeback and became wildly popular in 1931; named for the wife of Napoleon III, it looked like a modified cloche hat with feathers.

ESKIMO PIE – Ice cream food fad of the masses in the Twenties

EXPATRIATES – Disillusioned, creative types (Hemingway, Stein, Fitzgerald, Ezra Pound) left the U.S. and lived on the Left Bank in Paris because it was the *in* thing to do; starving artists found it cheaper to live there since the exchange rate with the Franc was 20-1

EXPLODING SUIT – When racketeers tried to force cleaning establishments to pay for protection (extortion), some of them refused. A unique method of punishment or intimidation was to send a suit to the cleaners. Into the seams of the suit the thugs would sew inflammable chemicals that exploded when subjected to the cleaning and pressing process.

EYE-TIE – Slander for someone Italian - He's just a dirty eye-tie.

FARM RADIO – The vast majority of farms did not have electricity until Rural Electrification came along in the late 1930s. Radio sets intended for farm use were manufactured for D/C current from a battery rather than household A/C.

FARO – A card gambling game where players bet on cards drawn from a dealing box

FASHION PLATE – Twenties expression for a fancy dresser

FATBACK – A strip of fat from the back of a hog carcass cured by drying and salting

FEDORA – A low soft felt hat with the crown creased lengthwise

FEEDING SOMEONE THE GOLDFISH – Chicago copspeak for beating someone with a rubber hose

FELIX THE CAT – Popular cartoon character of the Twenties

FIFTY Gs – Slang for fifty grand or $50,000

FIN – Slang for a five-dollar bill

FLAGPOLE SITTING – A strange endurance fad that became wildly popular in the 1920s. People found tall poles and erected small platforms on top of them and tried to see how long they could endure. A fellow named "Shipwreck Kelly," who claimed to be a survivor of the *Titanic*, became the most noteworthy.

FLAMING YOUTH – Term used to describe carefree youth of the 1920s who ignored convention typified by Clara Bow, Hollywood's "It" Girl (I don't know what "it" is, but whatever "it" is, she's got IT.) Elinor Glyn, a well-known author of pulp romance stories of the time, defined the *mot juste* "it" as an unusual **animal magnetism**. This type of carefree woman was footloose, drove fast cars, bathed in milk, and reveled in hedonistic madcap antics; Bow married cowboy star Rex Bell in 1931; spent her last years in a mental ward.

Aunt Jemima mix

FLAPJACKS - Pancakes

FLAPPER – A young woman of the era who showed freedom from convention by wearing flimsy dresses, head-hugging hats, heavy makeup, and rubber galoshes (overshoes) leaving them unbuckled so that they flapped when they walked. Onlookers said, "Here come the flappers." Corsets, bras, heavy cotton stockings, ankle-binding shoes, long skirts and petticoats were out. Smoking in public was "in." Some of the movie flappers were Joan Crawford, Mae Murray, Colleen Moore and Louise Brooks.

Flapper with cigarette

FLAT - CHESTED LOOK – This was another popular fad for women of the era. They didn't wear a bra but bound their chests with strips of linen or muslin cloth. This technique lent itself to the popular style of sheath dress that was often worn during the Roaring Twenties.

FLATIRON – When women ironed clothes they had two flatirons. One was used to iron with while the other sat on top of a stove and soaked up the heat. After the one being used cooled, it was traded for the hot one on the stove. To see if it was hot enough, women touched their index finger to their tongue to wet it, and then pressed it to the bottom of the iron to see if it sizzled.

FLAT TIRE – Boring person

FLICK – A slang expression for a movie due to the fact that the light mechanism produced a flickering effect. The carbon arc light that was used with early projectors burned

Chevrolet two passenger roadster

very hot and often caused disastrous theater fires because the film itself was made of highly flammable cellulose nitrate. That is why early movie screens were made with fire-resistant asbestos. Tri-acetate safety film did not come into use until 1948.

FLIPPED HIS WIG – To get very upset about something

FLIVVER – A slang expression for a small automobile; cars were also called gas buggies

FLYPAPER – A narrow strip of paper and covered with a sticky adhesive; flies landing on it were unable to free themselves.

FORTY-ELEVEN – An expression used to exaggerate a number. "I've told you forty-eleven times to stop doing that."

FORTY WINKS – An expression used to describe a nap

FOUNDLING – A baby left in front of a police station or on the steps of a church

FREEWHEELING – Saving gasoline by coasting in an automobile; pioneered by Studebaker; a knob on the dash was pulled out to engage freewheeling mechanism; abandoned after several years because it was considered dangerous

FRENCH HEEL – Women's shoes in the early Twenties were quite pointed and often had French heels - heels that were slightly flared at the bottom.

FRUIT JAR ALKY – A number of moon shiners bottled their spirits in old fruit jars with zinc lids that sometimes corroded and leached toxins into the drink.

FUR SCARF – The fur part of this accessory was taken literally. It was worn around the neck in winter and consisted of a skinned fox, with head and forepaws on one end, and tail and hind legs on the other.

GAMS – Female legs; She had a great pair of gams.

42 GANG – A group of thugs on Chicago's west side organized themselves into a gang around 1925. They were kind of a farm team for Capone's mob. They took their name from Ali Baba and the 40 Thieves. They thought they were one better, plus Ali Baba, than the literary gang.

GANGSTER TOWN – Slang expression for Cicero

Haynes open touring car

GARROTE – A thin wire used to strangle a member of the opposition.

GASPERS – An early epithet for cigarettes; also called "coffin nails;" Henry Ford opined in a 1914 pamphlet that cigarette smokers were unemployable; Thomas Edison thought that the burning paper surrounding the tobacco caused brain damage. Clever advertising in the 1920s made cigarette smoking wildly popular.

GAT – Gangster lexicon for a gun, ostensibly a tribute to Richard Gatling of Chicago, inventor of the gatling gun

GIGGLE WATER – An alcoholic drink

G – MEN – Slang for government men who either worked as prohibition agents like Eliot Ness or who simply were FBI agents such as Melvin Purvis

GIN-JOINT – Slang expression for a tavern; sometimes referred to as a thirst clinic

GIRL NEXT DOOR – Some women exuded a certain wholesomeness with their demure prettiness. Their manner of dress was less flamboyant than that of flappers and vamps. Mary Pickford, Lila Lee, Lillian and Dorothy Gish, and Laura La Plante portrayed girls of this type in the movies.

GLOVES – Gloves were fashionable with any formal wear – church, weddings, dinning out, funerals, opera. etc.; amazingly, the length of gloves in this era was measured in terms of buttons.

GOB OUTFIT – Name given to women's sport outfits that had a navy/nautical look and consisted of swagger pants, jacket and middy with contrasting tie

GOLDDIGGER – A woman who's attracted to a man only because of his wealth; women of this type were exemplified in the Anita Loos book, *Gentlemen Prefer Blondes*

GOOD HOUSEKEEPING – This smart, big, glossy, conservative magazine with advice for American housewives arrived on the scene in 1924

GRAFT – Money that was given to policemen, judges, and politicians for looking the other way was referred to as graft.

GRAMOPHONE – The name given to Thomas Edison's invention. A hand crank on the side of the box wound a spring that supplied mechanical power to a turntable that enabled it to play a record. Portable models could be taken to the beach or on picnics. Sound reproduction was mechanical and amplification was achieved by a large brass horn. The term for Grammy Awards comes from this device.

GRAVITY PUMP – Gasoline back then was dispensed mechanically. The attendant pushed a long handle back and forth which brought the gasoline from the storage tank below into a large glass container at the top with markings to show the number of desired gallons. The nozzle was then placed into the gas tank and the gasoline went into the car by gravity. This was sometimes called the "visible supply" gasoline pump. S.F. Bowser Company of Fort Wayne, Indiana, was the largest manufacturer.

Oil at filling stations was stored in glass bottles that looked like quart canning jars with a long tapered metal spout for pouring it into the crankcase.

GREASE CUP – Car chassis back then were lubricated with grease cups located on the undercarriage. The cups were later replaced by oil wicks and these, in turn, gave way to pressurized fittings.

GREAT WHITE WAY - Broadway (due to the bright lights)

GREENBACKS – Paper money

GREEN BEER – Beer that hasn't been properly cooked and fermented

GRIPPE – Old fashioned expression for a mild case of the flu

GRIP – Old-fashioned term for a suitcase.

GUMSHOE – A slang expression for a private detective. They usually wore rubber-soled shoes to make less noise when following someone surreptitiously.

McClure's Magazine

GUN MOLL – Gangster girlfriend who typically had a drugstore complexion and frizzy hair combed slantwise across their foreheads; "moll" is a corruption of the name Mary, the most common name, by far, of women in England several centuries ago.

HABERDASHERY – Men's clothing store; Gentlemen's Quarterly was founded in 1926 as a haberdashery trade catalog.

HACK – Slang expression for a cab driver or his car

HAMS – A technique used by rumrunners to escape being caught by the Coast Guard. If pursued, the illegal booze was placed in gunnysacks with salt to weigh it down when tossed overboard. In time, the salt would melt and the contraband would float back to the top. When the danger had passed, the booze would be reclaimed.

HANDLE – A person's name as in "What's your handle?"

HEADACHE BAND – A slang expression for a fashion accessory that was several inches wide and wrapped around the woman's forehead. They were often made of fabric that matched the dress. Some were beaded while others were bejeweled with emeralds and pearls.

HEADS AND TAILS –
Many bootleg operators didn't bother to discard the beginning or end of a production run, which was contaminated by deadly aldehydes and fusel oil, resulting in severe illness and sometimes death for those who consumed it.

Olga Petrova and her Packard

HEAD CHEESE – A jellied loaf made from edible scraps of meat from a pig's head, feet, tongue and heart and cured in a hickory smokehouse

HEATER – Slang expression for a gun

HEEBIE-JEEBIES – Slang for "feeling nervous"

HEEL – A cad, a self-serving jerk who uses women and then tosses them aside, looking for his next conquest

THE HIDEOUT – A 400-acre estate constructed for Al Capone in the Roaring Twenties as his north woods retreat. It was located on a hill overlooking a beautiful lake in Couderay, Wisconsin, and fashioned of native stone. The place included a main lodge, a bunkhouse, a gun tower, a jail cell, and a main garage.

HIP FLASK – About the size of a cigarette case, only thicker, with a cap that screwed on and off, carried in a man's hip pocket for a quick nip of booze.

HOI POLLOI – A Greek term that referred to the common people but in vernacular usage came to mean the rich or the elite

HOKUM – Pretentious nonsense

HOMBURG – Popular hat for males with a stiff curled brim and a high crown creased lengthwise

HOME BREW SCOTCH – A mixture of water, caramel, prune juice, and creosote

HOOFER – Chorus line girl

HOOVER BLANKETS – Hoboes who had to sleep on a park bench covered themselves with newspapers to keep warm.

HOOVER HOGS – Jackrabbits that hoboes managed to catch and cook over an open fire.

HOOVERVILLES – After the Depression hit in October of 1929, cardboard, tin, and tarpaper shanties that sprang up along riverfronts and were occupied by the homeless were given the epithet Hooverville, blaming the president. Chicago had a Hooverville at Harrison and Canal Street.

HOT SQUAT – Electric chair

HOTSY TOTSY – Pleasing, pleasant

HOUSE DICK: Slang for hotel detective

HUNKIE – Derogatory expression for someone of Hungarian descent; sometimes phrased as Bohunk.

HUNKY-DORY – Everything's a-okay, hunky dory

ICE – Protection money paid by the mob to police and politicians to get them to lay off

ICEBOX – Before electric refrigerators, food items that needed to be kept cold were placed in a metal lined wooden box, about four and a half feet tall. An iceman came around each day and delivered 25 or 50 pound chunks that were placed inside to keep the perishables cold. A metal tray at the bottom caught the water from the melted ice. It was always emptied just before going to bed.

INDIAN FILE – Twenties expression for a group marching in a straight line

INFANTILE PARALYSIS – Another term for polio; children who contracted polio often had to wear metal braces to support their legs

IN THE PINK – Someone "in the pink" was looking good, rosy cheeked and feeling good.

ISINGLASS – Pronounced iz-n-glas: A gelatinous semi-transparent substance prepared from the air bladder of the sturgeon, commonly applied to thin sheets of mica and used for small side windows in touring cars; also used in stove fronts so you could see inside to determine if the fire was getting low

JACKASS BRANDY – A poisonous drink made from peaches that sometimes caused internal bleeding

JAKE – Okay – commonly used in the expression "everything's Jake"

JAWCRACKER - Dentist

JAZZ – Jazz music was intended in the 1920s as a unique, purely American art form. It derives from the word "jass," a Negro euphemism for sex. The Negroes who invented it were revolting from convention and the sadness and boredom of blues music. It originated in New Orleans but quickly spread to Chicago and New York. Many blamed this "primitive" music for the decline in morals during the era. George Gershwin's 1924 *Rhapsody in Blue* is actually a jazz concerto.

JODHPUR – Riding breeches that are cut wide at the hips and close fitting from the knee to the ankle

Fats Waller

JOHNNY CAKE – Another term for baked corn meal

JUNIPER ADE – A non-alcoholic temperance drink

JUTNEY – A nickel slot machine

KEEPING UP WITH THE JONES – Edith Jones was born into a family that was notorious for its social climbing. She later became famous as a writer and better known for her married name, Edith Wharton.

KIKE – Slang expression for a Jew

KILL-DEVIL – Gin and beer

KIMONO – Imported from Japan and very popular among women of the 1920s; they took the place of the traditional housecoat. They had wide sleeves and a broad sash.

KNICKERS – Loose fitting pants worn mostly by boys and golfers that were fitted just below the knee.

KNUCKLEDUSTER – A barroom brawl

KRAUT – Derogatory term used to describe someone of German descent. Sometimes they were referred to as "dumb Dutchmen."

LAM – To flee - "He's on the lam."

LINDY HOP, CHARLESTON, TURKEY TROT, BLACK BOTTOM, FOX TROT, VARSITY DRAG – Popular dances of the 1920s. The Black Bottom was introduced in the second edition of "The Blackbirds," and was performed by Edith Wilson. The title refers to the Mississippi riverbed and not the actresses' posterior. It was an ugly foot-stomping dance that fortunately didn't last long.

LINKS – Slang for golf course, going back to the early landscape of Scotland where the game was invented

LOANSHARKING – Capone would give money to street loan sharks at an interest rate of about three percent. They, in turn, would loan it out at a rate of one percent a week or 52 percent a year.

LOCKJAW – An early symptom of tetanus poisoning characterized by spasm of the jaw muscles resulting in an inability to open one's jaws

LOUNGE LIZARD – Name given to gigolos who were thought to mainly be after a girl's virginity; men who sported side-whiskers were often branded with this epithet.

LYE SOAP – Many Illinoisans, especially those living in rural areas, still made their own soap. Lye was obtained by pouring water in a barrel of wood ashes (leeching vat) and letting the water percolate through them. The water was then boiled after refuse grease (such as grease leftover from frying bacon) was thrown into it. The mixture was then allowed to cool and harden and then it was cut into bars.

MACKEREL SNAPPER – Derogatory name for a Catholic because of the practice of eating fish on Friday; also called "fishbacks"

MAD MONEY – Women who went on dates took along enough money to get back home on a trolley in case their date got fresh with them and they chose to get out of the car.

MAGNETO – A device with a permanent magnet used to generate a spark from the plugs for starting a car. This was used in conjunction with a hand crank that was inserted at the bottom of the engine to turn it over and get it started. If the car backfired at that point, one could receive a broken thumb or arm. The electric starter, coil, distributor and generator replaced the crank and magneto. No battery was required for a magneto.

Mahjong

MAHJONG – A domino-like game from China with 144 tiles that became popular with Americans during the 1920s

MANGLE – Household machine used for ironing sheets and pillowcases

MANHATTAN BEER – The brand of beer sold by Al Capone. Fort Dearborn was his brand of hard liquor.

MARGIN – Buyers were allowed to purchase stock on credit (margin) with as little as ten percent down. This led to a lot of speculation and inflation; the stocks themselves were used as collateral. Most investors expected to pay off the debt by cashing in on some of their stocks after their value had risen. Everything worked reasonably well in a bull (rising) market, but when the bear (declining) market came along the whole thing crashed. If you bought General Motors stock in 1925, you were able to sell it three years later for double the value.

Room size stove

MEDICINAL ALCOHOL – The only legal alcohol allowed during Prohibition. It could only be obtained if a physician wrote patients a prescription for it. Patients who asked for prescriptions to aid the digestive process were said to have "thirstitis." A rum toddy was the standard cure for a sore throat.

MEDICINE BALL – A widely used instrument of physical fitness during this era. It was leather-covered and about 24 inches in diameter and two or more people would toss it back and forth for exercise. Used extensively with boxers, the trainer would throw the ball into the boxer's abdomen and the boxer would catch it and tighten up his muscles as if taking a blow from another fighter.

MEGAPHONE – A conical device used by cheerleaders, speakers and singers to amplify and direct their voices. Rudy Vallee became famous for using the megaphone while singing "My Time is Your Time."

MESH BAG – Cloth vanity case

MICK – A corruption of the common Irish name Michael, usually meant to be offensive

MICKEY FINN – Knockout drops of chloral hydrate named for a 19th century Chicago thug

MILL TAX – Municipalities, strapped for cash, often imposed a mill tax on goods and services sold in their town. The mill was worth a tenth of a penny and was often made of cheap metal about the size of a nickel. A half-penny mill with a large 5 stamped on it (five-tenths of a penny) was also usually produced. When metal mills proved too expensive to produce, plastic mills were minted.

MINIATURE GOLF – Invented in 1927 by Garnet Garner, a hotel operator on Lookout Mountain, Tennessee, as a diversion for his guests. Three years later there were 40,000 courses scattered throughout the nation. Garner devised a Tom Thumb franchise name for his brand of Lilliputian links and was smart enough to sell out before the craze died out a few years later.

MONACLE – A single eyeglass lens attached to a fancy string necklace. Hard to believe, but this fashion accessory was briefly popular with women who pursued the androgynous look.

MOTORCARS – Autos of this age included the Packard, Essex, Ford, Durant, Chevrolet, Nash, Olds, Dodge, Reo, Studebaker, Buick, Auburn, Chrysler, Hudson, Stutz, DuPont, McFarland, Franklin, Jewett, Peerless, Hupmobile, Cadillac, Dorris, Pierce-Arrow, Willys-Knight, Lincoln, Daniels, Duesenberg, Maxwell, Briscoe, Templar, Rolls Royce, Locomobile

MOUSE – A partial black eye from a fight. You've got a mouse under your eye.

MULES – Women's bedroom slippers; they often had large pompoms on the front

NEAR BEER – Legal beer with a low alcohol content of less than 1 percent – hated by nearly everyone. Normally beer was about 3.2 percent alcohol.

NECKING AND PETTING – These two words came into existence after the war. Generally they meant the same thing but some defined necking as "kissing from the neck up" and petting involved anything else you please. The war was also blamed for the spread of smoking among women.

1929 Pierce-Arrow Runabout

NEEDLE BEER – Near beer to which raw alcohol is added

NEOPOLITAN – An Italian, like Capone, born in Naples; later used to describe someone who was widely traveled

NEWSHOUND – Slang for reporter

THE NEW YORKER – "Not for the old lady from Dubuque" was the slogan of this weekly that began publication in 1925; incredibly, this magazine, noted for its witty cartoons, still survives

NICKELODEON – Early movie houses charged a nickel for admission. An odeum was a small roofed Greek theater for reading poetry.

NORFOLK JACKET – A collegiate style men's jacket with box pleats down the sides and a belt in the back. In the Thirties, zoot suits became popular. The coat was overly padded in the shoulders and the lapels were outrageously wide. The sharply pleated pants taped down to narrow cuffs. The ensemble was completed with a knee-length key chain.

OAKIES – Poor white sharecroppers who left the Dust Bowl area after the '29 Crash and headed west, looking for jobs; epitomized by the Joad family in Steinbeck's *Grapes of Wrath*

OATER – Slang expression for a western movie. The Western had one basic plot: a good man opposes a bad man exploiting or terrorizing a locality. The bad man is often the hero's rival for the girl he loves. The hero prevails via moral and physical superiority, but only after the heroine is menaced, and only after the bad man comes perilously close to triumph.

OIL OF CLOVE – Toothache medicine

OLD BLACK CROW – KKK parlance for a Catholic nun

OMERTA – The code of silence of the underworld

ON THE LAM – Fleeing the law

OUIJA BOARDS – (pronounced we'ja) Popular parlor game that gave simplistic answers to questions; broken down, the title consists of the French and German words for "yes;" the board had letters and signs on it that was used with a planchette to give spiritualistic or telepathic messages.

Ouija board (World Wide)

OXFORD BAGS – Sporting the "collegiate" look, men's pants had three-inch cuffs at the bottom and were flared by as much as 20 inches at the ankle.

PALAVER – A discussion or conference

PALMISTRY – There were those who believed that one's future could be foretold by reading the hands – their size, shape, texture, diameter of the fingers, and the direction and depth of the five lines that cross the palm, as well as the manner in which they cross.

PANAMA HAT – A lightweight hat made from hand-woven strips of fiber from a South American plant.

PARASOL – Women often carried small umbrellas during the daytime to protect their delicate skin from the sun.

PATENT MEDICINE – Nostrums that could be sold by druggists without a prescription

PEA COATS – A three-quarter-length coat, usually navy blue with large navy blue buttons with an anchor scribed on them

PEEPERS – Eyes

PERNICIOUS ANEMIA – A serious condition in which the blood is deficient in red blood cells. The standard treatment back then was to have all your bad teeth pulled out.

PHRENOLOGY – A popular pseudo-science that claimed you could determine a person's intelligence by the shape of his skull.

PIANO – Another slang expression for a Tommy gun because one could play a violent tune with it.

PIGEON – Someone who is a target or an intended victim

PIG LATIN – A nonsensical language that was invented where words were manufactured from the original by taking the first letter and placing it at the end, then adding "ay" to the ending. Thus nix (no) became ixnay.

PIKER – A small time operator

PINCH – Slang for an arrest

PINEAPPLE – Slang expression for a hand grenade or bomb

PITCHING WOO – The art of dating and romancing

PLAINCLOTHESMAN – Police detective

PLAYER PIANOS – Player pianos first came on the scene around 1900 by remained popular into the 1920s. The Aeolian Company's "Pianola" was among the earliest. The first units had a 65-note capacity but that was soon expanded to 88. **Chicago** became the manufacturer of player pianos that were used in taverns, ice cream parlors and dance halls that required the insertion of a nickel before play would begin. Crown Piano Company had a factory at the corner of Washington and Sangamon streets that was six stories high and occupied a square city block. Melville Clark, a Chicago player piano maker, moved his factory to **DeKalb**.

Most units sold to homeowners had words to the music printed on the roll so that parents and children could join together in a sing-along.

Power in the form of air pressure was supplied by a foot treadle, similar to that used on sewing machines. As the hole in the roll traveled over a tracker bar, a small bellow moved a rod that pushed down on the appropriate piano key.

PLUCKED EYEBROWS – Movie stars such as Jean Harlow plucked their eyebrows and then had them drawn on by someone like Max Factor to achieve the desired shape. This practice, of course, caught the fancy of ordinary women who followed the trend.

Prohibition cartoon

PLUG-UGLIES – Stout Irishmen in turf wars protected their heads in combat with leather-reinforced plug hats.

PNEUMATIC TUBES – Large department stores in Chicago used pneumatic tubes driven by air pressure. A customer handed a clerk the money for the item he or she wished to purchase. The clerk wrote the name of the item and cost on a slip of paper and everything was transported upstairs to the accounting department. The customer's change was quickly and efficiently sent back in the same tube. Smaller stores used a wire and pulley system with the money being sent in small envelopes clipped to the wire by a spring operated clothespin.

PODUNK – Mythical small town about which H.L. Mencken once wrote a 3,000 word monograph

PONGEE – Silk-like material made into underpants for women, looking much like a fancy pair of men's boxer shorts; a thin material also made into men's shirts – William Jennings Bryan wore a pongee shirt at the Scopes trial.

PORNO-GRAPHIC – The word originated in the 1920s when the *New York Graphic*, a tabloid, began concentrating on lurid stories about sex crimes.

POSTAGE DUE STAMPS – Back then if someone sent you a letter with insufficient postage the post office affixed postage due stamps on it, and the letter carrier collected the amount from the addressee.

POULTICE – A mixture or concoction that was used to apply to a wound to draw out infection.

PRIVATES – A euphemism for male sex organs; He was injured in the privates from buckshot.

PROHIBITION WATER – A euphemism for gin

PUBLIC ENEMY – A phrase coined by the Chicago Crime Commission to designate Al Capone. Later, newspapers and magazines used the term to describe such notorious characters as John Dillinger, Pretty Boy Floyd, and Bonnie and Clyde.

PULP MAGAZINES – Their popularity goes back to the Civil War era; Ned Buntline's dime novels about Buffalo Bill were the most popular; called pulp because they were printed on cheap newspaper pulp instead of regular paper

PURGATIVE – Old-fashioned term for a laxative

PUSHING UP DAISIES – Gangster slang for someone who gets killed and planted

PUT ON THE SPOT – Lured or betrayed to a place where one might be murdered with a favorable chance for the gangster's getaway

PUTTEE – A cloth strip that was wrapped around the leg from the knee to the ankle; a holdover from World War I "doughboy look"

PUTTING ON THE RITZ – The Ritz Hotel in New York gained a reputation for being classy, opulent and posh - ritzy. Puttin' on the ritz meant going first class.

RACCOON COAT – Overcoats for men and women made from raccoon skins were popular to wear at college football games

RACKET – Old social clubs held gala benefit events to raise money. These were usually noisy affairs. Gangsters began organizing their own "racket" by forcing local businesses to purchase a ticket that guaranteed "protection" or suffer the consequences

RED SCARE – Growing fear of Communism due, in part, to events such as increased violence in labor strikes and the Wall Street bombing. It started when Leon Trotsky issued a call for world-wide revolution from the Kremlin.

1923 Hupmobile Roadster

RINGWORM – Teachers used special lights at school to check the scalps of children infected with lice or ringworm; although its name suggested otherwise, the condition was caused by a fungus, not a worm.

ROADSTER –An automobile peculiar to the Twenties that had an open top, two seats and a luggage compartment on the rear.

THE ROCK – Gangster slang for Alcatraz

ROCKY MOUNTAIN OYSTERS – A euphemism for sliced and cooked pig testicles

43

ROLL-YOUR-OWN – People who couldn't afford to buy cigarettes rolled their own. They would take out a pouch of tobacco with drawstrings and tap some out in a specially-sized tissue paper. The paper was then rolled into the shape of a cigarette and the ends would be pinched closed. One edge of the paper was licked to seal the tube.

ROSCOE – gun, gat, heater, rod

ROTOGRAVURE – Metal engraved printing cylinder - a section of the newspapers devoted to pictures; the term is mentioned in the popular song, "Easter Parade"

ROUGE – Today it is the fashion to use a blush, but it is blended so that it gives the cheeks a natural glow. Back then the rouge was painted on and not blended so that it remained on the cheek as a prominent spot. **Rouge was also often applied to a woman's knees.**

RUBE – A country bumpkin; someone less sophisticated than a city dweller

RUB OUT – Gangsters often did cops a favor by rubbing each other out

RUMBLE SEAT – A roadster or coupe with a fold out seat in the rear that was without a top. Sometimes called a Dickey; the 1927 Model-T Ford had a two-passenger capability that folded out from the trunk which left it unprotected from the weather.

Packard with rumble seat

RUNNING BOARD – Cars of this era sat higher off the ground and had larger wheels because many people who bought them lived in the country where low-slung cars were impractical. Running boards were merely step-ups that were often connected to the bottom of the front fender and rear fender.

SALT GUNS – Double-barreled shotguns, loaded with salt, used by teen gangs in the 1920s. When hit by a load it didn't kill, but it stung like crazy.

SANDWICH SIGNS – Creative advertisers hired men to wear hinged boards with messages on the front and back, advertising their product. When the Depression hit in 1929 desperate men walked the streets with homemade signs that said something like WANTED – A DECENT JOB. Printed below in smaller letters would be something like "family man," a brief resume and an address or phone number.

SATURDAY NIGHT BATH – Daily showers or baths were almost unheard of in the 1920s. For most families a cleansing bath was a once-a-week ritual done on Saturday night, before church on Sunday morning. For many, the bathing was done in a large metal galvanized tub. If the family was large, it was not uncommon for several people to use the same water before it was thrown out.

SAWBUCK – Ten dollars because the Roman numeral for ten was an X that looked like a sawbuck

SAWDUST TRAIL – Slang term used to describe the soul-winning circuit used by evangelists of the era; the dirt floor of their tent meetings was often strewn with sawdust

SAWED OFF SHOTGUN – Long, cut-short

SCHICK TEST – An injection given under the skin to determine whether one was susceptible to diphtheria, a contagious disease that produced a sore throat and caused inflammation of the heart and central nervous system

SCOFFLAW – A law that was scoffed at or widely ignored such as Prohibition

SCORCHING – Slang term for speeding

SCRAPPLE – A seasoned mixture of pork scraps and cornmeal set in a mold and fried

SCREW – Gangster slang for a prison guard

SCRIP – Strapped for cash after the onset of the depression in 1929, many towns paid their workers with emergency paper money called scrip. Merchants were asked to accept this money at face value with the promise that the local government stood behind it.

SEPSIS – Blood poisoning; Calvin Coolidge's son died from a blister that got infected because there were no antibiotics.

SHEIK – A Jazz Age male who slicked his hair back with pomade like Rudolph Valentino, snake danced, strummed a ukulele, patronized cabarets and made out with the women. The equivalent term for females of the era was Sheba. The stereotype that developed held that a sheik was a character of the Valentino mold whose one aim in life was to carry young ladies off to his tent in the desert and deflower them.

Valentino suffered an untimely death at a young age in 1926.

SHILL – Someone who worked in conjunction with a confidence man. The shill acted like a typical customer who was thrilled with the sale if a product was being sold. In gambling, the shill bragged to others about being a big winner, whetting the appetite of potential gamblers.

Bix Beiderbecke (trumpet) & the Wolverines

SHIMMY – A torso shaking dance step, imitated from black cabaret dancers, which supposedly separated "nice girls" from brazen flappers.

SHINGLE – A masculine-looking haircut for women with a single curl pulled forward from each cheek

SHIVAREE – An old custom introduced by the French when they first settled in America along the Illinois Mississippi River valley at **Cahokia**. The word, loosely translated, means "headache." Newlyweds were given a surprise visit by friends who sang them a noisy mock serenade and played tricks on them. Afterwards, it was traditional for the newlyweds to invite the pranksters inside their home for a drink. You don't hear much about these after the early 1950s.

SHOOFLY PIE – A rich pie of Pennsylvania Dutch origin made with molasses and a crumbly mixture of flour, sugar and butter. A few crumbs from this in a far corner of the room would shoo flies away from the main food on the table by drawing them to it.

Elgin bicycle

SHOTGUN – Passenger side, front seat of a car – so named because that spot on top of a stagecoach was manned by a guard with a shotgun.

SHUT-EYE – Slang expression for sleep

SIDEBOARD – A piece of dining room furniture having compartments and shelves for holding articles of table service. Today it is called a buffet.

SILLABUB – Port wine, milk and sugar

SKIMMER – A stiff straw hat; the type you see today used at political rallies as a throwback to the old days.

SLAVE BRACLETS – These wrist fashions were thick and wide. During the Jazz Decade they were omnipresent and made from every kind of material imaginable.

SLOP JAR – Another term for a chamber pot for those who lived in homes without indoor plumbing and water closets

SMACKERS – Slang for dollars; Her exquisite fur coat set him back $950 smackers.

SMOKING SUITS – Oversized pajamas that women wore while clutching long cigarette holders between their teeth

SNEAKERS – Tennis shoes

SNOOTS – Sliced pig snout seasoned, breaded and fried

"SNORKY" – A nickname for Al Capone. It means "elegant."

SOB SISTER – Sentimental female reporter

SODA JERK – Used to designate the young man behind the marble counter at a drug store or Five and Dime store. He produced a nickel Coca Cola on the spot by mixing syrup and carbonated water and placing it in a stainless metal container that held a paper cone. He also dipped cones, made banana splits and ice cream sundaes.

SODA POP MOON – Philadelphia whiskey that contained a good dose of isopropyl alcohol

SOUSE - Seasoned and pickled pork trimmings; sometimes used to refer to a drunk

SPAGHETTI SNAPPER – Derogatory name for an Italian

SPATS – A popular fashion accessory for men in the 1920s was a cloth or leather gaiter that snapped around the ankles and covered the instep of a shoe.

SPEAKEASY – An illegal gin joint that usually featured music, dancing, drinking and gambling. Classy places issued membership

Texas Guinan – Queen of the Speakeasies

cards; some had a special coded knock on the door to gain access, and others required prospective customers to whisper a password or speak easy and say something like "Joe sent me."

SPEAKING TUBE – Many of the cars of the twenties had front compartments for the chauffeur that were isolated from the passengers. They communicated via a speaking tube.

SPIFFLICATED – Another highbrow description of someone who is inebriated or plastered

SPIKED BEER – Regular beer to which ginger ale and raw alcohol is added

SPIC – A slanderous term used to describe someone of Hispanic descent; a corruption of the word Hispanic

SPITOONS – Brass containers with a large oval openings for people who chewed tobacco to spit in. They were usually in hotel lobbies, at bars, in banks and in taverns.

STEP-INS – Female underwear

STICKPIN – A stickpin was a decorative item worn on a man's tie. Those who were affluent often sported stickpins featuring a large diamond.

STIR, PEN, SLAMMER, POKEY, JUG, HOOSEGOW, BIG HOUSE, BUG HOUSE – Slang expressions for prisons

STOOLIE OR STOOL PIGEON – Gangster slang for someone who talks to the cops and causes someone else to get caught. This harkens back to the old days when pigeons were caught and eaten as food. A pigeon would be caught, have his eyes sewn shut, and then placed on a stool to attract other pigeons that could then be caught and killed.

Male garter

STOP RIBBING ME – Stop joking or teasing me.

STRUGGLE BUGGY – Slang for a car used by a man to seduce girls

SUICIDE DOORS – Cars of this period had doors hinged so that if you got out of a car and the driver absentmindedly took off, the door would knock you down.

SUPPORTERS – These were male garters made of elastic and worn by men to keep the top of their calf-length stocking from slipping down.

SUPPRESSOR – Many female dresses of this era were straight line and required no corset, reflecting the modernity of the Twenties. Keeping in fashion, a binding under-garment known as a suppressor was often worn to flatten the bosom into a more boyish line. There was a popular saying: Men won't dance with you if you wear a corset.

SWAIN – A beau or boyfriend

SWOONING – A nationwide epidemic caused by rakish Rudolph Valentino's actions on the silent screen. When this devilish male with pointed sideburns and slicked down hair popped his eyes, bared his teeth, flared his nostrils, and carried a beautiful Englishwoman into his tent in *The Shiek*, women in the audience emitted loud gasps and

45

moans, as they vicariously experienced being made love to and ravished

TAILGATE – A trombone was referred to by this name. Jazz bands often climbed into wagons and drove through the streets to advertise a dance. The trombone player, needing extra space due to the slide, sat on the tailgate and played with his feet dangling.

TAKE A POWDER – This means that one should "get lost," or leave in a hurry

"TALCUM CHEEKS" – Capone, sensitive to the white scars on his left cheek, often applied a coat of talcum powder to his face to hide the scars.

TANGO – A sensuous Argentine dance popularized by Rudolph Valentino in *The Four Horsemen of the Apocalypse.*

TANK – Local jail; Louie had to spend the night in the tank; sometimes referred to as the jug or can

TEA – A euphemism or code word for whiskey at the speak-easies

TECHNOCRACY – A new word added to the national lexicon that referred to the scientific wave of new devices that were making life easier and more enjoyable for working Americans

TEX GUINAN CHAMPAGNE – Named for Mary Louise "Texas" Guinan, an ex-silent movie star who dressed in diamonds and furs and ran classy joints in New York and Chicago. She greeted patrons with "Hello, suckers!" and wore a police whistle around her neck. Her "champagne" was merely sparkling cider laced with alcohol.

THE THIRD DEGREE – Questioning someone intensely, often with force. When the police hauled a suspect in, they gave him the third degree.

THREE-MILE LIMIT – On the seas, ships brought large cargoes of liquor to the three-mile limit, just beyond the reach of American law.

TIN PAN ALLEY – A place in New York where tunesmiths worked to create lyrics to songs. It was located on West 28th Street between Broadway and Sixth Avenue. When musicians first tried to play these songs it created a racket – hence tin pan alley. This was an era when a song's success was not measured by the number of records bought, but by the number of copies of sheet music sold.

T-MEN – Treasury men – IRS agents

TOGGERY – Clothing store

TONNEAU – The rear or trunk area of an automobile

Patent medicine political cartoon

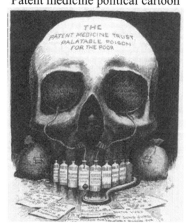

TONSILINE – Patent medicine sold by drug stores as a cure-all for coughs and sore throats

TORPEDOES – Slang expression for hit men. They were often outsiders so if someone happened to see them do the job, they wouldn't be recognized from a police mug shot book.

TOURING CAR – A large 4-door car suitable for distance driving, usually having a folding top. If the top was hard, the rear windows were usually curtained for privacy.

TRAFFIC SIGNALS – Traffic signals at this time did not have lights but used a device with a bell that had signs that flipped up into view. One said "stop" and the other read "go." In some places policemen were placed in a small white booth or on a foot-high white box at an intersection and used a whistle and a wave of their hands to direct traffic.

TROLLEY – Another name for the interurban streetcar, powered by electricity and rolling on metal rails

TURNKEY – Gangster slang for a jailer

TWENTY-THREE SKIDOO – A popular expression interpreted as "Let's get going."

TWO BITS – Slang for 25 cents because the old Spanish Pieces of Eight were scored into eighths with each bit being worth 12 and a half cents

TYPEWRITER – Yet another slang expression for a tommy gun because they both made chattering sounds

UNLUCKY CARD – The ace of diamonds has been considered an unlucky card ever since Joe Masseria was found murdered in 1931 holding the card in his right hand.

VAMP – The vamp was seen as a woman of the world who could drive men wild with desire. In movies and in novels,

Gloria Swanson

vamps would almost always lead men to ruin both morally and financially. Theda Bara, Pola Negri, Barbara LaMarr, Gloria Swanson and Greta Garbo became international stars for playing this role on the screen.

VANITY FAIR – A popular magazine of the era, employing a number of Algonquins as writers; it was slightly uppish in tone and bootlicked the successful, but it was both American and international in outlook

VAPORS – Women back then were stereotyped as prone to fainting easily from excitement. More likely, women fainted from the 25 pounds of pressure per square inch applied by tightly laced whalebone corsets to produce the desired hourglass figure. Expensive homes frequently had specially-made fainting couches in their parlors.

VAUDEVILLE – This form of entertainment began to die out in the 1920s. It started at the turn of the century and consisted of comedians, singers, juggling acts, animal acts and skits. The growing popularity of phonograph records, movies and radio all contributed to the decline. Performers such as Ed Wynn, Al Jolson, the Marx brothers, Will Rogers, and W.C. Fields got their start in vaudeville. By the end of the Twenties vaudeville was dead.

VELOCIPEDE – Old-time name for a bicycle

VERANDA - Porch

VINE-GLO – A California grape product that had the consistency of jelly. It produced wine when mixed with water and allowed to sit for a couple of months

WALK-A-THON – These were carnival-type events that were an offshoot of dance marathons. Billed as endurance contests, couples would walk around in a circular track until they were forced to drop out from exhaustion.

WARD HEELER – A worker for a political boss

WATER CLOSET – When indoor plumbing made it possible for the outhouse to come inside, the term water closet was used to describe the toilet. Instead of the water tank being affixed to the back of the toilet seat, it was located about seven feet high. To flush, occupants had to reach up and pull on a handle that was affixed to a long, sturdy chain. Comedian Jack Parr, 1950s host of "The Tonight Show," resigned in protest when a joke he wanted to tell about a water closet was censored.

Water closet

WHITE SLAVERY – People like Mary Hastings and Jim Colosimo were responsible for kidnapping young girls and forcing them into prostitution. After about four years the girls were literally worn out and they were thrown into the streets, their lives ruined.

WINDOW STRAPS – Crank-type window raisers did not come into common use until the mid-1920s. Before that windows were raised and lowered by straps.

WINE BRICKS – California grape growers produced and sold wine bricks, a solid mass of grape concentrate about the size of a pound of butter. Labels included instructions for adding water and "warnings" that fermentation could occur if allowed to sit for too long.

Wine brick

WIRELESS – Early name for a radio; the early sets required earphones for listening

WISH BOOK – What people back then called the annual edition of the Sears catalog. People in the country often used the pages from old catalogs for toilet paper.

WOP – A corruption of the Italian word "guappo," referring to a handsome scoundrel with a swagger; later used disparagingly to describe a person of Italian descent.

WRIST CHRONOMETER – Early designation for a watch

X MARKS THE SPOT – When newspapers ran a photo of a place where someone was killed, an X was used to indicate the place where the body was found.

YACK YACK BOURBON – Chicago moonshine flavored with iodine and burnt sugar

YOU'RE GOING FOR A RIDE – A phrase and technique first used by Chicagoan Hymie Weiss. The victim was taken for a ride out in the country, shot in the back of the head, and flung out of the car.

A special thanks to **Dr. Robert Malench** of **Edwardsville** for many of the medical terms on this list.

TYPICAL EXTORTION NOTE FROM A BLACK HANDER

Most Gentle Mr. Sullivan:
Hoping that the present will not impress you too much you will be so good as to send me $2,000 if your life is dear to you. So I beg you warmly to put them (sic) on the door within four days. But if not, I swear this week's time not even the dust of your family will exist. With regards, believe me to be your friend. . . .

SOME CARS OF THIS ERA

American Austin – A small car made in Butler, Penn. by Roy Evans

Auburn – Made in Auburn, Ind. by Frank and Morris Eckhart.

Blackhawk – A cheaper version of the Stutz Bearcat

Briggs & Stratton – Made by the Briggs & Stratton Company of Milwaukee (1920-22)

Buick – Made in Detroit by David Buick, inventor of the cast iron enameled bathtub

Cadillac – First built by Henry Ford and named for Antoine Cadillac, founder of Motor City

Chandler - Built in Cleveland until acquired by Hupmobile; featured a Pike's Peak engine that had been tested in the Colorado Rockies

Chevrolet – Established in 1911 by Will Durant and race car driver Louis Chevrolet

Comet – Made by the Comet Motorcar Company of **Decatur** (1917-21)

Cord – Named for Errett Cord, the head of Auburn Motors which built the car; Tom Mix drove a Cord

DeSoto – First manufactured in 1928 and slightly lower in price and quality than a Chrysler

Detroit Electric – Attained a glorious maximum speed of 25 mph; had a tiller for a handle since drivers sat in the back seat

Diana – Built by the Moon people in St. Louis

Doble – A steam powered car that required a 24-gallon tank – of water

Dodge – First built by the Dodge brothers of Detroit in 1914.

1929 Buick

Duesenberg – This is not a German car. The Duesie was built by Paul and August Duesenberg of Indianapolis, Indiana. Film stars Greta Garbo and Mae West popularized the fabulous car.

DuPont – A luxury car built by those hoity toity DuPonts of Delaware

Economy – Economy Car Company of **Joliet**, Illinois

Elgin – Elgin Motor Car Company of **Chicago** (1916-24)

Essex – Built by the Hudson Motor Co. of Detroit

Ford – The 1903 Ford looks exactly like a 1903 Cadillac because Henry Ford quit that company, took his plans with him, and launched his own firm.

Franklin – An air-cooled car made by H.H. Franklin of Syracuse, NY, and driven by famous people like Amelia Earhart and Charles Lindbergh. Since there was no radiator, an air screen was attached to the front of the car so it wouldn't look strange. Another unusual feature of this car was its laminated wooden frame.

Graham – Built by the three Graham brothers in Detroit and for a while sold quite well.

Hudson – Named for a Detroit department store mogul – not the explorer.

Haynes – This car had an aluminum body

Hupmobile – Named after the company founder, Robert Hupp of Detroit.

Jordan – Started at Cleveland in 1916 by an ex-newspaper man. It had a long and low silhouette and it featured "rattle proof" aluminum bodies. With extra wide doors for easy access, the Jordan had a distinctly French atmosphere.

1927 Hudson with gauges in center of the dashboard

Kissel – The two passenger Speedster featured two jump seats that emerged from each side of the body, just behind the driver's compartment, to give two additional passengers a precarious ride *just above the running boards*.

LaSalle – A lower priced version of a General Motors Cadillac

Lincoln – Founded in 1920 by Henry Leland but he ran into financial problems and was bought out by Ford.

Marmon – A large car built in Indianapolis; liked by big time gangsters

Marshall – Marshall Manufacturing Co. of **Chicago**

1923 Moon sport touring model

Moline Knight – Moline Auto Company of **East Moline**

Nash – Founded in 1917 by Charles Nash of Kenosha, Wis.

Oakland – A GM car whose sales declined rapidly in 1924 after the Pontiac was introduced. Tires on the Oakland, like most other cars, were only expected to last 10,000 miles.

Oldsmobile – Designed in 1901 by Ransom Olds as a one-cylinder car; "What a thrill to take the wheel, of my merry Oldsmobile . . . ." GM stopped making the car in 2004 because young people didn't like a car name with "old" in it.

Overland – Made in Toledo, Ohio, this car featured a Triplex spring system that banished road shocks

Packard – This luxury auto dates all the way back to 1899

Peerless – A Cleveland bicycle firm that decided there was more money to be made in cars

Pierce-Arrow – A prestigious car that came out of Buffalo N.Y., and was made by George Pierce. The 1920 Arrow had a Waltham clock built into the dashboard and an "air friction" speedometer that **measured speed by wind resistance** rather than by a cable.

Plymouth – A cheap car offered by Chrysler and named for those hardy settlers in New England because the car was said to embody their qualities of ruggedness and durability. It became the number three seller in America.

Porter – This was the featured vehicle in the old television series, "My Mother The Car." The incredible 1921 Porter had 125 horsepower.

Reo – Headed by Ransom Olds and made in Lansing. Mich. It was considered a well-made and lasting car by its owners. The Reo featured aluminum alloy pistons and large valves and exhaust ports.

Roamer – This beauty came out of Kalamazoo, Michigan, and bore a slight resemblance to the Rolls-Royce. Many of its models featured a Duesenberg engine.

Rickenbacker – Named for Captain Eddie, the race car driver turned ace aviator. The 1923 Rickenbacker featured FOUR WHEEL BRAKES and an AIR CLEANER.

Rock Falls – Rock Falls Motor Company of **Sterling**, Illinois

R&V Knight – Built by Root and Van Dervoort of **East Moline**; "Built For The Woman Who Drives" was their slogan

Stephens – Made in **Freeport**, Illinois, by the Moline Plow Company and could attain speeds of 60 mph.

Studebaker – Studebaker started out selling wheelbarrows to miners during the California Gold Rush. Then the family progressed from making carriages to horseless carriages. The 1922 model featured an oval courtesy light for passing motorists fixed on the outside cowl.

Stutz – Founded in 1911 by Harry Stutz. The Bearcat was the darling of Sheiks and Shebas during the Roaring Twenties. The 1921 Stutz was driven from the right side of the vehicle and this company, like Pierce Arrow, was one of the last to standardize the left side drive. The Bearcat model is one of the most prized by current collectors.

Tarkington – Tarkington Automobile Company of **Rockford**, Illinois

Velie – Velie Motors of **Moline**, Illinois (1908-1929)

Wills St. Claire – A strong, lightweight steel was used and this was hailed as the "Molybdenum Car"

Willys-Overland - Organized by John Willys who built cars in Indianapolis and Toledo. The com-pany would produce the famous World War II vehicle, the Jeep, so named because it was a General Purpose Vehicle.

1929 Chrysler $1,550

(I relied heavily on *Cars Of The Early Twenties* by Tad Burness, *100 Years of the American Auto* by James

48

Flammang, and Bob Elder of **Belleville** for information on automobiles in this book.)

GANGSTER BIOGRAPHIES

Tony Accardo was born in Chicago in 1906 and was raised on the northwest side – Little Sicily. He dropped out of high school, worked various odd jobs, including truck driving, and frequently got in trouble with the law. He was good pals with Machine Gun McGurn. He became an enforcer with the Capone group and **wielded a baseball bat** so efficiently he acquired the nickname, Joe Batters. Accardo frequently sat near the entrance of Capone's headquarters with a machine gun in his lap. Capone survived an assassination attempt in 1926 when Accardo pulled him down and shielded him with his body. According to many, he was a key player in the St. Valentine's Day Massacre. There are those who believe it was Accardo who wielded the bat – not Capone – when Anselmi and Scalise got their heads bashed in. Accardo was Capone's personal bodyguard when Capone attended the Atlantic City mob confab. When Joey Aiello of the Unione Sicilane was murdered, most thought that Accardo was responsible for the deed. In 1934 the 28-year-old Accardo married 22-year-old Clarice Porter, a beautiful Polish girl. Compared to most mobsters, Accardo was a good husband. Accardo's star rose after Capone was sent to prison for tax evasion. When the Outfit took control of things after Capone went to jail, Accardo was placed in charge of the gambling empire.

Accardo was given the nickname "Big Tuna" by reporter Ray Brennan of the *Sun-Times* after he caught a 400-pounder off the coast of Nova Scotia in 1949.

Joe Aiello - Aiello was a Capone foe who, along with brothers Dominic, Antonio, and Andrew, allied themselves with Dion O'Banion and Bugs Moran. It was Aiello who carried the effort to kill Capone to new heights by trying to persuade the chef of Bella Napoli Café to put prussic acid in the Big Guy's soup. Although offered $35,000 for the job, the astute chef figured that if he committed the deed he wouldn't live long enough to enjoy the money so he reported the bribe to Capone. Frustrated, Aiello let it be known that anyone brave enough to kill Capone would collect a $50,000 reward. Capone decided to take revenge and one evening in 1930 Aiello stepped outside his expensive apartment on the west side on North Kolmar

Avenue. He was caught in a blazing crossfire of sawed off shotgun blasts and Thompson machine gun fire.

Joe Aiuppa – Born in 1907, this guy dropped out of school after the third grade. But he had plenty of street smarts and quickly rose to a prominent position in the Chicago Outfit. He started out as a gunman for Capone and was questioned by police on numerous occasions after a corpse turned up. He was also known as a fixer and paid $500 a month to have secret copies of Chicago Crime Commission reports delivered to him. His nickname was "Ha Ha" because he usually wore a dour look on his face.

Many think that Aiuppa and Accardo were behind Sam Giancana's murder, upset over Giancana's refusal to share money from gambling operations he had set up with mob money in Mexico. Once Accardo and Aiuppa considered someone to be a has-been, they were as good as dead. Johnny Roselli, Giancana's closest associate, was murdered in Florida. Aiuppa was convicted in 1986 of conspiring to skim off Las Vegas gambling casino profits.

Gus Alex – Gussie was a protégé of Jake Guzik. This man of Greek descent ran the vice rackets for the Capone mob in the Loop area. He later was responsible for handling the Las Vegas skim for the Chicago Outfit. He was an avid skier and took numerous trips to Switzerland to squirrel away mob money. When the suspicious Swiss government barred him from the country, he obtained help from Senator Everett Dirksen who vouched for his good character. He appeared before the McClellan Committee and took the 5th Amendment 39 times.

Louis "Two Gun" Alterie

– He was one of those western psychopaths who joined up with the northside O'Banion mob and flamboyantly wore a pistol on each hip. He claimed to be deadly with either hand and often shot out saloon lights to prove it. **Alterie masterminded the hit on a horse** that was responsible for the riding mishap death of his buddy, Nails Morton. Alterie went to the stable, led the horse to the scene of the accident, punched him in the nose, and then shot him dead on the spot. Bugs Moran finally convinced this out-of-control villain (who had Capone's initials carved on his bullets) to go back to his ranch in Colorado. He was bumped off while visiting Chicago in 1935.

"Samoots" Amatuna – Samoots was a professional fiddler and was probably the first gangster to conceal his weapons inside a violin case. He was a fop who overdressed, owning over 200 monogrammed silk shirts. When a Chinese laundry man scorched one of his shirts he

John Dillinger cartoon

chased the man down, gun in hand. After having second thoughts about killing the man for such a petty offense, **he shot his delivery horse instead**.

Samoots took over as head of Unione Siciliane after Bloody Angelo Genna was murdered in 1925. Samoots was later murdered by two gunmen when he had a hot towel on his face while at a barber shop. He jumped out of the chair and caused the first gunman to miss all his shots, but the second gunman drilled him with four bullets. He requested a quickie marriage with his fiancée from his hospital bed, but he died before the ceremony could take place.

Moe Annenberg grew
up in a poor Chicago neighborhood and went on to become one of the richest men in America. And he did it with mob money. His Jewish-German family came to America to escape persecution.

Moe quit school at age 12 and ran messages for Western Union. He found work in the *Chicago Tribune's* circulation department. Then he switched over to working for William Randolph Hearst as circulation manager. When the "circulation wars" broke out between the four major Chicago newspapers around 1904, it was Annenberg who devised the roughhouse tactics. He hired a bunch of thugs to burn rival newspapers, overturn their trucks and beat up their vendors. One of his employees was Frank McErlane. Before the battle between Hearst and Colonel Randolph was over in 1913, **27 news dealers were killed**.

Annenberg came to realize that the big money was in racing information and news. In 1922 he bought the Daily Racing Form and by 1926 his income had grown to the point where he could afford to quit the Hearst organization. He bought several east coast publications and formed a partnership with Frank Erickson, a close associate of Lucky Luciano. Nation-Wide News Service was the result.

Al Capone brought Annenberg down to the famous Atlantic City Conference in 1929, discussing ways that they could assist each other to their mutual benefit. Nation Wide took in huge amounts of money, dealing with 29 racetracks and sending information and taking bets in over 233 cities. Since most of these bets were made by telephone and telegraph, **Annenberg became AT&T's fifth largest customer**.

In the 1930s Annenberg bought the *Philadelphia Inquirer* and soon became a respected power broker in the Republican Party.

But Moe, like Capone, got greedy and failed to pay his taxes. He and his son Walter were both indicted in late 1939. Walter agreed to change a "not guilty" plea to

"guilty," in return for charges being dropped against his son.

When Moe went to prison, Nation-Wide News went under and was replaced by Continental Press Service, an organization that was heavily criticized by the Kefauver hearings. James Ragen replaced Moe Annenberg as the new racing czar.

Moe died in 1942 but son Walter went on to be the founder of "TV Guide" magazine and "Seventeen." He was also a big friend of Richard Nixon and was appointed ambassador to England. In later life he became a big philanthropist, hoping to erase the stain on the family name caused by his father's criminal record.

Anti-Prohibition cartoon

Albert Anselmi –
Squat and bulky, this murderous thug teamed up with tall and lanky John Scalise and the duo were referred to by the press as the Mutt and Jeff of Chicago crime. **This pair was responsible for introducing the "handshake hit"** whereby one killer would greet the victim with a firm handshake while the other gunned him down. The pair also brought over the Sicilian custom of rubbing garlic on bullets in the odd belief that it would cause gangrene. They fled their native homeland under the threat of murder charges around 1920 and quickly went to work for the Gennas. Tales of the vicious manner in which they killed their victims became the talk of the underworld. They were arrested for participating in the St. Valentine's Day massacre but did not live long enough to stand trial. Capone suspected the pair of duplicity, invited them to a gala feast, and then beat the pair to death with an Indian club.

Frank Capone – Many say this eldest brother was
even more savage than Al Capone. In the 1924 city election (in Cicero) Frank Capone and his cohorts were actively engaged in intimidating voters at the polls who had the courage to vote Democratic in opposition to the Capone-backed Republican candidate. Citizens were asked how they were going to vote, and if they answered incorrectly their ballot was taken from them and they were threatened with a gun to vote Republican. Seventy policemen were rushed to Cicero to stop the fraud at a polling place near Western Electric. When the police arrived in unmarked cars both Capones opened fire and a lengthy gun battle ensued. Frank was cut down by shotgun blasts and Al fled the scene. Frank was given the biggest funeral in gangsterdom up to that time.

Ralph "Bottles" Capone

Ralph "Bottles" Capone – Ralph never rose very high on the list of crime leaders and was used mainly to relay orders from Al to others in the organization. He was called "Bottles" due to several soft-drink establishments Al set up for him to run. Ralph's bottled waters and Coca-Cola were about the only soft drinks that were sold at the Chicago World's Fair of 1933-34. Ralph maintained Al's estate in Palm Beach while his brother was at Alcatraz, and it was used to host various meetings by mob bosses. While Ralph lived the good life his son, Ralph Jr., had trouble accepting the fact that his father and uncles were gangsters. Shortly after Ralph appeared to testify before the Kefauver Committee, **his son committed suicide** with an overdose of pills. Ralph died a rich man in 1974 at the age of 81.

Big Jim Colosimo

Big Jim Colosimo - Colosimo was the criminal overlord of Chicago in 1919 and 1920. He was a flashy dresser, wearing white linen suits and lots of diamond jewelry. He brought in his nephew from New York, Johnny Torrio, to run his restaurant and speakeasy business. Torrio begged Colosimo to get into the bootlegging business, telling him that millions could be made. But Colosimo didn't think that prohibition was going to last long enough to make it worth the effort.

Colosimo's ex-wife provided the capital to get him started in the restaurant business. He divorced her and fell in love with a choir singer who started doing the nightclub circuit. Her name was Dale Winter and she was quite attractive and much younger than Colosimo.

Colosimo was killed three weeks after he married Dale Winter in April of 1920. A restauranteer and vice lord of the Chicago district known as The Levee, he was gunned down in the lobby of his own establishment.

Colosimo was Chicago's first great underworld king (1900-1920). His restaurant was frequented by idols of the day, such as **Enrico Caruso, George M. Cohan, Sophie Tucker** and **Al Jolson**. Some thought his first wife, Victoria, was responsible for his death, but she was in L.A. at the time of the killing. Colosimo's murder on May 11 enabled Torrio and Capone to enlarge their holdings in vice and racketeering.

Others thought Frankie Yale murdered Colosimo so he could expand his own empire. He was charged with the murder, and it was Johnny Torrio who now presided over the operation of countless brothels, speakeasies and gin joints in the old Levee District. Colosimo was Torrio's uncle, and it was he who first persuaded Torrio to leave New York and come to Chicago. Although a Catholic, Colosimo's funeral was conducted by a Protestant clergyman because the local archbishop forbade any diocese priest from performing rites on the gangster. This was due to Colosimo's divorce, not his underworld and vice activities.

Some say the cause of his death was his lovely new wife, a former Methodist church choir singer named **Dale Winter**. She was hired as a featured performer at Colosimo's club, and he immediately became moonstruck and she with him, even though Dale was half his age. **Florenz Ziegfield Jr**. heard Winter sing at Colosimo's club and offered her a contract, but she turned him down. Dale said her aspiration was to become a serious opera singer. Colosimo divorced his wife and catered to Dale's every whim and fancy. Colosimo soon lost respect. Everyone in the underworld said Colosimo had "gone soft." To the sharks of gangland Chicago, that was like blood in the water. When Colosimo went daft in the head over a dame, Torrio stepped in and took over operations. Colosimo's murder was never solved.

There were fifty-three pallbearers and honorary pallbearers at his funeral. Nine aldermen, three judges and a couple of Congressmen were there. The grieving Dale Winter soon discovered that technically their nuptials had no legal basis because they were married before the mandatory year-long waiting period after Jim's divorce from his first wife. The family, however, decided that the happiness she had given to her husband was worth about $6,000. Winter later married a Broadway producer and went on to have minor roles in three Hollywood films. Some say it was Colosimo who laid the foundation for the reign of Al Capone.

Currently, most researchers believe that Johnny Torrio grew impatient with his uncle's refusal to get into the lucrative bootlegging business and ordered the hit. Al Capone himself might have been the shooter since he was seen wearing Colosimo's diamond horseshoe ring after the killing.

Rollin Kirby "Mr. Prohibition" cartoon

Vincent "Schemer" Drucci

Vincent "Schemer" Drucci – Capone always considered Drucci to be his toughest rival. Drucci once encountered Capone in a Turkish steam bath and nearly strangled him to death. Capone's bodyguards showed up in time to save his life. **Drucci ran out of the building, stark naked**, jumped in his car, and drove away. Drucci was one of O'Banion's top lieutenants. He earned the nickname

"Schemer" for his bizarre plots for robbing banks or kidnapping millionaires and holding them for ransom. He once got into a gun battle with Capone's men and **laughingly danced a jig to avoid bullets that were splattering the pavement near him**.

But it wasn't Capone's men that got Drucci. He was arrested in 1927 for using force against election officials in an effort to keep Big Bill Thompson's political machine in power. While in the police car, he got into an argument with detective Dan Healy. Healy slapped Drucci causing him to make a grab for Healy's gun. Healy pumped four bullets into Drucci. His widow bitterly complained about the killing and wanted Healy charged with murder. "They shot him like he was a dog, but we gave him a king's funeral," his blonde wife proclaimed.

The "Terrible" Genna Brothers

– The six Genna brothers were Mafia from Sicily and foes of Al Capone. They earned the nickname "terrible" because of the violence and killings associated with them. "Bloody Angelo," "Mike the Devil," Jim, Tony "the Gentleman," and Pete came to America around 1900. Some of their murderous recruits were Guiseppe (Joseph) "the Cavalier" Nerone, Mike "Smoots" Amatuna, and Albert Anselmi and John Scalise. The latter two gunmen introduced the practice of **rubbing bullets with garlic in the hopes of inflicting their surviving victims with deadly gangrene**. Their main plant was at 1022 Taylor Street, but they also secured alcohol from numerous family stills in Little Italy. A three-way competition soon arose between the Gennas, the Torrio-Capone group, and the O'Banion-Weiss mob on the North Side.

Re-enactment of St. Valentine's Day Massacre

Their downfall came when Anselmi and Scalise switched allegiance to the Capone faction. Then, starting in 1925, Angelo, Mike, and Tony were all assassinated. The remaining three brothers fled Chicago but later came back and went into the produce business, staying away from the booze racket.

Jake "Greasy Thumb" Guzik

– Capone's Jewish accountant and financial wizard. His parents were involved in sleazy rackets and he saw both of them arrested on charges of white slavery. His nickname stems from his habit in early life when he worked as a waiter, of carelessly allowing his thumb to slip into a bowl of soup. Many challenge this and say it came from his job where he spent most of the day counting money.

He came to the organization by accident, saving Capone's life by informing him that he had overheard an assassination plot.

When a hoodlum named Joe Howard got physical and slapped Guzik around, he went running to Capone who found the man and emptied his gun into his head.

Guzik was forever grateful and when Capone began losing his mental capacities after getting out of Alcatraz, it was Guzik who saw to it that all of Capone's needs were met.

Guzik and his wife Alma were the proprietors of the Roamer Inn at the hamlet of **Posen**.

When people asked him if Big Al was taking back the reins of power after his release from prison in 1939, it was Guzik who said: **"Are you kidding? Al is nuttier than a fruitcake."**

Guzik, like Capone, got into tax trouble in the mid-30s and spent five years behind bars. In the 40s and 50s he was one of the Big Six that headed the National Syndicate. Guzik died of a heart attack in 1956.

Mike "de Pike" Heitler

– Known as the "Grand Old Man of Flesh Peddling," Heitler controlled joints in **Peoria** and Chicago. The price, when he started before the turn of the century, was 50 cents and he was believed to be the one who invented the assembly line system. Heitler operated the cash register and had men lined up as customers. When one girl finished and came down the stairs, he would collect 50 cents from the man at the head of the line. The girl was given a brass chit that could later be redeemed for 25 cents. By the late Twenties, the price for a girl had risen to $2.00.

Mike employed a character named Charlie "Monkey Face" Genker (yes, he was ugly) to insure that there were no unnecessary delays and that things kept moving. He kept track of every girl's time and if it seemed a particular customer was taking too long he would step on a stool and look over the transom and tell the customer to hurry it up.

He began to lose money and influence when Torrio and Capone muscled their way into the business in the 1920s. Capone relied more on Jake Guzik than Heitler to oversee the white slavery operations. Yet he was still important enough to be frequently seen sitting next to singer Al Jolson on the nightlife circuit.

Itching for vengeance, Heitler began squealing on the mob and its activities. It was Heitler who told Judge Lyle, a Capone hater, about the torture that was going on at the Green Mill.

Next he wrote an unsigned letter and sent it to the State's Attorney giving details of Capone's flesh-peddling activities. When Capone summoned Heitler to his office at the Lexington, he had the damning letter on his desk. Capone told Heitler he was through.

Heitler might have survived but then he wrote another letter and named eight people he thought were involved in the murder of reporter Jake Lingle. In April of 1931,

Heitler's charred body was found in the smoldering wreckage of a house in a Chicago suburb.

Heitler had last been seen playing cards with Lawrence Mangano, the man listed as the Public Enemy #4 by the Chicago Crime Commission. Mangano was the prime suspect and was questioned by Chicago authorities for three days but was not charged.

Murray "the Camel" Humphreys – Welsh-born labor specialist who worked the union rackets for the

Capone mob. At one time, Humphreys was the head of sixty-one locals. When Capone realized there might be an end to Prohibition, he moved into other areas. Humphreys was his man in charge of milk distribution through his own company, Meadowmoor Dairy. Capone was astonished when he discovered how large the demand was for milk. "Honest to God," he exclaimed. "We've been in the wrong racket all along."

Humphreys owned a dog and gave him the moniker "Snorky," the same one used by Capone's friends to address him.

Humphreys is called the "Forgotten Gangster" because his name today is not commonplace despite the fact that he wielded great power after Capone went to prison.

Humphreys was Capone's opposite and worked quietly, not wanting to draw unnecessary attention.

Roger Touhy had once been arrested by Melvin Purvis and charged with the kidnapping of William Hamm, the beer baron. He got off when his lawyer convinced a jury that Hamm had been kidnapped by the Karpis-Barker gang.

It was Humphreys who developed the plot to have Touhy set up as the fall guy for a fake kidnapping of Jake "The Barber" Factor. Touhy served twenty-five years before his lawyers convinced authorities it had all been a set-up. Touhy was gunned down three weeks after he was released from prison, a job thought to be authored by Humphreys. Humphrey died of a heart attack in 1965, shortly after being charged by the government with perjury.

Some say Humphreys' nickname came from the fact that he liked to wear camel hair coats.

Jake Lingle – Known as the "World's Richest Reporter," Lingle worked for $65 a week as a police

reporter for the *Chicago Tribune*. He vacationed during the winter in Florida or Cuba, had a summer place in Indiana, had a permanent room in the Stevens Hotel on Michigan Avenue, and was chauffeured around town in a fancy Lincoln.

He was known to bet $1,000 on a single horse race and didn't bat an eye when he lost $75,000 in the stock market crash of 1929. He explained away his extravagant lifestyle by saying that he had inherited a large sum of money and had invested wisely.

St. Valentine's Day Massacre (Chicago Historical Society)

When he was shot to death in 1930, Chicago newspapers lionized him as a gallant member of the wordsmith corps. But it soon became apparent that he was playing footsie with the Chicago underworld. Lingle was a go-between, a funnel between the Chicago mob and Chicago Police Commissioner William Russell. Russell was later forced to resign. Lingle used his connection with the police commissioner to obtain gambling and liquor licenses for the Capone mob and the Bugs Moran group. Moran and Capone occasionally fed him some inside dope that kept him at the top of the reporter heap, and in return he glossed over some of the misdeeds of the two gangs in his reporting.

Lingle had made a lot of enemies by forcing local brothel owners to give him a cut in return for dropping a story he was about to write on them.

Lingle was shot in the back of the head in a pedestrian tunnel while on his way to catch a train to Washington Park racetrack. Leo Brothers, a St. Louis hit man, was convicted of the murder and did 14 years, a relatively light sentence.

Tony "The Scourge" Lombardo –

Here was a man who concealed his Machiavellian heart behind the benign apron strings of a wholesale grocer. After Torrio left Chicago in 1925, it was Lombardo who became Capone's mentor. In return, Capone made Lombardo his *consigliere* – his prime advisor.

Lombardo urged Capone to find some way to make accommodation with the Irish North Side Gang, even after they managed to dispatch their leader, Dion O'Banion. Lombardo tried to appease the North Siders by telling them he would deliver O'Banion's killers – Anselmi and Scalise – for retribution. Capone himself nixed the deal because he thought it was too treacherous.

Capone copied Lombardo's practice of having one of his men serve as an official "taster," sampling the food before Capone would eat it.

Lombardo was killed in a rush hour crowd at the busy corner of State Street and Madison in 1928. Two dum-dum bullets tore away much of his skull. Capone vowed vengeance on the Aiello mob responsible for the hit.

Jack "Machine Gun" McGurn – McGurn, who was gunned down at age 40, was the role model for many of the tough guys in later Hollywood movies. McGurn was handsome, a snappy dresser and a ladies man – preferably blondes.

He ran afoul of the law when he decided to take matters into his own hand and avenge his father's murder by underworld figures in the Genna Gang. According to gangland lore, **McGurn soaked his hands in the blood of his bootlegger father and swore revenge**. McGurn was reputed to have killed a total of 25 men, the first five for the murder of his father.

He perfected his marksmanship by shooting birds off phone wires with

Aftermath of St. Valentine's Day Massacre

his BB gun. He honed his fisticuff skills by going into the ring and fighting a few years under the name "Battling Jack" McGurn.

McGurn joined the Capone faction since he knew they were bitter enemies of the Gennas. He was fascinated by the Tommy gun and became an expert at using it. McGurn took out the Gennas, one by one, placing a nickel in their hand to show his contempt.

It was McGurn who planned the St. Valentine's Day Massacre and he was arrested for it. When authorities tried to force his girl friend, Louise Rolfe, into testifying against him, he married her, gaining spousal immunity.

When Capone bashed three gangsters (Anselmi, Guinta, Scalise) with a baseball bat, it was McGurn who held them while Capone wreaked revenge.

McGurn spent a lot of time at nightclubs, so he began investing in them. One of the clubs was the Green Mill. When a comic named Joe E. Lewis threatened to go to another club for more money, McGurn threatened, "You'll never open." A couple of weeks later, three men went into Lewis' dressing room, fractured his skull and cut him up badly with a knife.

Things went downhill for McGurn after Capone went to prison. Even Louise Rolfe left him.

In 1936, on the eve of the St. Valentine's Day Massacre, McGurn was gunned down by several men at a bowling alley. **They left a nickel in his hand and a comic valentine next to his body**.

George "Bugs" Moran – Born of Irish and Polish parentage in Minnesota, Moran grew up in the predominantly Irish part of North Chicago and had served time on three separate occasions for armed robbery by age 21.

He began to run around with Dion O'Banion and gained the nickname "Bugs" for his flaky and erratic behavior. (He helped execute the riding horse that threw and kicked to death his friend, Nails Morton.)

He ascended to the top thanks to the death of others in the ranks. Capone engineered O'Banion's murder and then gunned down his successor, Hymie Weiss. Schemer Drucci rose to the top spot but was killed by a policeman in 1927. That incident elevated Moran to the top of the heap.

It was Moran who rushed from his car to deliver the coup de grace to Johnnie Torrio after his gunmen blasted him four times. **Torrio only survived because Moran's gun misfired**. And Moran was in the lead car when a motorcade attack was made on Capone at the Hawthorne Inn. Capone survived despite 1,000 rounds being fired into the building.

Moran had a running feud with Capone, and most newspaper men were rooting for Moran to emerge as the victor. Moran was good-natured, enjoyed the banter with reporters and disdained Capone for his involvement in the flesh trade.

Capone set up the hit on Moran and his men in what came to be known as the 1929 St. Valentine's Day Massacre. **Moran survived by a quirk of fate because he was five minutes late to the meeting**. Moran and his pal Ted Newberry saw men getting out of the police car, and they kept walking. Newberry was killed in 1933 by some of Nitti's men.

Moran allied himself with Joe Aiello and Jack Zuta in an effort to get revenge on Capone, but both men fell victim to Capone's gunmen.

Moran survived the Capone Wars and in 1946 was arrested for a robbery in Ohio. After being released he was arrested again on a different charge and given another ten years, this time at Leavenworth. He died in 1957 and was buried in a potter's field outside the prison walls.

Dion O'Banion – Born in **Maroa**, Illinois, in 1892, he was known as Dean during his school years. His

mother died of tuberculosis in 1901, and his father moved to Chicago to live near his parents' home. Dean's sister Ruth was taken to **Decatur** to live with an Aunt.

Dean grew up on the North Side of Chicago in the area known as Little Hell. He attended Holy Name parochial school, joined a gang, and earned money with a newspaper route. He was injured while showing off by sitting on the fender of a moving car. He fell and was run over, crushing his left leg. An operation left the leg about an inch shorter than the other, causing him to limp the rest of his life.

He quit school when he was 14 and earned money by doing various odd jobs at local saloons and cabarets. He started out as a choirboy, and soon became a singing waiter at McGovern's Cabaret. **Dion sang Irish ballads to lull drunken patrons to sleep so he could pick their pockets**.

An Irish gunman (Gene Geary) and thug from the tough Canaryville district of Chicago took a liking to him and became his mentor. He taught Dean how to use his fists and how to shoot with either hand. Although only five foot four, he was muscular and a good scrapper. He soon started carrying two or three weapons on him at all times.

Dion and his buddies witnessed the 1919 Chicago race riot. It is not known to what extent he may have participated in the event.

In his late teens O'Banion got in trouble with the law on several occasions for burglary and various assault charges. He spent time in a juvenile correction facility. With the advent of Prohibition he and his minions quickly gained a monopoly on bootlegging activity on the North Side of Chicago. He loved flowers and became partners with a friend who was a florist. They made a killing by supplying flowers for gangster funerals. In addition to supplying Gold Coast patrons with gambling equipment and booze, he occasionally hijacked rival hootch and did a few safecracking jobs. The newspapers called him Chicago's arch criminal, and **he reportedly killed or was responsible for the killing of 25 men**.

Johnnie Torrio put out a contract on O'Banion but no one tried to collect on it because O'Banion was under the protection of Unione Sicilione Don, Mike Merlo. But Merlo suddenly died and was replaced by Angelo Genna, an enemy of O'Banion. Several men walked into O'Banion's flower shop to pick up a wreath for Mike Merlo's funeral. They fired six shots into O'Banion's face throat and chest.

The "handshake murder" at his floral shop across the street from Holy Name Cathedral in 1924 set off a gang war

Concerned father talks to son by McCutcheon
AN OBJECT LESSON FOR A MOURNING HERO WORSHIPER

that lasted until 1930 and **resulted in the death of about 600 people.**

Frank Ragen

Frank Ragen – Ragen, and his Irish gang known as Ragen's Colts, were formidable enemies of Al Capone. Fortunately for Capone, their pinnacle of power came in the first two decades of the twentieth century as they dominated South Chicago in the stockyards area.

Like many other gangs in early Chicago, **they started out as a baseball team**. Frank Ragen was the star pitcher for the team. His Colts became a powerful ally of the Democratic Party. When he and his men dropped in to a polling place, the opposition Republicans quickly dropped out.

It was the racist Ragen's Colts that were responsible for stirring up trouble in the Black Belt in 1919, leading to the four-day race riot. It had been bathing Colts on the South Side beach that stoned and drowned a Negro youth who had strayed into their territory. With the advent of Prohibition, Ragen's Colts were busy hijacking Al Capone's liquor. Ralph Sheldon formed a splinter group that also gave Capone a lot of headaches.

Paul "the Waiter" Ricca

Paul "the Waiter" Ricca – Born Felice de Lucia in Naples, Italy, in 1897, he came to this country on the lam from a murder rap. He killed a young man who had dishonored his sister. After being released from prison two years later, he then killed the witness who fingered him.

Ricca first came to New York but left for Chicago and took a job there as a waiter. Then he went to work for Capone as manager of Little Italy's World Playhouse. When he married in 1927, Capone was his best man. Ricca then became the chief liaison man between the Chicago mob and the New York group. He became one of the top members of the Capone team and was a close friend and confidante of Tony Accardo.

Johnny Rosselli

Johnny Rosselli – Rosselli was born in Italy and came to this country with his parents in 1911. He grew up as a street punk in Boston and New York but came to Chicago around the age of 18. He soon became a bodyguard and driver for Al Capone. He was a snappy dresser and soon acquired the nickname of Mr. Smooth. When he contracted TB Capone sent him out to the warm climate of California to be the mob's point man for Hollywood. He also spread mob money around in Nevada so the legislature would pass the wide-open gambling bill. Rosselli became friends with Joe Kennedy and the two of them came to realize that the Hollywood dream factory was the "new booze."

Arnold Rothstein
– Rothstein is remembered today as the **mastermind behind the Black Sox scandal** of 1919, managing to "fix" the World Series. He had several nicknames including The Fixer, Mr. Big, The Brain, and Mr. Bankroll. Although he operated strictly in the background, having important connections to bootleggers, police, judges and politicians, he was probably one of the most important criminals of his era. He was an early tutor of Johnny Torrio, Frank Costello, and Lucky Luciano. Rothstein made sure that many bootlegging cases never went to trial. Rothstein was the inspiration for the Meyer Wolfsheim character in Fitzgerald's *The Great Gatsby*. The same can be said for Nathan Detroit in Damon Runyon's *Guys and Dolls*.

Arnold Rothstein

Rothstein, a big gambler, was killed in 1928 after he refused to pay a huge gambling debt incurred in a poker game that he claimed was fixed.

James "Fur" Sammons
– A member of the "Klondike" O'Donnell gang

Roger "The Terrible" Touhy
was a bootleg king who protested his nickname, claiming that he never killed anyone. It is hard to believe that the FBI went after Touhy in lieu of other more sinister hoods. Roger wasn't even on the Chicago Crime Commission's list of public enemies.

Touhy and his five brothers distributed beer to Chicago suburbs (especially in the Des Plaines area), and many considered his brew to be the best tasting in all Chicago. Capone came to regard him as a vital enemy when he opposed Capone's expansion of the flesh trade into the outlying areas.

Touhy went to prison for kidnapping Jake "The Barber" Factor for 14 days. The kidnapping was probably fake, and was thought to be organized by Murray Humphreys and engineered by the Barker-Alvin Karpis gang, allies of Capone.

Touhy wrote his memoirs, *The Stolen Years*, just before his release from prison, twenty-three years later. Shortly after his release, Roger was gunned down on his sister's front porch. Some blamed the hit on his memoirs for being too detailed and specific. Before he died, he muttered: "I've been expecting it. The b—ards never forget."

Tony "Mops" Volpe
– One of Al Capone's first-string bodyguards

Hymie Weiss
– Hymie Weiss was born Earl Wajciechowski in his homeland of Poland in 1898. He emigrated to the U.S. with his family, and the name was changed soon after their arrival. Weiss became buddies with Dion O'Banion when he was yet a teenager and the two of them performed numerous burglaries, car thefts and jewel robberies. They also worked together in the newspaper wars where they would intimidate vendors to sell only the papers that they represented. As years went by Weiss became O'Banion's right hand man in the ruthless North Siders gang. The gang went into bootlegging and had frequent conflicts with Capone and Johnny Torrio.

Weiss was credited with inventing the phrase "a one way ride" when, in 1921, he decided to teach a fellow gangster named Stephen Wisniewski a lesson for hijacking some of O'Banion's booze. Wisniewski was invited to go for a ride with Weiss along Lake Michigan and somewhere along the way he was whacked.

After the murder of Dion O'Banion, Weiss became the boss of the North Siders and began plotting the demise of Torrio and Capone. On January 12, 1925, Weiss, Moran and Drucci tailed Capone's limousine to a restaurant on 55th Street and State. They opened up with their guns and managed to get 26 hits on the limo. The chauffeur was wounded but Capone and his bodyguards were unscathed by the tirade of bullets.

Weiss next tried a hit on Torrio. Weiss managed to kill Torrio's dog and chauffeur, but Johnny escaped with a measly two holes in his hat. Weiss made another attack on Torrio on January 24th of 1925, and this time he was a little more successful. Torrio was ambushed outside of his apartment and was gravely wounded by shotgun blasts and .45 slugs from Weiss and his accomplice, Bugs Moran. The two were about to deliver a *coup de grace*, a shot to the

Hymie Weiss

head, when they were scared away by what they thought was a police vehicle. It turned out to be merely a laundry truck. Torrio was in the hospital for two weeks. When he got out, he turned everything over to Al Capone and quit the business.

In September of 1925 Weiss and a cavalcade of cars drove past the Hawthorn Inn in Cicero and fired over 100 rounds into the restaurant. Capone escaped harm by throwing himself prostrate on the floor.

Three weeks after the Hawthorn Inn hit, Weiss was shot to death by an unknown gunman lying in wait at a second floor window across the street from Weiss' headquarters, O'Banion's old flower shop. This became known as the "rented ambush." Weiss was DOA at the hospital, and an autopsy revealed ten different bullets in his body. Weiss was only 28 at the time of his demise.

Jack Zuta
Jack Zuta – Vice division head and chief idea man for the Moran gang; credited with bringing peace to the Moran/Aiello/Capone gangs. John Zuta was of Russian Jewish peasant heritage with an original spelling of Zoota. His family migrated to Chicago in 1913.

He got into the junk business on the near west side of Chicago. He decided there was more money to be made in vice and moved into the prostitution business. Soon he was owner of a string of bawdy houses on Madison Street. More powerful mobsters pushed him out of the business and he moved on to become an accountant, first for Capone and then for Bugs Moran.

It is believed he was the paymaster in the hit on Jake Lingle. After the killing, Zuta and cousin Eli were brought in for questioning. The word got out that Zuta was feeding information to the police in an effort to save his own skin. He quickly became a marked man. After Zuta's lawyer secured his release on bail, he was driven by a detective from south Chicago toward the safety of his north side territory. When they reached Quincy and State Street they were attacked by gunmen in two different dark sedans. A streetcar motorman was killed in the crossfire and Zuta fled in the confusion. He never showed up for his court appearance the next day.

Zuta fled Chicago and hid out in **Aurora**. He now went by the name of J.H. Goodman and told people he was a salesman. In early August of 1930 he was staying at a resort hotel near Milwaukee, Wisconsin. He was in the dance hall section, playing the jukebox and watching couples dance, when in walked a group of armed men. They spotted Zuta and gunned him down on the spot just as he was placing another nickel into the machine.

CHRONOLOGY

1919 – November: Johnny Torrio sends for Al Capone, asking him to leave Brooklyn and come to Chicago to work as a bouncer in one of his nightclubs.

1920 – **Big Jim Colosimo**, a notable restauranteer and vice lord of the Chicago district known as The Levee, is gunned down by Frankie Yale in the lobby of his own establishment. His death enables Torrio and Capone to enlarge their holdings in vice and racketeering. Yale probably murdered Colosimo so he could expand his own empire.

Colosimo fell in love

Jim Colosimo

with a young singer named Dale Winter and had recently divorced his wife and married Miss Winter. When he fell head over heels in love, this was a sign to the rest of the underworld that he had gone soft. The murder was never officially solved. It was Johnny Torrio who now presided over the operation of countless brothels, speakeasies and gin joints. Colosimo was Torrio's uncle, and it was he who first persuaded Torrio to leave New York and come to Chicago. Although a Catholic, Colosimo's funeral was conducted by a Protestant clergyman because the local archbishop forbade any diocese priest from performing rites on a gangster.

Some say the cause of his death was his lovely new wife, a former Methodist church choir singer. She was hired as a featured singer at Colosimo's club. He immediately fell for her and she for him even though she was half his age. He catered to Dale's every whim and fancy. Everyone in the underworld said that Colosimo had "gone soft." To the sharks of gangland Chicago, that was like blood in the water.

There were fifty-three pallbearers and honorary pallbearers at his funeral. Nine aldermen, three judges and a couple of Congressmen attended the ceremony. His grieving widow soon discovered that technically their marriage had no legal basis because they were married

Rock Island Arsenal
(Rock Island Historical Society)

before the mandatory yearlong waiting period after Jim's divorce from his first wife. The family, however, decided that the happiness she had given to her husband was worth about $6,000.

The Cook County Jail **forces 200 inmates to watch the hanging of a desperado so they will learn how to behave.**

The sport of **pigeon racing** becomes popular in **Moline** and **Rock Island**. It was brought to the area in the 1850s by Belgian immigrants where it had been a traditional sport in their native land. Belgians who came to Illinois were of two types – traditional Flemish and French-speaking Walloons from southeast Belgium, adjacent to France. Racing birds had a banded number affixed to one of their legs. They were driven to a distant point, hundreds of miles away. All were released at the same time. The first thing they did was circle to get their bearings, then they headed straight for home. Prizes were usually awarded to the owners of the fastest pigeons.

Belgians traditionally drank even more beer per capita than Germans. When Prohibition came along and near beer was the only thing legal, they began making home brew.

Anthony Billburg of **Rock Island** is the owner of a tavern with the **longest bar in the world**. It was built in 1915 on the corner of 20th Street and Third Avenue. The solid mahogany bar was 117 feet long. There were huge windows facing the street so that women could look inside and see that their husbands were only drinking and not involved in vice activities. Women were not allowed inside.

In 1918 the federal government drew a circle with a one-mile radius around Arsenal Island and ordered all taverns within that area closed. When the war ended in November of that year the restrictions were lifted. When Prohibition came along in 1920 the place was closed once more.

There were no stools at the bar and **those who became too intoxicated to drink were thrown out into the street**.

Average life expectancy at this time is fifty-four years.

The U.S. population is 106.4 million.

Nine million Americans own cars.

The **Volstead Act**, designed to enforce the national Prohibition laws, goes into effect on January 17th. **The first violation of the law** occurred about an hour later in Chicago by men who raided a railroad car and hijacked a load of whiskey that had been marked for medicinal use.

Rock Island's longest bar in world (Pamela M. Langston)

THE NEW BILLBVRG
LONGEST BAR IN THE WORLD
THE BAR THAT MADE ROCK ISLAND FAMOUS.

What accounted for the passage of prohibition? (1) The Anti-Saloon League, WCTU, and other similar organizations had pushed for it since the 1840s. (2) It was part of the agenda for the Progressive Movement (3) Organized suffragettes added this reform to their agenda (4) Many states and many counties were already "dry," having previously adopted "Maine laws" (5) Rural areas, which favored prohibition, were over represented in the state legislatures. In Illinois, Cook County had one representative for every 312,000 people. The rest of the state had one for every 223,000 people. The concept of "one man, one vote" had not yet been enacted into legislation. (6) Numerous Protestant churches preached against the evils of Demon Rum

Johnny Torrio, in a masterful diplomatic move, meets with various local gangs and proposes a plan whereby territories are marked out and a monopoly is established for supplying illegal beer and hard liquor to area saloons, bawdy houses, restaurants and cabarets. Any outsider that tried to move in would be dealt with collectively. Torrio would supply all the beer for $50 a barrel. Peace and prosperity would last among thugdom until 1923 when Spike O'Donnell got out of **Joliet Prison** and began hijacking Torrio's beer trucks, starting the so-called **Beer War**.

In a smoke-filled room at Chicago's Blackstone Hotel, (suite 804-805) Republican Party bigwigs strike a deal that makes Warren G. Harding of Ohio their "dark horse" candidate for president.

Few, if any, states could lay claim to playing a more significant role than Illinois in the passage of the so-called Progressive constitutional amendments for the income tax, the direct election of senators, women's suffrage, and Prohibition.

East St. Louis, the fastest growing city in America for the last thirty years, doubling its size every decade, reaches a population of over 70,000 people. It is now the 86th largest city in America, and the **third largest city in Illinois**. The total population for Illinois is 6,485,280. Downtown merchants organize the Jaycees, making it the **second oldest Jaycee group in the nation**.

The official baseball of the National League is manufactured by A.G. Spaulding of **Rockford** who opened his first sporting goods store in 1875.

Prohibition has a significant impact on all of Illinois. "Black Leg" mobsters see opportunities for enormous profits and open illegal "speakeasies." The Shelton brothers are dominant in **East St. Louis** and brought in illegal slot machines and prostitutes to their establishments. One of the Shelton Gang, **Jardown "Blackie" Armes**, was a good automobile mechanic and put his talents to work modifying cars to outrun prohibition agents. This was done by others all over the South with the same goals in mind. From these efforts at modifying car engines came **stock car racing** as we know it today. Armes was also adept at rigging cars with hidden containers for smuggling liquor.

Prohibition was largely responsible for the growth and development of organized crime and the Mafia empire as it now exists. Prohibition corrupted police and city officials in all major cities because it gave them a chance to supplement their meager salaries with bribes and kickbacks in return for looking the other way.

"Daddy's In There" – Prohibition cartoon

September 15. **S. Glenn Young**, a neophyte Prohibition Agent, along with two **Granite City** police officers, make a raid on a home in nearby **Madison**. They found a small still, mash, whiskey, and arrested the occupant. They then went to the house next door where a relative of the arrested man lived and found a 25-gallon container of liquor. The occupant, **Luka Vukovic**, pulled a gun and tried to shoot Young, but the weapon misfired. Young, in self-defense, shot and killed the man.

Decatur starch manufacturer A.E. Staley sells his football team to **George Halas,** a former U of I standout under coach Robert Zuppke. Halas met with ten other owners in Canton, Ohio (this is why the Hall of Fame is there), and formed a professional league called the American Professional Football Association. Halas' team won the title that year with a 9-1-1 record, playing their games at Cubs Field (later Wrigley Field). Halas changed the name from the Staleys to the Bears (to create a connection with the Cubs) in 1921 and the APFA became the NFL. Halas would go on to win ten NFL championships.

President Warren G. Harding (1921-1923)

On a Sunday, March 20, a tornado strikes **Elgin, Melrose Park, Maywood, Evanston** and **Wilmette** on the northwest side of Chicago killing 103 people. Around 1 p.m. the bright sunny skies grew dark, releasing rain and hail the size of robin eggs. The roof of the First Congregational Church in Elgin collapsed injuring scores and killing three. The Red Cross provided temporary shelters, and the militia was summoned to maintain law and order, **with instructions to shoot looters**. Relief trains from all over the state arrived, bringing food, clothes and medical supplies. Damage was estimated at $10 million.

Chicago has its own version of New York's Tin Pan Alley with dozens of music publishers and lyricists flourishing in the city, centering in the Randolph Building and the Garrick Theater Building. Tin Pan was a slang expression for the music pounded out on cheap, tinny upright pianos. Stephen Foster is considered to be the first person to make a living at writing songs. He penned *My Old Kentucky Home* and *I Dream of Jeannie*. The success of popular songs began with the rise of vaudeville in the 1890s.

Chicago produced the hit, Rudolph the Red-nosed Reindeer. It was written in 1939 by Robert May, a Montgomery Ward copywriter, who wrote it to accompany a Christmas story for the store's holiday promotion.

East St. Louis ranks third in population and third in the state in industrial output behind Chicago and **Peoria**. The biggest concerns in the Metro-East at this time are Hunter, Armour, Obear-Nester Glass, Shell Oil, American Zinc, Alcoa, Granite City Steel, Alton Boxboard, American Steel, Monsanto, Standard Oil of Indiana, American Smelting and Refining, and Laclede Steel.

The steel making complex along the Calumet River in Chicago becomes known as the **Ruhr of North America**. It became the *nation's largest steel producing area*.

The **Mascoutah** Brewery changes its name to Mascoutah Products Company, and to comply with

prohibition begins manufacturing a beverage called Old English Ginger Beer and Masco near beer (3.2 percent). The company is fined in late 1920 for making 4 percent beer, and in 1924 federal authorities closed the plant. After it was later found to still be making beer, new owners from **Joliet** were given jail sentences, and the plant was dismantled.

The United States now has 191 miles of federally assisted highways.

The Duesenberg Model A is introduced. It is the first American production car with all-wheel hydraulic brakes. Slanted windshields are gaining in favor as are wire wheels.

A ship called the *Sprague* is the **largest boat operating on the Mississippi River**. It is owned by the Aluminum Ore Company of **East St. Louis** and is used for hauling Arkansas bauxite to their plant site.

Jim Thorpe, Olympic champion and **great grandson of Chief Blackhawk**, becomes president of the National Football League. Thorpe was voted the greatest athlete of the first half of the Twentieth Century.

Only about 50 percent of eligible Illinois voters bother to go to the polls. This number has steadily been declining since 1896 when it had peaked at 79 percent.

Montgomery Ward, with 1,050 workers, is the largest Chicago employer of colored women. Because it did mail-order business, customers had no direct contact with them and never had to know they were served by black clerical workers.

Ronald Reagan's parents leave **Tampico** and move to **Dixon** when he is nine years old.

A bomb, set by radicals, goes off in the Wall Street financial district of New York, killing 33 people and wounding more than 200. This leads to the national phenomenon known as the **Red Scare**. Attorney general Mitchell Palmer begins a deportation campaign against suspected alien radicals. The ACLU is formed to help protect individual liberties in this era of excess.

Woodrow Wilson and his attorney general, Mitchell Palmer

The 19th Amendment gives women the right to vote.

Republicans Harding and Coolidge defeat Cox and Roosevelt in the November presidential election. After the passage of the 19th Amendment, women participate for the first time in a presidential election. The winning of the suffrage has the effect of consolidating women's position as man's equal. A majority of them favored Harding. The League of Women Voters was established shortly thereafter for the purpose of educating female voters.

The nation's first radio station goes on the air – KDKA in Pittsburgh, owned by the Westinghouse Corporation.

Sinclair Lewis publishes *Main Street*, a harsh, highbrow and unfair criticism of small town America (Gopher

Prairie), completely overlooking its friendly sentiment, neighborliness and generosity. Two years later he publishes the novel *Babbitt*, another one-sided harangue about America's flaws. Realtor George Babbitt represents all that is wrong with the commercial world of the 1920s.

F. Scott Fitzgerald's *This Side of Paradise* is published. For many people, it offers their first shocking glimpse of the new morality with petting parties and automobile romances.

The summer Olympic Games are held in Antwerp, Belgium.

The Negro Baseball League plays its first game.

The first meeting of the League of Nations is held in Geneva, Switzerland, minus the United States.

The 1920 census reveals that for the first time more Americans live in urban settings than rural areas.

George Gershwin writes the music for the Broadway play, *Scandals of 1920*.

The Hatfields and McCoys, two feuding families in the hill country on the Kentucky/West Virginia border, make national headlines.

1921 – Illinois governor **Len Small** is indicted and accused of embezzling a half million dollars when he was state treasurer. He wins acquittal, but many believe he was successful in bribing some of the jurors.

Governor Len Small

One-third of American homes now have electricity.

Al Capone, age 22, arrives in Chicago via Brooklyn. He was asked to come there by Johnny Torrio. Capone started out as a doorman and cleanup man at Colosimo's restaurant. After the death of his father, Al Capone left New York and built a two-story brick home at 7244 South Prairie Avenue in Chicago, anticipating his mother coming to live with him, along with his wife and son.

Congress cuts foreign immigration by 97 percent; these restrictions remain in effect until the 1970s.

Construction begins on Wacker Drive in Chicago, making use of concrete double decking to carry traffic.

Edith Rockefeller divorces Harold McCormick and gives him $3 million for title to their homes on Lakeshore Drive and in **Lake Forest**.

A woman in **Danville** goes on a 48-day fast to convince her husband to give up drinking, smoking, and join her church.

Adam "Mule Pole" Fritz, owner of a popular saloon in the heart of the city, complete with a spacious, ornate gambling parlor in the rear, is the most notorious gangster in **East St. Louis**. He eventually becomes a partner with the Shelton gang—Carl, Bernie, and Big Earl.

June 6. **S. Glenn Young** is tried in a federal court in

Springfield for killing Luka Vukovic of **Madison**. He had entered the man's home without a warrant, and the dead man's widow claimed that her husband was unarmed and that Young had planted the gun on his body. Young was exonerated, but it was a bittersweet victory because his wife divorced him (she claimed physical abuse), and he lost his $150 a month job as a Treasury Agent. He remarried later that year to a woman named Maude. One of the reasons given for his firing was an unauthorized interview he gave to the **East St. Louis** *Journal,* which gave the department "improper publicity."

Female telephone operators in **Danville** are forbidden to chew gum and must reply to callers in pleasant singsong tones and phrases.

Beeman's gum

BEEMAN'S PEPSIN GUM
THE PERFECTION OF CHEWING GUM.
A DELICIOUS REMEDY
FOR ALL FORMS OF INDIGESTION
CAUTION—See that the name Beeman is on each wrapper.
Each tablet contains one grain pure pepsin, sufficient to digest 1,000 grains of food. If it cannot be obtained from dealers, send five cents in stamps for sample package to
BEEMAN CHEMICAL CO., 3 Lake St., Cleveland, O.
ORIGINATORS OF PEPSIN CHEWING GUM.

The state's first radio station, WDZ, begins operation in **Tuscola**. It is known as station 9JR. **WDZ, the third station in the United States**, moved to **Decatur** in 1949.

Jack Dempsey successfully defends the heavyweight title he won in 1919 against Jess Willard. It was Willard who had earlier taken the title from Jack Johnson, the first Negro champion. Dempsey's opponent is the handsome Frenchman, Georges Carpentier. Surprisingly, the American crowd is decidedly in favor of Carpentier because **Dempsey was thought to be a slacker for having avoided military service**.

Fanny Brice is a star in the Ziegfeld Follies. She will later shine in the radio program, "Baby Snooks."

Five members of the Socialist party are elected to the New York state legislature. A vote is taken and they are deprived of their seats in the Assembly. Socialists, at this time, are seen as being one step away from Communists and representatives of the Soviet government.

The Unknown Soldier from the Great War is buried at Arlington Cemetery.

People read with shocked delight about the first-ever Miss America Beauty Pageant, held in Atlantic City, describing a host of beautiful young women wearing revealing one-piece bathing suits. Miss Washington took home the honors.

Auto sales sag badly due to the brief but severe economic depression.

Ford, Chevrolet, Buick, Dodge, and Studebaker are the top selling cars in America.

Warren G. Harding becomes the first American president to ride to his inauguration in an automobile – a Packard Twin Six.

The Eskimo Pie ice cream bar is born. It is a vanilla triangular-shaped bar on a stick, covered with chocolate. It was produced by the Haines-Ce-Brook plant in Lynn, Mass.

Bachelor Walt Wallet, the main character in the Chicago *Tribune's* comic strip *Gasoline Alley*, finds a baby left on his doorstep. He names it Skeezix, and the character becomes the first in the comics to age naturally, growing up to fight in World War II.

The Washburn Crosby Company begins a new advertising campaign using Betty Crocker, a mythical housewife.

William H. Taft becomes Supreme Court Chief Justice.

Congress passes an immigration bill that severely restricts immigrants from Asia, southern Europe, and central Europe. (They were considered undesirables.)

Albert Einstein receives the Nobel Prize in physics.

The Communist Party is organized in the United States.

RCA produces the first U.S. commercial radio sets.

Franklin D. Roosevelt, the Democratic nominee for Vice-president in the 1920 election, contracts poliomyelitis at the age of thirty-nine and becomes a cripple. He contemplates suicide, but his friend Louis Howe convinces him that his political career is not over. He regains some use of his legs through physical exercise, particularly swimming. He will go on to become the first handicapped person to be elected to lead a nation.

Sam throws out aliens by Rollin Kirby

WHOSE COUNTRY IS THIS, ANYHOW?

1922 – **Big Bill Thompson**, corrupt and "wet" mayor of Chicago, makes the charge that villainous England, under the leadership of King George V, is planning to invade the United States. This absurdity is pure politics designed to win over the Irish vote in upcoming elections. Thompson, a snaggle-toothed hulk who was a former athlete, was first elected mayor of Chicago on the Republican ticket in 1915. He soon fell in league with pimps, gamblers, thugs and assorted racketeers. He actually had little interest in politics and only **decided to run for mayor to win a bet**.

The maximum salary for Chicago school teachers is about $2,200 a year. Males and females earned the same salaries, but men were given sign on bonuses for each dependant they had at home.

The nation, already in the grip of a nationwide coal strike, is shocked by the **Herrin Massacre** that takes place on June 22. The infamous incident occurred during a bitter coal miners' strike against the **Southern Illinois Coal Company**. The company tried to break the union by firing its unionized workers. Next, the management imported armed guards and replacement scab workers from Chicago to work the Lester strip mine. There

Early soap ad

Pears' Soap

were work stoppages all over the nation at this time, ordered by **John L. Lewis** and the United Mine Workers of America.

The millionaire owner of the mine sought to profit by continuing to mine coal that would be sold at a premium price due to shortages.

Gunshots were exchanged as striking workers attacked the mine, and in the ensuing mayhem **three union miners were killed**. Enraged, the belligerent miners surrounded the facility, cut power and telephone lines, and lay siege to the place.

Terrified, everyone in the besieged strip mine surrendered on the promise that they would leave Williamson County. As they filed out, the angry mob began striking the scabs, shouting ugly epithets. Then they dragged off C.K. McDowell, the mine superintendent, and shot him twice, killing him. A man in an automobile drove up and told the mob not to kill the captives on the highway where it might be seen by women and children. The men were herded into a wooded area and told to run as fast as they could back to Chicago. But most of them were shot and killed trying to flee. One small group was held captive in the Herrin schoolhouse until the mob of about 200 people worked itself into a frenzy and dragged the men to a cemetery about a mile away. The group of six men, pleading for their lives, while yoked together by a large rope, were beaten and shot. Those who managed to survive, with bodies broken and bleeding, had their **throats cut** by a man with a pocketknife. When it was over, authorities found a total of **nineteen strike-breaker bodies**. Two separate trials were held for the remorseless murderers, but acquittal was the verdict in each case.

S. Glenn Young was one of the guards at the mine before he became a prohibition agent. Young is credited with bringing the first machinegun into Williamson County. Young will go on to become the leader of the KKK forces in the county.

An article in the June 24, 1922, St. Louis *Globe-Democrat* described the massacre as . . . "the most brutal and horrifying crime that has ever stained the garments of organized labor." After the massacre, Williamson County gained a national reputation as **"Little Hell."**

William Allen White, the Kansas newspaper editor, saw the emergence of a new doctrine in the conflict. Labor was beginning to believe that skill had the same status as property. The right of a worker to apply his skill in a place where it would produce value was beginning to be seen as a human right. The right of a laborer to work for profit was

---

THE KU KLUX KLAN

The KKK invites all able-bodied, law abiding, Christian men of the Protestant persuasion to come join us in our fight to purify our nation from those who seek to drag it down through law-lessness, Romanism and the mixing of inferior blood.

Defenders of true Americanism are invited to come to our meeting this Thursday, April 23, at 9:00 p.m. in the large field south of Mine #3 at Carter-ville. New members will be initiated.

61

gaining equal status with the right of owners to make a profit.

Robert Zupke, **University of Illinois** football coach, **introduces the huddle** as a means of communication during the game. Under his leadership, Illinois won or tied for the Big Ten title seven times in the next fifteen years, including the **national championship in 1927**.

Louis Armstrong, encouraged by coronetist Joe "King" Oliver, follows in the footsteps of "Jelly Roll"

Woman as an independent voter cartoon
(Newberry Library)

Morton and comes to Chicago. Armstrong and others would make Chicago a hotbed of the new distinctly American art form called jazz. Other notable performers in Chicago include Eddie Condon, Hoagy Carmichael, Ben Pollock, Benny and Harry Goodman.

The Illinois State police are organized. Their purpose is to enforce the provisions of the Illinois motor vehicle law. **Troopers are expected to purchase their own firearms**.

The Sag channel, a 24-mile long extension of the Chicago Sanitary and Ship Canal to connect with the Calumet River (south of Chicago), is completed. Like the Chicago River, the Calumet River no longer drains into Lake Michigan.

After nearly three years of work, a new state constitution is submitted to voters. Downstate voters accept the new document, but ratification fails when Chicago area voters overwhelmingly reject efforts to "modernize" the 1870 constitution.

King Tut's tomb in Egypt is discovered by a team of British archaeologists.

After the Great War, Ed Stinson, a navy test pilot, moves to Chicago and begins the manufacture of Stinson airplanes. It was Stinson who discovered that lack of air speed caused stalls and tailspins and saved thousands of lives by teaching pilots how to recover from stalls and spins.

King Tut's tomb

The American Fiber Company of East St. Louis is the **world's largest maker of burlap-type bags**. Instead of making them from jute, they are made from yucca fibers from plants grown on their plantation in Arizona.

The Lincoln Memorial in Washington D.C. is dedicated. Henry Bacon, an architect from **Watseka**, is the man who designed it. Daniel French sculpted the statue.

Al Capone makes newspaper headlines for the first time in Chicago when he accidentally rams a taxi and then pulls a gun on the driver. The story got his name wrong and referred to him as Alfred Caponi.

Pilots at Chanute Field in **Rantoul** are ordered to wear parachutes.

James Doolittle sets a record by flying across the United States in less than twenty-four hours.

Lottie Holman O'Neill becomes the first woman elected to the General Assembly, a position she holds for 38 years.

The U.S. navy converts a collier into the *U.S.S. Langley*, the nation's first aircraft carrier.

Benito Mussolini and his Fascist "Black Shirts" come to power in Italy via elections.

Britain agrees to Irish independence and acquiesces in the creation of the Irish Free State. Ulster, the northern part of Ireland, remains under British hegemony and this will lead to continuing conflict.

Isadora Duncan is banned from Boston after exposing herself on stage and making pro-Red comments.

Hollywood director William Desmond Taylor is murdered in his home.

William Desmond Taylor

The first Technicolor film, *Toll of the Sea,* is released.

The International Court of Justice is established at the Hague in the Netherlands.

Pius XI is elected Pope in Italy; he will strongly condemn Communism and Fascism.

T.S. Eliot's *The Wasteland* is published

The International Brotherhood of Magicians is formed, a group dedicated to keeping the principles and mechanics of their craft a secret.

There are so many airplane crashes, both here and abroad, that writer John Galsworthy writes a letter to the *London Times* proposing the banning of all aircraft for "any purpose whatsoever."

Chuck Carney of the University of Illinois is chosen "Player of the Year" in collegiate basketball. Carney will be a first team All-American for three seasons at Illinois.

Winifred Mason Huck of Chicago becomes the first Illinois woman voted to the U.S. Congress. She was elected to finish the term of her deceased father.

Balloon tires are introduced on American automobiles.

Studebaker begins using molybdenum steel in its autos.

Henry Ford publishes *My Life And Work* which becomes an international best-seller.

1923 – The Ku Klux Klan stages a huge rally on the outskirts of East St. Louis at the prehistoric site on **Collinsville Road** known as Monks Mound. Estimates placed their crowd of supporters as high as 10,000. Yet the Klan was largely unsuccessful in **East St. Louis** because the city had large contingencies of Irish, Catholics, and Negroes, the groups it hated the most.

Dupont Corporation invents cellophane.

Mary Margaret Bartelme of Chicago becomes the first woman judge of Illinois. She presides over the Juvenile Court for ten years.

Servus Rubber Company in **Rock Island** opens a plant at 1136 Second Avenue. They employ several hundred people manufacturing protective footwear (from rain).

The first *Illinois Voter's Handbook*, a reference book on state government, is published. It is published every two years thereafter.

There are few Negroes in Johnson County until this year when many migrate from the South to assist in the new industry of raising cotton.

Fords are so cheap and reliable that every other car made in 1923 is a Ford.

President Harding dies of a stroke, and Calvin Coolidge is sworn in as the new president.

Felix Salten of Vienna, Austria, writes *Bambi*, a children's novel.

Calvin Coolidge gives the first official presidential message on radio.

It is estimated that Chicago has 20,000 speakeasies.

Jack Dempsey, the colorful heavyweight champ since 1919, frequents the Chicago nightclub scene. Most politicians have his autographed picture on their desks.

Dempsey fights Louis Firpo, the "Wild Bull" of the Argentine pampas. The fight only lasted two rounds, with Dempsey winning by a knockout. There were **twelve knockdowns in about four minutes**, making it the most ferocious action ever in a fight of such limited duration. The 6'3" and 220-pound Firpo knocked Dempsey down several times, once through the ropes and out of the ring. Ashcan artist George Bellows immortalized the incident on canvas.

The KKK arrives in **Marion** and holds a rally some 2,000 strong with a cross burning ceremony. Dismayed over the inability of law officials to enforce prohibition, the Klan hires S. Glenn Young, a former Prohibition Agent, to clean up the area. The war between the wets and drys was on.

The power of the Ku Klux Klan was broken in **Franklin County** in what came to be known as the Battle of Mattox Farm. Jack Mattox was a prominent farmer who owned land at a place called Crawford Prairie. The local Klan, in their usual manner, was planning to pay him a midnight visit to give him a serious warning. But among the Klan group was a fellow Mason and friend of Jack Mattox. He warned Mattox of the impending visit, and he promptly organized a posse of about forty men. They lay in ambush

Firpo knocks Dempsey out of the ring

along the roadside and waited for the nightriders. There was an exchange of gunfire, and several Klansmen were injured and one killed in the ensuing melee. One of those wounded was convinced through trickery that his wounds were fatal. To salve his conscience, he gave authorities a long list of members. The governor of Illinois authorized a special group of 100 men to round up and arrest the klansmen. The power of the KKK was broken forever in **Franklin County**.

Packard twin six

Charlie Birger purchases 40 acres of land in Williamson County and makes plans to build Shady Rest, a clubhouse for his gang.

Bootlegger Charlie Birger is one of the people caught in a Young-led raid at **Benton,** and he vows to get even.

The first serious gang wars begin in Chicago after Spike O'Donnell gets out of prison and starts making raids on Johnny Torrio's beer shipments.

Johnny Torrio, after an assassination attempt that severely wounded him, quits the business and hands everything over to Al Capone. Torrio leaves the country and visits Naples, Italy.

The U.S. Treasury issues a $5 Silver Certificate with a "porthole" portrait of Abraham Lincoln. This large size paper currency, first issued in 1862, is known to collectors as a "shin plaster." The Lincoln note is currently worth about $450.00.

Reform-minded Democrat Michael Dever becomes Chicago's new mayor, replacing Big Bill Thompson. It was Dever's pressure on Capone that forced him to leave Chicago and move his base of operations to the Hawthorne Inn at Cicero.

An earthquake in Japan kills 100,000 people. After the U.S. donates massive aid, the Japanese send dozens of cherry trees that are planted in Washington D.C. The big earthquake in Tokyo destroys most of its buildings. Left standing is Frank Lloyd Wright's Tokyo Hotel that he designed to be quake resistant.

Eighteen years hence the Japanese will repay our act of kindness with a savage and unprovoked attack on Pearl Harbor.

The state buys historic Monk's Mound (near **Collinsville**) from the Ramey family that owned it and lived in a brick house on the site.

Robert Millikan becomes the **first Illinois-born native to win the Nobel Prize**. It is awarded for his oil-drop experiment by which he determined the amount of electrical charge in a single electron.

About 500 members of the Ku Klux Klan are sworn in as Prohibition Agents to combat illegal drinking in southern Illinois. Politics makes strange bedfellows as Baptist churches, also strong supporters of Prohibition, find themselves in an unholy alliance.

Robert Abbott, founder of the *Chicago Daily Defender*, begins the practice of including a column for Negro children in his newspaper. A few years later he creates a character named Bud Billiken (a Billiken is a guardian angel for children) and holds a Bud Billiken Festival the first Saturday in August. It was marked by a parade, special singers and performers, and a picnic after the parade with soda, candy, ice cream and competitive games and races. This festival is still going strong.

Adolf Hitler, a frustrated artist and architect, is jailed after an attempt to overthrow the government in the Munich Beer Hall Putsch. While in prison, he writes *Mein Kampf* (My Battle).

Construction is started on the *Tribune* tower in Chicago. It will feature 34 stories and a 450-foot tower above its main level. Near the top are gothic flying buttresses.

A young Adolph Hitler

The waistline on women's dresses has slipped down to the top of the hips.

William Stout of Adams County, an aviation buff since the 1890s, introduces the Stout Air Sedan which becomes the prototype for commercial airplanes of today. He later founded the Model Airplane League of America that offered youngsters affordable model kits of cardboard, tissue paper, and balsa.

Frigidaire introduces the first electric icebox.

The first neon signs are produced for advertising.

Henry Luce publishes the first issue of "Time Magazine."

Lon Chaney stars in *The Hunchback of Notre Dame*.

Nash Auto Company introduces a vacuum-powered windshield wiper.

Floor type heaters on cars begin to lose popularity due to dangers from the exhaust fumes.

1924 - Harold Red Grange, from Wheaton,

leads the University of Illinois to a stunning victory over Michigan. Grange scored four times in the first quarter, and in the second half, ran for yet another and passed for a 6th touchdown. Michigan at the time was ranked number one in the country and had a 22 game winning streak. Illinois won the game 39 to 14. Grange ran for 402 yards and passed for 64 more. His first four touchdowns were on runs of 95, 67, 56, and 44

Red Grange (r) & brother Garland (Library of Congress)

yards, a feat that will probably never be matched.

In 1925 Illinois played Penn, the Ivy League school. The mighty Penn team was undefeated and had crushed powerful teams like Yale and Chicago. Easterners said Grange's exploits were exaggerated and due to luck. Illinois won 24 to 2 with Grange running wild for 363 yards and three touchdowns. Grange would go on to play pro ball for the Chicago Bears. Grange quit the Illini team after Thanksgiving and was signed by George Halas for $100,000. This led to a new rule that pro sports could not sign college athletes until after their class graduated.

Georgia O'Keefe, a former student at the Chicago Art Institute, executes her first large flower painting. She is already famous for her numerous other paintings.

The state chartered Illinois Birth Control League is organized despite strong opposition, particularly from Catholic groups. Six of the twenty-two board members were women. Margaret Sanger had helped give impetus to this organization when she gave a speech to a crowd near the Union Stockyards in 1916.

The State of Illinois passes a law that prohibits males from appearing in public wearing masks. This is clearly aimed at the KKK. Representative Bandy of **Williamson County** cast one of the two negative votes against the bill.

S. Glenn Young seizes control of governmental machinery in **Herrin** and, acting as self-appointed judge, finds Sheriff George Galligan guilty of murdering Klansman Caesar Cagle in a shootout and orders him thrown in jail. In all, some 40 men were arrested for some connection with Kagle's killing, but Galligan and the others were later released.

Young is attacked by the Shelton gang while traveling with his wife from **Marion** to East St. Louis. His car is raked with gunfire near **Okawville.** He is wounded and his wife is blinded by buckshot.

In August there is a big shootout between Klan and anti-Klan forces at a garage in **Herrin,** and six people are killed. The sheriff's anti-Klan forces take refuge in a hospital, and there is another shootout at that site.

Chicago's Soldier Field, seating capacity 45,000, opens in the fall to host athletic events. Its name at the time is Municipal Grant Park Stadium.

A 3.6 mile lock and canal is completed at LeClaire along the **Rock Island Rapids**, a dangerous stretch for river traffic.

The **Tri-Cities/Quad Cities** area gains the reputation of the **Farm Implement Capital of the World** when International Harvester buys Moline Plow Works and begins making Farmall tractors in **Rock Island**. J. I. Case would arrive on the scene in 1937 with the purchase of Rock Island Plow Works, following Deere and Company which came to Moline in 1848.

Henry Ford announces the production of his ten millionth car and lowers the price of a Model-T to $290.

Architect **Louis Sullivan dies broke and unappreciated**. He started out as a member of William LeBaron Jenny's office staff. His talent and contributions would not be recognized until long after his death. He studied in Paris and then joined the Chicago firm of Dankmar Adler.

Al Capone's men use violence and intimidation at the

polls in Cicero in an effort to oust reform Mayor Dever who has been cracking down on their operations. An hours-long afternoon pitched battle ensues. **Brother Frank Capone is killed** in a shootout with police. Al Capone escapes under cover of night. Florist/gangster Dion O'Banion orders $20,000 worth of flowers in anticipation of a brisk funeral business due to the carnage. Fortunately for Capone, his slate of public officials won the election.

Charles Lindbergh, working for Robertson Aircraft of St. Louis, flies airmail on the St. Louis to Chicago run by following railroad tracks. Stops along the way include **Springfield** and **Peoria**.

Richard Loeb – Lib. Of Congress

An explosion in a food plant at **Pekin** kills 42 people.

Leopold and Loeb, the two youths who killed young Bobby Franks just for the thrill of it, and defended by Clarence Darrow, plead guilty to murder and are sentenced to life plus 99 years in jail. Chicago has six newspapers at this time reporting about the **Crime of the Century**.

Community players begin what comes to be an annual event in **Bloomington**, the American Passion Play depicting the life of Christ at the Scottish Rite Temple.

Capone kills Joe Howard on May 8 by pumping six bullets in him. Capone's friend, Jake Guzik, complained that Howard had slapped him around. Capone confronted the man, and when he mouthed off, filled him full of lead. Capone escaped prosecution when no one at the scene of the crime identified Capone as the shooter. The incident took place at Heinie Jacob's Saloon on South Wabash, not far from the Green Mill.

Congress passes a law extending the full rights of citizenship to native-Americans for the first time.

William Wrigley, the chewing gum magnate, builds the terra cotta **Wrigley Building**. It quickly becomes a Chicago landmark.

The divorce rate in Illinois stands at one in every seven marriages. (This is considered a scandalous statistic.)

Cicero, a town of about 70,000, the 5th largest city in the state at the time, is west of Chicago, but it is still in Cook County. Capone moves his offices there due to pressure from Mayor Dever in Chicago. Capone's new headquarters became the Hawthorne Inn at 4833 Twenty-second Street.

The small town of **Ina**, south of **Mount Vernon**, is rocked by a religious scandal. Lawrence Hight, a married Methodist minister, falls in love with a young member of his flock, Elsie Sweeten, a married woman with three children.

After a torrid affair that included clandestine trysts following Wednesday night prayer meetings, the love-struck couple decided to **murder their spouses**. Wilford Sweeten, a coal miner, was the first victim. Ptomaine (food) poisoning was common back then, and many assumed that was the cause of death. But when Anna Hight died an agonizing death six weeks later, ugly rumors forced the county coroner to order autopsies. Sweeten's body was exhumed, and an analysis of the stomach found traces of poison. Arsenic was also found in Mrs. Hight's body. The reverend was sentenced to life imprisonment at Menard in **Chester**, and Elsie was given 35 years at **Joliet**. Two years later the Illinois Supreme Court ruled that Elsie should have been tried separately. A second trial, despite much damaging evidence, ended with an acquittal.

Dion O'Banion, Capone's Irish rival, is killed in the famous **"handshake murder"** on November 10. Three men came into his flower shop in Chicago (on State Street) and when O'Banion (who always carried three guns) offered a handshake, one of the men held him fast, the other helped immobilize him, and the third shot him dead. Hymie Weiss now assumed leadership of the O'Banion Gang. O'Banion had been responsible for about 25 killings.

Nikolai Lenin, the man who engineered the Bolshevik revolution in Russia, dies. Leon Trotsky and Joe Stalin now jockey for power.

Surrealism as an art movement begins in Paris. Its Freudian purpose was to state freely the human imagination as it expressed itself in dreams.

Coolidge returns Confederate flag

J. Edgar Hoover is appointed head of the FBI.

Calvin Coolidge defeats the Democratic challenger, John W. Davis, in the presidential contest. Calvin Coolidge is re-elected with the slogan, "Keep Cool With Coolidge."

IBM is founded by Thomas Watson.

The first winter Olympic Games are held in Chamonix, France. The summer Olympics are held in Paris.

Former President Woodrow Wilson dies.

Using four different planes and taking six months, Colonel Billy Mitchell becomes **the first person to fly around the world**.

The *Shenandoah*, a great U.S. Navy dirigible, crashes, killing dozens of people.

The *Grand Ole Opry* begins making radio broadcasts in Nashville, Tennessee.

The Teapot Dome oil scandal and other improprieties during the Harding administration come to light.

John Dillinger is sentenced to nine years in prison for an attempted armed robbery in Indiana. While in prison he falls in league with a pair of career criminals, Harry Pierpont and Homer Van Meter.

Although the electronic theory for television goes back to an 1884 German patent, it wasn't successfully demonstrated until 1924. Experimental television was first broadcast at Chicago in 1931 by station W9XAP, but regular broadcasting did not begin until 1941.

The **Joliet High School Band** wins the regional music contest and goes on to become the most dominant in the nation. They win the National Championship trophy in 1926, 1927, and 1928, and are banned from the competition in 1929.

Memorial Stadium, built to honor Illinois youth killed in the Great War, is dedicated at **Champaign** during halftime ceremonies of a Homecoming football game vs. Michigan. The two rows of Doric columns represent the number of Illinois youth killed in the war. Two more columns were added to represent "sportsmanship" and "fair play."

Baseball commissioner Kenesaw Mountain Landis (UPI)

Jim Thorpe signs a contract to play football with the Rock Island Independents. **Rock Island** was one of the charter members of the American Professional Football Association that later evolved into the NFL. This is the same Jim Thorpe who was the decathlon and pentathlon champion in the 1912 Olympics. Thorpe was also a great grandson of Chief Black Hawk.

Another name player for the Independents is quarterback Jimmy Conzelman, formerly a player for the **Decatur Staleys.**

Florence Fifer Bohler, daughter of Illinois governor Joe Fifer, becomes the first woman elected to the state senate. It was Florence who introduced the bill that made "Illinois" the official state song.

Auto makers begin using baked-enamel paint.

1925 – Illinois adopts an official state song, "Illinois," written by Charles H. Chamberlain and sung to the tune, "Baby Mine." "By thy rivers gently flowing, Illinois, Illinois . . ." The song pays tribute to Lincoln, Grant and General John Logan. No state in the union produced three men as important as these to the Civil War effort. "Not without thy wondrous story, Illinois, Illinois, Can be writ the nation's glory, Illinois, Illinois . . . ." This great song makes the hair on the back of your neck stiffen.

The first Women's World Fair is held in Chicago. The event was the brainchild of Helen Bennett and it was organized and run by Louise Bowen. It was jointly sponsored by the Teddy Roosevelt Women's Republican Club and the Illinois Women's Republican Club. The fair ran for eight days, attracted 200,000 visitors, and raised $50,000 for charity. There were over 200 exhibitors. A women's symphony gave concerts and staged a pageant. Special speakers at a featured luncheon were Jane Addams and Nellie Taylor Ross, governor of Wyoming.

Victor Motors of 28th and Locust in St. Louis, a truck manufacturing firm since 1923, completes the renovation of an old factory at 24th and McCasland in **East St. Louis**. The facility was was used by St. Louis Cotton Oil Company before Victor revamped the 360,000 sq. ft. building for about $500,000. In April of 1926 the company started producing buses holding 28-35 passengers. The building was later occupied by Nelson Concrete Culvert Company.

Students at Yale University's cafeteria invent a new toy by sailing empty pie tins made by the Frisbie Baking Co.

Over 30,000 members of the KKK march down Pennsylvania Avenue in Washington, D.C., in the largest Klan parade in history.

It is estimated that warfare against the KKK by the forces of Sheriff Galligan, allied with the Birger and Shelton gangs, is responsible for 52 deaths in Williamson County. Allied with S. Glenn Young and the Klan were large numbers of Protestant ministers.

In a shootout at the European Hotel in **Herrin**, there is a gunplay between Birger's men and S. Glenn Young and his supporters. **Four people are killed** in the fracas, including S. Glenn Young. The power of the KKK wanes after his funeral. It is completely broken after another shootout (1926) in front of the Masonic Temple in Herrin where seven men were killed.

"Bryan takes notes" Scopes trial cartoon

Chicago's most successful criminal defense lawyer, Clarence Darrow, defends John Scopes in the famous evolution Monkey Trial in Dayton, Tennessee. The press heavily covered this sensationalized trial. It turned out to be a battle between old-fashioned fundamentalists who believed in a literal interpretation of the Bible, and modernists who believed the Old Testament to be a collection of fairy tales. William Jennings Bryan of **Salem** prosecuted the case and died a week after the trial was over.

March 18. A series of tornadoes ravage southern Illinois and the Midwest, killing more than **891** people in the **worst series of storms** to ever hit this part of the country. Twenty-six towns were hit over a five state area **injuring 2,832 people.** Fires in numerous places finished off whatever might have been missed by the tornadoes. Missouri, Illinois, Indiana, Kentucky and Tennessee were the devastated states. The heaviest loss of life and greatest destruction was reported in **Murphysboro**.

This part of Illinois becomes known as **Tornado Alley**.

Seven other states have tornadoes more frequently, but Illinois **ranks first in tornado-caused deaths**.

Igor Stravinsky makes his American music debut in NYC.

East St. Louis *Journal*: The swirling death wind which late Wednesday swept over southern Illinois has caused property damage in excess of ten million dollars. The death and injured figures were based on bodies recovered from the stricken area, and upon the number of persons still unaccounted for in the storm-ridden territory. The original figures are revised upward daily. The rural communities still have to report their loss of life, and this is expected to swell the totals.

Twenty-three towns in three states were swept by the storm, many of the places being virtually flattened.

SALESMAN SUCKED THROUGH ROOF
East St. Louis *Journal*, March 20

A traveling salesman in Carbondale, B.B. McPherson of St. Louis, told the amazing story of being sucked head first through a roof in the 1925 tornado.

He was inside a frame store when the tornado struck. It pulled him head first through the roof and then set him down outside in front of the building.

He said his trousers were torn entirely off him leaving nothing but the belt. Physicians in St. Louis said that he suffered from two scalp wounds, a possible fractured skull, a fractured shoulder and an injured ankle.

The city council of **East St. Louis**, led by **Mayor M.M. Stephens**, voted to send $1,000, and the state legislature was expected to vote $500,000 in relief funds. The St. Clair County Board voted to send an additional $1,000. **William R. Brown**, potentate of the Ainad Temple in East St. Louis, organized a group of his fellow men for relief work. A relief train, filled with doctors, nurses and supplies, immediately left from Chicago. Others were sent from St. Louis and East St. Louis.

Governor Len Small dispatched the state militia from **Quincy** to affected areas. Men were also sent from **Jefferson Barracks** in Missouri to help clear the wreckage and establish order. There was some reported looting initially, but after more guardsmen arrived the practice of thievery came to an end.

Murphysboro was the hardest hit with nearly half the town being flattened. Nearly a third of **West Frankfort** was gone. The fires that subsequently broke out were so bad that dynamite had to be used in some instances to create firebreaks.

More women than men were killed in Illinois because many men were down in the coal mines when the tornado struck.

The largest industrial site damaged was the Southern Railroad shop at Princeton, Indiana, which employed 450 people.

The Red Cross, of course, was on the scene in every town and immediately set up soup kitchens and tents.

Nearly half of those killed in **Desoto** were children as the winds struck a large school complex shortly before 3:00 p.m.

In Indiana, scores more were burned to death as they became trapped in the debris, and fires swept through the ruins with indescribable scenes of horror. The deathly odor of burning flesh was smelled for miles around as volunteer fire fighters struggled to check the flames. The fires were started mostly by overturned stoves whose burning embers set fire to the rubble.

Spectators described the tornado as a sausage-shaped greenish cloud that roared in with the sound of a locomotive from the west. They said it was humid and that hail began to fall just before the cyclone struck.

Automobiles did not escape the destruction as they were often piled together in small heaps. Some of them were tossed completely through the sides of buildings.

East St. Louis Commissioner **John Connors** came back from a visit to the devastated district and said there was a pressing need for serums, especially the anti-toxin for tetanus. He also said there was a shortage of undertakers.

Around midnight the skies around **Benton**, **Harrisburg**, and **DuQuoin** were reddish-orange with flames from the fires that were still destroying **Murphysboro**.

Forty-six of the injured were taken to hospitals in East St. Louis. Seven of the most severely injured died on the train while in route to St. Mary's and Deaconess (Christian Welfare).

For several days after the tornado, all roads and highways were clogged with sightseers wanting to get a glimpse of the carnage. Most were turned away for fear they would hamper relief efforts. Tented cities sprang up for the homeless. A crew of about forty men set about digging graves in **Murphysboro**.

Author Dean Koontz would later write about the tornado in *From The Corner of His Eye*.

April: The Sheltons have a falling out with Art and Bess Newman. Bess Newman orders the brothers out of the Arlington Hotel in **East St. Louis**. A few days later, one of the Shelton's men, **Charlie Gordon**, provoked Art Newman into a street fight, and Newman shot and killed Gordon. Newman was acquitted on self-defense, but he decided that it was time to get outta Dodge. Art and Bess sold the hotel, and the couple left for Memphis. After the heat was off, they decided to return to the area to **hook up with Charlie Birger**, making him a much more formidable foe for the Sheltons.

Harry Houdini – Lib. Of Congress

Harry Houdini, the renown escape artist, comes to **Chicago**. While not engaged in the business of death-defying escapes, Houdini takes it upon himself to debunk those who claim to be fortunetellers and spiritualists. One such person sued Houdini, saying that his crusade was making it impossible for him to communicate with the spirits, thus costing him money. Houdini won his case in court when he proved the man to be a fraud by challenging him to reveal the nickname Houdini's father had given him. The irony of all this is that before his death in 1926, Houdini promised to try and communicate with his wife from beyond the grave, prompting annual séances on every Halloween, the anniversary of his death.

A new ordinance makes it illegal to kill a white squirrel (cute rats with bushy tails), or take one out of the city of **Olney**.

George Halas, owner of the Chicago Bruins, helps establish the American Basketball Association pro league. The Depression wipes out the league, and in 1937 the NBA is formed. In 1947 the Chicago Gears signed George Mikan and won the championship. Maurice White took his Gears into a new league that he formed. It collapsed and Mikan was signed by the Minneapolis Lakers (now the L.A. Lakers).

The Chicago Cardinals win the NFL championship.

Harold Red Grange becomes football's first $100,000 a year player when he signs with the Chicago Bears. His contract is unusual in that it also calls for a percentage of the gate take. He quits the team a year later and forms his own league when they turn down his request to become 1/3 owner.

The editor of the student newspaper *Daily Illini* calls the popular shimmy dance "that insult to our whole moral code."

Al Capone applies for life insurance but is rejected by three different companies.

Capone orders a specially made Cadillac with bulletproof glass and armor plate on the body. The car cost $30,000 and weighed seven tons.

Elgin wins its second straight prep basketball championship.

May 25: Angelo Genna is ambushed and killed by Hymie Weiss, Bugs Moran, and Schemer Drucci. Mike "the Devil" Genna is killed a few weeks later on June 13th in a shootout with police.

Chicago banker Charles Dawes formulates a plan that is accepted by Europe to reduce German reparation payments to help that country recover economically. He will win the Nobel Peace Prize for the Dawes Plan.

Nellie Taylor Ross of Wyoming becomes the nation's first female governor by completing her deceased husband's term. A few weeks later, Ma Ferguson is installed as governor in Texas.

More farmers at this time have radios than bathtubs. It wasn't a matter of preferring entertainment to cleanliness. Radios could be bought for a few dollars but the expense of indoor plumbing was prohibitive.

Genna crime family

Howard Johnson opens his first restaurant in Massachusetts.

A dogsled delivers an emergency set of diptheria vaccines by making an exhaustive trip from Anchorage to Nome, Alaska. This event becomes the basis for the annual Iditarod dogsled competition. First place prize money for the winning musher is currently a little over $72,000. The route of the 1,100-mile race takes all the contestants through the ghost mining town of Iditarod.

The Chrysler Corporation is formed. Ford Motor Company is building 9,000 cars a day.

F.S. Fitzgerald's *The Great Gatsby* is published.

The death rate from alcoholism stands at 3.6 deaths per 1,000. Although slightly on the rise since the advent of prohibition, this is still down from the 5.2 percent in 1917 before the enforcement of the Volstead act.

Lincoln Ellsworth of **Chicago** joins Norwegian explorer Roald Amundson in an attempt to fly over the North Pole. This mission fails due to severe weather and faulty equipment but another attempt in 1926, this time with Umberto Nobile, is successful. Ellsworth went on to fly the entire length of Antarctica, giving America claim to huge chunks of that land.

Johnny Torrio is severely wounded in an assassination attempt by Bugs Moran, Hymie Weiss, and two other men. He is attacked in front of his apartment after he and his wife Ann had returned from a shopping trip. After a slow and painful recovery, he quits the rackets and hands everything over to Al Capone.

Football star Red Grange is featured on the cover of Time Magazine.

More closed cars than open models are sold this year – a first.

Uniform markings for federally assisted highways are adopted – even numbers for east/west and odd numbers for north/south.

The Lincoln Highway is completed – the first transcontinental highway.

1926 - A.A. Milne publishes *Winnie the Pooh*.

The Norwegian explorer Amundsen

Rank of Illinois cities in 1925 according to annual manufacturing value of products

1. Chicago, $3 ½ billion 2. Joliet $82 million 3. East St. Louis $77 million 4. Rockford $74 million 5 Cicero $57 million 6. Peoria $57 million 7. Moline $44 million 8. Granite City $43 million 9. Chicago Heights $41 million 10. Decatur $38 million 11. Alton $31 million 12. Aurora $30 million 13 Pekin $25.2 million 14. Elgin $ 25 million 15. Waukegan $24 million 16. Quincy $23 million 17. Springfield $22.7 million 18. Rock Island $22 million 19. Freeport $18 million 20. Kewanee $16 million 21. Danville $15 million 22. Maywood $14.4 million 23. Belleville 14 million

circles the North Pole in a dirigible named the *Norge*.

The Chicago Tribune Tower opens on July 6.

Winston Churchill is Chancellor of the Exchequer (finances) in England under the Stanley Baldwin government. He dabbles at writing and painting. Brilliant but erratic is how most summed him up. It was not thought that he would ever come to dominate Britain's destiny.

Chicago evangelist Billy Sunday lambastes the automobile for the decline in church attendance and the loosening of morals. "We've put the red light district on wheels," he warns.

Valentino and Vilma Banky in *Son of the Sheik*

Thousands of Chicagoans turn out to see the body of actor Rudolph Valentino who had recently died from a perforated ulcer in New York. He was on the way to his burial place in Hollywood. Police officers, fearing a repeat of a riot in New York, cordon off the area and only a few catch even a glimpse of his casket. The swarthy Italian-born Valentino rose to fame by starring in the *Four Horsemen of the Apocalypse* and *The Sheik*.

The federal government and various states work in conjunction to create **Route 66**. It begins in Chicago at the intersection of Jackson Boulevard and Lake Shore Drive. It courses 2,400 miles in length and ends in California near Los Angeles. Approximately 1/8 of the highway is in Illinois. It was fully paved by 1936.

Samuel Insull, the Chicago utilities giant, proposes that the city build a subway system. Aldermen turn him down. His company is now operating in eleven states and furnishing electricity to 385 cities. Insull ran utilities and electric streetcar systems in the northern half of the state, while **Champaign** politician William B. McKinley controlled the southern half. McKinley's Illinois Traction System became the largest in the Midwest. The McKinley Bridge over the Mississippi at Madison/Granite City was built by him. It was a large three-lane bridge that featured separate roadways for cars and trucks.

Insull spent his mornings at his People's Gas Light & Coke Co. and his afternoons at Chicago Commonwealth Edison. His wife, the former Gladys Wallis of stage fame, tried to resurrect her stage career 25 years after the birth of her son, but with little success. To smooth things politically, Insull kept a preferred list of 1600 Chicagoans whom he sold stock to at below market price.

When Harold McCormick was no longer willing to support the Chicago Opera Company, Insull stepped in and agreed to underwrite it for a 5-year period. He built a new structure that would have an opera house combined with office space. The idea was that the office rents would pay for the support of the opera. A month before the grand opening, the stock market crashed. Insull was 70 years old at the time. In July of 1932, his fortunes declining, the Board of Directors forced him to resign. The crash of Insull stock caused one bank failure and brought losses to thousands of investors. Insull's brother (Martin) was guilty of using more than $500,000 of company money to cover the margin on his personal brokerage account. After various lawsuits were filed, both brothers fled, Samuel to Europe and Martin to Canada. Samuel Insull was finally apprehended, but he was acquitted by the jury in a controversial trial.

Frank Smith wins the U.S. Senate race against William McKinley. But the U.S. Senate refuses to accept him on the grounds that his Insull-backed campaign had spent too much money and essentially "bought" the seat. The same thing happened to Senator William Lorimer who was expelled on similar grounds ten years earlier.

The first transatlantic conversation by telephone is held between New York and London.

Richard E. Byrd and Floyd Bennett make the first flight over the North Pole.

A hurricane devastates Florida, killing 300 and injuring 6,000, and effectively ending the land boom.

It is claimed that 900 different items bear the label, "**Made in Peoria**."

William Stout, a native of **Quincy**, establishes the nation's first airline service, offering flights from Detroit to Grand Rapids, Michigan.

The first Eucharistic Congress opens in **Chicago** and is attended by over a million people.

The **East St Louis Flyers** and the **Belleville Maroons** begin a football rivalry by playing an annual Thanksgiving Day (morning) football game that, more often than not, determined the conference championship. Most of the crowds were as large as 11,000 people.

According to August Maue in his *History of Illinois*, geography experts predict that by the year 1950, Chicago will have a population of 10 million.

William B. McKinley

Chicago upstart **Rand McNally** publishes his first atlas.

Coffee baron Frederick McLaughlin buys a Portland hockey team and moves it to Chicago where they become known as the **Blackhawks**. They play their games at the

Coliseum, a former Civil War prison. When the NHL is formed, Chicago is one of the six original teams. McLaughlin was married to movie star Irene Castle.

There is a falling out between Charlie Birger and the Sheltons when it becomes apparent that Charlie Birger is skimming profits from the slot machine business they were supposed to share equally.

The Sheltons hire a barnstorming pilot to fly over Shady Rest, Birger's hangout, while one of them **tosses homemade bombs** out of a two-seat JN-4 Jenny. Blackie Armes was the bombardier, but his nitro/dynamite bombs missed the target, killing only one of Birger's pets. In a later story that appeared in Ripley's "Believe It Or Not," this incident was considered the **first aerial bombing attack carried out on American soil.**

Emil Fricker becomes the last man publicly hanged in **Madison County**. Fricker, a dairy farmer in **Highland**, was convicted of murdering the husband of a milkmaid on his farm with whom he had fallen hopelessly in love. He was also suspected of killing her first husband.

Bill McSwiggin, the "hanging prosecutor," part of the Robert Crowe Republican faction, is killed while riding in a car with Tom Duffy,

William McSwiggin

Myles O'Donnell, and his brother Klondike. Tom Duffy is also killed. Jim Doherty, who was with the group, was wounded. The O'Donnells, including brother Spike, were Capone rivals. Capone was a member of a motorcade of five cars that was responsible for the ambush but four grand jury investigations failed to lead to an indictment.

The Book-of-the-Month Club is started. A year later it is followed by the Literary Guild.

RCA pays AT&T a million dollars for radio station WEAF and launches NBC, the National Broadcasting Corporation.

Kodak introduces 16 mm color movie film.

Ernest Hemingway's *The Sun Also Rises* is published.

Queen Marie of Romania visits New York and is welcomed by Mayor Jimmy Walker.

The spectacle film *Ben Hur* is produced by MGM at a cost of $6 million.

The nation celebrates its sesquicentennial (150 years) at Philadelphia, but attendance is poor and the exposition loses money.

Langston Hughes' *The Weary Blues* is published.

Capone and his men agree to the Hotel Sherman treaty with the Joe Saltis gang and several others. Each gang is assigned a specific territory in an effort to cut down on mob warfare. The main reason Al Capone agreed to the treaty was due to Sonny having a mastoid infection and he wanted to spend more time at home with his son.

Calvin Coolidge delivers his State of the Union message and recommends the following: extension of Civil Service

reform, more humane immigration laws, judicial reform, penal reform, the extension of rights for Negroes, economy in government, railroad consolidation, reduction of taxation, adherence to World Court rulings, and harbor and river improvements. Congress ignores most of his recommendations.

Chicago Mayor Bill Thompson

The Aragon Ballroom opens on Chicago's north side at a construction cost of a million dollars. Built in Spanish-Revival architectural style, it simulated a Hollywood movie set of a Spanish square. The spacious hall could accommodate 8,000 dancers. The gala grand opening was attended by Big Bill Thompson.

Classes for beginning dancers were held every Tuesday night. The fast-paced one step, fox trot, and waltz were taught. Another famous opulent Chicago ballroom of the Twenties was the Trianon, built in 1922 and billed as the "World's Most Beautiful Ballroom." It was named for a small palace given by Louis XIV to his wife, Marie Antoinette.

The Merry Garden Ballroom in Chicago was billed as "Chicago's Chummiest Ballroom" and became famous for hosting dance marathons, broadcast over radio stations WBBM and WCFL.

Rubber mounts are used in a car for the first time, holding an engine in place on Pontiac's six cylinder L head engine.

Cadillac introduces shatter resistant safety glass.

Glass "eyes" are placed at the rear of headlights on several makes of cars to let drivers know if the headlights are on.

Oldsmobile introduces chrome plating on automobile parts.

Chrysler introduces adjustable front seats.

Grauman's Chineese Theater opens in S. California.

Stick hobby horse

1927 – Jack Dempsey, who lost his title to Gene Tunney, gets a rematch. The fight is at Soldier Field in Chicago. It was rumored that Capone had big bets on Dempsey and had sent him a note that warned him not to lose. Capone even met with the referee, Davey Miller, and told him he had bet $50,000 on Dempsey and that he wanted him to give Dempsey a fair shot. Interestingly, it was the same Davey Miller shot by

Dion O'Banion four years earlier outside the LaSalle Theater.

Shortly before the fight, Miller was replaced as referee. Dempsey knocked Tunney down in the 7th round and would have won the fight had he gone to a neutral corner. Referee Dave (Long Count) Barry had to push Dempsey in the right direction before starting his count. Tunney barely got off the canvas before the count of ten, having

Tunney is down

been given five extra revitalizing seconds. Tunney went on to win by decision in the controversial fight.

Giant City State Park, south of **Carbondale** in the Illinois Ozarks, is created and so named for its orderly 35-foot high blocks of sandstone. The Civilian Conservation Corps (CCC) built the large stone lodge during the Depression. Back in Civil War times, the site was a hideout for treasonous Knights of the Golden Circle, Confederate sympathizers.

Chicago opens a new municipal airport that becomes known as Midway. It has a single runway and occupies a quarter of a square mile.

Entertainer Joe E. Lewis becomes known as "**the man the mob couldn't kill.**" Lewis was a comedian at the Green Mill in Chicago but wanted to sign a new contract with another club. He ignored threats on his life and planned to continue his career at the New Rendezvous. He was beaten and horribly slashed by several of Machine Gun McGurn's men. It took him nearly ten years to recover. He doggedly resumed his career as soon as he was able. His story was later told in the Frank Sinatra vehicle, *The Joker is Wild.*

Jim and Marian Jordan of **Peoria**, playing **Fibber McGee and Molly** on radio, help **make Chicago the radio capital of America.**

William McAndrew, Chicago Superintendent of Schools, is suspended and placed on trial by the School Board. He is accused of being unpatriotic and pro-British in his views. McAndrew is a victim of former Mayor Big Bill Thompson's bid for reelection based on a zany crusade against the British in an "America First" platform. Famed lawyer Clarence Darrow proclaimed, "Why it's the craziest thing I ever heard." The school district's head librarian suggested that all of the pro-British books be placed in a cage and only "mature" historians be allowed to read them. A former congressman combed the system's books for six months and declared that England was conquering America, "not by shot but by

Fibber McGee & Molly – Lib. Congress

a rain of propaganda." After months of hearings and 6,000 pages of testimony, the Board voted to remove McAndrew from his position.

April: Big Bill Thompson, backed with Capone muscle and money, ousts reform mayor William Dever and wins a third term as Chicago mayor. Schemer Drucci is killed while resisting arrest for assault and battery during election-day violence. Thompson won election for his third term as mayor but was defeated in 1931 by Anton Cermak.

George and Ben Probst, proprietors of the **New Athens Brewery**, are fined $1,000 each and sentenced to 90 days in the Franklin County jail for violation of the Volstead prohibition act.

Illinois becomes the last state to adopt a motor fuel tax to pay for road improvement. This was due partially to farmers not wanting fuel used in tractors to be taxed. A tax of two cents a gallon is imposed to build and maintain roads in Illinois.

Litchfield resident **Ray "the Cracker" Schalk** becomes the manager of the Chicago White Sox. He established records by catching 1,719 baseball games in seventeen years. He also played in the 1917 and 1919 World Series.

Miles Davis and his parents move to **East St. Louis** a year after he is born in **Alton**. His father is a dentist.

Famed Jazz musician Duke Ellington records a peppy tune on the RCA label called "East St. Louis Toodle O." The tune is a vague reference about having a good time in the notorious Valley district of the town. The song became nationally famous because it heralded his popular radio show throughout the 1930s.

When a tornado approaches a school in **White Hall**, teacher Annie Keller urges the children to take refuge under their desks and she faces the tornado's rage at the room's doorway. She is killed, but all of the children survive. A monument to her was later sculpted by the renowned Lorado Taft.

Lois Delaner of **Joliet**, a high school student and only 16 years old, is chosen "Miss America."

The ship *Favorite* capsizes off North Avenue in the Chicago River, killing 27.

The Buckingham Fountain is built at Grant Park and Lake Shore Drive in **Chicago**. The fountain spouts water almost 150 feet into the air and at night has a dazzling light display. It is modeled after a fountain at Louis XIV's palace at Versailles and named for its donor, Katherine Buckingham, a patron of the arts.

The new airport in **Springfield** will be named for Charles Lindbergh who helped plan its construction before his famous transoceanic flight.

"Roosting Joe" Powers remains atop the flagpole at Chicago's Morrison Hotel for 16 days, two hours, and 45 minutes. Flagpole sitting is a fad that sweeps the nation at this point in time.

The Avalon, the greatest of John Eberson's "atmospheric" movie palaces, opens in Chicago.

Charlie Birger and several other members of his gang are convicted of murder and Birger now faces execution. The state has recently replaced hanging with electrocution, but Birger gets a date with the hangman because his crime was committed before the new law was passed.

Carl Sandburg

Carl Sandburg composes the song "El-a-noy:" Then move your family westward, / Bring all your girls and boys/ And cross at Shawnee ferry'/ To the state of El-a-noy/

The U.S. Supreme Court rules that income from illegal sources is taxable and rejects the notion that filing such a tax return would violate the "self-incrimination" clause of the Fifth Amendment.

Al Jolson stars in *The Jazz Singer*, the first talking movie.

The Holland Tunnel between New York and New Jersey is constructed.

The first Academy Awards are held and *Wings* with Clara Bow is voted Best Picture.

Babe Ruth hits his 60th home run and establishes a baseball record that lasts for over three decades.

Henry Ford's first Model-A car is produced.

The first rules of contract bridge are drafted by the Knickerbocker Whist Club of New York. Before this new version, people played auction bridge.

Nan Britton, President Harding's mistress, writes her memoirs – *The President's Daughter*. She dedicates the book to all unwed mothers of the world.

A chemist discovers the healing power of scented lavender oil and invents the term *aromatherapy*.

The State of Illinois purchases Watch Tower Park at **Rock Island** and renames it Black Hawk Park. First opened in 1882 by Bailey Davenport, it was named Watch Tower Park because it overlooked the Rock River Valley. The park had a large covered pavilion, walking trails, a health spa with mineral springs, a merry go-round, a roller coaster, and a bowling alley. Its most famous ride was **Shoot-the-Chutes**. People rode in a wooden boat that zoomed down a steep incline that had greased wooden rails. At the

Shoot-the-Chutes (R. Is. Hist Soc.)

bottom the boat made a huge splash as it landed in the Rock River. The boat had a conductor who stood up all the way down and then poled the boat back to the base of the slide when the ride was over. The passengers departed and a new set of riders was loaded and pulled to the top of the incline by a metal cable.

Watch Tower Park was located at the end of a streetcar line and as automobiles became more affordable and popular, ridership declined and park revenues fell.

Charles Lindbergh, a pilot who flies the mail between Chicago and St. Louis, with stops at **Peoria** and **Springfield**, becomes the first person to solo the Atlantic. He took off at 7:52 a.m. on May 20th from Roosevelt Field on Long Island, New York. He flew the great circle route and landed in Paris thirty-three and a half hours later. Remember, on a globe, the shortest distance between two points is a curved line.

Carl Breer begins to study auto-related aerodynamics which will lead to Chrysler's Airflow design.

1928 – Charlie Birger becomes the last man in the State of Illinois to be legally hanged. He is executed at the Benton Jail for the murder of Joe Adams of **West City**. Birger was seen by many as a **modern-day Robin Hood** (overlooking the fact that he was a cold-blooded killer) and was perhaps the most colorful gangster in Illinois history after Capone and Dillinger. While in jail awaiting execution, Birger was visited by evangelist **Billy Sunday**. Birger was also allowed to have conjugal visits from his wife. Birger's favorite drink was said to be an **Egyptian cocktail** – corn liquor mixed with port wine.

Charlie Birger at Shady Rest

The 7-piered Chain of Rocks Bridge is built, spanning the Mississippi River in North St. Louis at Route 66. It is a steel structure of the cantilever type and is one-and-a-tenth mile in length. The name is derived from Rocks Shoal.

The Frenchman Maurice Ravel, who dies in 1937, composes "Bolero." It remains an obscure orchestral piece until Bo Derek turns it into a sensual masterpiece in her performance in the movie *Ten*, released in 1979. Derek is one of the few Hollywood actresses who supports current President George W. Bush.

Herbert Hoover is elected president, defeating New York Democrat, Al Smith. Smith, a Catholic, favored the repeal of prohibition.

Mae West stars in "Diamond Lil" on Broadway.

The Lewis and Clark bridges open in **Alton**, giving access to St. Charles County and north St. Louis.

7-Up is invented and marketed in St. Louis by C.L. Grigg. It took him two years and eleven different formulas before he perfected the lemon-flavored drink. The original red spot on the drink came from the inventor who had red eyes because **he was albino**.

Coal mine operators begin installing new loading machines and conveyors in Illinois mines to modernize and make operations more efficient. This results in large layoffs of miners who have never known any other kind of work. With the Depression about to begin, this will lead to economic hardship and labor strife.

The Manny Company of **Rockford** is absorbed by the J.I. Case Implement Company.

Two whites, Charles Correll and Freeman Gosden, launch a Chicago radio career with a blackface vaudeville act they had been performing. Within a year **Amos 'n' Andy** is a hit on NBC radio.

April: The famed "pineapple primary" occurs during a bitter Republican primary. Reform Senator Charles Deneen, backed by Diamond Joe Esposito, challenged the conservative wing of the party that was aligned with Governor Len Small, Capone, and State's Attorney Robert Crowe. Homes and staff offices were bombed, and Diamond Joe was assassinated.

Frankie Yale

Summer: Brooklyn hit man Frankie Yale is gunned down on the street by someone in an out of town car with Illinois license plates. Yale had opposed one of Capone's men, Tony Lombardo, becoming head of the *Unione Siciliano* in Chicago. Two months after he became Capone's puppet, Lombardo was gunned down on the street, not far from the Unione office in the Hartford building at Dearborn and Madison.

Amelia Earhart becomes the first woman to fly across the Atlantic.

The U.S. and 14 other nations sign the Briand-Kellogg Pact, outlawing war as a means to solve international problems.

The Graf Zeppelin airship makes a round trip between Germany and the U.S.

Amazing Stories pulp magazine

Chicago's Amelia Earhart (Lib. of Cong.)

The Chrysler Building is erected in New York; its 75 stories and gaudy spires make it the **world's tallest**.

The automatic fastener (zippers) becomes fashionable on overshoes.

Women finally win the right to vote in British elections.

Steamboat Willie, the first film with Mickey Mouse, is released.

Women's skirts are at their briefest, barely covering the knee.

Willa Cather's *Death Comes For The Archbishop* becomes a big seller.

Popular shows on Broadway include "Showboat," "Paris Bound," "Porgy," and "Funny Face."

The first cloverleaf interchange for automobiles goes into operation at Woodbridge, New Jersey.

Tim Moore, a native of **Rock Island**, lands a part in Lou Leslie's "Blackbirds," a Broadway production that becomes only the fourth musical to last for more than 400 shows. In 1951 Moore achieved lasting fame when he began playing the role of George "Kingfish" Stevens on the "Amos 'n' Andy Show" for CBS television.

The Oreo cookie by Nabisco, first introduced in 1912, is still doing well. It becomes the best seller of all time.

Germany builds the 776-foot-long *Graf Zeppelin* airship.

The Chrysler Corporation launches Plymouth and DeSoto, both as 1929 models.

Cadillac introduces synchromesh transmission which eliminates the need for double clutching when shifting gears.

Hudson introduces the first steering wheel with finger scallops on the edges.

Coast to coast bus service begins for the first time.

1929 – Congress passes the Jones Law, providing for heavy fines and up to five years in jail for bootlegging and other violations against the Prohibition Amendment.

The Modern Woodmen of America, a large life insurance company at **Rock Island**, begins the practice of covering women and children.

Herbert Hoover becomes the first president to keep a telephone on his desk.

The **Moline** Implement Company merges with Minneapolis Threshing Machine and the Minneapolis Steel and Machinery Company to form Minneapolis Moline, a company that went on to produce superior tractors.

At roughly 10:30 a.m. on the morning of February 14, four men in a car, two wearing police uniforms, pull up in front of a garage on Clark Street. A sign on the building read SMC Cartage Company and it was a favorite hangout for the Bugs Moran gang. Their Cadillac touring car even had a Klaxon gong on the running board. Thinking it was just a police raid, the seven men inside meekly lined up against the wall and were cut down in a hail of bullets. One

Pete Gusenberg of the Moran mob–killed at St. Valentine's Day Massacre

of the men killed was Reinhardt Schwimmer, an optometrist who hung around with the gang for the sport of it. Another victim, Frank Gusenberg, lived three hours with 14 bullets in him. When asked who shot him, he kept the underworld's code of silence and said, "Nobody." It is believed that the shooters were Tony Accardo, Machine Gun McGurn, Fred Burke and John Scalise.

Universal is the first airline to show a movie on a flight.

Al Capone was purposely at his Florida estate so that he would have an alibi. He was informed every step of the way by McGurn who made frequent phone calls. Moran, one of the main targets, escaped the slaughter when he arrived a few minutes late for the meeting, saw the "police car" pull up, and walked away in the other direction.

Highball – the only survivor of the massacre

As a result of public outrage over the St. Valentine's Day Massacre in Chicago on February 14, the **nation's first major crime laboratory** is established at Northwestern University. The lab was affiliated with the Northwestern University School of Law in the hopes that this would prevent political interference.

Calhoun is the only county in the state without rail service.

The first Aerocar house trailer is produced for campers.

Al Capone attends a big gangster meeting in Atlantic City, New Jersey. Sensing that other mob bosses are unhappy with the notoriety he is bringing to organized crime, he fears for his life. Capone gets himself arrested on a concealed weapons charge in Pennsylvania on the way home from the meeting. Thinking the judge will give him a month in jail where he will be safe, he is astounded when a stiff yearlong sentence to Holmesburg

Prison is pronounced for him and his bodyguard, Frank Rio.

J. Doolittle is the first pilot to rely solely on instruments.

Eliot Ness, a Norwegian-American graduate of the University of Chicago, becomes the head of a special task force to make raids on Capone's breweries and to gather information that will help the U.S. government make a case against Al Capone for tax fraud. The word soon gets out that Ness and his men can't be bribed, and they are labeled **The Untouchables** by the press.

Chicago real estate entrepreneur Oscar DePriest becomes the **first black man from a northern state elected to congress**. Unfortunately, he consistently voted against Roosevelt's New Deal and lost his seat four years later.

Roughly 26.5 million Americans now own automobiles.

Construction is nearly complete on the two-block long Merchandise Mart in Chicago, which remains for decades as the **largest commercial building in the world**. Completed in 1930, it has 95 acres of total floor space. Originally intended to serve wholesaling business needs, in 1991 it opened several floors to retail shoppers.

Cartoonist Elzie Segar introduces a new character into his ten-year-old "Thimble Theater" comic strip. He is **Popeye**, a spinach-eating sailor with bulging muscles in all the wrong places (forearm instead of biceps). The Popeye characters are based on real people known by Segar in **Chester**. Olive Oyl was modeled after a shopkeeper named Dora Paskal. The Wimpy character with the hamburger fetish was based on Bill Schuchert, owner of the Chester Opera House. Popeye was the alter ego of Frank "Rocky" Fiegel, a riverboat operator.

Ernie Nevers of the Chicago Cardinals **scores 40 points** in a football game against the Bears, a record that still stands.

Chicago loses a national lawsuit filed in 1908 by surrounding states. It was finally decided by the U.S. Supreme Court. The decision held that Chicago had legally been authorized by the secretary of war to divert 4,167 cubic feet of water per second from Lake Michigan, but for years had unlawfully increased that amount to 8,500. Chicago attorneys argued that the levels of the great lakes were rising, not falling, and that the latter volume of water was necessary to maintain navigability of the Illinois River. Chicago is directed to build more sewage treatment plants to cut down on pollution, thus lessening the need for extra water from Lake Michigan.

Chicagoan Ruth Hanna McCormick serves a two-year term as a Republican representative in Congress.

Oscar DePriest

Al Capone commits the most vicious act of his infamous career. Suspecting several of his men to be traitors, he staged a large banquet at a roadhouse near Hammond, Indiana. Joe Guinta, Albert Anselmi, and John Scalise were among the dozens of mobsters invited. Late in the evening, he accused the trio of disloyalty, bound them to their chairs and **beat them to a bloody pulp with a baseball bat**.

Illinois claims **more miles of paved roads than any other state**

in the nation. Every county has at least one paved road.

October 8: Ralph Capone is arrested for tax evasion.

Not until now does it become fashionable for women to start wearing colored nail polish.

The nation's first coast-to-coast airline is established.

President Hoover authorizes the Wickersham Commission to study the effects of Prohibition.

The movie business becomes the fourth largest industry in America.

William Faulkner's *The Sound and the Fury* is published.

Testors, the company famous for making model kits and model airplane glue, starts out as a business selling household glue.

Richard Byrd at tickertape parade

Five million radios a year are being sold in the U.S.

Richard Byrd reaches the South Pole in Antarctica by air.

Bell laboratories experiment with color television.

The Graf Zeppelin airship leaves New Jersey and flies around the world in 12 days.

Bill Tilden wins his seventh and last American amateur tennis championship.

It seems as if everyone in the nation is reading *All Quiet on the Western Front*.

October 24th – Black Thursday; the stock market crashes as investors, whose margins were exhausted or about to be exhausted, engage in a selling frenzy that has not been seen before or since. There is a record one-day loss of $32 million. General Electric, which only a few weeks before had been selling at 402, opened that morning at 315 and slid to 283. Panic selling set in around noon; bankers and brokers tried to explain the phenomenon as a technical adjustment of the market rather than a fundamental problem. The volume of selling on this day is nearly 13 million shares, a new Market record.

Things looked better on Friday, but by Monday the rout was on and on **Black Tuesday** the bottom fell out. By November 13th, most stocks had lost half of their value from their high water mark on September 3rd – the **BIG BULL MARKET WAS DEAD.** Day by day the newspapers began reporting grim suicides.

By the end of the year, the losses amounted to a staggering $15 billion. Overproduction by farmers led to falling commodity prices, and business over expansion during the booming decade also added to the economic woes. Stock prices had soared to unrealistic dizzying heights, fueled by feverish investor speculation that bought on margin (ten

percent down) and gambled everything on even higher prices. The State of Illinois, like the rest of the nation, would now suffer through a decade-long depression. Illinois coal mines closed one after another due to lack of industrial demand.

Because most people could no longer afford to ride trains, the Illinois Central was forced to lay off nearly half of its 60,000 work force.

A great many banks were financially unsound because they too had speculated and made risky loans at the prospect of high profits. When large numbers of people started withdrawing their savings to cover living expenses, shortfalls occurred which led to runs on banks and financial panic. Numerous banks were forced to close causing many people to lose their life savings.

CAUSES OF THE DEPRESSION

1. Overproduction of capital goods such as cars, radios and washing machines
2. Artificial commodity prices (coffee, cotton, sugar, wool), maintained by pools or trusts
3. A collapse in the price of silver due to numerous governments trying to put themselves on the gold standard
4. An international financial problem caused by the shifting of gold to France and America
5. Revolutions and threats of revolutions in various parts of the world, jeopardizing international investments
6. Low prices for farm products caused by over-production
7. The self-generating effects of the Depression itself – less purchasing power led to less demand for goods which in turn led to layoffs, which then led to even less purchasing power; the panic had written a *finis* to the Prosperity Decade.

BIG STOCKS OF THE TWENTIES

American Can
Anaconda Copper
General Electric
General Motors
Montgomery Ward
Union Carbide
New York Central Railroad
United States Steel
American Telephone & Telegraph
Westinghouse
Woolworth
Radio Corporation of America

The stock market crash and the ensuing worldwide

depression is a boon for Adolph Hitler. The economic crisis rescues him from political obscurity. The German people start paying attention to his speeches that promise, through National Socialism, to bring back economic prosperity and world respect for the Fatherland. *Mein Kampf*, which had been languishing under weak sales, suddenly became a best seller.

The U.S. Post Office issues a stamp to commemorate the capture of Fort Sackville by **George Rogers Clark** during the Revolutionary War in 1779. Clark had earlier captured British possessions at **Kaskaskia** and **Cahokia** without firing a shot. The French villagers at Vincennes, on hearing this news, threw in their lot with the

American cause. The British commander Henry ("the Hair Buyer") Hamilton reversed Clark's success at Vincennes by recapturing the fort. Never dreaming that a winter counterattack by Clark was feasible, Hamilton cut the garrison force there to 80 men. Undaunted, the courageous Clark marched across the state with 140 Kentuckians from Kaskaskia to Vincennes through flooded lowlands and rampaging rivers to reach his objective, 180 miles away. Although soaked, weary and half-starved, Clark's valiant men laid siege to Fort Sackville and finally forced the British to surrender on February 25, 1779.

As a result of Clark's brilliant exploit, the Northwest Territory (**including all of Illinois**) was secured, and British power and influence receded back to Detroit. When the peace treaty ending the war was signed in 1783, Britain **relinquished the entire region to the United States**.

1930 - February: Ralph Capone is convicted of tax evasion.

March 17: Al Capone is released from Pennsylvania prison.

June 9: Jake Lingle, the "**World's Richest Reporter,**" is shot and killed in a Chicago pedestrian subway under Michigan Avenue. Lingle was killed shortly after Al Capone was released from prison in Pennsylvania, getting time off for good behavior. Thousands of people showed up at his funeral. At first he was thought to be a martyr for freedom of the press. But it soon came to light that this $65 a week *Tribune* reporter led a fancy and expensive lifestyle. He was on the take as a middleman between the Chicago police and the underworld. Lingle was killed one day prior to a meeting he was supposed to have with Colonel McCormick and some Treasury agents. Leo Brothers, a St. Louis hit man, was later convicted of

the killing.

The **Coliseum** is a famous dance hall/gambling casino in **Benld**. Al Capone owns a still on the outskirts of town that ships illegal rotgut back to Chicago. This is a very popular night spot on Route 66 frequented by popular musicians and entertainers.

Dominic Tarro, one of the owners of the roadhouse, was called to **Springfield** to testify before a grand jury. The state's attorney wanted to question him about $50,000 worth of sugar he allegedly sold to a Capone still on the outskirts of Benld. Dominic never made it to testify. His body was found in the Sangamon River a few months later.

October 30: Joe Aielo, who was responsible for killing **Pasqual Lolorodo**, Capone's man who headed the Unione Siciliano, is caught in a crossfire with 59 bullet holes making a sieve of his body. Aielo had conspired with Guinta, Scalise and Anselmi to overthrow Capone.

November 18: Jake Guzik is convicted of tax fraud and is sentenced to an 18-month prison term.

December 20: Frank Nitti pleads guilty to evading $158,823 in federal taxes.

The Chicago School of Journalism compiles a list of the world's ten most outstanding personalities. Included are Benito Mussolini, Charles Lindbergh, Admiral Richard Byrd, George Bernard Shaw, Bobby Jones, President Hoover, Mahatma Gandhi, Albert Einstein, Henry Ford and Al Capone.

A very dead Pasuqal Lolordo

Gaston Means writes his book, *The Strange Death of President Harding*. In it he asserts that the philandering president was poisoned by his wife after she discovered his affair with Nan Britton. An alternate theory was that she poisoned him to save him from impending impeachment due to the numerous financial scandals in his administration.

The German Max Schmeling defeats Jack Sharkey for the heavyweight boxing championship.

Lard and jelly press

Miniature golf becomes the latest fad as courses spring up all over the country. According to the Department of Commerce there are nearly 300,000 courses throughout the land.

Coste and Bellonte make the first successful non-stop *westward* flight across the Atlantic Ocean.

Dull year – not one first-class murder trial of nation-wide interest, not one first-class prize fight, not one new sporting hero crowned.

Gallant Fox wins horse racing's Triple Crown.

The London Treaty for renewed limitations of naval armaments passes the Senate with flying colors.

With lines of the unemployed waiting for soup and bread getting longer and longer, there is renewed interest in the communist experiment in Russia and Stalin's latest Five Year Plan.

The Lateran Treaty between Mussolini and Catholic leaders makes Vatican City an independent state. Roman Catholicism is reaffirmed as the state religion of Italy.

Two thirds of American homes have electricity.

The Literary Digest conducts a national poll about Prohibition. About 38 percent of the people favor the law as it now exists; 40.8 favor modification to allow beer and light wine; 20.6 per cent favor repeal.

Three Capone mobsters are shot to death in the **Easter Massacre** of April 20th.

On October 3, Baby Face Nelson robs a bank in **Itaska**, Illinois, of $4,600. In November his gang robs a bank in **Hillside**, Illinois, of $4,000.

Al Capone opens the first "soup kitchen" in Chicago for the hungry and unemployed. It costs about $10,000 a month to operate, but Capone defrays expenses by leaning on butchers and other suppliers of food commodities to contribute.

Mother Mary Jones, a fearless union organizer, dies and is buried at **Mount Olive Cemetery**. The hallowed burial site is also known as Coal Miners Cemetery since the miners killed in the 1898 strike/riot at **Virden** are also buried there.

Robert Wadlow (Madison C. Hist. Soc.)

There is a young teenager living in **Alton**, Illinois, by the name of Robert Wadlow. He towers above his classmates in high school and is on his way to becoming the **world's tallest man (8' 11.1," 490 lbs., 44 1/2 AA shoe)**. Wadlow was nicknamed the "Gentle Giant." His height was a quirk of nature because everyone else in his family was "normal" size. He made many special public appearances, and these events helped pay for his medical and clothing expenses that were huge because everything had to be tailor made. He had to be fitted with special braces on his legs so that he could walk.

In 1936 he traveled to Dallas, Texas, which was holding a Centennial Celebration. On the fair's Illinois Day, Wadlow met Illinois Governor Henry Hoerner. At a rival centennial celebration in Fort Worth, Wadlow met Vice-president John Nance Garner and dancer **Sally Rand**. He later visited the State Fair in **Springfield** and made $1,800 appearing on stage in one of the shows. In

1937 he joined the Ringling Brothers/Barnum & Bailey Circus on the east coast.

Wadlow died at the age of twenty-two in 1940 from blood poisoning caused by an infected blister that was made by his braces. He was buried in a ten-foot coffin that took 12 pallbearers to carry. A life-size statue of him is in Alton on College Ave. across from the old Shurtleff College.

Singer Kate Smith

The lovely Jane Froman is becoming a star while singing with her own orchestra.

Just two words advertise the new *Anna Christie* movie – **GARBO TALKS**.

Edward G. Robinson starts the cycle of gangster movies with *Little Caesar*.

Ruth Etting is fast becoming a radio star with her "music that satisfies." So is James Melton, soloist for the Atwater-Kent Hour, and Morton Downey, whose theme song, "Wabash Moon" has a fascinating Irish overtone.

Kate Smith is beginning to get noticed singing about the moon coming over the mountain.

Many of the new songs have a wistful quality in keeping with the sober mood of the year: "Dancing With Tears in my Eyes," "It Happened in Monterrey," "What Is This Thing Called Love," and "Ten Cents A Dance." There is also a new sound in the air, Boop-boop-a-Doop. Its chief exponent is a plump girl with a baby mouth, **Helen Kane**, who made this distressing novelty (called sillysyllabic by Sigmund Spaeth) a sudden but mercifully brief rage.

Clyde Tombaugh of Arizona discovers the planet Pluto.

1931 – April: Anton Cermak is elected Mayor of Chicago as a "wet" candidate and the ostensible choice of Chicago mobsters.

June 12: Al Capone and 68 others are indicted and charged with 5,000 violations of the prohibition laws.

June 16: Capone pleads guilty to violating the liquor laws and income tax evasion for the years

Why is Bon Ami like puss in boots?

If you cant guess hold before a mirror

Because it cant scratch

1924-1929, thinking a bargain had been struck and he would get off with a fine and light jail sentence.

HOW THE THIRTIES DIFFERED FROM TWENTIES

1. **The Depression, worsened by the Dust Bowl, lasted the entire decade**
2. **Skirt lengths fell along with the price of stocks**
3. **Frills and ruffles were in, bobbed hair was out**
4. **Romance and glamour were in, cheap sex was out**
5. **Church attendance began to rise**
6. **Hard-boiled, jaded literature and plays were on the wane**
7. **Victorianism and the Gay Nineties were now sentimentalized, not looked down upon**
8. **Freud fell from his throne as people realized he didn't have the answer to everything**
9. **The bootleggers of the Prohibition era gave way to the notorious headline-grabbing bank robbers such as Dillinger and Bonnie and Clyde**
10. **Miniature golf became the new fad**
11. **The Twenties had belonged to the Republicans; the Democrats would rule the Thirties**
12. **With the advent of the New Deal, Negroes switched their Abe Lincoln-based support of the Republican Party to the Democrats**
13. **Musicals became popular because they were upbeat and helped people forget the woes of the Depression**
14. **The game of Monopoly is invented and becomes a favorite with the Depression-era public because it enables them to become rich property owners. Statistically, Illinois Avenue is landed on more than any other square.**

Vachel Lindsay, the "Prairie Troubadour" poet, commits suicide at his **Springfield** home. He was suffering from depression due to loss of popularity, diabetes, and epilepsy. He left a wife and two children.

Robert Frost wins the Nobel Prize for his poetry.

July 30, 1931: Judge Wilkerson tells Capone he won't be bound by any deals. Capone changes his plea to *not guilty*.

October 24, 1931: Capone is found guilty and sentenced to 11 years in prison and a $50,000 fine. Capone is stunned. He was expecting a sentence of two years.

Chicagoan **Jane Addams** wins the Nobel Peace Prize.

Vachel Lindsay

1932 – March 9. Al Capone is languishing in the Cook County Jail, awaiting an appeal of his 11-year sentence for tax evasion. He tells the cops that if they let him out of jail, he'll use his influence to find the kidnapper of the Lindbergh baby. His offer is refused.

Jane Addams (Illinois State Hist. Library)

Both major political parties hold their nominating conventions in Chicago. The Democrats nominate New York Governor Franklin D. Roosevelt and Republicans re-nominate incumbent Herbert Hoover.

Capone had been convicted of tax evasion the previous October, but his speak-easies and cabarets remained open so delegates would not be deprived of illegal booze.

December - Two crooked cops (Harry Lang and Harry Miller), working with a special unit formed by Mayor Cermak, try to kill Frank Nitti by shooting him. Nitti somehow manages to survive his wounds.

The movie *Scarface* makes actor George Raft a big star.

Equipoise sets the world record at the Arlington Race Track in Chicago.

Baby Face Nelson escapes from authorities while being taken to the prison at **Joliet**. He had been given a sentence for robbing a bank at **Wheaton**, Illinois. It is believed that he used a gun that was slipped to him by his mother when she visited him.

1933 – February 15: Chicago Mayor Anton Cermak is slain by Sicilian immigrant Joe Zangara (a bricklayer) while standing next to F.D.R. at a reception in Miami. Most say it was an assassination attempt on F.D.R. that missed. Others maintain that it was a Chicago mob hit in retaliation for Frank Nitti being severely wounded in a 1932 raid by one of Cermak's newly created gangster squads.

Joe Zangara

By year's end, thirteen Chicago policemen are killed in the line of duty.

Eleanor Jarman, labeled the **"Blonde Tigress"** by members of the working press, is the member of a gang that commits several robberies in Chicago. In one instance a store owner was shot and killed.

After they were caught, the leader of the gang was executed and Eleanor received a long prison sentence.

John Dillinger is released from an Indiana prison and immediately begins a crime spree that will earn him the title, Public Enemy Number One.

Dillinger considers robbing the cash-rich stockyards bank in **East St. Louis**. He discards the idea after examining a map and noting that the city of thirteen square miles is criss-crossed with an astounding 550 miles of railroad track and that every possible escape route could be blocked, either by a train crossing or a traffic congested bridge.

1934 – January 15: Dillinger and his men rob a bank of $20,000 at East Chicago. He kills a guard during the getaway. The gang holes up a while in Chicago and then leaves for Tucson, Arizona. He is caught and sent back to Crown Point prison in Indiana where he **escapes in March by using a wooden gun that he had carved and darkened with shoe polish**.

May: Bonnie Parker and Clyde Barrow are gunned down while in their car, a Ford V-8, on a dusty road near Arcadia in Louisiana. Sou-
venir hunters quickly snatched empty shell cases from the under-brush where the posse had poured a withering fire of 67 bullets from six automatic weapons into their stolen car. A gun found in Bonnie's lap had three notches on it. An examination of

Amelia Earhart

her body during the autopsy revealed that she wasn't wearing any underpants at the time of her death.

July 11: John Dillinger and his girlfriend, Mary Longnaker, brazenly attend the Chicago World's Fair.

July 22: Dillinger, betrayed by Anna Sage – the Lady in Red - is shot and killed by G-Men outside the Biograph Theater in Chicago.

1935 – An unarmed Doc Barker, Ma Barker's son, is captured in Chicago (January) by Melvin Purvis while out taking a stroll near his apartment in Pine Grove. Doc was killed in 1939 while trying to escape from Alcatraz.

1943 - Frank "the Enforcer" Nitti, faced with a ten year prison term for racketeering, commits suicide.

1947 - January 19: Al Capone dies in his sleep at his Palm Island estate in Florida.

1957 - February 25: Bugs Moran dies from lung cancer while serving a ten-year sentence at Leavenworth.

May 16: Eliot Ness dies of a heart attack.

1960 – G-man Melvin Purvis, suffering from mental depression and having undergone electroshock therapy,

Dillinger at the Biograph Theater – Dell Comics/Desilu

shoots himself in the head with a .45.

For further reading consult *The Dry Decade* by Charles Merz.

THE GREAT BUNION DERBY OF 1928

According to historian James Thomas, perhaps nothing typified the ballyhoo years more than promoters who dreamed up schemes to make money and generate publicity. Sports promoter C.C. Pyle decided to stage a three-month footrace that would begin in California and end in New York City.

The nation already had heroes like Richard Byrd, Gene Tunney, Red Grange, Tom Mix, Babe Ruth and Charles Lindbergh. Here was a chance for ordinary citizens to make the front page by pulling a stunt. After all, Shipwreck Kelly became a legend merely by sitting on top of a flagpole.

C.C. Pyle

Pyle owned a movie theater in **Champaign** and had been on hand that day when number 77 ran for four touchdowns and threw for another as Illinois crushed heavily favored Michigan on the gridiron. Now he persuaded the college dropout to help promote his footrace.

Along the way they would sell Red Grange shoes, helmets, candy bars, jerseys, dolls, caps, and sweaters. Each town along the way was asked to contribute a sum to pay for promotional costs. The thousands of spectators expected to show up and spend money would more than make up the cash difference.

Pyle's plan was for contestants from all over the world to start the race in L.A., and go from town to town along Route 66. It would be a grueling 3,400-mile marathon. As an incentive, a top prize of $25,00 would be offered. Each contestant had to pay a $25 entry fee. Pyle expected 1,000 runners to show up but there were only 275 hopefuls.

The Route 66 Association gave its support to the tune of $60,000, figuring that the extra attention would help secure more government funding to properly complete the paving process.

When the runners reached Illinois, Pyle learned the bad news that the Route 66 Association wasn't going to pay the money it had promised, deciding that Pyle had strayed too often from the 66 route because towns like Albuquerque refused to pony up the cash and were bypassed.

Red Grange (L) and C.C. Pyle

A Good Samaritan named Freeman Gunn of Chicago stepped up and offered to pay the bills for the last 1,000 miles of the race. It seems that Gunn had a twenty-two year old boy in the race and a $75,000 bet with a friend that son Harry Gunn would finish the race – which he did.

Towns were encouraged to support the contestants with free food and lodging. Crowds lined the streets and high school bands welcomed the runners. The race took nearly three months and the original number of contestants was whittled down to 55 by the time it ended.

An incredible 500,000 spectators lined up in L.A. to see the start of the competition. By the end of the first day, the number fell to 199. The contest even drew a number of American Indians who were known as a race for their long-distance running ability. When the grueling event was over, an Oklahoma kid of part Cherokee ancestry named Andy Payne ended up in first place.

Pyle went on to organize the *Ripley's Believe-it-or-Not* exposition at the 1933 Century of Progress fair in Chicago. Pyle died of a heart attack in Los Angeles in 1939 at the age of fifty-five.

MADISON AVENUE INVENTS ADVERTISING

As prosperity became the watchword of the Twenties, the art of advertising took on a whole new meaning. No longer were companies putting out ads to merely let consumers know their products existed. Their intent was to get people to consume as never before. Through hype and chicanery, the modern ad man succeeded where the medieval alchemist failed, transforming base metal into gold. Needs and wants were exploited. Buy because you need it. Buy because it makes you feel good. Buy because your neighbor has one. Buy because it will make you healthy. Buy because it will make you more attractive to the opposite sex. Suddenly, washing clothes was not simply laundering, as it had always been, but an expression of love.

Ad executives worked on catchy slogans. "Bon Ami (cleanser) – hasn't scratched yet." "For a gleaming smile,

get Ipana" (toothpaste). "Ivory soap: 99 &44/100 percent pure – it floats." "Hooverize your carpets. It beats . . . as it sweeps." "Often a bridesmaid, never a bride." "Could it be halitosis? (bad breath)– get Listerine."

Burma Shave ads, with those unique signs spaced a few hundred yards apart, popped up all over highways in the Midwest. Typically, the first sign asked: "Does your husband." And the next one continued, "Misbehave. Then came "Grunt and Grumble," followed by "Rant and Rave?" Who could resist the clever punch line? "Shoot the Brute some . . ." "Burma Shave."

Skywriting became in vogue with messages such as

DRINK HIRES! Billboards sprouted along highways. Layaway plans were offered by chain stores. Insurance policies were offered for as little as a nickel a week and salesmen knocked on the door to collect. Houses had long been sold with mortgages, but for the first time in history, consumer goods were sold on the installment plan.

Advertising created a Utopia: bright teeth, school girl complexions, cornless feet, fresh breaths, dishes that practically clean themselves, regular bowel habits, perfect bust lines.

No wonder the Twenties roared.

For more details on this subject see the highly readable *Only Yesterday* by Frederick Lewis Allen.

THE MAN WHO DISCOVERED MONEY

Charles Ponzi

Charles Ponzi dreamed of being a great financier like J.P. Morgan, but he was merely a clerk at J.P. Poole, a foreign trade house in Boston. One day he concocted a scheme whereby he told people that he could buy international money orders in one country and sell them for a higher price in another by taking advantage of international exchange rates. Investors fell for his get-rich-quick scheme and the money began to roll in. Ponzi merely shufled money from new investors to old and pocketed much of the money for himself. He lived the good life

IPANA
For healthier teeth, healthier gums

and bought his old company and fired his former boss. Authorities finally caught up with him and sent him to jail.

Ponzi schemes later resurfaced in the form of chain

letters but today such pyramid scams are illegal.

THE RAGMAN – One of the great things about memory is that it can transport you back in time to an almost forgotten era. The days of quarantines, fountain pens, trolley cars, coal bins and the iceman are but distant memories.

Sometimes at night I lie awake listening to the wind in the windows that reminds me of bits and pieces of favorite old melodies. It whistles an eerie scale, as if all the songs I ever heard were endeavoring to transcend time. I grew up in East St. Louis where the milkman came at 5 a.m. and the iceman came at 10 a.m.

About once a week there was a dusky man wearing tattered clothes who came down the alley with a horse-drawn wagon. His horse, clip-clopping over the bricks in the alley, wore an old floppy hat against the summer sun. The bells on his harness gave a cheerful punctuation to the day's business routine.

He picked up a bottle here, a discarded tire there; perhaps some old piece of iron. "Any old rags? Any old iron? Scissors or knives that need sharpening?" Sometimes he had props for clotheslines to sell.

Housewives dickered over pennies the ragman offered for "good junk" like magazines, used clothing, or metal.

Occasionally, the distinctive sounds of the traveling tradesmen were drowned out by the yells of children playing tag in the neighborhood. *Ready or not, here I come!"*

FAMOUS QUOTES OF THE TWENTIES

"I have never yet heard of a girl being ruined by a book." New York Mayor **Jimmy Walker** speaking out against censorship

"The Twenties was an era of wonderful nonsense." – Radio commentator, **Westbrook Pegler**

"To write is to write is to write is to write." – **Gertrude Stein**

"Whatever will bring in the most money will happen." – **Elinor Glyn** commenting on Hollywood movies

"America is my country and Paris is my hometown." – **Gertrude Stein**

"The flapper came in to the tune of 'I'll Say She Does,' and frequently she did." - **Lloyd Morris**

"Come on you miserable sinners, get down on your knees and pray. The Devil has two strikes on you already." - **Evangelist Billy Sunday, a former big league ballplayer who liked to use baseball metaphors**

"Jesus is the healer. I am only the little office girl who opens the door and says, "Come in." – **Sister Aimee McPherson**

"I will never consent to the pardon of this man." – **President Woodrow Wilson** commenting on the imprisonment of Eugene Debs

"There is no right to strike against the public safety by anybody, anywhere, at any time." - **Governor Calvin Coolidge** commenting on the 1920 Boston Police strike – the quote that won him the office of the Vice-president

"I do not like football well enough to play it for nothing." – **Red Grange**

"When more and more people are thrown out of work, unemployment results." – **Calvin Coolidge**

"Workers of the world unite – you have nothing to lose but your chains." – **Karl Marx** in the Communist Manifesto

"Wine is a mocker, strong drink is raging, and whosoever is deceived thereby is not wise." – **from the book of Proverbs**

"A reformer is a guy who rides through a sewer in a glass-bottomed boat." – **New York Mayor Jimmy Walker**

"The reign of tears is over." – **Billy Sunday commenting on the advent of Prohibition**

"Prohibition is a great experiment . . . noble in purpose." – **President Herbert Hoover**

"Everybody gets so much information all day long that they lose their common sense." – **Gertrude Stein**

"Not since the days of the Bourbons has the woman of fashion been so visible above the ankles." – **Vogue magazine**

Little Iodine funnies

"He could make the word cow have four syllables." **A reporter commenting on President Coolidge's New England accent**

"Nobody cared a whit about politics." - **F. Scott Fitzgerald commenting on America's obsession with fun and frivolity in the Twenties**

"The American businessman believed that the struggle by workingmen for higher pay and better working conditions was the beginning of an armed rebellion led by Lenin and Trotsky." - historian **Frederick Lewis Allen**

"President Harding's English reminds me of a string of wet sponges." – writer **H.L. Mencken**

"The business of America is business." - President **Calvin Coolidge**

"The American people want a president who does nothing and Coolidge is doing it very well." – **Will Rogers** commenting on the Coolidge presidency

"It was understood and agreed that the big thing in life was liquor." – **John O'Hara in** *Butterfield 8*

"We cannot make sense of nature without some conception which transcends nature, such as the existence of God." – **Alfred North Whitehead of Harvard**

"I thought fellows like that shot themselves." **Britain's King George V**, who made the comment on learning a fellow he knew quite well was sexually attracted to men; George refused to knight "buggers."

"The way to keep young people home is to make the home atmosphere pleasant – and let the air out of their tires." – **Dorothy Parker**

"Atheism tempered by hymns." – **George Bernard Shaw's wry observation of the religious atmosphere in the 1920s**

"The surest way to make a monkey out of a man is to quote him." – **Robert Benchley**

"From the moment the door closed behind you, you had the feeling of being in the Fortunate Islands where there were no rules and regulations, no yesterday and no tomorrow . . .." – Novelist **John Dos Pasos** describing a speakeasy

"National prohibition was a measure passed by village America against urban America." – **Sinclair Lewis**

"Man, if you don't know what it is, don't mess with it." – **Pianist Fats Waller** commenting on the new art form called jazz

"As for me, except for an occasional heart attack, I feel as young as I ever did." – **Robert Benchley**

"The cure for boredom is curiosity. There is no cure for curiosity." – **Dorothy Parker**

"Literature is news that stays news." – **Ezra Pound**

"The worst thing you can say about him is that he's stupid." - An anonymous critic of Mayor Big Bill Thompson

"He always has a certain dour look – like he was weaned on a pickle." – a contemporary describing the demeanor of **Calvin Coolidge**

"She was a siren of a magnetism such as few women since Cleopatra have possessed." – Writer Carey McWilliams commenting on **Sister Aimee Semple McPherson**

"If I had more time, I would have written a shorter letter." – **T.S. Eliot**

Dorothy Parker

"Utter originality is, of course, out of the question." – **Ezra Pound**

"The first two things I do every morning is brush my teeth and sharpen my tongue." – **Dorothy Parker**

"Some editors are failed writers, but so are most writers." – **T. S. Eliot**

"We are nearer to the final triumph over poverty than ever before in the history of any land." – **President Herbert Hoover**, shortly before the stock market crash

"Conscience is the inner voice that warns us someone may be looking." – **H.L. Mencken**

"Brevity is the soul of lingerie." – **Dorothy Parker**, writing for *Vogue* magazine

"All men are frauds. The only difference is that some men admit it. I myself deny it." – **H.L. Mencken**

"I don't care what is written about me so long as it isn't true." – **Dorothy Parker**

"The Jazz Age was simply due to America's unexpended energy in the War." – **F. Scott Fitzgerald**

"He thought he was alive because he worked with his brain – but his body was fit for the undertaker." – **Line in a bodybuilding ad by Charles Atlas**

"I know if I make $80,000 next year that will be more than President Hoover's salary. But I had a better year than Hoover." – **Babe Ruth**

"Communists are people who fancied that they had an unhappy childhood." – **Gertrude Stein**

Buster Brown and his dog Tige

"There is no God. But it doesn't matter – man is enough." **Edna St. Vincent Millay**

"I aimed at the public's heart, and by accident I hit it in the stomach." – **Upton Sinclair commenting on the success of** *The Jungle*

"April comes like an idiot, babbling and strewing flowers." – **Edna St. Vincent Millay**

"Art is the stored honey of the human soul, gathered on wings of misery and travail." – **Theodore Dreiser**

"People will buy anything that is advertised as one to a customer." – **Sinclair Lewis**

Upton Sinclair – Library of Congress

"Hemingway's remarks are not literature." - **Gertrude Stein**

"I have only one superstition – I touch all the bases when I hit a home run." – **Babe Ruth**

"Drinking makes such fools of people and most people are such fools to begin with, it compounds the felony." – **Robert Benchley**

"Advertising is a valuable economic tool because it is the cheapest way of selling goods – particularly if the goods are worthless." – **Sinclair Lewis**

"I do want to get rich but I never want to do what there is to do to get rich." – **Gertrude Stein**

"How you travel is who you are." **Lucius Beebe, America's connoisseur of good taste** (back then there were first, second, and third class accommodations on ocean liners and trains)

"Blondes are for weekends, brunettes are for keeps." – **Popular saying that developed during the Twenties**

"In the United States there is more space where nobody is than where anybody is. That's what makes it the United States." – **Gertrude Stein**

"It takes a lot of time to be a genius; you have to sit around so much doing nothing, really doing nothing." – **Gertrude Stein**

"The Colonel is one of the great minds of the nineteenth century." – **1920s critics of Robert R. McCormick, conservative owner of the Chicago Tribune**

"Here was a new generation grown up to find all gods dead, all wars fought, all faiths in man shaken . . . " – **F. Scott Fitzgerald in** *This Side of Paradise*

"A poet more than thirty years old is merely an overgrown child." – **H.L. Mencken**

"France was a land, England was a people, but America was . . . a willingness of the heart." – **F. Scott Fitzgerald in the Saturday Evening Post**

"Find a writer who is indubitably American . . . who has something new and peculiarly American to say and who says it in an unmistakable American way and nine times out of ten you will find that he has some connection with the gargantuan and inordinate abattoir by Lake Michigan – that he was bred there, or got his start there or passed through there in days when he was young and tender." – **H.L. Mencken talking about Chicago**

"Sooner or later a crash is coming, and it may be terrific." – **Roger Babson**, well-known economist

"Do you want a room for sleeping or jumping?" – Question asked by a hotel desk clerk of a registering guest; **Eddie Cantor joke** after the crash

1929 Peerless

SPECULATION IN THE STOCK MARKET

Some historians refer to the 1920s as the Prosperity Decade. The enormous confidence in Coolidge prosperity was not unlike that of the Clinton prosperity of the 1990s. One could almost invest in anything and make money because of the rising tide of the market that floated all boats. After dinner conversations in the 1920s were dominated by talk about making a killing in the market by investments made in Union Carbide or Anaconda Copper.

These conversations were not restricted to the Park Avenue crowd in New York or Knob Hill in San Francisco. People in all walks of life were now investing in the stock market. All sorts of people to whom the stock ticker had previously been an alien mystery were now carrying hundreds of shares of Studebaker or Continental Oil. They were learning the significance of symbols such as GL and X and ITT, and whipping open the early editions of afternoon papers to catch the latest quotations from Wall Street. It was not uncommon for a stock to jump in price from 40 & 1/8 to 60 & 7/8 in less than a week.

If you are wondering why the market prices have long been figured in eighths, it goes back to when the market was first established in 1790. A popular currency of the day was the Spanish coin known as Pieces of Eight. It was scored into eights so that chunks could literally be bitten off to make change. If the price of a stock goes up by 1/8 it has increased its share by 12 and ½ cents or one-eighth of a dollar. Back in the 1920s one could get a shave at a barber shop for two bits or twenty five cents.

Another thing that encouraged speculation with stocks is that brokers often allowed clients with good credit to buy on margin – with as little as ten percent down. In a rising or Bull market that works fine. But when things go south and the Bears (declining market) run wild, there is potential for disaster.

The speculative fever had been intensified by the action of the Federal Reserve System that lowered the rediscount rate from 4 per cent to 3 ½ percent in August of 1927 and purchased government securities in the open market.

Things were sluggish in the early months of 1928 but the market rebounded in mid-March with a big surge. Speculative fever once again gripped the whole country. Stories of fortunes made overnight were on everyone's lips. Wives were asking their husbands why they were so slow in getting in on the bonanza, only to discover that their husband had bought 100 shares of General Motors the day before. Barber shops were filled with stories about staggering advances in stocks. And so it went on, day after day and week after week.

When nay-sayers warned that prices were inflated and that a day of reckoning would be coming, they were drowned out with shouts of "Be bullish on America" or "Never sell the United States short." The big bull market had become a national mania.

When prices did begin to slip in September of 1929, soothsayers proclaimed that there was "nothing to worry about," and that the market was readjusting itself into a

Cartoon – Congress tinkers with prosperity

"more secure technical position."

The impending disaster was destined to be as bewildering and frightening to the rich and powerful and the customarily sagacious as to the novice and the foolish and unwary holder of fifty shares of margin stock.

When prices began to plummet on Thursday, October 24, 1929, it was mostly due to the fact that investors, whose margins were exhausted or about to be exhausted, dumped thousands of shares on the market at one time. Normally there were bargain hunters who stepped in and saved the day but this was not to happen. The powerful bankers who usually intervened to rescue prices stayed on the sidelines.

For the next couple of days things seemed to stabilize but the worst was yet to come – Black Tuesday. By the end of that frantic day a record number of shares had been sold and the average prices of fifty leading stocks had dropped by forty percent. The big bull market was dead! The panic had written *finis* to a frenetic chapter of American economic history.

National income fell sharply after the crash. In the following three years 86,000 businesses failed. Nine million savings accounts were wiped out. Wages fell by an average of sixty percent. Factory girls in 1932 Chicago were earning 25 cents an hour. Even the great Babe Ruth took a ten thousand dollar salary cut.

Just as individuals were bankrupt so were municipalities. Property owners defaulted on their taxes and many a city found that it could not pay its teachers or garbage collectors. By 1932 750 teachers in Chicago could no longer make mortgage payments and lost their houses to banks.

In the fall of 1930 the International Apple Shippers Association discovered they had a large crop surplus on their hands. They concocted a scheme to give apples to individuals on credit with the understanding that they would go into the streets and sell them for a nickel apiece. Soon there were so many apple sellers that some cities passed ordinances declaring them to be a nuisance.

Poverty now stalked America. There were soup lines on ten thousand street corners. Hobo jungles sprouted near the riverfront of every large city. Shabby men, once proudly employed, lined their overcoats with newspapers and placed cardboard insoles in their shoes. Women were abandoned by the thousands as their men, depressed from lost respect, hit the road and rode freight trains to seek employment. Factories lay idle. Dust blew over the land.

For further reading consult *The Great Crash* by John Kenneth Galbraith.

"WE'RE WIPED OUT"

Perhaps her father had been right when he had forbidden her to set foot in the financial district today. The latest news report stated that, in spite of the traumatic first three hours of trading, the market had closed on an upward beat. It said that U.S. Steel had even shown a gain on yesterday's trading. There was growing belief the rally would continue tomorrow.

Edith was relieved. Her father had gone to work apprehensive. She suspected yesterday's break had been a bad one for him.

When Edward Stone opened the front door of the apartment, his daughter saw immediately that something was seriously wrong.

It pays to be a Christian by William Ridgeway

"Uncle Billy's Bible Class"

Is what the ribald heathen call these advertisements.
You see we believe that Business and Religion mix.

We have discovered that in spite of cussin' and swearin' and gamblin' and sportin' down in the ranks among the poor old plugged under strappers, the "Big Boss" of almost every big long established concern "Belongs to Church." Here is a sample of some Steam-Hydraulickers. Every one of these is headed by a Churchman:

Standard Oil Co.	International Harv. Co.	Remington Typewriter Co.
Cluett, Peabody & Co.	Standard Underground	Lukens Steel Co.
H. J. Heinz Co. ("57")	Cables Co.	Procter & Gamble Co.
Crane & Co. (Dalton)	John Wanamaker	(Ivory Soap)
Packard Motor Car Co.	John Morrell & Co.	E. I. Du Pont de Nemours
Swift & Co.	Christie Brown & Co.	& Co.
United Gas Imp. Co.	(Toronto)	United States Gov't.
Larkin & Co. (Buffalo)	Firestone Tire & Rub. Co.	Sears, Roebuck & Co.
General Electric Co.	Consolidated Gas Co.	United States Steel Co.
Penn. R. R.	(N. Y.)	Lovell Mfg. Co.

The other day we wrote to ex-Postmaster-General Hays, who is a Presbyterian Elder, asking him to tell us what Church the members of the present Republican Administration belong to. Here is the report:

President Coolidge, Congregational	Secretary of Interior Fall
Secretary of State Hughes, Baptist	Secretary of Agriculture Wallace, United
Secretary of Treas. Mellon, Presbyterian	Presbyterian
Secretary of War Weeks, Unitarian	Secretary of Commerce Hoover, Quaker
Atty. General Daugherty, Methodist	Secretary of Labor Davis, Presbyterian
Secretary of Navy Denby, Episcopalian	

She started to move toward him.

"Stop! Stop everything! We've got to move out."

Frightened by the hysteria in his voice, certain her father was acutely ill, Edith remained still.

Slowly, as if to memorize every detail, Edward Stone's staring eyes scanned the room, taking in the expensive paintings, the new furnishings, the crystal wall lights, the hand-sewn carpets and drapes.

Once more his voice broke the silence. "We can't keep any of it. I haven't a penny. The market's crashed. We're wiped out. Nothing!"

Edith gasped. As she turned toward the kitchen and called to her mother, her father lunged past her.

"I'm going to kill myself! It's the only way. You'll have the insurance . . . ."

Screaming, also close to hysteria, Edith chased after her father. Mabel Stone rushed in from the kitchen.

"Ed, for God's sake!"

Her husband reached the French doors leading onto the apartment's terrace. They were closed.

It gave Edith and her mother a chance to catch up. Edith grabbed her father around the waist; his wife tried to pull his hands from the door.

He broke their hold, turned the key, and wrenched open the door.

For a moment, Ed Stone stood in the doorway. Then, panting, he turned to his wife and daughter.

Edith would never forget how he kept repeating the same terrible words, he wouldn't stop saying them.

"The money's gone - all of it. We can't get it back. You'll have the insurance. . . ."

"Ed, for God's sake, you have a wife and daughter . . . !"

"Get back!"

He turned and took hold of the balcony railing. The street was twenty stories below.

Edith and her mother simultaneously lunged at him. This time Edith did not let go. She hooked both arms around her father's neck, determined if necessary to choke him into unconsciousness. Mabel Stone tackled her husband around the knees.

The force of their combined assault brought Edward Stone to the floor.

Lakeview Castle off New Poag Road near **Hartford, Illinois** (courtesy *Alton Telegraph*). It was built close to Cahokia Creek in 1897 by Frenchman Ben Biszant for his English bride. A team of horses dug a moat around the house and the depression quickly filled with water. The extra dirt was used to build up the plot where the house was built. Biszant's wife died around twelve years after the castle was built. Biszant lost interest in the place, sold it, and moved to California. According to author **Troy Taylor**, the fourteen room structure, surrounded by 35 secluded acres, was the most famous **speak-easy** in the area during the 1920s. It was later used as a military school and a home for unwed mothers. It was unoccupied for several years and vandals burned it to the ground in March of 1973. Taylor says local lore maintains that the place was rumored to be haunted by the spectral remains of the woman who died there. Taylor has written numerous books including *Haunted Alton, Haunted Decatur, Ghosts of Springfield,* and *Haunted Chicago.*

For a moment they were locked in an impasse.
"Please, listen . . . ."
Edith loosened her grip.
It was a mistake. Her father broke his wife's hold on her legs, got away from his daughter, and leapt again to his feet.
"Mama, we've got to stop him! He's going to jump!"
Even as she shouted, Edith managed to get a grasp on her father's foot. Twisting it savagely, she toppled her father back to the floor.
She dived on him, helping her mother pinion him to the terrace. Edith would remember his eyes bulging, his mouth opening and shutting but now saying nothing, as if driven by compulsion to suicide.
Close to breaking herself, the slimly built Edith knew she could not physically restrain him much longer. She fell back on the only weapon she had: words. "I called him a sissy, yelled at him, reviled him, hated him for what he was making me say and do."
Edward Stone fell back and began to cry.

His wife slapped him twice - hard on each cheek.

He whimpered on for some moments. Then he slowly came to his senses. In silence they led Edward Stone inside. Only there was he able to tell them the facts. He had lost close to $5 million. They would have to fire the servants, move out at once from their new apartment, and completely readjust their lifestyle.

"Ed, it doesn't matter. We'll manage somehow."

Edith thought her mother was the most magnificent person in the whole rotten world.

Together, she was certain they had saved her father's life. She also knew what had happened would now make it impossible for her to contemplate further play about Wall Street.

Excerpted from *The Day The Bubble Burst*, by Gordon Thomas and Max Witts. Used by permission of Doubleday, a division of Random House, Inc.

CARS, ROADS AND ROUTE 66 IN THE TWENTIES

Note: All Route 66 pictures (taken by Dan Oberle of **Geneseo/Edwardsville**) in the book are of places that were authentic to the 1920s.

In the year 1900 there were almost no paved roads in the State of Illinois. David Wrone, a significant historian of the "hard road movement," points out that Illinois roads were hardly better in 1910 than the Goshen Road in 1818 at the time of statehood. Back then, the routes from one settlement to another through the woods were mere animal paths and Indian trails that were marked by one notch on a tree for a footpath, two notches for a bridle path, and three notches for a wagon.

After the horseless carriage was invented, automobiles in significant numbers began to appear in the state around the turn of the century. Charles and Frank Duryea, formerly of **Peoria,** are generally credited with **making the first automobile in America**. The first automobile in Illinois was a German-

Memory Lane road and sign at **Lexington**– D. Oberle collection

made Benz, displayed at the 1893 Columbian Exposition in Chicago.

Ironically, when horseless carriages became mired in the mud, they had to be pulled out by teams of horses. Equine travelers on a road where an automobile became stuck often yelled to the exasperated occupants, "Get a horse!" Much of the auto's early "get-a-horse" reputation came from the fact that the earliest pieces of machinery, with luck, could only manage to wobble along in a fusillade of explosions for a few miles before something shattered. Also, the balloon tires had a tendency to go flat with dismaying frequency. The first ads, run by the Duryea brothers, referred to the newfangled contraptions as "**gasoline buggies.**"

Illinois Paved Roads in 1925

Drivers soon began pushing for paved roads. However, the state legislature was largely dominated by rural interests, and farmers did not care to pay the costs for a city man's pleasure. Also, many thought that the best solution was to simply build more interurban lines. The problem was solved in 1911 when a state law was passed transferring money collected for license fees into road improvements. When that later proved to be insufficient, a tax on gasoline sales was imposed.

Rivers and rails still dominated as the twin avenues of commerce because roads were medieval in character. They spewed forth billows of dust in summer. Writer Donald Tingley notes that after a typical spin on a hot summer day, the driver emerged from his toy wearing a layer of the Illinois countryside. (In my youth I remember rural road crews spreading calcium chloride on dirt and gravel roads in an effort to deal with the dust problem.) These same roads froze into ruts during winter months and became impassable bogs during the spring and fall rainy seasons. Most automobile pioneers simply kept their machines stored in a garage or barn until spring.

In case you're wondering, the first paved road in the state was about 15 miles long and it ran from **East St. Louis** to **Belleville** in 1847. The St. Clair County Turnpike was a macadamized type, named for the Scottish inventor (John McAdam) of a mixture of pitch and crushed rock. The limestone came from the quarries at **Alton**.

Road conditions were vital to rural communities. Social functions, church attendance, mail delivery, shopping trips and elections were all affected by weather and accessibility of the roads. Farm products could be marketed only if roads permitted access to rail or harbor facilities. One rural farmer recorded his preoccupation with the weather in a 1910 diary. "Severe thaw this morning . . . was married this afternoon . . . the roads froze tonight."

After the turn of the century and more and more people began buying automobiles, they found that their driving was limited due to poor roads and the weather. Driving was confined to the months between late spring and late fall. Winter months were too cold and frozen roads were too dangerous. In early spring the mud, slush and potholes turned motoring into an adventuresome sport.

Drivers typically garaged their vehicles during this down time and stored their precious batteries with a local mechanic who hooked them up to a line with a low electrical current. People who bought the cheaper open touring car also usually garaged them for the winter.

The early Twenties saw the advent of a car that was expressly made to appeal to women – the Jordan. Ned Jordan was an ex-newspaperman and salesman. He secured financial backing from some friends and a Cleveland bank. The expensive Playboy model had an aluminum body, soft leather upholstery, and a fitted vanity case on the dash. High priced and vulnerable to the Depression, the Jordan expired in 1931.

Windshields of the early Twenties often consisted of a stationary lower section with an upper section that could be pushed out for ventilation.

Since many of the boxy cars of the 1920s looked similar, police were taught to distinguish them by their radiators, grilles, and emblems that often sat atop the radiator cap. Pierce Arrows were easy to distinguish because the headlights were built into the fenders.

Temperature gauges were an accessory and cost extra. The most popular type consisted of a glass thermometer enclosed in a brass tube that mounted atop the radiator filler tube. It faced backward so that it was always visible to the driver.

Hall of Fame Museum at **Pontiac**

Another popular accessory was the "**muffler cut out.**" This was a foot-controlled valve that was attached to the exhaust pipe just ahead of the muffler. The driver had the option of choosing to run the exhaust through the muffler for silence or to bypass the muffler for extra power. The cut out feature also made it easy for motorists to determine if they had a clogged muffler.

Then there was the Chain Pull. One end of a chain was placed around the powered rear wheels of a car while the other end of the chain was fastened to metal stakes that were driven into the ground ahead of the car. Thus, the disabled car could actually **pull itself out of the mud**.

Another popular 1920s accessory was the spotlight. Often they were clamped to the windshield post. They were useful for seeing street signs and finding house addresses. They could also assist the headlights when driving on dark country roads.

Road maintenance was left to township officials and with something like 1,600 townships, one can imagine the inconsistencies and funding problems that arose from one part of the state to another. Often the simple process of dragging the roads to smooth them was a perplexing challenge. And, as is so often the case today, inadequate tax revenue hounded officials.

The sheer number of road miles was a vexing problem. By 1912 there were over **95,000 miles of road in the state**.

Ironically, it was members of velocipede (bicycle) clubs throughout the state that first pushed for legislation to improve Illinois roads. But they met with fierce opposition from independent farmers who were suspicious of any efforts by city groups, suspecting that they would be saddled with most of the tax burden to pay for such programs.

The Mill roadhouse at **Lincoln** on old Route 66

The state legislature appointed a state highway engineer and authorized a three-man commission to study the road problem. **Lafayette Funk** of the seed-corn family was one of the men on the commission. Unfortunately, the team did little to solve the problem. Meanwhile, the University of Illinois established a laboratory to determine whether concrete, brick, or macadamized roads were the best solution for the future. Governor Dunne gave a speech in which he noted that **Illinois ranked twenty-fourth** out of the forty-eight states when it came to road improvement.

A statewide convention was organized by interested groups and 150 representatives met in **Peoria** to discuss the problem. They resolved to lobby the General Assembly and pressure it into passing much needed legislation. The state legislature decided to tackle the problem in 1913 with the passage of what came to be known as the **Tice Law**. Sponsored by Homer Tice of **Greenview**, the forty-seventh session of lawmakers established a uniform licensing procedure for vehicles and fees that would support a statewide road

improvement program. The Tice Law also created a new three-member highway commission and a highway engineer who would oversee the construction of highways by the state. Another provision of the Tice Law was to **use convict labor** for roadwork under the assumption that it would be good for the convicts and good for improved roads. Building roads with state funds started in 1914 when Governor Dunne turned a spade full of dirt in a ceremony that started construction on the **Aurora-Elgin highway.**

Vermilion County and the **Danville** area was the first to take advantage of the good road movement. The county quickly passed a bond issue and constructed a fairly good network of roads.

The state road design of engineer P.C. McArdle set bricks on a concrete base that was three inches thick in the middle and tapering to a mere two inches on the edges. The base was to be a mixture of one-part cement, three and one-half parts sand, and six parts crushed rock. The bricks were placed on the base and the entire surface smoothed with a hand roller. A mixture consisting of equal parts sand and cement bonded the bricks to the base and was also used in the brick interstices (joints). The Vermilion Good Roads Association doubted the wisdom of a two or three inch base and lobbied for a thicker four inches. The group's persistence paid off and construction began in 1916. By 1917 only three other counties had approved bond issues under the Tice Law – **St. Clair, Jackson, and Cook**. It soon became clear that the Tice Law only had the desired effect in areas where local support was effectively organized.

When it became obvious that paved roads were an expensive proposition the federal government decided to intervene. In 1916 Congress passed a law that offered matching funds for the construction of highways that were deemed to be of interstate significance. Illinois was declared eligible for up to $12 million, and this was a powerful incentive. The public sentiment for good roads was growing steadily as registrations for automobiles increased from 131,000 in 1914 to approximately 375,000 in 1918. The first Illinois roads that were earmarked for federal funds were the Cumberland Road (U.S. 40) and the **Dixie Highway** (U.S. 54).

Hamel Water Tower – Oberle Collection

Governor Frank Lowden supported legislation that called for even more roads in 1918. A popular referendum was placed on the ballot for November 5. The

88

architect of this plan was Samuel Bradt who was one of the three highway commissioners and chairman of the Illinois Bankers Association. Lowden shrewdly assuaged potential critics by assuring the public that no projects would be undertaken until after the war was over and that such public works projects would be good sources of employment for the men returning from Europe. The proposal overwhelmingly carried by a vote of 661,815 to 154,396 with only two counties defeating it – **Hamilton and DeWitt**.

Ernie Edwards' Pig Hip Restaurant at **Broadwell** – Dan Oberle

At first the good roads movement was hurt by the inevitable economic recession that followed major wars back then. But falling prices of material and wage costs enabled the building project to continue. As more and more people bought automobiles, public support continued to increase. In order to finish the project, a new bond issue was floated in 1924. Additional funds were secured through taxes on gasoline although this, at first, was found to be unconstitutional (gasoline companies argued it violated the 14th Amendment's due process clause). By the end of the decade Illinois could boast the **finest system of paved roads in America**. From **Galena to Cairo**, between the Wabash and Mississippi, 75 percent of the state's 10,098 miles of highway was paved with concrete. Secondary or county roads, constituting 17,369 miles, were ¼ surfaced, mostly with gravel. By 1925 it was possible to travel from Beloit, Wisconsin, to **Cairo** on roads that were 95 percent concrete.

The number of automobiles increased dramatically, and by 1918 there were 340,000 cars in the state. By 1929 the number increased to 1,630,816. Railroads and streetcars suffered from the increase in automobiles as ridership steadily declined. Horses, long a common sight on the average street, quickly began to disappear from the scene. Wartime prosperity and Henry Ford's innovative assembly line made cars affordable to more citizens. Soon the auto became much more than just a rich man's toy.

The need for hard roads was not deemed a necessity until large numbers of Americans began buying the "horseless carriage" after World War I. When alternate paths of Route 66 were built during the Depression to take the road

through a different set of towns, they were often bricked instead of concreted. A stretch of the road near **Hamel** was originally bricked before it was later covered with asphalt. The brick process was used because it was labor intensive and WPA projects like this put more men to work during the Depression.

During the 1920s and '30s Illinois roads were a mish-mash of assorted character. This jumbled variety consisted of graded earth, gravel, oiled gravel, brick, macadam (crushed stone mixed with tar, asphalt, asphalt over a concrete base, and Portland cement. The Land of Lincoln was in need of improved roads to enable it to wrest the title **"Crossroads of America"** from those neighboring Hoosiers - roads that would sail past verdant fields of winter wheat in the spring and tawny rows of corn in the fall. Some of the early Illinois concrete roads were made with a slight rise - curbing on the outer edge. It was thought by engineers that this would help drivers stay on the highway. Unfortunately, it had the opposite effect, causing some drivers to lose control of their vehicles and crash.

Illinois was *the leader* over all of the other states along Route 66 in the paving process. Such roads would sit on top of rich prairie soil that made Illinois the **"Breadbasket of America;"** soil so rich that pioneer farmers boasted, "You can plant nails and harvest crowbars." With more and more Model-Ts burping along, these roads could criss-cross the state and connect its pulsating cities with the hinterland and beat the economic drums of trade and commerce.

Before the fabled Route 66 artery existed, there was a dirt road that went from **Chicago** to **East St. Louis**. In 1915 this dirt path was officially dubbed **The Pontiac Trail**. Many called it the **Greater Sheridan Road**. Dirt roads back then were improved by what came to be known as a split-log drag process. Invented in Missouri, the device used several teams of horses or mules that dragged logs over a dampened roadbed to dramatically improve its utility.

Old Illinois Route 4/66 near **Staunton – D. Oberle collection**

Route 66 started out in 1926 as a patchwork of mixed road surfaces that linked Chicago with St. Louis and St. Louis with Los Angeles. This was the Age of Ballyhoo and showman/entrepreneur C.C. ("Cash and Carry") Pyle drew national attention to the new road in 1928 by organizing an international **Bunion Derby** - a footrace from LA to New

York, with the first two-thirds to follow Route 66 and go through Chicago. To this day it remains the **single most important event** known to Route 66 in terms of exposure and publicity. A first place prize of $25,000 was offered, drawing 275 contestants. Runners covered a predetermined distance each day. **Red Grange**, the former U of I star and Chicago Bears' football player, was hired to fire the gun each morning to begin the race anew. His celebrity status was used to promote interest in the race at various stops along the way. To help draw crowds, Pyle assembled a

C.C. Pyle's Bunion Derby

circus sideshow that arrived at each leg's destination a day in advance. The hoopla included carnival rides, sideshow attractions (**including a mummified dead outlaw**), games of chance and concession stands. Grange acted as master of ceremonies in some of the featured attractions. When the exhausted runners reached Chicago, a Brit of Italian ancestry by the name of Peter "Iron Man" Gavuzzi clung to a tenuous lead. After a grueling 84 days and a distance of 3,423 miles, with numerous contestants dropping out from exhaustion and raw feet, Andy Payne, a young Oklahoman of Native-American extraction, claimed the prize at New York's Madison Square Garden. There were only 55 finishers.

Originally labeled Route 60, this proposed road, which would become so revered, was planned by the "**Father of Route 66**," Cyrus Avery, President of the Associated Highways Association of America (what a mouthful). The name change was forced by North Carolina, Virginia, and Kentucky, whose governors whined that a Route 60 should logically start on the East coast - not Chicago - and go through *their* states. At a special meeting in Springfield, Missouri, an **Oklahoma engineer named John Page suggested the number 66 be used as a compromise**. This intervention by fate, causing a signage change, turned out to be an amazing stroke of luck. It is significant because "Route 60" simply lacks the charisma and magnetic appeal of those incredible double sixes emblazoned on a black and white shield. A Route 60 designation would have been roughly equivalent to Adolph Hitler adopting a yellow flag with an acorn on it instead of the mesmerizing twisted cross, a black swastika within a white circle on a blood red field. Furthermore, can you imagine songwriter Bobby Troupe struggling to pen

catchy and rhyming lyrics for Route 60?

The U.S. Congress passed the Federal Aid Road Act in 1916. Illinois was granted $12 million in matching funds and the Illinois Highway Commission immediately began to plan for a 4,000 miles system of hard roads across the state.

In 1918 the state legislature authorized $50 million to fund the new network of roads. The original Route 66 in Illinois followed most of SBI 4 (state bond issue 4, built in 1918 from these funds) from **Springfield** to **East St. Louis**. Route 4 traveled along a historic path, a portage trail once traversed by Marquette and **Joliet**. It was dubbed the **Pontiac Trail** back in 1915.

Have you ever wondered why the British drive on the left side of the road? It's a tradition that goes back to Medieval times when traveling was dangerous because of highwaymen. Most people are right handed and if a passing stranger suddenly attacked, you were in a good position to ward off his blow with your sword. And back in ye olden times, all the roads technically belonged to the monarch. Main roads were often designated as the king's highway. When Englishmen migrated to America they naturally brought their language and customs with them. This is why many towns in Illinois have roads with the name Kingshighway.

Another bit of Illinois road trivia. Roads that generally run east and west usually end in an even number while north to south roads are mostly odd. There are exceptions, of course, but highways 1, 3, 157 and 159 all run north to south. Routes 40, 50 and 70 are east-west.

Sixty-six was the **first fully paved road** ("slab all the way") in the state at a cost of about $40,000 per mile (6" thick). Some labeled it the "**Great Diagonal Highway**" or the "**Lone Star Route**." By 1924 this State Route 4 was completely paved. In 1926 the American Association of State Highway Officials (AASHO) re-designated Illinois State Route 4 as Route 66. Its original western terminus was at the **McKinley Bridge** on the Mississippi River.

Old Route 66 submerged by **Lake Springfield** – Dan Oberle

Illinoisans were a practical, pragmatic breed in those jaunty days of "tin lizzies" and hardly gave the new highway thought except for the fact that they could now get from point A to point B much quicker. It was a boon to traveling salesmen and a convenient venue for Chicago bootleggers to keep in touch with their counterparts in **Springfield, East St. Louis** and St. Louis. The burgeoning automobile age made possible thousands of new suburban communities with luxury homes surrounded by grass.

The first grouping of stores together in a "shopping center" took place in Kansas City, Missouri, in 1924. The first motel appeared in San Luis Obispo, California, in 1926. The first "parking garage" was constructed in Detroit in 1922. The first traffic lights were installed in New York City in 1922.

Leo Brothers, the labor slugger from St. Louis, was convicted of killing reporter Jake Lingle. He traveled Route 66 to make a $10,000 Capone contract hit in Chicago.

Charles Lindbergh flew along Route 66 and the parallel Chicago & Alton Railroad (later GM&O) tracks on his airmail delivery route from St. Louis to the Windy City.

Gasoline back then came as simply regular and ethyl instead of the three octane ratings commonly sold today. When Route 66 was completed in Illinois, regular cost about 17 cents a gallon; Ethyl was a penny more. Only Ethyl was leaded; The Dupont Ethyl Company that made tetraethyl lead introduced Ethyl in 1923. Lead raises the octane rating of gasoline. In the 1970s it was determined that lead in gasoline caused pollution and unleaded gasoline was required in all automobiles.

The higher the compression ratio of a car's engine, the greater the need for a higher octane rating. Graham Edgar introduced octane ratings in 1926. Both Ethyl and regular gas in the Twenties was originally clear, like water, as the natural end product of the refining process. Unfortunately, housewives unwittingly began using leaded gas as a cleaning agent to remove spots on clothes. Since tetraethyl lead was soluble, it penetrated the skin, causing lead poisoning. To discourage this practice, the company added a red dye to the gasoline giving it a pinkish cast. The **dye caused a permanent stain on clothing and housewives quickly stopped using ethyl gas as a cleaning agent**. In modern times this dye was placed in gasoline that was designated for farm implement use because it was taxed at a lower rate than automobile gas used on highways.

Illinois ranked ninth nationally in 1919 in the refining of petroleum products. By 1929 it jumped to seventh behind California, Texas, New Jersey, Pennsylvania, Oklahoma and Kansas. Much of Illinois oil was refined in Chicago, but a large refinery complex was built by Shell Oil and Standard Oil at **Wood River**, near the Mississippi River

north of **East St. Louis**.

In the 1920s and 1930s gasoline was dispensed mechanically. The attendant pushed a long pump handle back and forth, which brought the gasoline from a storage tank below into a large glass container at the top with markings to show the number of desired gallons. Anything between even gallons was a guesstimate. The nozzle was then placed into the gas tank and the gasoline went into the car by gravity. Quarts of oil (an ugly, thick greenish brown color) at filling stations were stored in glass containers that looked like a canning jar with a long tapered metal spout for pouring oil into the crankcase. It had the viscosity of sorghum molasses and was not nearly as efficient as modern oil, necessitating frequent "ring jobs."

The first tires were simply hard rubber applied to a twenty-four inch metal rim. The earliest balloon tires, invented by Dunlop, required 60 pounds of pressure, but by the mid-Twenties design improvement made it possible to buy tires that required only 30 pounds.

During World War II drivers were limited to about three gallons of gas a week and were encouraged to either use public transportation or carpool. No cars were produced from 1942-45 because auto factories were converted to wartime production. There was a shortage of rubber and car owners were asked to contribute the spare tire in their trunk to the war effort. Punctured inner tubes, instead of being replaced, were fixed with "hot patches." Some patriotic Americans jacked their cars up, **removed all of the tires**, and left their vehicles on cinder blocks for the duration of the war. And all

Old gasoline pumps at **Dwight** – Dan Oberle Collection

Americans were expected to strictly obey the nationally imposed speed limit of **35 miles per hour**.

What kind of autos used Route 66 when it was first completed? Originally called a horseless carriage, the term motorcar was now very much in vogue. Tin Lizzie or "flivver" was the vernacular for cheaper models such as the Chevrolet, Ford and Plymouth. Classic autos of this age of driving by the seat of one's pants included the Packard,

Leo Brothers (*Chicago Tribune*)

Essex, Durant, Nash, Oakland, Olds, Dodge, Reo, Studebaker, Brisco, Chalmers, Napier, Buick, Auburn, Chrysler, Hudson, Velie (made in **Moline**), Duryea (made in **Peoria**), Stutz, DuPont, McFarland, Franklin, Peerless, Hupmobile, Cadillac, Dorris, Pierce-Arrow, Willys-Knight, Lincoln, Daniels, Duesenberg, Maxwell, Rolls Royce, Pontiac, Moon, Marmon, Whippet, Rickenbacker, Stanley Steamer, and Locomobile.

Chevrolet with twin-beam headlights, fender mounted horn: stepping on a floor button changed the beam angle

Cars of this happy-go-lucky era, when the journey was almost as important as the destination, generally lacked radios and black box heaters (recycled hot air from the manifold), were optional. Windshield wipers were often found only on the driver's side and were originally operated by hand. Some old models were started with a hand crank. Brakes were mechanical, not hydraulic. Two-seaters with open cockpits were dubbed "roadsters." Some smaller coupes had fold out seats in the rear known as "**rumble seats**." The larger square-roofed sedans made for long-distance travel were called "touring cars." Vehicles that took people from hotels to train stations were known as "station wagons." Rear doors were often hinged in the back. If you stepped out of the car and the driver absentmindedly pulled forward with the rear gate open, you could be knocked down and run over, hence the term "**suicide doors**."

Carbon was a much greater problem for motorists of the 1920s than today. The low grades of gas and oil sold were conducive to carbon formation. Carbon damaged the valves, coated the piston tops and compression chambers, and frequently caused knocks. It was often necessary for a motorist to remove the cylinder head and clean out the carbon. Valve grinding was also a frequent bother. Motorists were advised to drive their cars at high speeds at least once a month to "**blow out the carbon**."

Back at the turn of the century there was so much prejudice against motorcars that numerous towns passed ordinances **requiring a man holding a red flag to walk ahead of the vehicle**. These restrictions often prohibited the use of offensive horns, bells, or whistles. Illinois even passed a 1903 law regulating the top speed of automobiles at fifteen miles per hour. Speeding was especially a problem in the suburbs as rich Chicagoans zoomed to their summer and weekend homes on the outskirts. In July of 1908 an **Evanston** cop on a bicycle apprehended ten

speeders, some of them going a scorching thirty-three miles-per-hour. In 1939 the speed limit was *reduced* from 80 to 70 miles per hour on the open road.

By 1924 automobiles in Illinois had caused the deaths of over 1,200 people, half of which were pedestrians. The sociological aspects of the impact of automobiles should not be overlooked in this free-wheeling era. Robert and Helen Lynd did a 1929 study of a typical Midwestern town (Muncie, Indiana), and concluded that "ownership of an automobile has now reached a point of being accepted as an essential part of normal living."

Ministers warned about the corrupting of the morals of the nation's youth and preached against the evils of the automobile – this newfangled "bedroom on wheels." Nay sayers blamed the auto for a decline in church attendance, claiming it made going on picnics, playing golf, and other diversions more attractive. An editorial writer for the Chicago *Tribune* claimed that the automobile was detrimental to the morals of our youth and to the health and stability of the family. The automobile, he claimed, freed modern youth from parental supervision and most young people lacked the necessary maturity to cope with temptations presented by this new freedom.

It can be argued that Route 66 gave birth to a national network of highways, giving rise to the trucking industry. Trucks made it possible for smaller regional stockyards to spring up. This ultimately eliminated the need for huge terminal stockyard facilities, ergo it spelled doom for Chicago's Union Stockyards and the National Stockyards at **East St. Louis**. The trucking industry also put many railroads out of business.

One aspect of Route 66 memorabilia that frequently gets overlooked is the old penny post card. The easiest way to find these treasures today is to search for them with your computer on E-Bay.

1929 Buick deluxe convertible Coupe $1,875

When this author went with his parents on vacations, they never failed to send postcards back to family and friends. In a way, I suppose, it was simply a way to keep in touch. Yet I often wondered how the people on the receiving end felt. Sometimes it seemed like bragging. "Hey, look at us! See how much fun we're having while you sad sacks are back home slaving away at your jobs. Can you believe the fantastic place we just visited, pictured on the front in glorious color! Aren't we the lucky dogs?"

When we took those trips, my sister and I often passed the time by trying to see how many out-of-state license plates we could spot. Since Route 66 went all the way to

California, it had more of these cars than most highways.

In the early days these post cards were printed on linen card stock. The photos were in black and white so artists were paid to colorize them by hand painting. Some of the most interesting are the ones showing electric streetcars. If you look closely, you'll notice that the streetcars seem to be going down the street powered by some unknown force in the universe. Downtown streets were criss-crossed with electric wires that provided power for passenger trolleys. These wires were deemed to be too ugly and a distraction by card producers, so for aesthetic purposes they were arbitrarily deleted from the picture.

Decamp Junction near **Staunton** – Dan Oberle Collection

In many cases, post card pictures are all that remain of many Route 66 landmarks in Illinois. Pictures were taken for postcards of hotels, motels, roadhouses, restaurants, service stations, factories, schools, churches, parks, landmarks, and a variety of other places. About a half dozen of the Route 66 pictures used in last year's *Incredible Illinois* came from postcards.

The price of Route 66 postcards varies. Some regular postcards can be purchased at shows for as little as 50 cents each. But anything with Route 66 on the back usually goes for about $2.00 - $5.00 each, depending on scarcity and demand. **Collinsville** has a postcard show every Easter and Labor Day weekend, and I'm sure many other places throughout the state have these events.

One advantage in collecting Route 66 postcards is that they don't take up much space. I just love the way Route 66 expert **Michael Wallis** refers to these gems. He calls them a "slice of Americana in visual shorthand."

Another thing that made traveling interesting in the 1950s was reading the Burma Shave signs – those wonderful verses by the road. Back in 1925 a liniment salesman from Wisconsin by the name of Clinton O'Dell decided to try and market a brushless shaving cream. The oils for the soap formula came from Burma, hence Burma Shave. The set of serial signs consisted of thirty-six inch boards that were hand painted with brass stencils.

The first red on white signs didn't have rhymes or jingles – just prose. "SHAVE THE MODERN WAY/

FINE FOR THE SKIN/ DRUGGISTS HAVE IT/ **BURMA SHAVE**."

Sales were steady but the essential spirit of what made America cherish the jaunty little signs was, of course, their light-hearted spirit. During the Depression humor in advertising was lacking. It was so scarce as to be virtually a trace element. Instead of the lapel-grabbing hard sell, O'Dell introduced America to an endearing brand of folksy humor.

When spotting the signs along Route 66 it was common for everyone in the car to read the verses in unison: "ARE YOUR WHISKERS/ WHEN YOU WAKE/ TOUGHER THAN/ A TWO-BIT STEAK? **BURMA SHAVE**."

Once travelers realized that the sign recipe followed a jingling cadence, frosted with a topping of humor, they grew addicted. "SUBSTITUTES/ CAN LET YOU DOWN/ QUICKER THAN/ A STRAPLESS GOWN/ **BURMA SHAVE**."

Route 66's first eastern terminus (to purists, point of origin) was at Cicero, but it soon was extended to Jackson Boulevard at Michigan Avenue and later to Lakeshore Drive at Chicago's Grant Park. From 1926 to 1930, Route 66 followed Route 4 from **Springfield** to **Staunton**. After that date the road was shifted farther east, and it now ran through **Litchfield, Mount Olive** and **Livingston**.

There was a lot of politics involved back then when determining exactly which route the road would take and what towns would be visited or bypassed. There was so much at stake - just as when the railroads were built back in the 1850s. Towns like **Carbondale, Centralia**, and **Mattoon** that had trunk lines grew and prospered. The American Automobile Association predicted in 1927 that tourist travel along Route 66 towns would amount to an astounding $3.3 billion annually. Places that were bypassed shriveled and died on the economic vine; some became ghost towns or, at the very most, irrelevant. Some towns had big parades to celebrate the opening of a stretch of the road through their

Smitty's 24 hour grill at **McCook** – Dan Oberle collection

boundaries. The new road quickly became a boon to mom

and pop stores, motels, filling stations, restaurants, refreshment stands, repair shops, sign painters, and virtually all of the building trades.

BASEBALL IN THE ROARING TWENTIES

1901 was an important year for professional baseball in Illinois. It was the year the Three I League (Indiana, Illinois, Iowa) was formed. It was organized in **Peoria** and included teams from Davenport, **Rock Island**, **Rockford**, Cedar Rapids, **Decatur, Bloomington, Peoria**, Terre Haute and Evansville. There was a 110 game schedule and players were paid $750 a month. Hall of Famer

Old-time glove

Carl Hubbell got his start in this league. Illinois teams dominated, winning the championship twenty out of the thirty years the league existed.

The White Sox won the pennant in 1901, 1906, 1917, and 1919. The Cubs won National League pennants in 1906, 1907, 1908, 1910, 1918 and 1929. In 1907 the Cubs, led by the double play combination of Tinker to Evers to Chance, defeated the Detroit Tigers, led by Ty Cobb, in the World Series four games to none. The White Sox won the World Series against the Giants (4-2) in 1917.

After the infamous 1919 **Black Sox Scandal,** where seven members of the Chicago team conspired to throw the World Series, baseball owners were convinced that something substantial had to be done to restore public confidence in the integrity of baseball. After all, famed tunesmith George M. Cohan had lost $30,000 betting on the White Sox. They passed over William H. Taft, John J. Pershing and chose **Kenesaw Mountain Landis,** This narrowly educated, tobacco-chewing man was a federal district judge for the

Shoeless Joe Jackson

Shoeless Joe Jackson

Northern Illinois district. He had a reputation for toughness and sternness, an image that was further enhanced by a nickname that evoked a sense of hard rock solidarity. The press quickly dubbed him the **"Czar of Baseball"** and he vowed to protect the sport from anything that might taint its image. When a Chicago jury voted the White Sox players who threw the Series "not guilty," Landis intervened and banned them from baseball for life.

In 1922 the U.S. Supreme Court considered whether organized baseball was a monopoly. Justice Oliver Wendell Holmes gave the unanimous decision that it was not. The justices ruled that the terms interstate trade and commerce did not apply to baseball in their commonly accepted manner. This ruling still stands.

The "**farm system**" for developing minor league ballplayers started back in the 1920s. The genius who developed the system was **Branch Rickey**, general manager of the St. Louis Cardinals. From 1926-1946, the Cardinals were second only to the Yankees for having the best winning percentage in baseball. Known as the **"Professor of Baseball,"** he applied scientific principles of management to the sport. Rickey was the first to build a large empire of farm teams with the express purpose of recruiting and nurturing new baseball talent. The system was so successful that other clubs soon copied the formula and it became a staple of baseball.

Pitcher Ed Cicotte

Prior to 1920 baseball was just another sport. The man who changed all that in the blink of an eye was **George Herman Ruth**. Ruth made baseball America's game. Babe Ruth made baseball a metaphor for life and the American Dream. Ruth reinforced the notion that somehow a poor boy could still rise to fame and fortune. Ruth was the pivotal figure in the establishment of the greatest dynasty in baseball history, that of the New York Yankees.

Before Ruth, most players choked the bat and slapped at the ball with a short choppy swing. That batting style was deemed the most productive. Ruth's prodigious swings produced an unprecedented number of home runs and soon players in both leagues began to copy his style. Each day, millions of readers turned to the sports page of the newspapers to see if Ruth had hit another home run. One can only imagine what his hitting totals might have been if he had not started his career as one of the best southpaws in the game. Few players in the game have exceeded his **lifetime batting average of .342**. Even seven time National League batting champion Stan Musial could only muster a .331 average.

The 1920s is often referred to as the **Golden Age of Sports** with such names as Bill Tilden in tennis, Johnny Weissmuller in swimming, Rogers Hornsby in baseball,

Red Grange in football, Bobby Jones in golf, and Jack Dempsey in boxing.

For further reading check out *Baseball: A History of America's Game* by Benjamin G. Rader, published by the University of Illinois Press.

AFRICAN-AMERICANS IN THE 1920s

Black persons constituted a growing percentage of Illinois' population during this era. They first started arriving from the South in large numbers when World War I broke out in Europe due to an increased demand for war materials and industrial goods, creating more jobs in the factories. Immigrant labor from Europe had long filled the need for factory workers, but immigration slowed to a trickle when the war broke out. Blacks from the South moved north to fill the void. The exodus from the South continued throughout the 1920s. In 1920 there were 182,274 Black citizens in the state. By 1930 that number grew to 328,972.

Cab Calloway

Marcus Garvey

There was a split in the Black leadership over the question of how to deal with the problem of white racism. African-Americans suffered through **three race riots** in Illinois. There was the **Springfield** riot in 1908, the **East St. Louis** riot in 1917, and the **Chicago** riot of 1919.

Booker T. Washington thought that Blacks could move up the economic and social ladder by learning trades and skills. **W.E.B. Du Bois**, the head of the N.A.A.C.P. that was formed after the Springfield riot, was critical of Washington's policy of "accommodation" and pushed for Blacks to also seek college degrees and enter the professions. Du Bois even called Washington an "Uncle Tom." Du Bois noted that due to decades of slavery there was a growing need to restore "black pride." One only had to look through the pages of the Chicago *Defender* to find a plethora of **ads for hair straightening** tonics and creams to lighten the skin.

Another leader, **Marcus Garvey**, decided that Blacks would never be accepted in America, and he pushed for a "back to Africa" movement.

The professions in Illinois were largely closed to Blacks. According to the 1930 census there were only 331 Black physicians, 795 teachers and 159 dentists. There were 854 musicians but they were mostly confined to playing in black and tan cabarets, houses of prostitution and bootleg speak-easies. Most Black males worked at menial jobs such as janitorial workers or elevator operators. About two-thirds of Black women earning wages were employed as household domestics – washing, cooking, ironing, and scrubbing the floors. On the railroads, Black men had almost a monopoly on jobs as porters and waiters on Pullman cars.

Despite an 1874 Illinois law that said children should not be excluded from schools because of race, segregation was the norm. The 1896 national case of **Plessy v. Ferguson** established the "separate but equal" standard for race relations. For example, schools in **East St. Louis** were not desegregated until 1950. Blacks also were faced with segregation when it came to housing, movie theaters, buses, parks, and playgrounds.

On a more distressing note, although there were twelve lynchings in Illinois between 1900 and 1915, there were even more during the Twenties due to Klan resurgence.

In 1928 Adelbert H. Roberts became the first Black elected to the Illinois Senate. The best-known Black politician in Illinois was **Oscar De Priest**. In 1928 this Chicagoan became the first African-American from Illinois elected to the U.S. House of Representatives. Like most Blacks of the era, he was a Republican. Prior to Roosevelt and the New Deal, Blacks remained loyal to the party of Abe Lincoln.

Most Blacks who attained wealth in this era did so through association with vices such as gambling and prostitution. John "Mushmouth" Johnson was a notable example of this. He operated the gambling rackets on Chicago's South Side for many years.

Despite all of these problems and all of this discrimination, Blacks still poured into the State of Illinois because life was better here than in the South.

For further information see *Black Chicago* by Allan Spear, 1970; Donald Tingley's *The Structuring of a State*, 1980, and Elliot Rudwick's *Race Riot at East St. Louis*, 1964.

THE GOLDEN AGE OF ADVERTISING SLOGANS

"Reach for a Lucky instead of a sweet." (Lose weight by smoking a Lucky Strike cigarette instead of eating.)

"Help your husband become a winner at his workplace – start his day with Post Bran Flakes."

"The successful man wears Arrow brand shirts with starched collars."

"Blow some my way." – Chesterfield cigarettes

"Chew Mail Pouch Tobacco – treat yourself to the best."

"The best way to lick the problem of constipation is to consume Fleischmann's yeast."

"Often a bridesmaid but never a bride . . . could it be halitosis?" – Listerine

"Come to church – Christian worship increases your efficiency." – church billboard in uptown New York

"Not until the last vestige of dandruff is gone can you be considered acceptable socially – use Listerine." (The Listerine people later discovered that they could sell even more of their product by saying it fought halitosis.)

"Use Bon Ami cleanser – hasn't scratched yet."

"Rinso white, Rinso white, happy little washday song."

"Bad breath is now judged to be one of the greatest social offenses." – May Breath mouthwash

"Use Kotex for correct appearance and hygienic comfort."

"Use NUJOL to produce internal cleanliness which leads to Health, Happiness and Success."

"Fleishman's Yeast solves problems with complexion, constipation, colds, and boils."

"Ovaltine banishes wakeful nerves and sleepless nights to give you lasting all-day energy."

"Formament – our germ-killing tablet helps prevent colds."

"Keeps your face velvet smooth all day long with a man-style fragrance." – Aqua Velvet

"Don't use inferior, unsafe bathroom tissue." – Scot Tissue

"Old Dutch Cleanser chases dirt and provides healthful cleanliness."

"Dangerous dirt can be found in rugs that are thought to be clean – solve this problem by Hooverizing your carpet."

"Maytag – the washer that glorifies washday."

"You too, can have a skin you love to touch." – Woodbury's facial soap

"America's finest and most expensive car." – 1920 Locomobile ad

"The blend that can't be copied – Chesterfield, they satisfy." Chesterfield cigarettes

"Sooner or later you'll own Generals." – General Tire

"The pause that refreshes." – Coca Cola

"Naturally lovable – that schoolgirl complexion." Palm-olive Soap

"I'd walk a mile for a Camel." – Camel Turkish blend cigarettes

"Good to the last drop." – Maxwell House Coffee (Teddy Roosevelt is credited with inventing this slogan when he commented on it in 1907.)

"A pink toothbrush is the first sign of pyorrhea – use Ipana toothpaste."

"Don't be shunned because of B.O. – use Lifebuoy."

"Ask the man who owns one." – Packard automobiles

"Log Cabin Syrup – buy it in the Abe Lincoln log cabin tin."

"His master's voice." – Victor Talking Machine Company with an ad showing the faithful dog Nippur listening to a gramophone recording

"Old Dutch Cleanser – chases dirt."

"Aunt Jemima's light and fluffy plantation pancakes – famous all over the South." – Quaker Oats Company of Chicago

"Buy a Sheridan – the peptimistic car."

"If beauty is only skin deep, we can make you beautiful." – Woodbury Soap

"If it isn't an Eastman it isn't a Kodak."

Sherwin Williams Paint

"Schlitz, the beer that made Milwaukee famous."

"Use Squibbs Dental Crème – it prevents acid tooth decay at the danger line."

"Children cry for it – Fletcher's Castoria." (laxative)

"Good morning – have you used Pears' soap?"

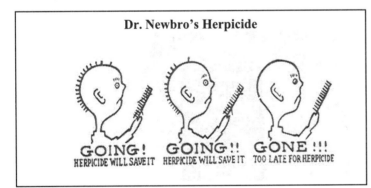

"Dr. West's toothbrushes fight the most mortal enemy of your smile – tooth decay."

"Don't just drive a car, drive a Studebaker."

Dr. Newbro's Herpicide

"Pay as you ride – buy a Maxwell on the installment plan."

"Piggly Wiggly keeps 2,000,000 hens busy daily to supply the needs of our customers."

"Motorists wise, Simonize their cars for protection."

"You can trust your car to the man who wears the star." - Texaco

"When better automobiles are built, Buick will build them."

"You can be sure if it's Westinghouse."

THE HARDING SCANDALS

In stark contrast to Pennsylvania Avenue being blocked off from traffic due to the current war on terrorism, President Harding permitted sightseers and well-wishers to chug up the White House driveway and chortle right past the presidential front door. Whereas Woodrow Wilson the aristocrat was aloof and reserved, Harding was gregarious and "just folks."

Harding put together an able cabinet, for the most part. Andrew Mellon was Secretary of the Treasury, Herbert Hoover was Secretary of Commerce; Charles Evans Hughes was Secretary of State. And **Charles G. Dawes**, the Chicago banker, became the Director of the Budget. He made one very bad choice, Albert Fall as Secretary of the Interior. The oil lobby licked their chops at that one.

Harding died on August 2, 1923, of a stroke, shortly after a trip to Alaska. Some have suggested that Harding was actually poisoned by his wife after she found out he was having an affair with a woman named **Nan Britton**. Others said that he lost the will to live because he found out his friends had betrayed him.

The president was memorialized but it didn't take long for his whole life work to topple into disgrace. There was scandal and misuse of funds by Charles Forbes who was in charge of the Veteran's Bureau. A senate committee investigated oil leases of government lands at Elk Hills, California, and Teapot Dome, Wyoming. Albert Fall leased these lands without competitive bidding and in return received a kickback of $260,000 from oilman Harry F. Sinclair of Sinclair Oil. Fall ended up being the first cabinet officer to go to prison. Harding's tomb in Marion, Ohio, was not dedicated until President Hoover and ex-president Coolidge performed the disagreeable task in June of 1931.

Harding's mistress – Nan Britton

1923 - THE KLAN COMES TO ILLINOIS

It was one of those typically hot, humid days in late June – the kind of day where you can hear the corn growing in the fields, and the heat shimmers off the highway in undulating waves, giving drivers the false perception of a desert mirage.

A great gathering of oddly dressed people clustered around the base of one of the lesser mounds that was just west of the Great Cahokia Mound that stood an impressive 100 feet tall. The Cahokia Mound was an historic bit of architecture that had been built by Native-Americans who had once inhabited the area in the anthropological era known as the Mississippian period. The natives had carried basket after basket of alluvial soil to create an impressive oblong structure that contained a volume of material that was larger than the Great Pyramid of Cheops in ancient Egypt.

Imperial Wizard of the KKK – Library of Congress

The mound was located on the outskirts of **East St. Louis**, an industrial town of about 74,000. It was about a hundred yards from U.S. Highway 40, also labeled Collinsville Road. Route 40, earlier known as the National Road, skirted the southern edge of **Troy** and the northern edge of **Collinsville**, then followed a path along the western edge of the bluffs before making a 90 degree turn toward East St. Louis along rich, flat land that was once the bed of the Mississippi River. Now it was called the **Great American Bottom**, and it stretched between **Alton** and **Chester**. Lewis and Clark had spent time in **Cahokia** and **Illinoistown**, but there is no evidence that they ever visited the great mound during their historic Corps of Discovery trek in 1804.

But on this day, the eager crowd that was waiting in white satin hoods was expectant, their eyes searching the cobalt blue sky. Suddenly they began to cheer. They had seen a tiny speck in the sky, a speck that grew into an airplane. As it came closer the Curtiss Jenny glistened in the bright sunlight, and they could see that it was gilded all over. It circled the level field, a spot that had been freshly mowed, and slowly seesawed in for a bumpy landing, its engine sputtering as it coughed to a stop.

A bulky man in a robe and hood of purple silk hoisted himself up from the rear seat of the plane. As he climbed to the ground, a new surge of applause filled the air. White-robed figures bobbed up and down on tippy-toes; small children were hoisted up on their father's shoulders for a view. A small delegation of dignitaries filed out toward the airplane, stopping at a respectful distance.

The man in purple stepped forward.

"Kigy," he said. In Klanspeak he just uttered, Klansmen, I greet you.

"Itsub," they replied solemnly.

He went forward to greet each member of the small group, Klasping left hands, showing Klan loyalty and greeting.

With the newcomer in the lead the group made its way to a raised wooden platform, decked out in bunting and flags, and especially built for the occasion. The guest stepped forward to the rostrum and raised his hand.

"My worthy subjects, citizens of the Invisible Empire, Klansmen all, greetings. It grieves me to be late. I have just come from Washington where we held a glorious parade, attended by thousands, down Pennsylvania Avenue. The President of the United States kept me unduly long, counseling upon matters of importance to the state." The crowd buzzed.

"Here in this uplifted hand, for all to see, I bear an official document addressed to the **Grand Dragon, Hydras, Great Titians, Furies, Kleagles, Exalted Cyclops**, and all citizens of the Invisible Empire of the Realm of Illinois. It is signed by His Lordship, Hiram Wesley Evans, **Imperial Wizard**."

The Grand Dragon paused, inviting cheers and clapping that thundered about him. Then he launched into a speech. He urged members of the audiences to fight for 100 percent Americanism and against foreign influences. He exhorted them to ignore writings in the press that falsely proclaimed the innocence of Sacco and Vanzetti. He called them anarchist vermin that justly deserved to be exterminated. He warned about the growing influence of Catholicism in this country and urged supporters to write their congressmen, urging an end to foreign immigration that was filling the land with Romanists, Jews, and those who believed in Godless Communism. Someone in the crowd raised a placard. It read: "The Pope will enter the White House when Hell freezes over." There had been disturbing rumors that New York Governor Al Smith, a "wet" and a Catholic, was the growing favorite for the nominee of the Democratic Party in the upcoming 1928 election. The Klan had had a strong influence at the 1924 Democratic nominating convention and had seen to it the Protestant John W. Davis had gotten the nomination over Alfred E. Smith, a hated Tammany machine politician.

The Knights of Columbus was denounced as a secret organization with a smoldering plot to kill Protestants and install the Pope in the White House. It was no accident that the lofty spires of the Catholic churches commanded the highest view in most towns. The Knights hid their guns in

Nicola Sacco and Bartolomeo Vanzetti

the basement of Catholic churches and when the time was ripe, guns fired from the belfries could dominate the streets.

Next, the speaker warned about the growing boldness of "Niggers." He talked about their desire to marry white women and mongrelize the race. Whippings, tar and featherings, beatings, and lynchings were the recommended antidote for those sluggards who had forgotten their place in society.

Small placards were handed out to the crowd for those who were merchants. Economic boycott was a strong weapon of the Night Riders. Members were urged to boycott stores owned by Jews and to place these placards in the windows of their own stores. The placards had three large black letters – TWK – trade with Klansmen.

When he finished his speech and stepped back, people began tossing coins, rings, dollar bills, watch charms, and anything else that was bright and valuable on the platform. When the tribute slackened, officials on the platform gathered up the treasure.

Anti-Bolshevik cartoon of the 1920s

Finally, a local reverend gave an invocation and a twenty-five-piece band played "America" and "The Star Spangled Banner." It ended with a pledge of allegiance to Old Glory. Then the man in purple strode of to a near-by pavilion to consult with his attendant Kleagles, Cyclopses and Titans.

The crowd dispersed and wandered off to various sites close by and spread blankets to consume picnic baskets. This was an all day affair. Later that evening there would be another message given by a lesser official. Those in the crowd who were not yet members would be invited to join in the crusade. Robes were sold to newcomers at a cost of $6.50. The affiliated Gate City Manufacturing Company of Atlanta made them at a cost of $3.28. Local Klaverns were supported by dues of a dollar a month. There would be blood oaths and an elaborate ceremony, followed by a cross burning.

Meetings similar to this took place in towns all over the state and the Klan had particular appeal in the southern tier known as Egypt. They held numerous rallies in **Herrin, Marion, Benton, Harrisburg, Carbondale, Cairo** and **Murphysboro**.

RADIO IN ILLINOIS DURING THE TWENTIES

The decade of the 1920s became the first in history to see the rise of popular culture. The rich and well-to-do had always possessed leisure time to pursue their interests but now the common man, the blue collar worker, and the less educated had a chance to enjoy life.

This was all made possible by several factors. Labor unions had long pushed for increased wages and shorter working hours. Writers such as Upton Sinclair, Theodore Dreiser, and Carl Sandburg had pushed and prodded for government and capitalists to have a more humanitarian outlook. Increased industrialization and mass production techniques created more leisure time for more people. Large numbers of Americans had more free time and increased disposable income. One reporter put it thusly: "Millions learned to play where only thousands played before." Another writer phrased it this way: "**The right to play is the final clause in the charter of democracy.**"

This new playground saw the advent of Mahjong, crossword puzzles, speakeasies, movies, jazz music, flag pole sitting, dance marathons, comic strips, and, finally, radio.

Radio first arrived on the American scene in 1920 when the Westinghouse-sponsored station KDKA in Pittsburgh began broadcasting election results on November 2, 1920. That was the day Warren G. Harding and Calvin Coolidge defeated James Cox and Franklin Roosevelt in the presidential election. The next year, in 1921, Westinghouse started station KYW in Chicago, mostly broadcasting the songs of Mary Garden from the Chicago Opera Company. Opera made up nearly all of the scheduled programming that first year but later on they did broadcast the World Series.

This writer was born in 1939 and when I was just a lad of nine my father bought me a one-tube radio set from the Walter Ashe radio supply store on 11th and Pine in St. Louis. My father was a foreman at the C.K. Williams paint mill in **East St. Louis**, but he repaired radios in his spare time.

1920s radio tube - WLS

The kit cost a mere $2.99. I followed the instructions carefully winding a coil of exposed copper wire that would serve as the tuner. The metal frame of my bed became the antenna and a wire that ran to a lead pipe served as the ground. There was no speaker for amplification and I was only able to hear through a plastic earphone inserted into one ear. Night after night I listened to the heroic deeds of Tom Mix (who urged young wranglers to eat shredded **Ralston**), the madcap adventures of Little Orphan Annie (energized by a daily cup of **Ovaltine**), and the youthful bravery of Jack Armstrong (bolstered by daily bowls of **Wheaties**).

Similarly, on old time radios of the Twenties (known as crystal sets), there was a wire that extended up through the box, and you would move the "cat's whisker," to tune in a particular station; the metal frame of one's bed could be used as an antenna. These cheap sets had no amplification and required headphones for listening.

The antenna for radios in the mid-Twenties was simply a wire that was about two feet long that came out of the chassis. For better reception, some owners attached extension wires and ran them outside via the nearest window.

Many of the early stations in Illinois devoted a significant portion of the broadcasts to service for farmers. Farm wives listened to radio entertainment while they did their work in the kitchen, and the farmer could now hear weather reports and hourly updates on market prices. By 1925 Illinois had 37 radio stations in operation. Many of these stations broadcast Chicago Board of Trade livestock, grain, dairy and vegetable prices as well as weather reports.

As radio stations flourished, radio receiving sets became more common in households. By 1925 nearly twelve percent of farmers had radio sets. Many small-town banks owned radios and posted changes in livestock and farm prices for rural clients. Clubs, churches, schools, civic organizations and farm bureau offices bought radio sets for the entertainment of their members and information on prices and weather.

The early sets, ranging in price from $25.00 to $250.00, were battery powered; not until 1927 was it possible to operate household radios on plug-in electrical current. Few farm households had electricity available in the 1920s and 1930s so farm sets were sold with batteries. Only with the advent of the New Deal program known as Rural Electrification was electricity available to nearly everyone. Companies now began to make DC sets that had

1926 Lamp and radio with speaker in lampshade

batteries but were also adaptable to AC current. By 1930 roughly half of all farm homes had radio receivers.

Sears Roebuck and Company of Chicago operated one of the early stations. Catering largely to farmers, it broadcast under the call letters WBBX. It quickly became fashionable to assign words to each call letter of a radio station. The **East St. Louis** station, broadcasting out of the Broadview Hotel, had call letters WTMV that stood for Watch The Mississippi Valley. In 1924 Sears changed its call letters to WES, which stood for World's Economy Store. Later the letters were changed once again to WLS for **World's Largest Store**.

WGN in Chicago was owned by the Chicago *Tribune,* and their call letters stood for World's Greatest Newspaper. WGN concentrated in its early years on sports, current news and market reports. The station broadcast music programs from a location in the **Drake Hotel**. Actually, most Chicago stations broadcast popular music from hotels. KYW beamed the music of the "Night Hawks" each evening from the **Congress Hotel**. WLS sponsored Isham Jones and his orchestra, which broadcast from the College Inn in the **Sherman Hotel**. WLS was especially noted for the "National Barn Dance," a program eagerly looked forward to every Saturday night by rural residents.

In an interesting sidelight, WGN as a public service interrupted its programming to broadcast police calls. The Chicago police force had no broadcasting ability of its own in 1922, so squad cars with receivers tuned in to WGN to hear about a robbery that had taken place or to learn the description of a burglar. This procedure made listening an exciting adventure but it destroyed continuity.

The Federal Communications Commission was created as a result of a landmark case filed by Robert McCormick. In the case of the *Tribune Company v. Oak Leaves Broadcasting*, the Colonel claimed that another station was infringing on the broadcast frequency of WGN. Partly as a result of this case Congress created the Federal Radio Commission to regulate the airwaves, and it soon evolved into the FCC.

The networks were created when groups of stations joined forces. The Mutual Network was formed by a conglomerate of WXYZ of Detroit, WGN of Chicago, WLW of Cincinnati, and WOR of New York. NBC was formed by RCA in 1926.

With the arrival of networks the "star system" evolved.

Early crystal radio set

Two of the biggest were Chicagoans Freeman Gosden and Charles Correll who played "**Amos 'n' Andy**." Their act started on WGN as "Sam 'n' Henry" but when the pair switched to WMAQ they changed the program's name. Despite its racist overtones the program was successful for decades.

Situation comedy got its start when Jim and Marion Jordan of **Peoria** created "**Fibber McGee and Molly.**"

Radio commentator Lowell Thomas

"Good morning breakfast clubber!" became a daily welcome for millions of listener's to the long-running Don McNeill's "Breakfast Club" program. Produced and aired in Chicago, it was one of the few that stayed while others began moving to New York or Los Angeles. Fran Allison of later **Kukla, Fran and Ollie** fame played Aunt Fanny, who dispensed homespun advice and humor. Anita Bryant and Johnny Desmond starred on The Breakfast Club early in their careers.

Jack Armstrong, The All-American Boy, was aired five nights a week from Chicago radio. Other programs broadcast from Chicago that kids went wild over included *Tom Mix, The Lone Ranger* and *Captain Midnight*. Another favorite that started in 1930 was *Little Orphan Annie*. The immensely popular program sold tons of Ovaltine. "**Who's that little chatterbox? The one with the pretty auburn locks. Who can it be? It's Little Orphan Annie!**" These kids programs were broadcast right after school and again immediately before bedtime.

Station KYW in Chicago was established in 1921 for the specific purpose of broadcasting opera. Mary Garden was the featured singer more than any other vocalist.

Chicagoan **Floyd Gibbons** became the prototype for radio war correspondents. He set

Radio stars Edgar Bergen and Charlie McCarthy

the standard for swashbuckling war reporters by wearing a flamboyant hat, a trench coat, and a white patch over an eye lost in World War I.

By 1929 there was a vast change coming to the air as well as to the comic strips. Until this time, the stories had followed a rigid formula. Each day's adventures were complete in themselves. Now the *continued story* caught on, following the trail blazed by Buck Rogers and Tarzan in the newspapers and The Goldbergs and Amos 'n' Andy on radio. The inevitable next step was the daytime serial.

The nickname "soap opera" for daytime drama is one of the great injustices of history because drug companies like Sterling and Whitehall and food companies like General Mills and General Foods sponsored nearly as many programs as Lever Brothers or Procter and Gamble.

Chicago was the birthplace of this new dramatic form. Frank Hummert of the Blackett and Sample Advertising Agency saw opportunity in the empty daytime hours of radio. Before 1930, evening was considered the only time of real use to sponsors. During the day, men were in offices and women were busy with housework.

Hummert thought differently. Women handled the household money. The logical time to get their attention

Tarzan by Illinoisan Edgar Rice Burroughs

TARZAN
LORD OF THE JUNGLE

with advertising was in the morning before they went shopping at the market. Hummert was exploring this line of thought when he hired a new secretary, Anne Ashenhurst. She was promoted after two weeks and she and Frank Hummert began to outline some of the forty-seven dramas that they were to bring to the air. By 1935 when they were married, both were vice-presidents of Blackett, Sample and Hummert. Some of their programs included Stolen Husband, Terry And Mary, Amanda of Honeymoon Hill, The Strange Romance of Evelyn Winters, Valiant Lady, and John's Other Wife.

By the end of the Twenties decade more than 15 million Americans owned radio sets.

For further information read George E. Mowry's *The Twenties: Fords, Flappers and Fanatics*. Old issues of Radio And TV Mirror were also consulted.

THE DOLLAR DECADE

When Alexis de Tocqueville visited America in the 1830s he noted: "The whole American nation is devoted to business." By the 1920s nothing had changed much except maybe the emphasis on business pursuits was even greater. The American public's favorable perception of business and corporations probably reached its apex during this decade. These were the halcyon years of business prestige. Despite unfavorable depiction by the novelists of the era, the American businessman was the hero of the day.

Europe was left in shambles after the war, and its economies were in disarray. As a result, the United States became the new world economic leader. Europeans, as a whole, began drifting toward socialism, but America became the bastion of entrepreneurship and investment capitalism.

Rollin Kirby – A worried stock market investor

Businessmen had learned some hard lessons since the old days of the Robber Barons. *Caveat emptor*, "the public be damned," and "every fellow for himself" was replaced with the golden rule and honesty is the best policy (at least superficially). The goal of modern corporations was to become a good employer, a good neighbor, and a good citizen. Even Arthur Train's 1924 novel, *The Needle's Eye*, pitted the old relentless industrialist against a modern democratic businessman.

To be sure, there were some literary highbrows who failed to tow the line. Sinclair Lewis was devastating with his Babbitt. George S. Kaufman and H.L. Mencken mercilessly lampooned and satirized businessmen as childish, greedy, ignoramuses.

Yet Booth Tarkington, in *The Plutocrat,* lays out a tale about a businessman, Mr. Tinker, who at story's end is seen as someone to be admired – a great businessman.

All three presidents of this era were friendly to business. Many of the cabinet members of this period were highly successful businessmen. Andrew Mellon, the aluminum magnate, was declared to be second only to Alexander Hamilton in greatness as secretary of the treasury. Harding declared that it was a blind idealist who could find no thrill in the magnificent tapestry of business and blind indeed was the man who recklessly pulled at its threads to unravel it.

As Secretary of Commerce, Hoover held nearly 200 conferences in which his department exhorted business to become more modern, streamlined and productive. Charles

G. Dawes, the budget director, thought that government should be run like a successful business.

Even religion played a supporting role in this adoration of American business. The social gospel underwent a decline in this decade in favor of emphasis on personal sins of the lost generation – smoking, drinking and dancing. Apparently, the business climate of the 1920s had improved working conditions to the point where the need for protest was not felt by churches to be particularly great.

Lloyd C. Douglas wrote the novel *Magnificent Obsession* in 1929. In it the protagonist Bobby Merrick discovers a success formula in the Bible. By helping others, he learned that you enlarge yourself, and in the process the people you have helped will in turn affect your success.

Many businessmen joined service clubs such as Kiwanis, Lions, or Optimists. "Service above self" is the motto of Rotarians. The oldest of these clubs was Rotary, founded at Chicago in 1905. These civic clubs, and at least a dozen others like them, tried to instill moral codes in the business community.

The Bible itself was not silent about business matters. It contains numerous passages that condemn slothfulness and laziness and praised hard work and diligence. There is also the parable of the talents. Yet the parable about the rich man also condemns the practice of hoarding wealth. "Ye cannot serve God and Mammon." Interestingly, Jesus held himself free from the worldly trappings of possessions.

Large numbers of writers in this era were either atheists or agnostics and had little good to say about religion in their writings. Sinclair Lewis gave us Elmer Gantry, a charlatan, scoundrel, and a wolf in sheep's clothing. His cruel satire was not very successful because it was so extreme. Most successful pastors of churches were good men with pure motives.

Lewis also made fun of religion and ministers in Zenith,

H.L. Mencken's Smart Set – Mencken was a huge critic of big business

the mythical town in *Babbitt*.

With the onset of the Great Depression, veneration of the businessman rapidly changed to distrust. When Roosevelt became president he promised to give the "forgotten man" (workers) a new deal. He also promised to drive the money changers (businessmen) from the temple. Instead of appointing business moguls to his cabinet, he chose university professors.

This division between the two political parties along economic lines continues to this day. Democrats are generally perceived as supporters of organized labor and are willing to increases taxes to implement programs that help the downtrodden and redistribute the wealth. Republicans are mostly seen as champions of Wall Street and industrial capitalism and claim the Democrats have never seen a tax that they didn't like.

ILLINOIS AVIATION IN THE ROARING TWENTIES

Prior to 1908 Illinoisans interested in aviation had to be content with watching balloon ascensions and flights. Back in 1884 Dr. Arthur De Baisset of **Chicago** came up with a design for a heavier-than-air vehicle. **Mt. Carmel's** Edward Pennington devised a plan for an aeroplane in 1890. The first actual flight on Illinois soil took place in 1908 when famed Glenn Curtiss piloted a plane briefly at the Hawthorne Race Track in Chicagoland.

1930 Air Races in Chicago

The first military air bases in Illinois were established by the army in 1917. Chanute Air Base, named for aviation pioneer **Octave Chanute**, was built at **Rantoul**. The site was chosen by the War Department because the terrain was level, it was close to the Illinois Central Railroad, and the town of Rantoul could be used to furnish water and electricity. It was built at a cost of $1 million and was completed by July 4. During the first six months of training there were 50 crashes. Chanute Air Base trained 525 pilots for World War I aviation duty.

Scott Field, named for corporal Frank Scott who was the **first enlisted man killed in a flying accident**, was built in 1917 on the outskirts of **Belleville** and **O'Fallon**. A huge hangar for dirigibles was built at Scott Field and during Prohibition they were used for flying over rural areas of Southern Illinois in an effort to spot illegal stills.

The Curtiss-Steinberg Airport, visited by both Charles Lindbergh and Amelia Earhart, was built at **Cahokia** on the outskirts of **East St. Louis**.

Numerous pilots from World War I took up barnstorming as a way to maintain their interest in flying while also earning a modest living. Barnstorming consisted of

daredevil stunt flying, flying exhibitions, races, mock aerial

Early photo of Scott Air Base near **Mascoutah**

battles, and offering brief rides to interested spectators. Flyers of this sort frequented county fairs. Landing fields in those days were often a mere vacant field or a city park.

The first airmail in Illinois arrived at Chicago in 1918 on a flight from New York. Service from **Chicago** to Cleveland came in 1919; to St. Louis via **Rantoul** in 1920, and from Chicago to Kansas City in 1922.

Early flying was dangerous and fatal accidents were frequent. Back then, anyone could buy or rent a plane and fly it where he pleased. In 1919 the Goodyear airship "Wing Foot" fell from the sky and **crashed through the skylight** of the Illinois Trust and Savings Bank in **Chicago**, killing 13 persons.

Federal regulation of planes and licenses did not come until 1926 when aeronautics was placed under a division of the Commerce Department with **Chicago** attorney William McCracken Jr. in charge.

Charles A. Lindbergh was a prominent figure in Illinois aviation both as a barnstormer and a mail pilot. In 1926 he regularly flew airmail runs from St. Louis to **Chicago** with stops at **Peoria** and **Springfield**. Lindbergh and other pilots flew the route five days a week, but flying airmail was expensive and postage charges barely covered the expenses. The easiest method back then for Lindbergh to fly from St. Louis to Chicago was to merely follow the Gulf, Mobile & Ohio railroad tracks that roughly paralleled State Route 4 (later Route 66).

At the time Lindbergh made his historic trans-Atlantic flight in 1927 he was already a prominent figure in Illinois. When he later stopped in **Springfield** on a celebratory tour, the airfield was named in his honor.

In 1928 Amelia Earhart, a graduate of Chicago's **Hyde Park High School**, became the first woman to fly the Atlantic. The Chicago *Tribune* quickly dubbed her "Lady Lindy." Interest in aviation grew exponentially and by 1928 there were 58 landing fields scattered throughout the State of Illinois.

The Chicago Municipal Airport opened in 1927 and it consisted of 640 acres – one square mile. Robertson Aircraft of St. Louis, the company that hired Lindbergh, began flying passengers to Chicago in 1927. By 1928

Chicago's National Air Transport was **the nation's largest carrier**.

By the end of the decade it was obvious that a revolution in transportation had occurred. The fast-rising trucking industry was beginning to hurt the railroads. Many families now owned automobiles and a whole new way of life was ushered in. Passenger travel via the airline industry was still in its infancy but instead of taking three days to cross the country by train, the distance could now be traveled in about twelve hours.

A REVOLUTION IN MORALS

There is little doubt that the early years of the post-war decade saw a first class revolt against manners and morals of the old order. The old Victorian code might be summed up in the following manner: Women were the guardians of morality; they were made of sterner stuff than the men and were expected to draw the line. Young women were to remain chaste and seek a romantic love match that would lead them down the aisle into the sanctity of marriage. When a man pursued a woman it was customary that a large amount of chaperonage would be involved, at least until the engagement. And no respectable woman was seen drinking or smoking in public.

Victorian dresses nearly dragged the floor at one end and climbed high up the neck at the other end. Femininity was displayed through shapely figures achieved by tight-laced corsets and petticoats.

All of this began to change after World War I ended. Much of it had to do with the growing independence of women. The draft created a shortage of male workers and women stepped into the breach to take their place. As wage earners they found a new freedom that they had never before experienced and they were loathe to give it up.

Women won the right to vote in 1920, sort of a reward for being such good sports by working in factories and helping the war effort. This gave them a certain equality with men, and it was a heady experience. Women now began to push the envelope in other social areas such as dress, behavior, and aggressiveness. What was good for the goose was good for the gander.

Women began to go to college in ever-increasing numbers and began to enter professions that long had been dominated by men.

Something generally underestimated is the effect of new inventions and appliances that gave women more free time and released them from the drudgeries of housekeeping. Women bought quilts instead of making them. They canned less and bought more foodstuffs in tins and boxes. Instead of beating rugs they vacuumed them. Instead of cutting cloth from patterns to make dresses, women began to rely more on store bought clothes. Electric washing machines replaced the tub and scrub board.

With men going off to war, not knowing if they would ever return, a spirit of "eat, drink and be merry" accompanied the departure of the soldiers. This led to an epidemic of hasty marriages and unconventional liaisons. There was a natural breakdown of traditional restraints and taboos.

Women were influenced by what they read and books and magazines that became more affordable and popular than ever. Freud became wildly popular, and he advanced radical new ideas about sex and how it was a universal driving force. Anthropologists advanced the thesis that moral codes had no universal validity and were often based on taboos and superstitions. The Freudian gospel taught that the first requirement of mental health was to have an uninhibited sex life – obey your libido.

Other forces which undermined the old order were speak-easies that catered to both men and women, the automobile which allowed young people to get away from the prying eyes of their elders, confession and sex magazines, more daring song lyrics, and movies that showed other adults kicking up their heels and breaking the old bonds of restraint.

Out went the Victorian manner of dress; the shocking knee-length skirt replaced it. The boyishly slender figure became the aim of every woman as the corset was discarded. Silk and rayon replaced cotton. Not content with merely having skimpy outfits, women sought, too, the freedom of bobbed hair. Many of the women disdained the beauty salons and began patronizing male barber shops.

Garter bootleg flask

Another act of female defiance was the rapid switch to smoking cigarettes. Despite the preachings against smoking from evangelical hinterlands, women began to freely smoke in restaurants, club cars, in theater lobbies, at the office and even the dinner table. From the beginning of the decade to the end the total production of tobacco more than doubled to meet the new demand.

POPULAR MAGAZINES OF THE TWENTIES

The Nation
Saturday Evening Post
Harper's
Scribner's
The New Republic
True-Story
Police Gazette
Ladies' Home Journal
Time
Pictorial Review
Literary Digest
Reader's Digest
American Mercury
New Yorker
American Magazine
Vanity Fair
Collier's
Weekly
The Dial
McCall's
Magazine
The Forum
Life
Variety
Vogue
McClure's
True
Confessions
National
Geographic
Good
Housekeeping
Atlantic Monthly
Popular Mechanics
Saturday Review of Literature
Red Book
Country Life

Judge Thayer of the Sacco/Vanzetti case

THE RED SCARE IN ILLINOIS

The early years of the 1920s saw a nation and a state that overreacted to the threat of internal subversion of democracy posed by foreign radicals as a result of Lenin and the Bolsheviks coming to power in Russia. Illinois was at the forefront of radicalism. Eugene Debs helped found the Socialist Party at Chicago before the turn of the century and Big Bill Haywood helped form the IWW – Industrial Workers of the World - at Chicago in 1905.

There were still lingering memories of the violence that occurred at the Haymarket Square bombing and the Pullman strike, both in Chicago. Most citizens didn't bother to make distinctions between one leftist group and another. It was easy to transfer the anti-German hatred spawned by World War I to a newly perceived threat.

The American Legion patriotic group was organized in the spring of 1919 and the first state convention of these veterans was held in **Peoria** on October 17-18, 1919. Their avowed intention was to "**kill radicalism by spreading Americanism**." The veterans launched into a massive campaign of educating the public through publication of pamphlets, historical pageants, lectures, and newspaper editorials.

Another group that harped on foreign radicals and "un-Americanism" was the newly revived Ku Klux Klan. Klan literature said they stood for "the Christian religion, pure womanhood, just law and liberty, upholding the Constitution, free public schools, free speech, free press, and law and order." Often overlooked was their willingness to use violence against Jews, Blacks and Catholics. The Klan was able to organize 287 klaverns throughout the state and managed to elect mayors in **Paris** and **Decatur**.

The Imperial Wizard spoke at a huge rally at the Armory Building at the University of Illinois at **Urbana**. Chicago had twenty klaverns with 100,000 members and the outlying suburbs claimed another 100,000 members.

There was strong Klan influence at the precinct level in **East St. Louis**. The Klan even staged a **huge rally at Monks Mound** on Route 40, several miles outside the city limits. The East St. Louis Klan was infiltrated by a Catholic who then published the names of businessmen who belonged to the group. The threat of economic boycott was stifling. East St. Louis had large numbers of Catholics in political circles and on the police force, and this was further discouragement to the Klan in that town.

Protestant churches in Illinois sometimes found themselves in league with the Klan – especially Baptist, Nazarene, and Methodist denominations in the lower one-third of the state known as **Egypt**. Members of the Klan would sometimes march into a church in the middle of a service and hand the minister a large donation along with a note giving Klan support to the congregation's efforts. One thing that united conservative Protestant churches with the

Klan was support for law and order and support for enforcement of Prohibition laws.

One of the radical leaders in Illinois was Earl Browder, editor of the *Labor Herald*. Browder was jailed on several occasions and ran for president on the Communist ticket numerous times.

Mitchell Palmer, President Wilson's Attorney General, was busy rounding up alien suspects and deporting them back to Russia. One ship that was used to transport them, the *Buford*, was nicknamed the *Soviet Ark*. Politicians jumped on the bandwagon of national hysteria and adopted the slogan **S. O. S. – ship or shoot**.

Not to be outdone, Illinois authorities made similar raids against radical activists. Sixteen such radicals were arrested in **Chicago** and placed on trial in 1920 for violating the Illinois sedition law. The great Clarence Darrow defended them, but they were found guilty. Seven were sent to **Joliet** prison and nine were incarcerated for a shorter time in the Cook County jail. Governor Len Small eventually pardoned them because he believed that the Sedition Act was passed to stifle dissent rather than to prevent subversion. A majority of the newly created American Legion posts passed resolutions condemning Small's actions.

The most outrageous and deadly act carried out by the subversives was the Wall Street Bombing in September of 1920. The stock market, at the junction of Broad and Wall streets, was symbolic of democracy and capitalism. The banking firm of J.P. Morgan was across the street.

Shortly before noon there was a terrific explosion that **killed thirty people outright** and wounded hundreds of others. Someone or some group had fashioned a bomb consisting of TNT that was brought to the scene by a horse drawn wagon. After years of intense investigation and interrogation of known radicals, no one was ever charged with the awful crime.

The scare lost its steam as citizens began to realize the socialists, communists and anarchists constituted only about one percent of the population and were a very limited threat to democracy.

THE 1925 SCOPES MONKEY TRIAL

For those who took sides in the Scopes trial, and nearly everyone did, it must have been similar to the current culture war that is going on today between traditionalists and modernists, red states v. blue states.

Protestant churches, which numbered in their membership five out of every eight adults in the U.S., had split into two warring camps – traditionalists (conservatives) and modernists (liberals). Traditionalists believed that everything in the Bible was true, and it was true because it was the word of God. Modernists began shifting away from terms like *hell*, *sin*, and the *devil*, and began to focus on God's love instead. They believed that stories about Jonah and the whale and Adam and Eve were fables.

The controversy started when the Tennessee legislature, dominated by Fundamentalists, enacted a law making it illegal to teach Darwinism – that man was descended from a lower order of primates.

In Dayton, Tennessee, two men sipping phosphates in a drugstore hatched a plot to challenge the law against evolution – George Rappelyea and John Scopes. Scopes was a twenty-four year old high school biology teacher. He was promptly arrested for his teachings creating a national *cause celebre*.

Clarence Darrow

The great Chicago lawyer, Clarence Darrow volunteered his services for the ACLU defense. The prosecution secured the services of three-time Democratic presidential candidate, William Jennings Bryan. Bryan was born and reared in **Salem**, Illinois, and was a graduate of Illinois College in **Jacksonville**. The trial attracted hundreds of journalists, was broadcast by the Chicago *Tribune* station WGN, and was put on film by several motion picture cameras. A primate from Coney Island named Zip was brought in as a defense exhibit to bolster the theory of the "missing link."

It was a bitter trial. Bryan accused Darrow of using the case to "slur the Bible," and Darrow called Bryan a "fool" for believing in such "stories" as Adam and Eve and Jonah and the whale.

John T. Scopes

Clarence Darrow mostly criticized the Old Testament and queried William Jennings Bryan about the Tower of Babel, the exact date of the Flood, and how Cain obtained his wife. Bryan said he believed that the world was created in 4004 B.C. and that the great Flood in Noah's time occurred on about 2348 B.C. Bryan affirmed his belief that the Tower of Babel was responsible for the world's languages and said that he believed in the biblical miracles about the parting of the Red Sea by Moses, the sun standing still for Joshua, a big fish swallowing Jonah, and Daniel surviving in the lion's den. Bryan stated that he didn't know where Cain's wife came from and left that thorny question to be pondered by agnostics.

Darrow declared that his purpose was to prevent ignoramuses from controlling the educational system in America. Bryan, his veins popping and his face purple, shook his fist at Darrow and called him "the greatest atheist and agnostic in the United States."

Most people forget that **Bryan won the case**. The question was even recently missed by a contestant on *Jeopardy*. Scopes was found guilty and fined one hundred dollars. His fine was paid by the liberal *Baltimore Sun*. The U.S. Supreme Court eventually upheld the constitutionality of the Tennessee law.

Sadly, William Jennings Bryan, The Great Commoner, **died a week after the trial was finished**.

Someone once said that truth is stranger than fiction. It is a little known fact that John Scopes and Bryan previously knew each other. John Scopes, like Bryan, grew up in **Salem** and attended the University of Illinois while Bryan attended Illinois College in **Jacksonville**. After the trial, Scopes gave up teaching and attended the **University of Chicago** and received a degree in geology. He went on to work mostly for oil companies, dying of a stroke at age 70.

THE DEPRESSION IN SOUTHERN ILLINOIS

Robert Hastings eloquently described his childhood experiences and life in Southern Illinois coal mines in the 1920s and during the Depression. The following excerpts are from his 1972 book, *A Nickel's Worth of Skim Milk*, courtesy of the Southern Illinois University Press.

The closing of the West Side mine, which was about twelve miles north {of **Marion**} at **West Frankfort**, was not unexpected. The mine had been working only a day or two a week, and wages had been paid on a percentage basis. So on the final payday, when the mine closed, many employees were bitter, since they got absolutely nothing for their last two weeks of work. Some said the owners had planned all along to cheat the miners out of their last pay. Others felt the company had operated the mine as long as it

could, sharing with the miners what little profit there was.

We weathered the storm because of Dad's willingness to take any job and Mom's ability to stretch every available dollar. My diary shows that Dad sold iron cords door to door, picked peaches, raised sweet potato slips, hung wallpaper, painted Don Albright's house for $5, picked up a day or two's work at the strip mines, guarded the fence at

the county fair, cut hair for boys in the neighborhood, and worked intermittently on WPA projects.

John L. Lewis of the United Mine Workers

With no dependable income, we cut back on everything possible. We stopped the evening paper, turned off the city water and reverted to using our well, sold our four door Model-T touring car with the snap-on side curtains and isinglass. Instead of toothpaste we used baking powder; we stopped buying toilet paper and used the Sears catalog.

Like many Southern Illinois men, Dad knew little about any trade except mining. On September 28, 1916, he had been issued Illinois Miner's Certificate 17229 in Book 172 after two years' experience and a written exam. The certificate says he was thirty-five years old, five feet ten-and-a-half inches tall, weighing 135 pounds, and having black hair and gray eyes.

Dad had no ambition to have any of his three sons follow him into the mines. There were few safety regulations. Dad wore a carbide lamp fastened to his mine cap, and its open flame was a constant invitation to a gas explosion.

My brother LaVerne did try it for two or three days. On his first day in the pits the hoisting engineer "dropped the cage," a traditional initiation for a new miner.

Dad carried a three-tiered aluminum dinner bucket. The bottom compartment held drinking water, the middle section sandwiches and fruit, and the top part pie or cake. When miners "threw out their water" it meant they emptied their buckets of drinking water and were ready to go home.

Southern Illinois mines reached out with their black, grimy hands for three of our relatives. Dial Hastings, Dad's brother, died in a powder explosion at the Scranton Mine. Marshall Jack, the first husband of Mom's sister, died in a mine. And Archie Rodd, who married Dial's daughter, Elva, was crushed to death in a slope mine near **Harrisburg**.

Anyone who grew up in Southern Illinois in the 1920s and '30s remembers the old shaft mines, most of which have long since given way to giant shovels that strip dirt from over the coal seams. There was Slogo and New Virginia and Peabody 3, 11, and 18. And Old Gent, Scranton, West Side, Orient 1 and 2, Stiritz, Paulton, Sloppy Hollow and White Ash. And Bell & Zoller 4, Lake Creek 1 and 4, Old Wasson, and Old Ben 8, 9, and 15.

Coal mining had spectacular growth in Williamson, Saline, and Franklin counties between 1900 and 1925. At their peak, a hundred mines were hoisting coal every day in these three counties; their mine payroll reached $40 million in 1926. Day after day, in 1926, the big New Orient Mine in Franklin County **broke the world's record for tonnage hoisted in an eight-hour shift**.

Most of the residents in these counties were descended from settlers who came between 1870 and 1910 from the

West Kentucky hills. In speech and folkways the area was culturally homogeneous with the western Appalachians and distinctly unlike central and northern Illinois.

A unique feature of the Depression in Williamson County was the emergence of about 150 small, makeshift "gopher holes," where farmers and unemployed miners dug shallow-vein coal for local sale. They would sink a slope about fifty feet deep and mine the poor grade of coal. Most loading was done by hand. Many had no storage space at the tipple, and would hoist coal only when someone was waiting to buy a load.

Geologists estimate that 135 to 200 billion tons of coal still underlie two-thirds of Illinois – enough coal to last more than a thousand years at the present rate of consumption. Illinois has one of the largest reserves in the world, greater than that of Pennsylvania or any other state east of the Mississippi, and greater than those of most countries in the world.

BLACK DIAMONDS IN ILLINOIS SOIL

Between 1833 and 1925 over one and a half billion tons of coal were removed in Illinois, yet the total amount was estimated as only one percent of our coal. With 15 distinct bituminous coal seams, only the state of Pennsylvania has produced more. By 1920 Illinois slipped to third place behind West Virginia. During the 1920s more than half of

Union organizer Mother Mary Jones on a deck of playing cards

the Illinois counties mined coal. About 98 new mines opened in Illinois between 1912 and 1930. During the 1920s the leading counties in coal production were **Franklin, Williamson, Macoupin, Sangamon, Saline and St. Clair.** Generally speaking, the quality of Southern Illinois coal was better than that mined in the northern part of the state.

Mules were used for many years to haul coal in Illinois mines but by the 1920s most had been replaced by electric locomotives. Sparks from these electric motors were dangerous and sometimes they caused explosions, as did the fumes from gas-powered locomotives. Mules were stabled underground and most never saw the light of day.

McCoupin County Courthouse at **Carlinville** in the heart of Illinois coal country – Dan Oberle Collection

Many of them went blind from being underground for so long.

Coal dust was often explosive and it needed to be sprinkled down with water at regular intervals.

By the 1920s the miner with the pickaxe was replaced by cutting machines in most Illinois mines.

Back in the old days when we threw a shovel of coal into the furnace, few of us realized that we were handling a product that had its origins billions of years ago. This was when the surface of the planet was mainly covered with water and swampland. The climate and conditions were perfect for the growth of carboniferous plants – giant ferns, trees and shrubs. The air buzzed with mammoth insects of infinite variety, while gargantuan beasts (dinosaurs) and reptiles inhabited the waters and land.

In the mines of France there have been found in the strata of coal and rock the fossils of many of these species in a splendid state of preservation. These fossils included flies, grasshoppers, roaches, spiders, locusts, and dragonflies – some of which measured nearly two feet from wing tip to wing tip.

It has been estimated that the original amount of coal deposits in the United States exceeded three trillion tons. Of this amount, the original coal deposits in Illinois alone were placed at 18 billion tons. Illinois ranks second only to Pennsylvania in that respect. The first discovery of coal in the U.S. was made in the latter part of the 17th century by explorer Father Hennepin at **Ottawa**, Illinois. In our state the coal beds were formed when the inland sea receded and Illinois became a great marsh or swamp with luxuriant plant growth. Peat beds were formed year after year as these plants formed layer after layer. (Peat is an early stage of coal formation.) There was relatively little earth disturbance, so most of our coal is found in beds that are fairly level.

Coal was discovered in an unusual manner on the American Bottom around 1811 by a group of Trappist Monks living on Cahokia Mound, near **Collinsville**. They noticed that in some way a tree near the bluffs took fire, and even its roots burned. The roots kept burning until it was found that the roots reached into a seam of coal, and the coal was on fire.

From about 1850 to 1950 about a third of all coal produced by the state was used by the railroads. And for years about half the coal produced has been consumed by the Chicago district.

What many people don't realize is that most seams of coal are only about two and a half to fourteen feet thick. In the early days of mining, for every ton of coal mined there was about one and a half ton of coal wasted or left in the mines as supporting pillars. Modern methods of mining and improved equipment have greatly reduced this percentage.

There are three methods for mining coal in Illinois: the drift, the strip and the shaft. Where the coal bed outcrops on a hillside or a ravine the drift or slope method is used. A drift mine differs slightly from a slope mine in that the former follows the seam in on a level, while the slope mine is driven downward at an angle from the surface to reach a vein of coal that does not outcrop.

One of the greatest obstacles to mining deep shaft coal is

Photograph of "Mother" Mary Jones

the great amount of water that collects in a mine that has to be continually pumped out. In Illinois alone, more than a billion gallons of water are pumped out of the bituminous mines annually. A general average figures about fifteen tons of water pumped out for every ton of coal mined.

Another problem faced by miners was the danger of the roof of a mine collapsing. Timbers were used to shore things up, but many mines chose to spray the underside of a roof with a cement mortar called "gunite." It was sprayed on one to three inches thick with a "gun."

Mines that were about 300 or 400 ft. deep had temperatures that hovered around 60 degrees. It was necessary to create numerous air passages in mines to provide adequate ventilation to insure the dilution of poisonous and explosive gases generated by the coal, mine water and explosives. It was Illinois miners who first began the practice of taking canaries down into the mines.

When the canaries stopped singing due to asphyxiation, the miners knew it was time to get out.

It was common in area mines to use the room and pillar method of mining. The greater the depth of the mine, the closer the natural pillars were spaced. It was not uncommon for the tremendous weight on the pillars to push down on the clay floor causing the floor to heave, a condition known as a "squeeze." If the floor was hard, the pressure on the pillars sometimes caused them to collapse,

---

Just Scabs: by Mary Libby, 1932

Old **Taylorville** has lots of scabs
    And **Tovey** just a few,
But it keeps them busy picking scabs,
    They have nothing else to do.

There was once a grand old union,
    But it turned to a dirty scab,
    And so the wise men left it,
    And the scabs were left to scab.

The man who wears the name of scab,
    Who works behind a gun,
Is the foulest, slimy, creeping thing,
    That crawls beneath the sun.

    Old scabs, young scabs,
You can smell them in the air,
    At Taylorville and Tovey,
You can find them everywhere.

    Oh, Taylorville and Tovey,
It's a time to close your door,
'Till every louse kills every scab,
And be clean, free men once more.

---

closing the mine.

Every year the shafts of the mines must be sunk deeper and deeper, as the more accessible veins of coal are worked and exhausted. Pumps for the work cost thousands of dollars each, so there is an enormous investment in this equipment alone. A large force of men, besides those actually employed in mining coal, must always be available to keep mine machinery in repair, as mining operations cannot be interfered with, except in cases of great emergency. Since the mining is done during the day, repairs and maintenance are usually carried out at nights and on Sunday. The water from the mines has such high mineral content that it cannot be used in the boilers at the collieries.

Strip mining, also called open-pit mining, is possible when the seam of coal is an exposed outcrop or close to the surface. The loosened cover or "spoil" can be thrown aside, and large power shovels can be used to load the coal on trucks or railroad cars. When there is no outcrop, the work must be started by digging a 70 ft. wide ditch next to the seam. This ditch is called a box cut. Surface coal usually has lower sulfur content because of oxidation. In the early years strip mining left ugly scars on the land with a series of furrows with topsoil mixed with subsoil. The state legislature enacted laws requiring mine companies to restore and reforest the land after the coal has been extracted.

Consumption of coal in America reached a peak around 1918 with over 700,000 men employed.

1920 drift coal mine at **Makanda** in Jackson County

One of the most famous mine owners back then was Joseph Leiter of Chicago whose father Levi Zeigler Leiter was an associate of Marshall Field. Leiter opened a mine at **Zeigler** in Franklin County. Leiter was one of those robber baron-types who once tried to corner the wheat market, a move that cost his father nearly ten million dollars. Leiter and his father bought 7,500 acres of land in Franklin County at a time when there were no coal mines in the area. As soon as the mine opened it was struck by the United Mine Workers, an action that led to bloodshed. There were a number of disasters in the Zeigler mines, mostly due to the neglect by the Leiters of safety precautions and regulations. Yet production remained high and the only mine that outproduced it in the 1920s was the Superior Mine #3 at **Gillespie**.

Peabody Coal opened a number of Illinois mines in the 1920s. By 1930 they had 23 mines in **Sangamon, Christian, Franklin, Saline, Vermilion and Madison counties**.

Another big operator in the coal business was Old Ben Coal Company who owned eight mines by 1930 and whose big producer was mine #8 at **West Frankfort**.

Back in 1915 a large ocean liner, in making a record trip across the Atlantic, used 4,725 tons of coal, enough to keep 945 families in fuel for an entire year. In a single year, one great steamship company paid seven million dollars for the coal necessary to operate its fleet of steamships, or fifty percent more than it paid for provisions for crews and passengers.

Coal first came to the **East St. Louis** area from a mine in the bluffs near a small village named Pittsburg (near present-day Routes 157 and 15). The coal was first hauled by mules and horses along tracks with wooden rails. Pilings had to be driven in **Pittsburg Lake** (Grand Marais)

so that a wooden bridge could be constructed across the body of water. East St. Louis was in a rudimentary stage of development at that time (around 1832), and the coal was delivered to the riverfront. From there it was loaded on Samuel Wiggins' ferryboats and transported across the Mississippi to the city of St. Louis. The railroad fared poorly in its early years because the company overestimated the demand for coal by St. Louis. Wood was still the preferred fuel, even in steam locomotives that came along. But demand for coal slowly increased, and by the 1860s the nine-mile long railroad was the **richest dollar-per-mile railroad in the nation**. By 1875 coal could be delivered to any part of East St. Louis on a railroad track for six cents a bushel. Manufacturers could buy in bulk at $1.50 a ton.

Coal is not only useful as a household fuel, and in manufacturing, but it also has a number of useful by-products. Here is what one-ton of bituminous (soft) southern Illinois coal will yield: 1500 pounds of coke; 20 gallons of ammonia water; 140 pounds of coal tar. Coal tar, by distillation, will yield 70 pounds of pitch, 17 pounds of creosote; 14 pounds of heavy oils, 9.5 pounds of naphtha yellow, 6.3 pounds of naphthalene, 4.75 pounds naphthol, 2.25 pounds alizarin, 2.4 pounds solvent naphtha, 1.5 pounds phenol, 1.2 pounds aurine, 1.1 pounds anthracite and 0.9 pounds toluene. Coal is also used in the production of perfume, plastics and dyes.

From toluene is obtained the substance known as saccharine, produced by the Monsanto plant near **Cahokia** and another in St. Louis. Saccharine is 230 times sweeter than sugar. Saccharine was long used for medicinal purposes and in the manufacture of confections.

Southern Illinois coal has a high sulfur content which is a

Undercutting a coal seam in Madison County 1921

pollutant. Around 1951 St. Louis passed an ordinance banning the use of soft coal and required the use of anthracite coal from places such as Pennsylvania. Other cities followed suit, delivering a crushing blow to the local coal industry.

Back then, there was a general formula used in estimating the amount of coal a family would need to get through a typical southern Illinois winter. Experts generally figured one ton per room per season, plus an extra half-ton. So, on this basis, a typical five-room house would ordinarily require almost six tons of coal. Coal was delivered by truck and emptied into the coal bin of the house, located in the basement. A metal door, usually located in the block foundation, was for gaining access. By the early-to-mid 1950s, many homes converted to a stoker. This was a machine with a hopper that was attached to the furnace. Instead of using lump coal, stoker coal was pellet sized and was automatically fed to the furnace by a motor-operated worm screw at the bottom of its hopper. Instead of an ash residue, stoker coal produced "clinkers" which were very abrasive to the hands. By the late 1950s, many homes converted again, this time to natural gas. Old coal furnaces were often retrofitted with gas burners.

Most of the towns along the bluffs near **East St. Louis**, **Granite City** and **Alton**, owed their prosperity to the coal mines which served industries in those towns along the riverfront. The **Glen Carbon** area was heavily mined, and the current subterranean landscape is honeycombed with mine shafts and connecting tunnels. Many homeowners carry mine subsidence insurance as an addendum to their homeowner's policy for protection. There was an elementary school in **Collinsville** and a state police station in **Maryville** that had to be abandoned due to subsidence problems.

Most people cannot imagine the huge quantities of coal that are used to produce electricity. Commonwealth Edison had a plant in **Kincaid** in 1969 that used a conveyor belt to take coal to generators for Chicago electricity. The consumption at this plant back then was four million tons a year. That is the equivalent of more than two train loads a day with each train pulling 100 cars containing 50 tons of coal each. The plant has two 500-foot high stacks that are equipped with air-pollution abaters, including electrostatic precipitators that cost $6 million to install. Lake Kincaid, covering four square miles and averaging about 13 feet deep, built by damming a creek, supplies water to the steam condensers.

The huge Cahokia Power Plant at **East St. Louis**, with its set of six huge smokestacks, consumed an almost equal amount of coal for the industrial suburbs across the river from St. Louis in its 1950s heyday.

The General Electric Corporation is currently running television ads that claim a new process has been devised that makes it cost efficient to burn Illinois coal and scrub the emissions. For decades most power plants have had to import low sulfur coal from Montana.

The artificial gas industry in East St. Louis dates back to 1865 when the East St. Louis Gas and Coke Company was chartered by the state. In 1907 the company was consolidated with **Belleville** Gas and Electric to form the St. Clair County Gas and Electric Company. By 1950 Illinois Power and Light Company had their gas plant at 2060 Lynch, across from Mepham/C.K. Williams Paint Company. They had a regulating station at 627 North 89th Street. Their offices were at 417 East Missouri Avenue. Union Electric, which generated electricity from burning coal at the Cahokia Power Plant, had their offices in East St. Louis at #7 Collinsville Avenue, next to the Southern Illinois Bank. They built a new office at 5th and Broadway in 1957. For the most part, Illinois Power supplied the city with gas, and Union Electric took care of its electric needs.

In both cases, southern Illinois coal was the source of the fuel that was used.

C.H. Quackenbush says that the most common gas used in southern Illinois was coal gas. This was manufactured by placing coal in a superheated clay retort, which was then closed to exclude air. The heated retort freed the volatile or gaseous matter from the coal. These gases were then carried through a series of pipes and appliances which condensed, washed and scrubbed the crude gas, and by mechanical and chemical means removed the impurities from the product and made it ready for the 400 uses which gas is applicable.

A second method of making gas from coal was known as the carbureted method. The gas is manufactured by passing steam through a bed of coal or coke in an incandescent

Mississippi coal barges (Neal Strebel of **Collinsville**)

state. The action of the hot fire on the steam passing through it decomposed the steam into hydrogen and oxygen. These gases were united with carbon gases from the fuel bed to create water gas. The mixture in that state had little illuminating value, so it was then passed to another machine where it was mixed with an oil vapor. This whole mixture was then fixed into a permanent gas by contact with superheated fire brick. It was then scrubbed and cleaned in a similar manner as the coal gas. Water gas was often used to enrich coal gas, thereby giving it greater illuminating value.

The distribution of gas from the storage holder was carried on through a system of about sixty miles of cast iron

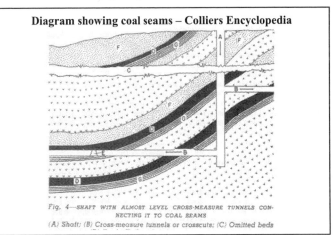
Diagram showing coal seams – Colliers Encyclopedia

Fig. 4—SHAFT WITH ALMOST LEVEL CROSS-MEASURE TUNNELS CONNECTING IT TO COAL SEAMS
(A) Shaft; (B) Cross-measure tunnels or crosscuts; (C) Omitted beds

pipe of diameter varying from four to sixteen inches. The

flow of gas through mains is similar to water flowing through pipes, but the pressure is much less, being about 1/9 of a pound per square inch. Wrought iron pipes were laid from the main to the consumer's basement at no charge. Contrary to public opinion, gas meters, which measure the amount of use, are very accurate. They cannot register unless gas at that time is passing through it.

Coal mining ranked number one when it came to dangerous occupations in Illinois. During the first three decades of the twentieth century, 5,337 men lost their lives in mining accidents. Part of the problem was due to miners being paid by their tonnage output. This caused miners to work at a faster pace with less regard for safety than otherwise might have been the case. The 1910 Cherry Mine disaster in Bureau County was caused by taking hay into the mine to feed the mules that pulled the coal cars. The hay was parked near an open flame that ignited the hay. Mules were eventually replaced by small electric locomotives, but electrical sparks from these devices frequently caused explosions. Nearly twenty percent of fatalities were caused by workers being run over by the locomotive or from being hit by a mine car. Improper use of mine supports caused numerous cave-ins and countless deaths. About ten percent of all mine accidents were related to blasting powder that was used as part of the operations. Some explosions occurred when miners carelessly tried to open a keg of powder with their pickaxe.

Safety was improved mostly through legislation, not because the mine owners took the initiative. Things improved greatly in 1909 when the legislature authorized the establishment of a Department of Mining Engineering at the University of Illinois.

Illinois produced some notable leaders in the coal industry including the irrepressible **"Mother" Mary Jones** who is buried in **Mt. Olive** along Route 66. Another was **John Mitchell**, but Mother Jones didn't think much of him. She said: "John Mitchell left to his heirs a fortune, and his political friends are using the labor movement to erect a monument to his memory, to a name that should be forgotten."

WOMEN IN 1920s NOVELS

During this rambunctious era women's lives were touched and altered by technology, popular culture, political events, and changes in national social patterns. While many writers tended to have their female characters behave boldly in thought and in deed, probably more so than in actual life, an examination of the literature of this era can provide interesting insight.

This new age increasingly saw women enter the workplace, obtain a college education, assert their right to vote and become involved in politics, and rid themselves of dullard husbands.

It also saw a revolution in women's morals as they now cast off Victorian restraints by bobbing their hair, smoking, drinking, swearing, dancing daring dances, and indiscriminately kissing a wide number of handsome young men.

Many of these tales appeared as short stories by writers such as **Kathleen Norris** or Temple Bailey in Good Housekeeping or Ladies' Home Journal. It is probably safe to assume that women who bought these books and magazines read them because their heroines were ones that they admired or with whom they could empathize.

Women readers identified with the modern flappers, yet they were still bound by the restraints of tradition. The cult of domesticity and traditional gender roles still had mass appeal and were still reflected in the stories of this decade.

The "Y" chromosome set in F. Scott Fitzgerald's novels (such as *The Great Gatsby*) demonstrated that women were beginning to assert themselves as sexual beings, with sexual needs that rivaled those of the men. In E.M. Hull's *The Sheik*, it became obvious that women were the equals of men – at least in the bedroom. Sensual protagonist Diana

Mayo thrilled female readers two years in a row on the best-seller chart.

Martha Ostenso gave readers yet another sensual heroine in *Wild Geese*. It was this period that first saw passionate women like Judith Gare burying their nails into their lover's flesh and biting soft skin with their teeth.

Perhaps the archetypal flapper existed in Anita Loos' best seller, *Gentlemen Prefer Blondes*. The heroine Lorelei is an energetic gold digger in the classic sense, trading her charms for expensive gifts. According to legend, Loos was motivated to write the story because H.L. Mencken was said to prefer witless blondes to brunettes. When Lorelei meets the wealthy scion of a wealthy family with rich tradition, she shrewdly transforms into a traditional woman and settles down to a conventional life.

Many of **Temple Bailey's** young women, despite their modernity, spend most of their time passively waiting and filling their hope chest, in the expectation of marriage to the right man.

Kathleen Norris wrote over eighty novels in her long career. Her heroines in the 1920s had much of the flavor of the flappers, but it was mostly superficial. Her women took on the postwar changes in appearance and behavior, but it was in moderation. This uncanny mix of modern with tradition probably helps explain why Norris remained popular for so long.

Writer **Dorothy Canfield** in *The Home-Maker* challenges traditional roles assigned to men and women in the marriage contract. She suggested that husband and wife should share in the housework chores and child rearing.

While her character Evangeline Knapp convinces herself that women's work is the noblest of professions, she nevertheless hates the drudgery of scrubbing floors, beating rugs, and washing dishes. So much of her energy is expended on housework that she has little left to give to her husband and children.

Writers did not neglect women who lived in rural areas. **Edna Ferber**, **Willa Cather** (her settings were in Nebraska), Bess Streeter Aldrich and Rose Lane penned works that focused on the hardships endured by women struggling with their husbands to transform the wilderness into productive farmland. Edna Ferber's farm novel, *So Big* won the Pulitzer Prize for 1925. Interestingly, the 1920s and '30s are the only era in our history where farm novels prospered in large numbers.

Most followed a set formula. Before any farm family could declare their efforts at homesteading a success, they had to survive blizzards, droughts, prairie fires, attacks from cougars or bears, and an occasional raid by marauding Indians. It was also common for many of these heroines to inherit a farm, left to them by a drunken father or a husband who was beaten down in the difficult effort to subdue the soil. These plucky women then, through their own abilities, manage to turn a failed farm into a successful one.

These novels also perpetuated the myth that farmers constituted the backbone of the country and that tillers were the embodiment of rugged individualism, grit, determination, and perseverance – characteristics that any red-blooded American needed to succeed in this country.

Another recurring theme in these earth sagas is the hard work and sacrifice by pioneer women so that their children and grandchildren would have better lives. Urban readers of these novels surely must have looked at the hardships endured by these families and reflected with thankfulness on their own comparative wealth.

The female heroes in these books are generally women of strong character, sometimes sustaining and reassuring their doubting husbands who are on the verge of giving up the struggle against nature.

Another interesting observation about novels of the 1920s is that most of the heroines possessed a natural beauty and disdained the use of rouge sticks, powder, lipstick, and other cosmetics in an effort to manufacture natural beauty. Somehow readers must have concluded the opposite for the use of beauty products and beauty parlors more than doubled during the decade. Women apparently believed that if they were going to look as good as the women in the novels, nature was going to need assistance.

Yet another common thread among these literary heroines is the notion of self-sacrifice – woman concerned about the welfare and happiness of others more than themselves. In one **Fanny Hurst** story, the heroine gives up her son, whom she has borne out of wedlock, to a wealthy Chicago family that can afford to send him to the finest schools. This simply underscores a recurring theme among a majority of these fictional characters who exist in the milieu of this period – women, by their very nature, are more unselfish than men. And perhaps they are.

For an in-depth look at this topic, see Patricia Raub's *Yesterday's Stories*, 1994; *The Damned And The Beautiful* by Paula Fauss, 1977.

DANCE MARATHONS

Dance marathons had pretty well disappeared from the American scene by the time I was born in September of 1939, but as a lad of about eleven my mother took me to a walkathon, one of its offshoots. Roller Derbies, so popular in the Forties and Fifties, were another offshoot. The walkathon event was held in St. Louis on fairgrounds, somewhere on South Broadway. We took a bus from **East St. Louis**, where we lived, and then transferred to another bus in downtown St. Louis. In all, it was only about a forty-minute trip. Admission was 75 cents for adults and 25 cents for children.

My Aunt Marie,

Pola Negri in *Woman of the World* - 1925

who lived in St. Louis, was one of those entered in the contest. At a walkathon couples walked around a track in a contest of endurance. It was a fun event for a kid because of the carnival atmosphere and a plethora of side attractions. A man named "Butterball" stripped down to a pair of swim trunks and was encased in ice to see how long he could endure. There was a nurse close by to monitor his health, and he had a small flag to wave as a signal that he was ready to quit.

My older sister (Jackie) teamed with our cousin Barbara Jean to enter an amateur singing contest. They chose *It Had To Be You*. They didn't win. Neither had previous experience on a stage, and they merely did it as a lark.

Walkathon at White City Casino in South Chicago

Almost everyone has heard of dance marathons that were aptly illustrated by the 1969 Jane Fonda movie, *They Shoot Horses, Don't They?* The classic moment comes when a dead tired Fonda asks her marathon partner to shoot her towards the end of an excruciating contest.

Dance marathons began as a craze in the 1920s as a fad for the purpose of breaking a world endurance record. They were often held on dance floors that were cordoned off with a seating area for spectators who rooted for their friends and crowd favorites. The events usually had an emcee, judges, nurses, hawkers of snacks and souvenirs, and, sometimes, special guests. The participants were usually a mix of professionals and amateurs. The big events had bands that played music at night and Victrolas cranked out scratchy music during the day. Some places handed out attendance prizes.

As these events drew larger and larger crowds, with large sums of money taken at the gate, the promoters began rigging and orchestrating the whole thing, much as "professional" wrestling and reality shows are choreographed in our own time to promote interest and drama.

On special occasions professional dancers were brought in to liven things up. **Red Skelton, Anita Day, Frankie Laine and June Havoc** (Hovick) all occasionally worked at marathons. By the way, June Havoc's more famous sister was **Gypsy Rose Lee**. Havoc set the all-time marathon record of 3,600 hours and went on to have limited success in an acting career.

Promoters soon learned to couple the authentic with the staged to hold down criticism from the crowds and participants. Citizens who were hooked on marathons turned to the local radio station for updates on how their favorite couple was performing. In **Winslow**, Illinois, where most townspeople had no radios, the local telephone operator called the **Freeport** Walkathon group twenty miles away and rang customers with news about how Winslow's favorite couple was doing.

Sadly, one promoter in a **Chicago** walkathon was shot to death. He either didn't get permission from the right people, or he didn't want to share gate receipts..

Surprisingly, these marathons generated widespread opposition from varying groups. Movie theaters opposed them simply for the competition for the entertainment dollar that they posed. Policemen grew tired of monitoring large crowds over a 24-hour period that lasted a full week. Finally, there were the moralists, the same Puritans that opposed alcohol. Some blue noses thought that dancing was immoral because it promoted unsupervised physical contact between the sexes. Religious groups said that dancing on Sunday violated local blue laws. Many promoters changed the name and used the euphemism "dance derbies" when critics said that dance marathons were inherently a danger to the health of participants.

In response to criticism and pressure from numerous groups, many city councils passed ordinances banning dance marathons within the incorporated city limits.

Sleep deprivation caused some strange behaviors. One exhausted woman at a marathon held at **Chicago's Coliseum** complained that she saw a roomful of men with guns who were threatening to shoot her. Health officials coined an expression to describe odd behavior such as hers caused by lack of sleep – **marathonitis**.

Dance marathons were merely part of a larger culture of the period where individuals sought fifteen minutes of fame by twirling Yo-Yo's, sitting atop flagpoles, and consuming

Marathon champ, June Havoc with her sister, Gypsy Rose Lee (*New York Post*)

dozens of hardboiled eggs. One Texan won a five hundred dollar bet by spending a week pushing a peanut up Pike's Peak. Numerous people died attempting to go over **Niagara Falls in a barrel.**

Shipwreck Kelly gained national recognition with his flagpole sitting exploits and earned as much as $100 a day. But for some, fame is fleeting. As the craze died out, Kelly returned to obscurity and lived the rest of his days in the Hell's Kitchen area of New York. In 1952 he was found by police, dead on the street, penniless and with few worldly possessions save a few yellowed clippings about his earlier achievements.

When it became obvious that many of the dance marathon record holders were women, people began o question the traditional stereotype about women being the "weaker sex."

Dance Marathon contestants

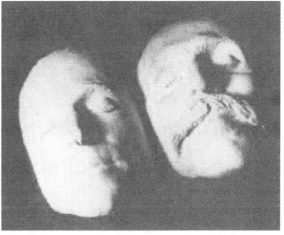

Most contests started out with couples actually doing the fox trot or something that closely resembled dancing. But as the hours wore on, contestants were reduced to a boring spectacle of two people, barely moving their feet, walking around the floor in a dreary fashion.

Rules were quickly adopted. Contestants had to dance 57 minutes out of every hour with a mere three-minute rest period. They had to dance, walk, or raise their heels and toes at least six times every minute. If you fell or if a knee touched the floor, you were disqualified. Ten-minute rest periods were allowed every four hours for food and water intake. Couples were declared to be inseparable. If one dropped out the other was also disqualified. Contestants had to submit to quickie health exams that checked heartbeat and blood pressure.

Highbrows of this era generally looked down on dance marathons and thought they exploited women because promoters and managers were generally men. The marathons appealed mostly to middle and lower middle class women – secretaries, sales clerks, typists, laundry workers, telephone operators, seamstresses, and the like.

For more information see *Fads, Follies And Delusions of the American People* by Paul Sann; *Dance Marathons* by Carol Martin, 1994. Also consult *Business And Religion in the American 1920s* by Rolf Lunden.

THE SACCO AND VANZETTI CASE

Except for the Red Scare and subsequent Palmer raids, there was only one other important thing that split liberals and conservatives in this decade – the Sacco-Vanzetti trial.

In 1920 there was a $15,000 payroll robbery in South Baintree, Massachusetts. A paymaster and his guard were shot to death during the hold up. A few weeks later a couple of Italian radicals were arrested for the crime. Both men were carrying guns at the time of their arrest, and they lied to authorities when initially questioned.

The hard-fought trial lasted six weeks with the dominant themes of patriotism and anarchy being sharply contrasted.

Many have long questioned the defense strategy of politicizing the proceedings. The trial took place before Judge Webster Thayer, and the pair was found guilty (after five hours of jury deliberations) and sentenced to death.

The case also launched the career of J. Edgar Hoover who was head of the General Intelligence Division of the Justice Department. This prosecution was his first major responsibility.

Three men in a Boston office began furiously writing to the world press about the case, saying that the trial had been a sham and that Sacco and Vanzetti were being persecuted simply because they were foreigners. Crowds marched on American embassies in Paris, Rome, and Lisbon. Twenty people were killed when somebody threw a bomb in Paris during a Sacco-Vanzetti demonstration. The controversial case soon became a *cause célèbre* in the United States.

As appeal after appeal dragged on, the case was discussed vehemently here in America by partisans on both sides. Those of the liberal persuasion cited irregularities in the trial, claimed the evidence against the two men was largely circumstantial, and said Judge Thayer was prejudiced in favor of the prosecution. Friendships were interrupted as arguments erupted over key pieces of evidence in the trial.

When Judge Thayer denied a final appeal, public opinion forced the governor to assemble a special committee to review the case. The trio included President Lawrence Lowell of Harvard University, a highly respected man. The committee went to extraordinary lengths and interviewed 102 witnesses. After a couple of weeks the committee came back with a report that said they unanimously believed the men to be guilty.

Sacco and Vanzetti death masks

Harvard became stigmatized in the minds of many liberals as a result of Lowell's actions. "**Not every wop has the switch to his electric chair thrown by the president of Harvard,**" one dissenter lamented.

Intellectuals such as Albert Einstein, John Dewey, H.L. Mencken, H.G. Wells, Madam Curie, John Dos Pasos, law professor Felix Frankfurter, and historian Arthur Schlesinger campaigned to set them free. They compared it to the Dreyfus case in France. No other crime story has spawned so many plays, poems, and books. Many thought that the men had been convicted because of their beliefs. Frankfurter wrote a book in which he advanced the thesis that the notorious Moreli gang was responsible for the robbery and murders. Surprisingly, the speculative "Moreli thesis" was placed in an article on Sacco and Vanzetti in the 1929 edition of the Encyclopedia Brittanica, published in Chicago.

The case was unusual in that Sacco and Vanzetti had capable representation at the trial. Fred Moore, a famous labor lawyer, volunteered his legal services. True, there was not a single Italian on the jury, but neither were there any businessmen – Moore had seen to that. The two defendants even took the stand in a futile effort to convince the jury of their innocence.

Nicola Sacco

Nicola Sacco and Bartolomeo Vanzetti, these two atheists, World War I draft dodgers (they fled to Mexico), and anarchists – the poor shoemaker and a fish peddler - were finally given the electric chair in 1927.

Richard Newby, an English professor at **Illinois State University,** has recently challenged some of the old assumptions. Forensics has been introduced to the controversy. Based on ballistics tests made in 1961 on the two weapons, and comments made after the executions by defense lawyer Moore, experts concluded that Sacco was probably guilty and Vanzetti might have been innocent. Sacco's gun was a ballistics match, but there was no direct evidence that he pulled the trigger.

THE MADCAP ADVENTURES OF IZZY AND MOE

When the prohibition law went into effect, Congress appropriated money for the salaries of about 1,500 agents to enforce the law. They were paid salaries of $2,000 a year. By far the two most spectacular agents were Izzy Einstein and Moe Smith.

Izzy's big advantage was that nobody who took a good look at him could believe he was an agent. He was short and weighed 225 pounds and most of it hung around his middle like a spare tire. This man who spoke fluent Yiddish, and about five other languages, ingeniously rigged an evidence collector that consisted of a small funnel, a rubber tube and a bottle, all concealed under his loosely hung suit. Whenever a bartender served him an illegal drink, he would sample the wares and then pour a small portion into the collection bottle when the bartender wasn't looking. "Most of the stuff I got in these places was terrible," he oft complained.

After several months on the job he began to miss a good friend of his from the lower East Side of Manhattan, Moe Smith. Izzy persuaded his friend to hire a relative to run the cigar store that he owned and join forces with him. New York reporters, in an effort to spice up their stories and reports, fixated on the exploits of these unlikely agents. Historian Herbert Asbury says the pair became so well known they made the front pages of the newspaper more than anyone else except for Al Capone and the President. The Brooklyn *Eagle* reported that had there been a couple dozen more Izzy and Moes, the country would have ended up "parched and bone dry."

They developed ingenious props to help their ruse. Sometimes the team went into a saloon carrying a bottle of milk or a big jar of pickles. "Who'd ever think that a fat man with a jar of pickles was an agent?" complained one bartender who was pinched. If they needed to get into an establishment frequented by musicians, Izzy carried a violin with him and set others at ease by playing simple tunes such as "How Dry I Am."

Soon the pair became so famous that they had to resort to wearing elaborate disguises to gain entrance into an illegal establishment. On another occasion they noticed that a small warehouse near a cemetery seemed to have a suspicious smell about it. The two men posed as ditch diggers and complained to a man who came out of the building that digging holes by hand was hard work, bringing on thirstitis. The man went inside and brought back several jugs and was promptly arrested. When they searched inside they found three illegal stills running full blast.

Government officials in Washington D.C. began to grow jealous since they were more important than Izzy and Moe but were hardly ever mentioned in the newspaper. Izzy and Moe were ordered to come to D.C. for a meeting. They

Izzy Einstein and Moe Smith

were told to stop talking to reporters in hopes that this might curb their publicity. But it did no good because newshounds now began to make up stories about the duo to feed the public's voracious appetite for sensational news.

Izzy and Moe were ordered to turn in their gold badges in November of 1925. Reporters were told that Izzy and Moe were dismissed "for the good of the service" because their vaudevillian antics made it seem as if prohibition enforcement was some sort of a joke. Both men promptly went into the insurance business and were quite successful. All four of Izzy's sons went on to become successful lawyers.

For more info on the exploits of these prohibition icons see "Izzy and Moe" by Herbert Asbury and "The American Mercury," 1949.

AMERICA AND FOREIGN AFFAIRS IN THE 1920s.

Generally speaking, Americans have long had little interest in U.S. foreign policy. Even during the height of the contentious Vietnam War, most citizens could not locate Vietnam on a world map.

The tone for this period was set during the last years of the Woodrow Wilson administration. The idealistic president had formulated a plan for world peace. Article ten of the peace treaty that was signed between the Central Powers (bad guys) and the Allies (good guys) called for a League of Nations. It was a model for a world body, similar to the United Nations, where countries of the world could discuss and debate contentious issues, with the hope that things could be ironed out peacefully before nations went to war.

German Zeppelin over New Jersey

Americans, naturally, were preoccupied with frivolous news about the NC-4 making a trans-Atlantic flight across the ocean via the Azores. They wondered whether Ty Cobb would win the American League batting title. And they pushed for higher speed limits on the new concrete highways that were being built. **Illinois regulations in 1919** drew the line at 15 mph in residential sections of cities; 10 mph in urban areas, and **curves had to be negotiated at a mere six mph**.

But the U.S. Constitution calls for the Senate to ratify all treaties with a 2/3 majority. Republican senators, led by Henry Cabot Lodge and William Borah of Idaho, were adamantly opposed to allowing the Puritan schoolmaster to talk America into joining the League. They were in tune with most citizens who were weary of international crusades and reforms. Warren Harding, in his quest for the presidency in 1920, hit the nail on the head when he said that Americans wanted not nostrums, but **"normalcy."** Idealism was on the ebb.

Republicans echoed the sentiments of George Washington when he had warned in his Farewell Address against entangling alliances. Men like William Howard Taft and Elihu Root believed that America should become involved in war only if we were attacked or our national honor was at stake. They certainly weren't about to let foreigners such as Clemenceau, Orlando, and Lloyd George, leaders of France, Italy, and England, direct our foreign policy.

Much of this was pure and simple politics, of course – such as Democrats like **Chicagoan Barack Obama** giving Secretary of State nominee Condi Rice a hard time at her confirmation hearing, or Senator **Dick Durbin of East St. Louis** criticizing George Bush's plan to reform Social Security.

When the treaty was defeated, Americans retreated back to isolationism. Some say that a U.S. led League of Nations might have prevented World War II, but there is little logic to this. The League merely became a debating society, much like the current United Nations. When it came to getting tough with **Hitler, Mussolini, or Tojo** in the 1930s, few League nations favored any kind of direct military action. Likewise, when it came to getting tough with Saddam Hussein, most U.N. members were willing to give him another chance, despite his already having broken his word on treaty obligations on *twelve* previous occasions.

When the nations of the world took a vote and condemned the aggressors, Germany, Italy and Japan merely quit the League. It seems like Winston Churchill, who was not yet British Prime Minister, was a lone voice in the wilderness, pleading for action – not compromise.

Another problem that cropped up after the war was that of immigration. America had always been a land of immigrants, but for a couple of centuries the newcomers had predominantly come from Western Europe and were Protestant. Since 1890 the new crop mostly came from southeastern Europe and were Catholic. Further, the radicals and anarchists that had been giving America so much trouble tended to be recent immigrants.

The problem was dealt with by the passage of a series of acts that imposed quotas and discriminated against those countries that were sending "undesirables." Special and even more restrictive quotas were imposed against Asian countries.

Anglophobe and isolationist Big Bill Thompson, Chicago mayor

In Germany, Adolph Hitler observed these changes in U.S. policy with consternation. By restricting "inferior" races and allowing immigration from "desirable" Nordic races from northwestern Europe, America would strengthen her population with superior stock. This would make her a formidable enemy.

To discourage arms races and naval build-ups, a series of conferences were held to establish ratios among the great naval powers, protecting the status quo. It was agreed at the **Washington Naval**

Conference that the U.S. and England should remain the dominant naval powers, while countries such as France, Italy, and Japan were assigned smaller ratios. England and the U.S. were given a 5, Japan received a 3, and France and Italy were assigned a 1.75. In short, Japan's navy would be 3/5ths the size of England's. The 1922 treaty placed a ten-year moratorium on the building of capital (big) warships. It also placed restrictions on the use of submarines in warfare and outlawed the use of poison gas.

William Borah, the Illinois-born Idaho senator, was the moving force that brought about the conference.

The major powers also agreed to respect each other's territorial possessions in the Pacific and the territorial integrity of China was affirmed in a reiteration of the Open Door Policy.

By 1924 it had become obvious that the problem of **German reparations** had to be dealt with. The harsh Treaty of Versailles that had ended World War I imposed stiff penalties on a defeated Germany. One of the provisions insisted that Germany sign a "war-guilt" clause to the effect that they were solely responsible for damages caused to other countries by the war and that reparations were due.

Germany floundered under the terrible economic weight of these payments causing ruin to that country's economy and leading to disastrous inflation.

Vice-president Charles Gates Dawes, **a former Chicago banker**, led a committee of ten nations that drew up a revision of these payments that led to their amounts being scaled back. The plan also called for an end to the allied occupation of the Ruhr Valley, Germany's coal and steel region.

Germany was unhappy that the reparations were not done away with entirely, but had no choice but to go along with the plan. Dawes would receive the Nobel Peace Prize for his efforts, the **Dawes Plan**.

When Adolph Hitler came to power in 1933, he announced that Germany would discontinue making reparation payments. A generous America had not insisted on any reparation payments from Germany so his decision did not affect our country.

In 1928 the foreign ministers of France and the U.S.

Leading isolationist and Supreme Court Chief Justice, William H. Taft

concocted a novel way to prevent future wars. They drew up the **Briand-Kellogg Pact** which outlawed war. Most of the countries of the world signed the document. It might have been naïve to think that such a simplistic approach to international problems could sustain world peace. Both Germany and Japan were signatories of the document. Hull House founder and peace activist Jane Addams supported the pact, and her decades of effort (she opposed U.S. participation in World War I) along these lines **led to her winning the Nobel Peace Prize**. Kellogg won the Nobel Peace Prize in 1929.

Most Illinoisans of this era leaned toward isolationism during this period. There was growing disillusionment with our participation in World War I. With war clouds looming on the horizon, it did not look as if we had achieved our goals. World War I apparently was not the "war to end all wars." People throughout the state weren't in any mood to send our boys to Europe a second time for the purpose of pulling British chestnuts out of the fire. Fascism and Communism may have been on the march, but Americans were generally tired of reform crusades and weary of military intervention.

Chicago mayor Big Bill Thompson reflected the Midwest mood of isolationism. Thompson blamed the British for dragging the nation into World War I, and he began damning them with acerbic diatribes in time for his re-election in 1919. He launched a campaign in the Twenties to have pro-British references removed from school textbooks. Thompson caused a national stir by twisting the lion's tail and threatening to punch King George in the nose if the British monarch ever dared to step foot in Chicago.

Mrs. John Howard Curran (UPI)

SOUTHERN ILLINOIS WOMAN POPULARIZES THE OUIJA BOARD

The Ouija game, invented shortly before the turn of the century, was first met with mild interest. It only became a sensation after Mrs. John Curran of **Mound City**, Illinois, who lived in a two-story frame house on Pearl Street, began making fantastic claims in 1916. She stated that the board enabled her to get in touch with the spirit of **a woman killed a hundred years earlier by Indians** in the New England area. This deceased woman, by the name of Patience Worth, now proceeded to dictate to Mrs. Curran thousands of words of poetry and prose that also produced six novels on the eve of World War I.

In 1919 the American Society for Psychical Research invited Mrs. Curran to come to New York and give a public demonstration. She did, giving an impressive performance before a large audience, receiving words and messages from Confucius and Walt Whitman, along with some esoteric Hindu transcriptions.

Skeptics, of course, called this **housewife with the world's busiest Ouija board delusional**. They claimed the long-departed Patience Worth was but a figment of Mrs. Curran's imagination. Harvard Psychologist William James explained the phenomenon by comparing her to rare persons with an "alternating personality" who could sit down at a piano, and with no previous training play a concerto.

Ouija Board

Mrs. Curran went to New York once again in 1928, this time for an audience at St. Marks in the Bouwerie. By now her message of spiritualism was very popular, and she had quite a following. She performed magnificently, producing poems on split-second notice in response to requests from the audience.

Mrs. Curran grew wealthy from her abilities and she moved from Mound City to St. Louis, and from there to Los Angeles where she died in December of 1937 at age forty-six.

As historian Paul Sann explains in his 1967 *Fads and Follies* book, "Miss Patience Worth of New England never called to the bench for a pinch hitter, so the Niagara of words finally dried up."

It is noteworthy that Mrs. Curran's emergence coincided with a rising interest in spirituality. There were those in the 1920s who held séances on each anniversary of the Halloween death of **Harry Houdini** and claim to have communicated with him.

Arthur Conan Doyle, of Sherlock Holmes fame, was a firm believer in having once lived in a previous life through reincarnation. And then there was **Edgar Cayce**, the man who once a day would lie down on his couch, fold his hands, and go into a self induced trance. An observer would then ask him questions about some individual from the past and he would relate answers, called readings, given to him as a result of having communicated with that person.

The Ouija board gained even greater notoriety when it became the subject of a murder trial. A lonely Dorothea Turley in the Southwest found an Ouija board and a handsome cowboy to keep her company. Just one problem; there was still a Mr. Turley. Dorothea asked the board to help her decide between her husband and her young lover.

The board replied that her future was with the cowhand, and that the problem could be solved by having daughter Mattie shoot her father – which she did. Despite the fact that the Ouija board had told them they wouldn't be prosecuted for the act, young Hattie was sent to reform school until she was 21, and mother was given three years behind bars.

In **Chicago,** the Ouija board was involved in another interesting case. In an odd decision, the court held that a woman could not be prosecuted for slander against a neighbor because she had been directed to do so by an Ouija board.

The Fuld brothers of Baltimore invented the Ouija board in 1892 but they eventually sold out to Parker Brothers. Used by thousands in the hope that it could tell them whether their loved ones had survived the Great War, it remained a popular game throughout the 1920s. The lapboard had nine numbers on it plus all twenty-six letters of the alphabet. The user asked the board a question and used the three-legged planchette to discover the answer. All you had to do was place your fingers lightly on the planchette and a "magical" energy guided it to the letters or number that gave you an answer. Women often used the board to ask it how many children they would bear or how many times they would be married.

For answers to simplistic questions, the board also had a *yes* and *no* which told young maidens whether they would marry someone rich or famous.

BIOGRAPHY OF GEORGE GERSHWIN

Gershwin, (Mr. Music) a true musical genius, was born on September 26, 1898 in Brooklyn. He was the son of immigrant parents. His brother Ira (Mr. Words) was a successful lyricist.

George Gershwin

The family's first piano was bought for Ira, but it was George who took immediate interest and learned to play by ear. At the age of 12 he began taking lessons and his first job was selling tunes as a "song plugger" for professionals

Giant Lauterbach statue in **Springfield** – Dan Oberle collection

on Tin Pan Alley. George soon began writing music on his own. His first hit was **"Swanee,"** sung by Al Jolson in the Broadway musical Sinbad. From 1920-24 he wrote songs for the Scandals of Broadway series.

Rhapsody in Blue was written in three weeks and it was first showcased by Paul Whiteman's orchestra. The work is still one of the favorite pieces played in the United States and worldwide by orchestras and ensembles.

From 1924-29 he wrote music for Broadway productions and scored with big hits such as **"Fascinating Rhythm," "Lady Be Good,"** and **"The Man I Love."** After "Lady Be Good," he teamed with his brother Ira to compose **"Strike Up The Band"** and **"Someone To Watch Over Me."**

George took a trip to Paris and

Victor Herbert, Irving Berlin, John Philip Sousa

the city inspired him to write *An American in Paris* which is his second most popular orchestral work.

George and Ira next packed for Hollywood and composed music and songs for the Silver Screen. **"Lets Call the Whole Thing Off"** and **"They Can't Take That Away From Me"** came from *Shall We Dance* starring Fred Astaire and Ginger Rogers.

One of his biggest failures was *American Opera*, better known as *Porgy and Bess*. The show closed shortly after it opened. Audiences in the depression simply weren't interested in the poverty of the ghetto and the daily lives and loves of Negroes. The musical enjoys great success today and audiences thrill to **"Summertime"** and **"I Got Plenty of Nuttin."**

George, a workaholic who never married, died in surgery on July 11, 1937 in Hollywood while doctors were trying to remove a cancerous brain tumor.

Chicago based United Airlines currently uses *Rhapsody in Blue* as its theme song for commercials.

Other popular Gershwin tunes include **"Our Love is Here to Stay," "Embraceable You,"** " **'Swonderful, 'Smarvelous"** (that you should care for me).

PROFILE OF CHARLIE BIRGER – THE "SCOURGE OF EGYPT"

Birger's heyday was the 1920s—a time of booming coal mining activity in southern Illinois and occasional economic relapse. Charlie was one of those bigger than life characters who grabbed headlines in the down state area while Al Capone was rubbing people out up in Chicago.

Charlie Birger was no ordinary bootlegger. He had a penchant for telling tall tales about serving in the military, and true to the dime novel traditions of the Old West, spent a month in a hospital as a result of having a horse fall on him while he served with the U.S. Cavalry at Fort Assinnibone, Montana, in 1901. Some of the post-military service time in his life was spent on a ranch in South Dakota where he rounded up cattle and tamed wild horses. He didn't want the military to know about this for fear it would cost him a disability pension. He bragged to reporters that he once tamed "Man eater," the toughest horse of all, one that rivaled Pecos Bill's steed, "Widowmaker."

The press gave Birger the Robin Hood label due to his habit of tossing coins to children in the schoolyard in **Harrisburg**, Illinois. To those down-and-outers who occasionally were on the receiving end of a bag of free groceries, he was a charitable man. Birger won people's admiration despite the fact that he was a modern-day Jesse James who substituted a machine gun and armored car for a revolver and a horse.

The "Scourge of Egypt" was born in Russia (now Lithuania), probably around 1883. His family came to America through the Ellis Island port of entry in New York. The Russian/Jewish family later moved to St. Louis where they lived on Biddle Street in the north end for a spell. Charlie's family went back to New York, but they eventually returned to St. Louis where he worked as a youth delivering newspapers for the *Post-Dispatch*. Then the family moved to **Glen Carbon,** Illinois, where older brother **Sam Birger** ran a general store and became a prominent druggist. Sam later donated land for an elementary school, so city fathers **named a street in his honor.**

Birger was married at least three times, first to Edna May

Birger and family: Bernice, Minnie and Charlene

Hastey of **East St. Louis** (around 1909) and then to **Beatrice Bainbridge** (1918-25). He married **Bernice Davis** in February of 1926, but they too were later divorced.

His was one of those unusual lives enshrouded with fascinating folklore. Birger had a deep hatred for manual labor and gravitated to the likes of others who cut corners and tried to make a fast buck in gambling and bootlegging. He shielded his wife and two daughters as best as he could from his shady activities. **Art Newman**, a gambler and hotel operator from **East St. Louis,** who was originally allied with the Sheltons, became his No. 2 man. Birger also owned a couple of entertainment spots near the "colored" section of East St. Louis where gambling, bootlegging and prostitution were the chief sources of income.

Birger (center, top - with vest) and gang at Shady Rest

No one knows for sure how many men Charlie Birger killed; some estimates go as high as ten. Charlie ran into Carl Shelton while recuperating from a gunshot wound in a **Herrin** hospital. As rival bootleggers they had a lot in common. Charlie was caught in a Williamson County dry raid and sentenced to a year in the **Danville** prison in 1924. While being "salted away" in prison he hatched a scheme to form an alliance with the Sheltons. Hauling uncut booze from Florida and other points south, their boys would lay over in **Harrisburg** before making the final run to St. Louis and East St. Louis where the big markets were. Birger and the Sheltons parted ways after they got into it over an argument about profits from slot machines—those one-armed, money-eating metal monsters.

For a brief spell, Birger lived in **Belleville** and worked at the Nigger Hollow coal mine near **O'Fallon**, Illinois, one of 300 in the area. **John Auble's** *History of St. Louis Gangsters* (page 12) says he served in the Civil War, but it was actually a stint with the United States Cavalry in 1901.

After military service, Birger put in a request for a disability pension due to back injuries received when he was thrown from a horse. He told authorities that when he was discharged after three years of service, he lived in Glen Carbon from 1904-1905, then resided for a spell in the East St. Louis **Edgemont** (which means foot of the hill) area from 1906-1908. Edgemont was significance back then as a switching point for all the streetcars that ran in the area. While living there, he ran a small store that sold groceries and confections, and he frequented **Traband's** saloon on 89th and State. Birger probably killed his first man while living in Edgemont. Gary DeNeal, in *A Knight of Another Sort*, tells about a running feud Birger had with a local character whose nickname was "Chubby" Oughten around 1908. It started as an argument over a bottle of beer in a dance hall near **Phil Traband's** place. The man came at Birger with a knife, and Birger shot him several times in the chest. Birger surrendered himself to Keeton, the village marshal. He was acquitted of any serious charges on a plea of self-defense. It would not be the last time Birger successfully used the self-defense plea. This incident may have been the reason Birger left Edgemont. From 1908 to 1913, he lived in **Staunton**, Illinois.

Charlie Birger didn't have the look or demeanor of a gangster. He was less than six feet tall, slim, and had a thick shock of hair on the other side of his part that hung down a little on his forehead. He was usually very animated, but sometimes his face would take on the bland look of innocence of an *enfant terrible* getting ready to give someone a hotfoot or to light a firecracker under his chair. He was a combination of Machiavelli, Don Juan and Blue Boy, crossed with a scorpion.

The 1910 census listed him as living in **Virden**, Illinois, with a wife, **Edna May Hastey**, a tall blond from **East St. Louis.** In 1912 he was living in **Christopher,** and in 1913 he left for the **Harrisburg, Ledford, Marion, Herrin** area where he lived out his remaining days.

In 1913 he went into the business of selling liquor to area miners from a place in **Ledford**. He became a respected member of the community and was known for tossing handfuls of change to gleeful, scrambling kids, and selling watermelons from an old Model-T roadster with a pickup bed. The kids in the area loved him because he also bought them candy and ice cream.

In 1915 Birger and his wife separated, but his divorce from Edna was not finalized until 1917. Whether Charlie's reputation for a roving eye or his proclivity for getting into trouble broke up the marriage is unknown. In December of 1917 Birger shot and killed a man who was his competitor in the liquor business, a certain **George 'Crip' Yates**. There are several versions of the story, but a coroner's jury verdict of justifiable homicide once again secured Charlie's release from jail.

In 1918 Birger served time in **Massac County Jail** when three stolen cars were found in his **Ledford** barn. The chief of police in **St. Louis** wrote to the chief of police in **Metropolis**, Ike Brannon, and told him that Birger had purchased tags and plates from a St. Louis firm, apparently with the intent of starting a car theft ring. While in jail, Charlie was his usual charming self, making donations to charities, spreading money around, and winning friends with his outgoing personality. A jury could not agree on a verdict of guilty or innocent, so he was released.

Charlie was in hot water again in 1919 when a trunk marked "glassware" arrived at the railway express office in **Eldorado**. The official in charge noticed a peculiar odor and thought it odd that the trunk had been shipped by a certain Charlie Birger, *from* the city of **East St. Louis**, *to* Charlie Birger. The sheriff was summoned, and he discovered the contraband and ended up pouring 78 quarts of hard liquor down a storm sewer.

In July of that year Charlie Birger took a date to the county fair at **Shawneetown**. It was a woman named **Beatrice Bainbridge**. They were married in March of 1921 in Clayton, Missouri. When they first met, Birger told

Ruins of Birger's cabin at Shady Rest

her that he was a jewelry salesman from Chicago. Their first apartment was located above the **Busy Bee Candy Kitchen** on the square in **Harrisburg**. Her entire family was upset with her for marrying a bootlegger, thief, and a killer. It wasn't much of a marriage. Ostensibly, Birger

married her to acquire a veneer of respectability and to have someone to raise his daughter, **Minnie**. A daughter of their own, **Edna Charlene,** was born in 1921. Beatrice miscarried a baby boy, stillborn due to an accidental fall in 1923. A disappointed Charlie Birger would father no sons.

From about 1919 to 1921 Charlie took care of his aging father, Louis. The bewhiskered man was a bit senile, and on several occasions "wandered away" from his son's home

Harvey Dungey – Birger gang member and gang artist – rare photo showing his drawing of the murder of Joe Adams, courtesy Bob Rea of **Benton**

in Harrisburg. Louis died on December 10, 1921, and was buried in Chesed Shel Emeth Jewish cemetery in University City, Missouri. Birger's daughter Charlene died in childbirth in 1949 and was buried in the same cemetery.

Around 1922, Birger's Army *disability* pension was finally approved, and he received a check for $25 a month for the rest of his life.

Charlie Birger got in trouble with the law again in 1924 – this time for bootlegging. His trial was at **Danville** where he was found guilty, fined $2,500, and sentenced to a year in jail.

After his release he continued his ways with bootlegging and gambling, and in December of 1925 formed an uneasy alliance with the Sheltons in the slot machine business. The partnership didn't last long because the Sheltons thought Birger was skimming profits and a bloody feud broke out. Another account has it that the pair broke up because Charlie and Carl were competing for the affections of Helen Holbrook, a divorcee who has been labeled as the **"Shawneetown Dame."**

On November 12, 1928, the Sheltons carried out an audacious, but unsuccessful, attack on Birger's Shady Rest gang hangout that was built in the fall of 1925. They flew over the place in an old Curtiss Jenny and threw nitro/dynamite bombs from the open cockpit. There was little damage and gunfire from the Birger gang drove the assailants away. The Ripley's "Believe it or Not" people

Lory and Ethel Price Home

reported it as the **first aerial attack ever carried out on American soil**. The Birger gang protected their empire with an armor-plated car that sat on a Lincoln chassis. The Sheltons next attacked the Birger roadhouse with a World War I vintage army tank, but it also failed.

Art Newman was a member of the Birger gang and wife (Bess) was the chief madam in East St. Louis with operations in the Arlington Hotel (3rd and Missouri Ave.) and later the Deluxe, not far from City Hall, in a strip known as **The Valley**. The Sheltons used to hang out in the lobby of the Arlington and frequently cleaned their guns there. **Bess Newman** got tired of this and one day ran them off, so they started hanging out at the **Savoy** across the street. Newman sold the Arlington in 1925.

Shady Rest, Charlie Birger's hangout, was dynamited and burned to the ground on January 8, 1927. At first it was thought to be the work of his enemies – the Shelton gang. But it was later thought to have been done by Birger himself, ostensibly to cover up the killing of Elmo Thomasson, a young man Birger had hired to kill Joe

H. Dungey drawing of shootout between Birger and Shelton "tanks" near Marion (courtesy D. Bain/Anderson-Austin News)

Adams, Mayor of West City and a hated ally of the

Sheltons. Adams was fixing an armored vehicle that belonged to the Sheltons. Birger demanded that Adams surrender the truck, but he refused. Adams was killed on December 12, 1928, by Harry and Elmo Thomasson. The young brothers knocked on Adams' front door and handed him a fake note from Carl Shelton, written by Charlie Birger. They shot him while he was reading the message.

Birger was also responsible for the murder of Lory "Slim" Price, a state trooper whom Birger suspected of duplicity. Price rode a Harley Davidson motorcycle as a member of the state Highway Patrol. His assigned area was Highway 13 between **Harrisburg** and **Carbondale**. Although a law enforcement officer, Price engaged in a few shady activities with Charlie Birger and was a frequent visitor at Shady Rest.

Also killed that same night was Lory's schoolteacher wife, who was pregnant at the time. On orders from Birger, Ethel had been abducted by Connie Ritter and several other Birger henchmen. They shot and killed her

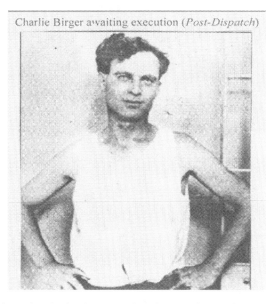

Charlie Birger awaiting execution (*Post-Dispatch*)

and threw her body down an abandoned mineshaft north of **Marion**. Lory was shot in the stomach by members of the Birger gang, then he was driven in Art Newman's car to an empty field near **DuBois** (Washington County), where he was dumped and shot again.

Harry Thomasson ultimately confessed to the crime of Killing Joe Adams and admitted he had been paid by Birger to commit the murder.

Art Newman and **Ray Hyland** were arrested for the murder of Lory and Ethel Price, and Birger was jailed for the killing of Joe Adams. Birger's associates were given stiff jail sentences, but Birger received the death penalty.

While incarcerated in the Franklin County jail at **Benton**, Birger received a surprise visit by famed evangelist **Billy Sunday**, but there is no record of any repentance or conversion.

Birger's attorney tried one last desperate maneuver to save his client from the hangman. He asked for, and was given, a sanity hearing. Unfortunately, Birger was merely a sociopath and passed the test with flying colors. On a specially built gallows, Birger became the **last man to be** *publicly* **hanged** by the State of Illinois that later employed the electric chair. Phil Hanna of **Epworth**, known as the "Human Hanging Machine," carried out the execution. During Hanna's career he performed over fifty hangings. Back in those days public hangings were big social and media events, and even Birger's former wife, **Edna**, was there for the gala affair. Birger faced his death with a false bravado as he flippantly made a gallows humor remark about what a nice day it was just before the noose, with 13

1926 shootout at Masonic Temple in **Herrin**, Illinois, by Harvey Dungey - courtesy D. Bain/Anderson-Austin News

knots, was slipped over his head. Birger was executed in **Benton**, but his body was buried near his father in a small Jewish cemetery in **University City**, a section of St. Louis. His plain and simple headstone bears the inscription, Shachna Itzik Birger.

Birger's other daughter, Minnie, died in Wyoming in 1992.

Historian **Gary DeNeal** has written the definitive biography of Birger in his 1981 book, *A Knight of Another Sort*. For an autographed copy of his book send a check or money order for $18.00 to Gary DeNeal, Springhouse Box 61, Herod, IL 62947

PROFILE OF THE SHELTON GANG

Carl Shelton was born on February 7, 1888, on a farm in the eastern part of Wayne County. He was the second oldest of the siblings born to Agnes and Ben Shelton. The oldest was Roy, born three years earlier. Younger children in the family included Earl, Dalta, Bernard (Bernie), and two sisters, Hazel and Lula.

Grandfather Wilson Shelton moved his family into Southern Illinois shortly after the Civil War ended, bringing his family from the verdant hills of nearby Kentucky to the gently rolling land near **Fairfield**, Illinois. The boys led carefree lives, helping with chores around the farm and hunting and fishing along the banks of the Little Wabash River. Carl dropped out of school after the seventh grade and brother Bernie lost interest after the second grade, while Earl quit after four years.

The family was Protestant in religious orientation and the children attended the Methodist Church at **Merriam**. The Shelton farm, at the Merriam crossroad, was a mere four miles east of Fairfield.

Life on the farm typically consisted of trips to the outhouse, hog butchering, bailing hay, plowing, harvesting, feeding the chickens, Saturday night baths in the horse trough, sheep feeding on the front lawn to keep the grass "mowed," cisterns and rail barrels.

When World War I broke out the only Shelton to wear a uniform was Earl, but the war ended before he saw any action. After the war the brothers went to St. Louis and worked at odd jobs in stores and drove taxis. From their late teens on, the Shelton brothers were trouble prone with Earl being the first to serve time in prison, having been convicted of robbery in 1915 and sent to the Reformatory at **Pontiac**.

After the brothers were run out of St. Louis they left for **Carterville** and worked in the coal mines. They found the life of a miner to be hard work, low paying, and sheer drudgery. Carl, Earl, and Bernie quit the mines and left for **East St. Louis**, a town long noted for its opportunities to make easy money when it came to vice. Roy, the brother who would spend the most time behind bars, was already languishing in prison (for larceny) at Menard in **Chester**. Dalta, for some unknown reason, never joined the gang and stayed at home to help his father run the farm.

The Sheltons opened a tavern at Nineteenth and Market, not far from the railroad tracks in East St. Louis. They were quick to take advantage of opportunities offered by Prohibition and got involved in rum-running activities from Florida and the Bahamas.

Following the Capone model, they bribed police and public officials. Soon they controlled most of the

124

gambling, bootlegging, and prostitution from **Peoria** to **Cairo**.

The brothers resided for a while at the Arlington Hotel in East St. Louis, an establishment run by Art and Bess Newman. The Sheltons also opened a roadhouse in **Herrin** and alternated much of their time between St. Clair and Williamson counties. At first the Newmans sided with the Sheltons but they later switched allegiances and threw in their lot with the rival Birger gang.

Shelton ally, Art Newman

The Sheltons soon were going head-to-head with another ruffian, Charlie Birger, who had formed a formidable gang of his own, and alternated his time between East St. Louis and **Marion**. The two gangs were mirror images – cold, calculating, and ruthless. In 1923 the two gangs formed an uneasy alliance, hoping there was enough ill-gotten loot to satisfy everyone. Bootlegging makes strange bedfellows, but the merger didn't last long. Some say it was due to Charlie Birger skimming slot machine profits, while other historians contend that Charlie and Carl were rival suitors/lovers and fought for the affection of a comely young widow from **Shawneetown** – Helen Holbrook.

During the brief alliance between Birger and the Sheltons they fought against a common enemy – the KKK. This same organization of super patriots who loved the Bible, Old Glory, and the U.S. Constitution, hated Jews, Catholics, foreigners and Negroes. Gun battles reigned supreme in Williamson County between pro-Prohibition forces, bolstered by Protestant churches and the Klan, and an unholy alliance between bought law officers and bootleggers.

Carl and Earl Shelton were indicted for killing Caesar Cagle in one of these shootouts but they were never convicted.

Shelton associate Frank "Buster" Wortman of East St. Louis/Collinsville (1962) - previously unpublished *Globe-Democrat* photo

Next, the Sheltons ambushed Prohibition Agent S. Glenn Young along the Atlantic-Pacific Highway near the Okaw Bottoms (Kaskaskia River), wounding Young and blinding his wife with buckshot. Carl and Earl were indicted for the attempted murder, but once again there was no conviction. Then they were indicted for the robbery of a bank at **Kincaid** on September 27, 1924. In January 27, 1925 a mail messenger in **Collinsville** was robbed of a $15,000 mine payroll, and once again authorities thought the Sheltons committed the deed.

An election-day riot and shootout at the **Herrin** Masonic Temple in April of 1926 decimated the ranks of the KKK and marked the beginning of the end of their power in Southern Illinois.

The feud between Birger and the Sheltons escalated when the Birger gang converted a REO truck into an odd-looking tank with gun ports and the Shelton gang modified a gasoline tank truck with armor and mounted a machine gun on its rear. Newman and his wife were attacked by the Shelton monstrosity on October 4, 1926, while traveling on the road. They escaped serious injury, and Birger and his cohorts retaliated the next night by using their vehicle to shoot up a Shelton roadhouse.

There was another incident where Earl Shelton fell ill with malaria and was hospitalized at St. Mary's hospital in **East St. Louis**. Art Newman and Freddie Wooten hatched a plot to dress in drag, find the room where Earl was staying, and cut his throat. The plot was foiled when an alert policeman spotted the pair and held them for questioning.

The next skirmish in this unbelievable conflict took place on November 12, 1926. Two pilots were barnstorming at **Benton**, Illinois, in a Curtiss "Jenny." Shelton henchmen hired the pilot to fly over Shady Rest, the famed gang hangout on the outskirts of **Marion**. Crude bombs were constructed by wrapping wire around sticks of dynamite and bottles of nitroglycerine. Shelton associate Blackie Armes was thought to be the bombardier. Members of the Birger gang ran outside after the first bomb was dropped and began firing their weapons at the JN-4. The bombs mostly missed their target, resulting only in the deaths of a pet eagle and bulldog.

The Shelton's trial for the mail robbery in **Collinsville** began in January of 1927. Art Newman, Charlie Birger and a Birger cohort, Harvey Dungey testified against the Sheltons. All three said they had conversations with one or more of the Sheltons where they talked about planning a robbery in Collinsville. Dungey, a drug addict and an East St. Louis cab driver, testified that he saw all three of the Shelton brothers in their Buick near Collinsville.

All three Sheltons were found guilty and sentenced to twenty-five years at Leavenworth, Kansas. They were put to work breaking up and cutting stone for construction purposes. Fortunately for the

125

Sheltons, Harvey Dungey, after being questioned by sheriff Jim Pritchard and a reporter from the St. Louis *Post-Dispatch*, admitted that he had given false testimony at the trial and that Charlie Birger had paid him to do it. Birger meanwhile had been arrested and jailed at **Benton** for his part in the murder of Joe Adams, mayor of **West City** and close friend of the Sheltons. The Sheltons were set free and the killing of Joe Adams earned Birger a date with Phil Hanna, the "Human Hangman" from **Carmi/Epworth**, Illinois. He would be the last man publicly hanged in the state as the electric chair became the new method of choice for executions.

Carl Shelton – Bowen Archives SIUE

Meanwhile, Helen Holbrook, the **Shawneetown Dame** who allegedly slept with both Carl Shelton and Charlie Birger, was **found dead from poison** in her home at St. Petersburg, Florida. It was ruled a suicide, but many speculated that she was bumped off by the Sheltons because she knew too much.

The Sheltons went from the frying pan into the fire. As soon as they were they released from Leavenworth they were charged with the **Kincaid** bank robbery back in 1924. Kincaid was another one of those coal towns in Christian County laid out by Peabody Coal. Art Newman was once again slated to be a main witness against them in the trial at **Taylorville**. This was the famous "blotter case" where the defense had police officials produce a police blotter that showed that Bernie and Earl had been arrested and were in police custody at the time of the robbery. Unfortunately, the records looked as if they had been clumsily altered and all five entries on the page were in the same handwriting with fresh ink. The brothers were found guilty and sentence from a year to life at Menard Prison in **Chester**. The Shelton lawyers filed an appeal and the Illinois Supreme Court ruled in October of 1928 that the trial had been flawed and the three brothers hadn't been given a fair trial.

The Sheltons had a new lease on life, especially since their nemesis, Charlie Birger, had been executed back on April 19th.

With Birger gone there was just one last fly in the ointment. The **Cuckoo Gang** in St. Louis now began to muscle in on their territory. The gang had received their curious moniker earlier in the decade when the Capone mob tried to gain control of the rackets in St. Louis. They sent representative after representative to St. Louis in an effort to work out some kind of a deal. Every one of them came back in a pine box. Al Capone threw up his hands in frustration and said, "leave those guys alone, they're crazy . . . nuts . . . *cuckoo*."

Carl told the Cuckoo gang to get out of Illinois, but leader Herman Tipton had other ideas. The Cuckoo gang might have been too much for the Capone mob, but now they were dealing with the Sheltons. The Sheltons employed a dissatisfied former member of the gang to shoot up a Cuckoo cabin in **Valmeyer** (along the Great American Bottom) and after several hundred rounds of ammo two were killed and two others were severely wounded in this 1930 episode. This event set off a fratricidal gang war that led to the death of fourteen gang members. Not one Shelton gorilla was killed in the process.

Just when it looked like the Sheltons were going to be on Easy Street in East St. Louis, a crusading sheriff by the name of Jerome Munie got elected in St. Clair County. Carl tried to bribe Sheriff Munie, but he wasn't interested. By the end of 1934 the Sheltons were history in East St. Louis. Carl went back to **Fairfield** and delved into the farming and oil business. Despite his semi-retirement, Carl quietly kept a hand on most of the gambling in downstate Illinois except for St. Clair and Madison counties. In a secret 1941 meeting at the Broadview Hotel in **East St. Louis**, gambling reps were told by state officials that handbook operations, gaming clubs and racetrack betting would be winked at in return for monthly payoffs. According to historian Taylor Pensoneau, Carl was the "principal figure" in delivering a $2,000 monthly payoff to officials in Dwight Green's administration. This is somewhat ironic since Green had earlier played a key role in sending Al Capone to prison.

Bernie Shelton – Bowen Archives SIUE

Meanwhile, Bernie met a pretty girl named Carrie Stephenson, owner of The Pines Motel and Restaurant in **Collinsville**. They were married in 1935 and set up housekeeping at a dude ranch near **Millstadt** called Happy Hollow. Bernie and Carrie shared a passion for sex, fast cars, and horses. They were divorced two years later and Bernie began looking for greener pastures, which he found in **Peoria**.

Big Earl was out of the picture at this time since he was arrested in Florida while on a rum-running mission. He was now cooling his heels in a federal prison in Atlanta. When he got out of prison, Earl returned to Fairfield and worked his 350 acre farm. In the evenings he ran a gambling establishment called The Farmer's Club, located on the town square in Fairfield.

Carl and Bernie next decided to make Peoria the focus of their gambling empire. Peoria was similar to East St. Louis in many ways. It, too, was situated on a river, was the subject of put-downs, was highly industrialized, had a cornucopia of saloons, and ranked slightly above East St. Louis in population.

126

The Shelton's home base in **Peoria** was the Palace Club near City Hall. Like **East St. Louis**, everybody knew that officials were running the city on profits from gambling and prostitution. On one of the trips from **Fairfield** to Peoria, Carl and Bernie's car struck and killed a young girl that ran out into State Route 121 near **Decatur** without looking. Saddened at the girl's death, they paid all the funeral bills.

In 1945 **Peoria** elected a reform mayor who came down hard on gambling. Carl quit the Palace Club but Bernie relocated to the Parkway Club, just outside the city limits. Carl went back to full time farming and oil speculating. Bernie remarried and acquired a Peoria ranch called the Golden Rule Farm.

Another problem now loomed large for the Sheltons. Two Shelton associates, Frank "Buster" Wortman and Blackie Armes, were released from prison in 1941, having been incarcerated since 1933 for assaulting Prohibition agents near **Collinsville**. The pair now switched their allegiance to the Capone mob that had pulled strings and done favors for them during their prison terms. They also allied themselves with former members of the St. Louis Eagan Rats, Cotton Eppelsheimer and Chippy Robinson, and muscled their way to the top of the heap in **East St. Louis**. According to St. Louis newspaperman Carl Baldwin, Wortman and the Capone outfit now conspired to put the Sheltons out of business.

Blackie Armes was

Bottom picture – Bernie Shelton Peoria assassination scene

Brothers Notorious
— THE SHELTONS —
Southern Illinois' Legendary Gangsters

Taylor Pensoneau

killed in a shootout at a **Herrin** night club. Wortman replaced him with two new recruits, Tony Armes, a brother to Blackie, and Charlie "Blackie" Harris of **Fairfield**. Both were former Sheltonites. The Capone mob let it be known that both Carl and Bernie were worth $10,000 each – dead. Charlie was another one of those rogues who had spent the better part of his life at Leavenworth and was credited by the FBI with killing 21 men, equaling the number attributed to S. Glenn Young.

On October 23, 1947, Carl was driving in his jeep on Pond Creek Road. Ray Walker and Little Earl Shelton were with him. A fusillade of shots rang out and Carl fell out of the vehicle, mortally wounded. Walker and Little Earl leaped from the Jeep and cowered in a ditch. "Don't shoot me anymore, Charlie. **It's me, Carl Shelton. You've killed me already**." An autopsy revealed that Carl was hit with 17 bullets. No one was ever convicted of the murder.

Less than a year later Bernie was killed outside the Parkway Tavern in **Peoria** on July 26, 1948. He was hit in the chest by a round from a large caliber Winchester as he was walking from the tavern to his car. Once again, no one was held accountable for the crime.

On June 7, 1950, Roy Shelton was shot and killed while driving a tractor on farmland near the spot where Carl was killed. Five shots were fired by a lone gunman with two of them fatally injuring Roy. He fell off the tractor that began to circle, and the blades left him a bloody, lifeless corpse.

Big Earl barely survived an assassination attempt back on May 24, 1949 at the Farmer's Club. Three shots were fired through an open window, one of them wounding him.

When sister Lula Shelton and her husband were shot at, every surviving member of the Shelton family secretly fled to Florida. This included Agnes (mother), Lula and her husband, Big Earl and his wife, Little Earl, and James Zuber. Dalta, the "good" Shelton, died from cancer in 1960 at **Jacksonville**, Illinois.

Big Earl went into Florida real estate and prospered. He died in 1986 at the ripe old age of 96.

Most of the Fairfield property the Shelton's left behind was burned to the ground by unknown arsonists.

Blackie Harris was convicted in 1965 of a double murder and sent to prison at age 69. He was paroled in 1981 and died a few years later.

Buster Wortman remained the top kingpin in Southern Illinois for about 28 years. He built a house surrounded by a moat off Lemen Settlement Road on the eastern fringe of **Collinsville** in the mid-fifties. Author Taylor Pensoneau notes that when Governor Stevenson cracked down on gambling, Wortman moved into jukeboxes, horse racing, pinball machines, loan sharking and labor racketeering. He owned a respectable and popular bar and restaurant called the Paddock, located on St. Louis Avenue near the downtown area of East St. Louis. His many years of drinking liquor and smoking cigarettes finally caught up with him. Wortman died in 1968 at the age of 63.

For an autographed copy of Belleville native Taylor Pensoneau's fascinating *Brothers Notorious: The Sheltons*, send a check for $18.00 to Downstate Publications, Box 320, New Berlin, Illinois.

WOMEN IN THE ROARING TWENTIES

In the decade prior to the 1920s activist women were involved in the temperance movement, educational reform, and the fight for women's suffrage. By 1920 the country was dry and women had the right to vote. The Gibson Girl look of the previous generation was replaced by the designs of John Held Jr. Long skirts, long hair, and high collars were out. Short skirts and bobbed hair were in. Lipstick and rouge, long associated with a "painted woman," were now fashionable. The New Woman was ready to throw off prior constraints and kick up her heels.

The flapper of this new age was eager to defy old conventions and was in revolt against the old order. For the first time in history American women had gained some measure of equality and sense of freedom compared to their male counterparts. Outrageous fashions, cosmetics, a flattened chest, cigarettes, and perhaps her personal flask of liquor were overt symbols of this new emancipation.

Actress Ann Forrest

Even those women who were content to play the traditional role of housewife and mother discovered that things had changed for the better. There was a never-ending amount of new gadgets and products that made household chores less tedious. The washing machine turned the scrub board into a museum piece. The vacuum sweeper replaced the rug beater. Indoor plumbing replaced drawing water from a well. Electric irons caused the stove-heated flatiron to be sold to the junk man. Entertaining programs on the radio enlivened whatever drudgery still existed from doing housework. Popular songs of the day could be played over and over on the Victrola.

Elinor Glyn – Culver Pictures

There was little left of the old reform spirit in this new decade. Part of this was due to the cyclical nature of reform movements. The two decades prior to the Civil War were marked by reform, but then people grew tired and lost interest for the next thirty years. The Twenties saw another lull in reform, but the spirit was re-energized once again in the New Deal years. The Forties and Fifties saw another lull, but the Sixties were full of protest and change.

Another reason for lack of interest in crusades during this period was due to the success of earlier reform. Wages were higher, working conditions had improved, life was easier; now there was actually time for vacations. Streets were paved, housing was better, gains were made in educational opportunities. Kindergartens were quite common and more people were graduating from high school. College was becoming affordable for the middle class. The number of college coeds was increasing exponentially. More and more people could afford cars.

Home economics rapidly became a popular course of study in high school. Movies were displacing vaudeville as the most popular form of public entertainment. Former suffragettes now joined social clubs that were more interested in card playing and Mah-Jongg than welfare work.

Despite the newly won right to vote, women failed to organize as a bloc to give their vote clout. Women simply failed to vote along social feminist lines. A significant number of men favored Harding and Coolidge over Cox and Roosevelt in 1920. Ditto for women. That rascal Big Bill Thompson was defeated for Chicago mayor in 1923 by William Dever, a reform candidate with an impeccable record. Yet only twenty-three percent of the women supported Dever, the Democrat.

It should also be remembered that the stereotype of the irrepressible and irresponsible flapper of this era held true mostly for single women. Once they married and settled down to raise children, they pretty much returned to the role of the traditional housewife. The husband was the breadwinner; the husband made most of the financial decisions; the husband decided which stocks were good

128

investments; the husband decided what brand of car to buy.

When the Great Depression came along in the Thirties the conservative, traditional role of the woman once again dominated. It would take World War II and "Rosie the Riveter" to bring women back to the workplace in large numbers.

PROFILE OF A 1920s ILLINOIS TOWN – EAST ST. LOUIS

Chicago may have gained most of the headlines in the Roaring Twenties but there was plenty going on in the rest of the state. Northwestern Illinois had the Looney gang to contend with, Springfield was dominated by Frank Zito, and Southern Illinois, crowned by East St. Louis, boasted the Birger gang, the Shelton Gang, and Frank Wortman.

The Kefauver Committee in the winter of 1950 launched a series of investigations into organized crime. Here is what the report said about this part of the U.S.

East St. Louis Stockyards, 2nd largest in America

"At the close of World War I, all areas of the Midwest proved to be lucrative for the furtherance of gangland activities because of the advent of Prohibition. Prior to the war, organized gangs were practically nonexistent, and hoodlums operated mostly on an individual basis. When it became evident that the illegal manufacture and distribution of liquor carried with it great financial possibilities, gangs began organizing and competing for this lucrative business."

Before one can understand a city like East St. Louis, one must first learn a little about its origins and early history. The town was founded in 1792 when Captain James Piggott, a resident of Cahokia, built several crude cabins across the river from St. Louis and established a ferry business there. Territorial governor Arthur St. Clair had visited Cahokia and made the suggestion about a ferry business to his friend, James Piggott. Piggott, a Pennsylvania native, had earlier fought the British at Germantown and Brandywine Creek during the Revolutionary War.

Piggott died not long after he started the ferry business, but subsequent owners managed to turn it into one of the most powerful and prosperous enterprises in the state. It even survived the construction of the Eads Bridge in 1874 and merged with and evolved into the prosperous Terminal Railroad, which later owned the bridge. **Actress Virginia Mayo**, who recently passed away, was a direct descendant of Captain Piggott, the city's founder.

East St. Louis has long had an image of a bawdy, brawling town. Around 1800 an island began to shoulder its way above the water in the Mississippi River. This large plot of ground became a no-man's land, the site of several fatal duels, cockfights and bare-knuckle brawls. It quickly gained the moniker, **Bloody Island**. After it was attached to the city of East St. Louis by a series of dikes and landfill, it became the locus of the **nation's second largest railroad complex**. By the 1920s there were twenty-seven railroads with terminals and warehouses there. All the great Captains of Industry has vested interests in East St. Louis. The list included such names as **John Jacob Astor, Andrew Carnegie, Jay Gould, Philip Armour, Gustavus Swift, John D. Rockefeller and J.P. Morgan**. When the large stockyards complex was built in 1873, the place became a magnet for immigrant labor.

Poles, Czechs, Lithuanians, Germans, Irish, Scots, Poles, Hungarians, Greeks, Armenians, Italians, Croatians and Bohemians all strove mightily for a slice of the economic and political pie. East St. Louis did not escape the jaded atmosphere of the Gilded Age after the Civil War. As the city grew by leaps and bounds new problems arose related to government, sanitation, crime, streets, housing and amusements. Scandals, violence and graft became the order of the day, culminating in the murder of former Mayor John Bowman in 1885. Part of the town's problems were due to many business owners being absentee landlords. They chose to live either in St. Louis or above the dirt and soot of an industrialized town up on the bluffs at **Signal Hill**, in **Belleville** or **Collinsville**.

Duke Ellington: "East St. Louis Toddle O" was one of his theme songs

In addition to political and civic strife there was labor violence as workers striking for higher wages and decent working conditions vehemently opposed being replaced by scab workers. Thomas Furlong, a detective for Jay Gould, sent a memo to his boss that said: **"East St. Louis is the toughest of the tough towns, tougher than Dodge City."**

Famed Illinois agnostic **Bob Ingersoll** (pictured right) said that **he didn't believe in hell** but that he might change his mind if he ever had to go to East St. Louis and serve riot duty.

East St. Louis was a town noted for its industrial prowess. The "Pittsburgh of the West" was dotted with smokestack industries and 550 miles of railroad track, ranking second only to Chicago as a national rail center. This raucous town of 75,000 people led the nation in the production of baking powder, paint pigments, and roofing materials. Its horse and mule market at the local stockyards ranked number one and the hog market was a close second to Chicago.

Starting with the Gay Nineties and lasting until 1920, East St. Louis reached a pinnacle of success. For three successive decades it was the fastest growing city in America. By 1920 it ranked third in population in the state, behind only Chicago and **Peoria**. Because of its location on the river, its access to cheap coal and electricity, and its reputation as a rail center, factory after factory was built there. These industrial plants made and processed steel, brass, aluminum, paint pigment, barrels, castings, baking powder, zinc, beer, sulfuric acid, soap, roofing materials and many other commodities.

But by 1920 its population stagnated, no doubt owing much to the ugly reputation it received due to the 1917 race riot that left 39 Negroes and 9 whites dead in its aftermath.

Despite the outward façade of prosperity the city was in debt. This was due to a huge project undertaken in 1889 to raise the downtown streets an average of eight to ten feet to solve the problem of periodic flooding. This controversial and expensive project cost an astounding sum of a million dollars.

Around 1903 the city fathers made a decision, partly by design and partly subconscious. Armed with the knowledge that its hard-working citizens wanted to quaff some brew, gamble, and perhaps spend some time with feminine company, they decided to allow East St. Louis to become a wide-open town. The quarterly charge for liquor licenses became obscenely high, but proprietors didn't complain much because business was so good. The citizenry didn't seem to mind because income from vice

newspapers at bay with occasional raids and token fines. The whole thing became self-perpetuating through a system of graft, payoffs, nepotism, cronyism and ghost payrolls.

Robert Ingersoll

Politically it became a single-party town, with control being exerted first by Republicans, and after the election of Franklin D. Roosevelt – Democrats.

This then was East St. Louis in 1920 – a rough and tumble hard-scrabble town with a tavern on every corner and a church on every other corner – **Sin City**.

The year 1920 was a landmark for East St. Louis, and marked the beginning of one of the most hopeful times in the city's history. Committees were formed to deal with the race problems and by 1940 a government report said that Negroes in the city were better off than most in comparable situations.

East St. Louis had incorporated in 1861 and was now nearly 60 years old and had gone through some excruciating growing pains. The city battled social problems such as prostitution, natural disasters (recurring floods and the 1896 cyclone), and the corruption of the Lambert administration between 1911 and 1913. The 1917 race riot seemed to be a peak of pain for everyone. Just as the murder of Elijah Lovejoy in 1837 Alton stifled growth and optimism in that town, the recent race riot hung like a dark cloud over the city for two decades. But sometimes it takes a tragedy to bring people together.

There was reason for hope with the dawn of a new decade. The view from 1920 was fairly good. Industry was still flocking to the city. A mushrooming population had pushed the city limits farther than ever before. Social groups were formed, cultural organizations sprang forth, churches and schools were built, parks were created, and new-fangled inventions such as the flivver were making life easier. Most important of all, jobs were plentiful. A saying had developed and it had gained national currency. **"If you can't find a job in East St. Louis, you won't find work anywhere."**

Voters adopted the commission form of government in 1919. The "new" mayor was M.M. Stephens, a wise and honest man who would become known as the town's best mayor. He had been the city's hero serving as mayor in the 1880s and 1890s. The city seemed poised for greatness.

The Roaring Twenties roared loudly in East St. Louis. Mayor Stephens governed most of them, leaving

Aluminum Ore Company on Missouri Avenue in **East St. Louis**

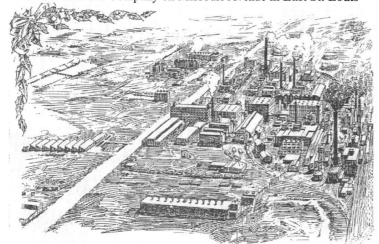

kept property taxes low.   Authorities kept crusading

office in 1927. It was a stark contrast to the events that were yet to come. The Great Depression, which gripped the country for a decade, came to an end only as the world took up arms again and wartime production spawned new jobs.

Lewis and Clark used Piggott's Ferry in **East St. Louis** while making preparations for their historic journey (U.S. Postal Service)

There were a couple of dark clouds on the horizon. In 1920, the Census Bureau reported that the government of that city was the second poorest in America according to cities of comparable size. This was due, in part, to sweetheart deals that previous administrations had made with large industrial concerns. Firms like the National Stock Yards, Monsanto, and Aluminum Ore had located just outside the city limits, establishing industrial suburbs within their own municipality. They paid no taxes to the city coffers.

A second concern occurred when city fathers blithely ignored the report of a St. Louis city planner that said major changes needed to be made in the infrastructure.

Prohibition might have been tougher on the city than the Depression. Many people lost their jobs at Heim's Brewery on State Street and the Central/ Lemp Brewery on Broadway due to the act.

The "Noble Experiment, which ended in 1933, deprived East St. Louis of its magnificent income from saloon licenses that made up half the city's budget. Boot-legging operations gave rise to organized crime in East St. Louis, giving a revenue source to Charlie Birger and the Shelton brothers. Prohibition corrupted East St. Louis because it gave police and public officials a chance to sup-

Actress Lillian Gish, as a young girl, lived in **East St. Louis** about four years with her mother and sister

plement their meager salaries by taking bribes. Once Prohibition ended, the corner tavern made a spectacular comeback. Revenues began flowing once again into the city treasury, but the gangsters merely devised new methods to supplement their incomes.

Civic gains were made with the creation of an Exchange Club that became the **largest in Illinois**. The city also had the **second oldest Jaycees group in the nation**. The Girl Scouts were formed in 1920. A 23-acre recreational facility was established for them up on **Signal Hill** and it was given the moniker Camp Minnie Wa Wa.

With the advent of Prohibition various dens of iniquity sprang up in the form of speak-easies. Among the most notorious was the Monkey Cage (a favorite of Charlie Birger) and several profitable establishments owned by "Mule Pole" Fritz. The town's most notorious gangster soon partnered up with the Sheltons.

What follows is an abbreviated mini-history of my home town, East St. Louis, in the Roaring Twenties.

1921 - Another new civic organization springs up, the Optimists Club. "Friends of the Youth" was their slogan. More businesses continued to develop with the advent of National Bottling and Swansea Stone Works at 33rd and Louisiana.

Broadhead Ford is organized by Willis and Jack Broadhead at 1135 Missouri Avenue.

A government study listed East St. Louis schools among the foremost in the nation vis a vis training in industrial arts and domestic arts. Overall, **the schools are ranked with the best in the state**.

1922 - The new Hawthorne Elementary School is built at 3800 Caseyville Avenue. The City Council passes an ordinance that requires youngsters to have an 8th grade education before they can drop out of school and go work in the factories.

Sterling Steel begins operations on the southwest edge of town. Construction also begins on the Cahokia Power Plant. When completed, East St. Louisans would have the **lowest electrical utility rates in the nation**.

1923 - There is another burst of civic pride when Shriners come from all over America to dedicate the new Ainad Temple. A huge parade of 5,000 people is held to mark the ceremony. It took the immense parade an entire hour to pass a given point on Collinsville Avenue.

Movies were popular in East St. Louis and its landscape was dotted with the Waverly Theater in the Lansdowne area, the Lyric, Drake, and Avenue theaters on Collinsville Avenue, the Columbia (Roxy) and Esquire theaters on State Street, the Odeon on St. Clair Avenue, the Liberty Theater on Missouri Avenue, and the Home (Gaty) Theater on Gaty Avenue, featuring dirt and sawdust floors, wooden benches and six pot-bellied stoves for warmth. In 1928 Harry Redmond built the spectacular, million-dollar Majestic Theater, fashioned in magnificent Arabesque décor.

Chicago-born silent film star Leah Baird comes to town to promote her new film, *Destroying Angel*. She models clothes at Seidel's dress Shop on Collinsville Avenue and does her Christmas shopping at Bernard's, on the corner of Collinsville and St. Louis.

1924 – The Croatian Hall at 1300 N. 9th is constructed.

East Side High Flyers play their first basketball game at the Ainad Temple. They lose to **Greenville**.

The first truck hauling livestock arrives at the stock-yards.

Heff's Chili Parlor in the Contratto Building on 40th and Waverly becomes a front for illegal gambling. Heff throws his weight around by parading up and down Waverly with his big German shepherd dog in defiance of the community.

Holy Angels in the Lans-downe area is founded at 3706 Caseyville Avenue. By 1950 it will be the second largest parish in East St. Louis. The first building is a long wooden structure that was used as a WPA center during the De-pression.

The World War I soldiers' war memorial is built on a

Candy Tockstein - Born in 1926; resided with parents at Lakewood Place in **East St. Louis**; appeared with Humphrey Bogart in *Knock on Any Door*; first married singer Mel Tormé and then game show host Hal March (below)

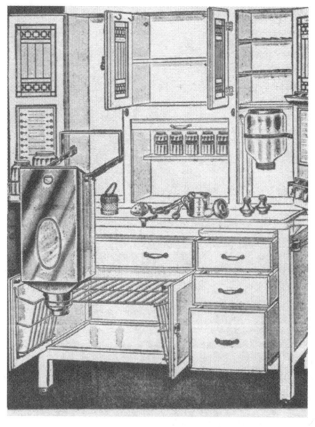

triangle of land at Caseyville Avenue and 25th and Lynch. It is a tall obelisk topped by an Eagle.

S. Glenn Young is supposed to appear in court at the Federal Building on Missouri Avenue. He is charged with attempted murder during a prohibition raid at the house of a Polish immigrant. Instead Young goes to the Labor Hall on Collinsville Avenue and sends word for the judge. He holds a press conference and charges that public officials at City Hall are in league with the bootleggers and are thwarting the divine mission of the KKK. The judge sets the bond and Young's followers post the money. Young leaves the building to the cheers of a crowd of about 1,000.

Southern Malleable Iron is established at 21st and Bond.

The city's first Pageant of Progress is held. It features a week of festivities each year at the beginning of October. It culminates with the crowning of a beauty queen chosen from the Southern Illinois area. The pageant is presented nightly at the Ainad Temple and is performed by locals. The extravaganza is discontinued in 1936 and is replaced by the Lady of the Lakes Pageant at Grand Marais.

Frank Holten is elected as a representative to the state legislature. He will be the longest serving member of that body, lasting 40 years. Grand Marais Park will be renamed Frank Holten State Park in his honor.

1925 – Mel Price begins working as a sports editor for the *News Review* of East St. Louis. He will later be employed by the *Journal* and *Post-Dispatch*. While in the Army (during World War II) he is elected as a U.S. Representative, serving in that capacity for over 40 years.

The KKK holds a four-day rally at Monks Mound. The featured speaker is the Imperial Wizard, from Georgia. The Catholic Church infiltrates the meeting and publishes a list of its local KKK members, urging boycotts of their stores.

The Fairmont Jockey Club opens on Collinsville Road. It runs horse races for 30 days in the spring and for 30 days in the fall. It will be the **first track in the nation to have lighting for night races.**

Sacred Heart Catholic Church building opens at 8th and Baugh.

First Church of God at North Park Drive and Kingshighway, with central headquarters in Anderson, Indiana, begins its soul-saving ministry.

The Knights of Columbus building on Washington Place near 14th and State is completed.

East St. Louis returns to the aldermanic form of government with more power in the hands of the mayor.

Sts. Constantine and Helen Greek Orthodox church is built at 1125 Gaty Avenue. It is the only Eastern Orthodox church in Southern Illinois and draws members from as far north as **Litchfield** and as far south as **Carbondale**.

1926 – James Kirk, founder of the East St. Louis *Journal,* dies at age 78 in his home on Pennsylvania Avenue.

The new million-dollar hospital called St. Mary's opens at 129 North 8th Street.

S. J. Peters, formerly of East St. Louis, King of the Bootleggers, surrenders to authorities at **Chester**, Illinois.

"Texas Slim" comic strip

The city has 16 fatal car accidents for the year. Among those killed is John Niederer, 57, of Niederer Dairy Co.

The city's income for the year is $916,080. Annual income from the years 1888-1925 exceeds expenditures except for monies owed due to the street raising started back in 1888.

A Negro Republican Women's Club is formed.

1927 – Miles Davis and his family move to East St. Louis a year after he is born in **Alton**. His father is a dentist.

The ILL-MO Hotel on Collinsville Avenue is destroyed by fire. It is replaced by the Goldman building and features Walgreen's Drug Store and lunch counter.

The East St. Louis Kiwanis Club is formed.

Amelia Earhart, Charles Lindbergh and Al Smith (Democratic mayor of New York) visit the city.

The library buys and moves into the old Elks Lodge at 9th and Illinois.

Wilson school at 48th and Hallows in Rosemont is built.

Duke Ellington records "East St. Louis Toodle O" on the RCA label.

The East St. Louis Junior Service Club for women is established.

1928 – The East St. Louis High chapter of the National Honor society is formed.

Al Oglander opens Al's Men Shop at 121 Collinsville Avenue.

Tailspin Tommy

James and Mary Helms open the Parkway Inn, a popular eatery at 25th and Lynch/Caseyville Avenue.

Ground is broken for the construction of the $1 million Broadview Hotel.

Emily Craig of **Mt. Carmel** is chosen queen at the annual Pageant of Progress.

The Village of Monsanto is organized south of East St. Louis. It will feature a chemical plant, rubber processing plant, an oil refinery, and a brass mill.

The city police force purchases its first sub-machine guns in an effort to combat a mounting crime wave spawned by Prohibition.

Daylight, due to a "smog pall" does not appear on December 22 until 8 a.m.

After the *Journal* runs a series of articles, City Hall decides to make payments on the principal on the debt from the 1888 street raising. Before this, only interest payments were made.

The First Church of the Nazarene is established at 15th and College,

Sterling Baptist Church on Bunkum Road is established as a mission of Washington Park Baptist on North Park Drive.

The Ralston-Purnia Company, located near the stockyards, is damaged by a $175,000 fire.

1929 – The Sears Store opens on the northwest corner of Collinsville and Illinois Avenues.

Central Catholic High opens at Wabasha and St. Clair Avenue. There are 75 boys and a teaching staff of three. It will later locate to 5th and St. Louis Avenue.

Oliver Parks establishes an aeronautical school near the Curtiss-Steinberg Airport in nearby **Cahokia**. It is the **nation's first federally approved school of aeronautics**.

Crispus Attucks School at 2600 Kansas is built. It is

named for the Negro who was killed in the 1770 Boston Massacre, a prelude to the American Revolution.

The East St. Louis Flyers play a football game at the St. Louis Arena as a second feature to an important college soccer match. Their opponent is a St. Louis All-Star team. Despite the Flyers losing quarterback Tom Cassady, to injury, they prevail 6-0 in front of 10,000 fans.

1930 – Wirt Downing begins his legendary career as an assistant football coach at East Side. The team goes undefeated. This will be repeated in 1931, 1941, 1943, 1952, 1953, 1954, 1955 and 1958. In 1955 **the team was ranked second in the nation with a 54 game winning streak**.

The State of Illinois builds a museum at Monks Mound.

Adolph Menjou as "Satan" - 1927

Audiences flock to the new Majestic Theater to see **East St. Louis native Lillian Gish** in her new film, *Coquette*.

Lansdowne Junior High is built at 39ᵗʰ and Caseyville. It is attended by Lee and Lynne Wild, twins who later go to Hollywood and **star in movies with Mickey Rooney**.

The Stockyards Bank, rich in assets, makes loans to other

East St. Louis banks to help them through hard times during the Depression. As a result, not a single bank in the city

"fails" during the decade. **This is the only large city in the entire country that can make this claim**.

Flagpole sitting becomes the local rage and Judge W. R. Weber issues an order to all juveniles to cease and desist.

The city adopts a policy that if a single female teacher gets married, her employment will be terminated. It is felt that women who work to supplement the household income should not be employed at the expense of others who are out of work.

The Live Wire Class of the First Presbyterian Church at 13th and Gaty consists of over 1,000 members. **It is the largest Sunday school class in the nation**.

Clark Junior High at 33ʳᵈ and State is completed.

The population of the city stands at 74,347 – 3ʳᵈ largest in the state.

WOMEN'S FASHIONS OF THE 1920s

Since the beginning of the Twentieth Century fashions have been an important part of the American culture. Unlike women's clothing, men's fashions have always been a bit more subdued and slower to change. Yet as a teenager in the 1950s, this author can remember wearing pencil thin belts, "Mr. B" (Billy Eckstine) shirts, pegged Levis, metal taps on the bottom of tan (St. Louis orange) plain-toed shoes from Boyds in St. Louis, and a red poplin jacket similar to the kind worn by James Dean in *Rebel Without A Cause*. It's hard to believe but pink and charcoal were popular colors for young men in my era. General Motors even produced a 1955 tri-colored Chevrolet that was white, pink and charcoal.

Women's fashions of this rambunctious Twenties era were a reflection of a new sense of freedom brought about by the right to vote, social realignment, co-eds, the automobile, bobbed hair, Freud, advertising, and carefree women as depicted in the movies.

There is a certain distortion to fashion of this time because the media paid little attention to what typical housewives and women in rural areas wore. Nevertheless, the designs of Coco Channel, Erté, Sonia Delaunay, Jeanne Lanvin, Madeline Vionette, Molyneux, Louiseboulanger, Paul Poiret, and Patou, worn by the rich and famous,

134

managed to filter down to the masses and common people living in hamlets or on farms.

Much of this can be attributed to mail order catalogs from Sears & Roebuck or Montgomery Ward. Millions of people eagerly awaited the arrival of the latest edition of a catalog. Its arrival meant hours of entertainment and a fount of information. Those who could not afford mail order clothes could buy yard goods and cobble together reasonable facsimiles on their sewing machines. Even companies that sold dress patterns offered designs that were modifications of the *haute couture*.

Thus even house dresses and work shirts had a modicum of style and were a reflection of the times. Even more affected were the clothes that typical Americans referred to as their "Sunday best" and worn to church, weddings and funerals. Thanks to Sears for giving permission to reproduce many of these designs from their catalogs.

As the decade began, women's fashions were still dominated by the war years. But changes were quick to arrive as skirts became shorter, figures slimmer, with diminished bosoms. Suits were sleeker and had more of a tailored look. The middy and the overblouse became important items. Bandeaux or brassieres began to replace the camisole.

High shoes were still worn, but there was an increased popularity in pumps. Most stockings remained dark, but flesh colored hosiery was on the increase. The Japanese kimono and sleeping suits (pajamas) made their first appearance.

By 1922 skirts were shorter, reaching mid-calf in length. Much of the classically simple clothes and new knitwear designs *en vogue* can be attributed to the influence of Coco Chanel. Stockings, still dark in color, began to take on fancy heels and clock designs. Cheaper rayon stockings arrived on the scene.

Lady's coat $35.00 - shamona suede

With the advent of 1923 the waistline had fallen to the hips. Mesh purses and silver-plated compacts became must-have fashion accessories. Bob hats for shorter hair were becoming the rage.

By 1925 the art movements in Paris and the Exposition Internationale des Arts Décoratifs made their influences felt on southern Illinois farms and in the ethnic ghettoes of Chicago. Hemlines were just below the knees. In

the silhouette, the hair styles, hats, shoes, gloves and jewelry, the accent was placed on the modernity of artforms expressed by the likes of Picasso, Matisse and Braque. The clean beauty of pure line and the hard edge of geometric lines came to dominate. The monotony of squares, circles and rectangles was broken with the addition of abstract patterns of appliqués, piecings, tucks and embroidered patterns. The focus now was on the slender, boyish look. Some women took this to the extreme by adding a monocle in an effort to look androgynous.

Due to the influence of Max Factor and the movies, a wide range of cosmetics were being offered in the form of nail polish, powder, rouge, lipsticks, and mascara. For some unknown reason, nail polish did not become wildly popular until the Thirties.

Rubber galoshes, unbuckled and flapping, bobbed hair, rouged knees, slave bracelets, cloche hat, rolled down stockings, and a long string of faux pearls became *de rigueur* for the woman who thought of herself as a "flapper" in the "cat's meow" category.

Dance frocks were copied from clothes worn by Hollywood flappers such as Joan Crawford, Mae Murray, Colleen Moore, and Louise Brooks. Large ties or bows just below the navel often accented the tubular style dresses. When dancing, the hat was discarded in favor of a headache band. Dyed to match satin slippers with high ankle straps completed the ensemble.

Toward the end of the decade the hemline once again dipped downward. In part, this was merely a new cycle of fashion designed to make earlier clothes seem out-dated so that consumers would spend money on new outfits. Flat planes were given detailed treatment and asymmetry became part of the fashion mix. Alligator patterned rubber and leatherette came into use. Except for the increasing popularity of gob outfits and slacks, femininity was once again becoming increasingly popular.

I relied upon Stella Blum's *Everyday Fashions of the Twenties* and Tom Tierney's *Great Fashion Designs of the Twenties* (Dover Books) for this section.

OIL IN ILLINOIS – THAR SHE BLOWS!

Marion Hubbert, of the University of Chicago, once explained that oil and natural gas in Illinois are found in pools or they are trapped in porous sedimentary rocks, originating from layer after layer of decomposed marine life dating back many years. This conversion process is believed to have taken as long as 300 million years.

Interestingly, there is one scientist of note (Immanuel Velikovsky) who theorizes that **our petrochemicals are a result of some ancient cosmic storm eons ago**, and the earth soaked up the gooey matter, acting much like a giant sponge.

Gas production first began in the state in 1853 when marsh gas was taken from wells drilled near **Champaign**. This gas was produced from rotting vegetation buried under the glacial deposits. In the 1860s, several wells were drilled in **Clark County**, but commercial production in that area did not begin until some forty years later. In the 1880s natural gas was discovered in the **Litchfield** area and was being sold for domestic use.

Significant oil production did not begin in Illinois until around 1905. Before that, Illinois **farmers grew castor beans** and the pressings from that crop produced oil that was used for lubricating and medicinal purposes. In the early years of searching for oil, water seeped into the wells and caused problems. It was not until the turn of the century that well casing technology solved the problem so that excess water could be drained off. By this time, geologists also discovered that oil and gas often collected at anticlines, beneath the crests of uplifted layers of rock.

There was some oil production in the 1880s around **Litchfield** in Montgomery County. The **LaSalle** anticline in eastern Illinois became a rich oil-producing region around 1904. By 1905 the state was producing 4.4 million barrels of oil. By 1908 the figure jumped to 33.1 million barrels. These discoveries pushed Illinois to third place among states in annual petroleum production, behind only California and Oklahoma. Standard Oil carried out most of the early oil exploration in Illinois. Later, Pure Oil and Indian Oil at **Lawrenceville** started drilling wells. In 1913 prospectors found oil in **Carlyle**, **Robinson**, **Bridgeport**, **Carlinville**, **Casey** and **Marion County** (the Sandoval Pool). By 1913 the boom years of oil production in Clark, Cumberland, Edgar, Crawford, and Lawrence counties was essentially over. As new sources of oil were found in other states, Illinois slowly fell behind in the rankings. The state's production fell off from 33 million barrels in 1910 to a paltry five million in 1936. Most of the oil in Illinois was easily refined.

Most oil men at the turn of the century were of limited education and searching for oil was carried out in a haphazard process. Geologists were distrusted since most operators could not understand a geological survey.

The oil economy quickly revived when the new technology of seismic exploration allowed geologists to find hidden anticlines. By 1940 the state's production had risen to 147.6 million barrels a year. **Clay, Richmond,**

Jasper, and Marion counties prospered during this period. Production fell off again after 1940 as finding new sites to replace old ones lagged.

Most people don't usually think of Illinois as a significant oil-producing region, but it has been pumping out crude oil since shortly after the turn of the twentieth century. A map of our oil producing areas looks pretty much like a bunch of scattered dots – some strange kind of psychological Rorschack test. However, most oil well sites are found in the southeastern part of the state in what is known to geologists as the **Illinois Basin**, centering in **Crawford** and **Jasper** Counties. Most prominent are sites along Interstate 64 between **Mount Vernon** and the Indiana border, and just north of the interstate in places like **Fairfield, Oblong** and **Robinson**.

Drilling for oil in Illinois was sometimes a dangerous business because **Illinois oil has high paraffin content**. It was necessary periodically to "shoot" the wells with nitroglycerin. This technique involved lowering a quantity of nitroglycerin into the well and setting it off. The resulting explosion would break open the clogged pores of the sand and let the oil flow again. Sometimes this required as much as 200 quarts of nitro. The **nitro was transported by horse drawn wagons and any sudden jerk or bump could set off an explosion**.

Another early problem was transporting the drilled oil in Illinois to refineries. The nearest refineries were about 200 miles away. Ohio Oil went into eastern Illinois and built tank farms at **Stoy**, located west of **Robinson**. There were approximately 1,000 tanks with a storage capacity of 35,000 barrels each.

Fractional tower for petroleum distillation

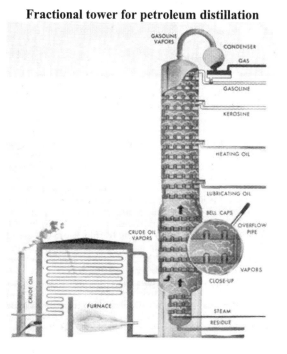

Using shock waves to find oil

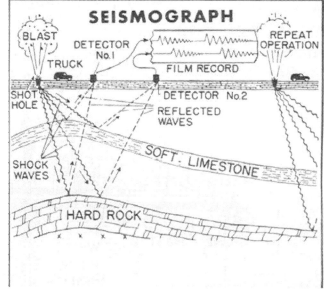

136

Ohio Oil built the Illinois Pipeline Company, which went from **Martinsville**, Illinois, to Preble, Indiana. Pipeline workers were paid 25 cents an hour to dig the trenches for the eight-inch pipeline. When the route encountered railroad tracks the workers burrowed beneath them.

In Illinois the depth of the deposits, or pay zones, varies from 500 feet to about 3,950 feet. From the highway one can see numerous grasshopper rotary pumps rhythmically bobbing up and down, with their upright cylindrical storage tanks somewhere nearby. Sometimes one can also spot what are called "heater treater" structures that are used to separate the warmed oil from its accompanying salt water by a simple gravitational process where the oil, being less dense, rises to the top. The water is pumped down another well, and the oil goes to storage.

Another method of oil extraction is known as water flooding or secondary recovery. In this technique, water is pumped under pressure into the pay zone, where it displaces the oil and pushes it to the pump area. Sometimes it takes as little as 1,000 barrels of water to accomplish this. Detergents can be added to the water to make it easier for the oil to seep through the porous rock. In the most common technique, the five-spot pattern, water is pumped into the reservoir rocks from different spots around the well, making a pattern much like the five spots on a domino. Unfortunately, this method leaves behind over half of the oil reserve.

A tertiary method of assisting the extraction process is called hydraulic fracturing. A fluid with the consistency of a milkshake is injected into the reservoir and the pressure is great enough to fracture the rocks around the well. The newly opened fractures make the reservoir rocks more porous, allowing oil to flow more easily into the well area.

Through hydraulic fracturing and water flooding, Illinois

Sketch of a typical oil rig

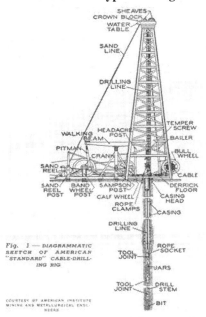

oil production rose to about 82 million barrels in 1956. Unfortunately, production in the state has been declining ever since, amounting to only about 12 million barrels annually in recent years.

A more recent extraction technique is the injection of carbon dioxide into areas around the well to push the oil closer to the well.

When a site is prospected for oil, the first thing done is the construction of a drilling rig with a spindletop. The old rigs were wooden structures, and they were left in place after the drilling was completed. Today they are made of metal and are dismantled and reused elsewhere. As the drilling process begins and progress is made through various layers of earth and rock strata, core samples are taken and analyzed. As the well progresses, a 4-6 inch casing is inserted into the drilled area. When it is believed

How oil is trapped in various geological formations

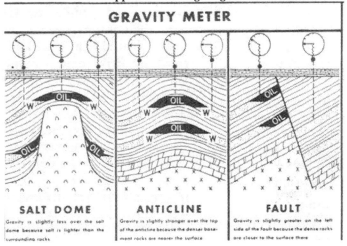

that oil has been found, a smaller pipe is inserted inside the casing, and an explosive charge called a Go-Devil is lowered to the bottom. This explosion blows a hole in the side of the casing, allowing crude oil to seep into it.

Whether or not you get what is known as a "gusher" depends on how much pressure is in the strata. If the oil is under strong pressure, they place a choke on the top of the well, and this regulates the flow of gas. Water and gas often come up with the oil as a by-product. In older times, the gas was burned or "flared" off. Nowadays the gas is sent to a compressor where it is converted into a liquid composed of propane, butane, methane and ethane. The water is often collected and injected back into the ground to help force the oil up the well.

The oil that is pumped out of the ground is sent to a collection tank. The pipe leading from the well to the tank often sits on top of the ground.

When a well penetrates an oil reservoir, it is much like a balloon that gradually begins to deflate. In some large oil fields there is a certain amount of subsidence (sinkage) because of this deflation. A similar phenomenon occurs when extensive coal deposits are removed. Most homeowners who live in an area that is honeycombed with mines take out mine subsidence insurance to protect their investment.

Gary Barber, a Houston, Texas, engineer (formerly of **Edwardsville**) explains that crude oil contains other contaminants such as sulfur, and these are removed during the refining process. Particulate matter in suspension is separated and is converted into asphalt for applying to roads. The term asphalt actually has two meanings. First, it is merely the sludge that exists at the bottom in a normal barrel of crude oil that is pumped from the ground. At room temperature this mixture is nearly a solid. The second definition is the mixture of this sludge with sand and gravel to form a material that is used to build or resurface roads.

Road asphalt is combined with crushed rock and sand for road construction purposes. Refineries also make pitch that is used for roofing tar. The asphalt at the bottom of a barrel can be mixed with diesel fuel to form "bunker fuel" that is used to power ocean going vessels. Ships are generally powered by a special internal combustion engine that runs on this heavy fuel.

Similarities between oil refining and an illegal still

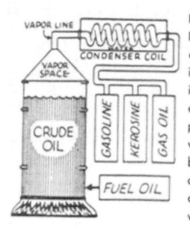

IN ITS SIMPLEST FORM the process of petroleum refining consists in heating the crude oil in a still to its boiling point, passing the vapors from the boiling oil thru condensing pipes and condensing the vapors into liquids.

Let's use a typical well that you might see in a farmer's field off Interstate 64 in Wayne County as an example. Over a 24-hour period the well might produce a minimum of five barrels (42 gallons per barrel) a day. That is roughly the break-even point due to electrical costs for the pump motor and other expenses incurred in the collection and

Oil refinery in **Wood River**, Illinois

shipping process. The average well produces about 20 barrels a day or 800 gallons. If the going price of crude on the world market is $20 a barrel, that's over $400 a day. Electrical costs per day run about $100.00. The farmer who owns the land receives about one eighth or $50 a day, and the company that installs and maintains the well gets the other $250. Wells around **Mattoon, Taylorville** and **Nashville** generally pump more than 20 barrels a day.

After the **Carlyle** dam was built and the lake created, you saw a lot of oil wells drilled around the perimeter of the lake. That's because all the weight of that water sitting on the lakebed placed the oil in the rock strata under greater pressure, making it more economically feasible to drill for oil.

In the old days geologists specifically looked for dome-shaped rock formations because they knew this often meant that oil was trapped in the strata of such a formation. The oil sometimes collects in pools, but it is often trapped in porous rock such as shale or sandstone.

By 1962, oil had replaced coal as the state's most valuable mineral, and it employed some 60,000 people.

Over the years some 150,000 wells have been sunk in Illinois to explore for gas and oil deposits. Oil has been found in 47 counties by 1,200 companies.

"Down Among the Oilfields" – old poem, author unknown

We're down among the oil fields
Where you never have the blues
Where the bandits steal the jitneys
And the marshals steal the booze.

Where the burglars pick your pockets
While you "lay me down to sleep,"
Where the bulldogs all have rabies
And the rabbits they have fleas.

Where the buildings horn the skyline
 Where the populace is boost
 Where they shoot a man for pastime
 Where the chickens never roost.

 And you come home in the evening
 Suffocating in the heat,
 Where the jitneys whiz about you
 And the street cars barely creep.

 Where the big girls like the wee ones
 Wear their dresses to the knees,
 Where you get up in the morning
 In a world of snow and sleet.

 Where the stickup men are wary
 And the bullets fall like hail;
 Where each pocket has a pistol
 And each pistol's good for jail.

 Where you whist out in the morning
 Just to give your health a chance,
 Say "Howdy" to some fellow who

Shoots big holes in your pants.

Where they always hang the jury
Where they never hang a man,
If you call a man a liar, you
Get home the best you can.

Where the owls are afraid to hoot
And birds don't dare to sing,
For its hell down here in Oil Land
Where they all shoot on the wing.

ERRORS & OMISSIONS: PEOPLE AND FACTS INADVERTENTLY OMITTED FROM 2003 *INCREDIBLE ILLINOIS*

John Vincent Atanasoff – The man who invented the digital computer while contemplating its principles in a **Rock Island** tavern in 1938. He was a professor at Iowa State College in Ames, Iowa, but drove to Rock Island because Iowa was a dry state at the time. He built a fully functional computer but failed to follow up on a patent application. A man named John Mauchly borrowed his ideas and built the famous ENIAC computer. In 1946 he was declared to be the inventor of the modern computer.

A long court battle started in the late 1960s and ended in 1973 with Atanasoff being declared the rightful **inventor of the computer**. Unfortunately, too much time had elapsed and it was much too late for him to receive royalty payments.

Leah Baird – (1883-1971) Chicago-born actress who first made a name for herself in summer stock and traveling companies. She was quite popular as a silent screen actress from 1915 to 1925, making about sixty movies, including *Destroying Angel*.

After her career faded she turned to script writing, and after that she decided to reenter acting by playing bit parts. She appeared uncredited in *Mildred Pierce, The Desert Song, Watch On The Rhine, Action In The North Atlantic*, and *Kings Row*.

Marlon Brando – Brando was born in Nebraska but his family moved to **Libertyville**, Illinois, north of Chicago, in 1937 when he was a child. His ancestry was French-Irish and the original spelling of the name was Brandeau. He had a tumultuous childhood and was kicked out of several schools (surprise, surprise). He finished his education at a military school. Brando's mother, who died of alcoholism in 1954, did some acting in a local theater and this is how he got interested in the business. The rebellious Brando was even kicked out of acting school. His

Marlon Brando

salesman father later became his manager.

Brando is considered **by some critics to be the best actor in the history of films.** My son (Steven) disagrees and thinks he made only two good films – *On The Waterfront* and *The Young Lions*.

Maurice "Mo" Cheeks – Chicago-born star basketball player for the Philadelphia 76ers in the 1970s and 1980s. In his later years he played for the Atlanta Hawks and New Jersey Nets. He was a great defensive basketball player and excelled in making steals. In 2001 he became the head coach of the Portland Trail Blazers but was released in mid-season due to the team's poor performance.

He owns **one of the most memorable NBA moments in history**. A young girl was singing the National Anthem before one of the Trail Blazer games. Suffering stage fright, the girl forgot the words halfway through the song. **Cheeks went over, put his arm around her, and helped her finish in fine style**.

Billy Graham – Although we traditionally associate the Reverend Graham with North Carolina, he has an important Illinois connection. In 1941 he was the pastor of the Gospel Tabernacle in **Wheaton**. While pastor, Graham attended Wheaton College outside of Chicago. There he met and fell in love with Ruth Bell, the daughter of a Presbyterian medical missionary. He was a freshman and she was a highly pursued junior. The wedding took place after Graham's graduation in 1943. He soon became the pastor of a small basement congregation in **Western Springs**, Illinois.

Little John Gregory

Little John Gregory – Following in the tradition of Alvin Shipwreck Kelley, John Gregory fixed a perch above a shopping center in **Rockford** in an effort to beat a 211-day record he had set earlier in Fort Smith, Arkansas. This was in 1961 and it took a small army to finally haul him down from his perch. **His weight had ballooned from 419 pounds to an alarming 499.** Apparently, his doctor didn't want him to go over the 500-pound mark.

Dorothy Hamill – Born in Chicago but reared in Connecticut; she won Olympic gold at Innsbruck in 1976; married Dean Paul Martin (Dean Martin's son) in 1982; starred in the Ice Capades. Most recently Dorothy did commercials for Vioxx.

June Haver – Born June Stovenour in **Rock Island**, she performed a piano solo with the Cincinnati Symphony at age seven. She made her first feature film *Home in Indiana*, in 1944. She went on to star in other musicals including: *Look For The Silver Lining, I Wonder Who's Kissing Her Now, When Irish Eyes Are Smiling, and Oh, You Beautiful Doll.* She was wed to actor Fred MacMurray in 1954.

Sidney Hillman (1887-1946) Born in Lithuania, Hillman became the founder of the Amalgamated Clothing Workers of America. As a close friend and adviser to President Roosevelt, Hillman helped shape New Deal legislation that protected the rights of workers and improved working conditions.

Hillman came to Chicago in 1907. He worked for a while as a stock clerk for Sears & Roebuck. Then he apprenticed himself to a garment cutter in a factory run by Hart, Schaffner and Marx.

Hillman believed in working with management to try and head off union conflicts and strikes, preferring instead a policy of constructive cooperation.

Hillman emerged as a union leader during the 1910 garment workers strike. During the strike he met his future wife, Bessie Abramowitz.

Juwan Howard – Raised on the south side of Chicago by his grandmother; became a member of the 1991 Fab Five basketball team at Michigan along with the likes of Jalen Rose and Chris Webber. In 1992 the five freshmen advanced to the NCAA championship game but lost to Duke. Everyone vividly remembers the 1993 loss to North Carolina in the final game where Chris Webber was **charged with a technical for calling a time out they didn't have**. Their legacy has been tarnished by failure on the court and recent charges of illegal payments made when they were yet amateurs. A former Michigan athletic director has called the era a disgrace. The University took down the two Final Four banners. Howard played in the NBA with Washington, Denver, Dallas and Houston. He had over 600 steals in his career. He has been known in recent years for his philanthropy and work with disadvantaged youth.

Matt Hughes – **Hillsboro**, Illinois, man who is the current UFC mixed martial arts champ with a record of 30-3. At 170 pounds he is considered the **most powerful fighter in the history of the sport** in the welterweight division. In mixed martial arts contestants are barefoot and can kick, box or wrestle during the match. They wear padded gloves without fingers.

Leonard Keeler – A professional at the Northwestern University crime lab; inventor of the polygraph lie detector test. William Marston made such an instrument possible when he invented the systolic blood pressure test. In 1940 Keeler was working as an advisor for Detective Comics and came up with the idea for the female super heroine **Wonder Woman**.

Mike Krzyzewski (Sha-shef-ski) – Born in 1947, he attended high school in Chicago; outstanding coach of the Duke Blue Devils basketball team for twenty-five years. He was twelve times the ACC Coach of the Year with over 700 total wins; has three national championships; ten Final Four appearances; inducted into the Basketball Hall of Fame in 2001.

Bernie Mac – Chicago actor and comedian; star of "The Bernie Mac Show" on the Fox network and the film, *Mr. 3000.*

Sidney Hillman of the Amalgamated Garment Workers

Virginia Marmaduke – Died at **Pinckneyville** Community Hospital in 2001 at age 93. She was born in **Carbondale** in 1908 and spent her childhood in a two-story house on Poplar Street. The family moved to Chicago when the Illinois Central Railroad gave her dad a promotion. She learned her writing skills at the Ursuline Academy in Arcadia, Missouri. She then attended the University of Iowa where she studied journalism and then married Harold Grear, whose family owned the ***Herrin Daily Journal***. Virginia started her career by writing about local events. They divorced in 1943 and Virginia left for Chicago where she was hired by the *Sun*. She told the editor that she couldn't cook and didn't know anything about fashion. Virginia said she wanted to cover "blood, guts, and sex" as a beat reporter. Luck was with her. She got her wish because the war had left the newsroom shorthanded.

Her big break came three years later when she was first at the scene when police found the severed head of youngster Suzanne Degnan in a sewer. She conducted 600 interviews in covering what came to be known as the "crime that shocked Chicago."

Virginia Marmaduke

Virginia later covered the presidential campaigns of Harry Truman, Dwight Eisenhower and John Kennedy. She soon became known as the **"Grand Duchess of Journalism."** Most of her 35-year career in print and broadcast journalism was spent in Chicago. She was the first woman on the *Chicago Sun's* editorial staff, the first woman in Chicago with a sports byline (earned covering harness races at Maywood Park), and was Chicago's first female crime reporter.

Marmaduke wrote about murder and mayhem, the famous and infamous. She was as colorful as anything she wrote in her columns. Virginia once fended off a gangster with a spiked heel shoe. She moved over to the *Tribune* when they offered her more money. She then became the host of a radio show named "Coffee With the Duchess." She interviewed Queen Elizabeth and Frank Sinatra, and dated actor George Raft.

In 1964 she was hostess of the Land of Lincoln pavilion at the World's Fair at Flushing Meadows, NY. After the fair she retired and moved to a cabin in **Pinckneyville** on land that had been in her family since 1831. She spent her remaining years involved with various causes and as a booster of southern Illinois. She became a spokeswoman for Southern Illinois University at **Carbondale**.

Virginia was inducted into the Journalism Hall of Fame in 1992.

Donovan McNabb – Illinois kid (born in 1976) who grew up in the Dolton neighborhood of south Chicago; played on a state championship prep basketball team. Weighing 240 pounds and standing 6-2, he starred at Syracuse University but was lustily booed by Philadelphia fans when drafted by the Eagles. McNabb played the entire regular 2004 NFL season without throwing an interception in the red zone. He does Campbell Soup commercials with his mother. **Rush Limbaugh stirred up a controversy when he criticized McNabb** and said that he was just an average quarterback who received special attention because he was African-American. McNabb led the Eagles to a 13-3 season in 2004 with two of the losses coming after Philadelphia had wrapped up a division crown and home field advantage (McNabb saw limited playing time in the losses to St. Louis and Cincinnati). Prior to the 2004 season Mc-Nabb's team had lost three consecutive NFC championship games. He threw three touchdown passes and three interceptions in a losing cause in the 2005 Super Bowl.

Jay Mariotti – Chicago *Sun-Times* sportswriter who also appears daily on ESPN's "Around The Horn" (avidly watched by this writer). He leads all guests with the most wins on a show that pits four national sports writers against each other in competitive banter as they comment about sports news of the day. Mariotti was banned (tongue in cheek) from reentering the state after predicting (while covering the Super Bowl in Jacksonville) that 21-0 Illinois would lose to 10th ranked Michigan State.

Mariotti correctly picked North Carolina to defeat Illinois in the NCAA championship basketball game at St. Louis in April of 2005.

Mariotti maintains that most people mispronounce the state name. It's Ill (as in sick) i-noi, not El-a-noi.

Danica Patrick

Tim "Kingfish" Moore – **Rock Island** native who played the part of George "Kingfish" Stephens in the television production of *Amos 'n' Andy*. About 800 other actors auditioned for the part but were turned down. Moore was recommended for the part by Charles Correll and Freeman Gosden, the two who originally invented the radio characters.

Tim "Kingfish" Moore

Clarence E. Mulford – Wrote a series of western stories about the Bar 20 Ranch. The hero was Buck Peters who had an interesting sidekick that walked with a limp after a rustler's bullet shattered his knee. He was known as Hopalong Cassidy and Bill Boyd played the character on the silver screen. Boyd's co-star was his white horse Topper and he (Boyd) never drank anything stronger than sarsaparilla. Boyd had the foresight to buy the rights to the character from Milford and made millions when Hopalong Cassidy became a popular television program.

Reinhold Neibhur – 1892-1971 – Liberal, socialist, iconoclastic Protestant theologian from **Lincoln**, Illinois who did not believe in the virgin birth of Christ. He is generally believed to be the author of the Serenity Prayer (God grant me the serenity to . . .). Neibhur was awarded the Medal of Freedom in 1964; wrote *Moral Man and Immoral Society* in 1932.

Danica Patrick – Racecar driving sensation who wowed the sports world by nearly winning the Indy 500 in May of 2005. This petite 100-pound, 5-2 beauty took the lead near the end of the race but ultimately finished fourth due to her car being low on fuel. She was born in Beloit, Wisconsin, but grew up in nearby **Roscoe**, Illinois.

Melvin Van Peebles – Chicago-born (1932) director, screen writer, film editor, actor, producer and composer; father of actor Mario Van Peebles who starred with Clint Eastwood in *Heartbreak Ridge*.

Kirby Puckett – Grew up on the south side of Chicago and went on to become an All-Star player for the Minnesota Twins, winning two World Series titles in 1987 and 1991. Born in 1960, he was the youngest of nine children. Elected to the Hall of Fame in 2001. The gregarious Puckett was also named to ten straight All-Star teams from 1986 to 1995. He played only 12 seasons for the Twins due to irreversible damage to the retina in his right eye.

Cheryl Rhoads – Born in 1954 at **Hinsdale**, Illinois; her mother, Mary Gurrie Rhoads, was a newspaper columnist in Chicago. Brother Mark Rhoads was an Illinois senator. Cheryl was a member of Chicago's Second City comedy improv. Cheryl is an actress, writer and producer. She was Mother Goose in the 1987 *Mother Goose Video Treasury*; teaches acting classes. She currently is a conservative advocate trying to counterbalance liberal Hollywood.

Cheryl Rhoades

Gary Schroen – A 1959 graduate of **East St. Louis High** who recently wrote about his experiences as CIA station chief for two decades in Pakistan and Afghanistan. He knew the warlords who helped drive the Soviets from Afghanistan. Schroen's book, *First In: How the CIA Spearheaded the War on Terror in Afghanistan*, is a tale of both derring-do and miscues, too. In paving the way for the invasion of Afghanistan, Schroen handed out $3 million in hundred dollar bills to local Afghan commanders to solidify their support. Our biggest mistake, he claims, was in allowing the Afghans to go after Osama Bin Laden instead of using the U.S. military. Schroen feels that the invasion of Iraq was a mistake and that it has become a magnet to draw out radical jihadists who hate the U.S.

Gary Schroen (St. Louis Post-Dispatch)

Len Small – Called "the Pardoning Governor," Small was known for carrying his collaboration with crime figures to the limit. Small entered the Springfield executive mansion in 1921 and was promptly indicted for embezzling money when he previously held the position of state treasurer. While his lawyers defended him in court, he allegedly worked behind the scenes with crime figures to make sure that jurors were either bribed or intimidated into a "not guilty" verdict. He repaid the boys for their efficient work by issuing pardons on an unprecedented scale. Chicago journalist George Murray exposed these shenanigans in his sensational work, *The Legacy of Al Capone*.

Susan Sontag – (1933-2004) Born in New York, grew up in Arizona; received her college degree from the University of Chicago. She married and divorced her sociology instructor in the 1950s. Susan excelled as a short story writer, novelist, human rights activist and commentator on modern culture. She has also written screenplays and directed films. Susan became associated with the radical Bohemian scene in New York in the Sixties. Became nationally famous as a Vietnam War critic in the Jane Fonda mold.

Francis Townsend – Social critic who was born and educated in **Fairbury**, Illinois. The youngest of seven children, he was birthed in a two-room log cabin in 1867. Concerned about the many people on relief during the Depression, he devised the Townsend Plan. It would supply $200 a month to all those over the age of 60. The money would come from a special tax on business. The 18-member faculty of the University of Chicago analyzed the plan and decided that the plan would cost taxpayers $20 billion a year – 40 percent of the nation's 1934 income. Undaunted, he held rallies and conventions and his supporters numbered in the millions.

It was partially due to pressure from the Townsend Plan that F.D.R. proposed his plan for Social Security. Although Townsend attacked the New Deal program, he was drawing $98.50 a month from it when he died in 1960 at age 93.

Dwyane Wade – **Southwest Chicago** kid born in 1982. Wade attended Oak Lawn High School and then went to Marquette University and was drafted by the NBA in 2001. Now he is one of the top guards - make that top stars - in the NBA, playing alongside Shaquille O'Neil for the Miami Heat. When O'Neil got hurt in the 2005 playoffs, Wade started posting Michael Jordan-like statistics.

Jack Welch – Former CEO of General Electric and author of the 2005 number one selling book *Winning*. Welch is a big fan of George W. Bush and is a graduate of the University of Illinois.

Michael Wilbon - Chicagoan and Northwestern grad who appears daily on the ESPN sports show, "Pardon The Interruption" with Tony Kornheiser; Wilbon and Kornheiser are columnists for the *Washington Post*.

Gretchen Wilson – Country singing star sensation from **Pocahontas**, Illinois, in Bond County. She grew up listening to Charlie Daniels, Patsy Cline, and Tanya Tucker. She dropped out of school and began waitressing at the Powhatan Restaurant and singing cover songs at local bars for tips. She moved to Nashville, Tennessee, and became a member of the Musik Mafia, writing songs. Signed by Sony Records, she is known as "Redneck Girl" and recently nabbed two big ACM Awards – Top Female Vocalist and Top New Artist. **(Picture - right)**

Billy Zane – Chicago-born (1966) actor best known as *The Phantom* and for portraying the snobbish, villainous Cal Hockley, fiancé of the beautiful young socialite in *Titanic*

REAGANISMS - RONALD REAGAN QUOTES
(Reagan was born in **Tampico** and grew up in the town of **Dixon**, Illinois.)

"The most terrifying words in the English language are: I'm from the government and I'm here to help."

"The trouble with our liberal friends is not that they're ignorant; it's just that they know so much that isn't so."

"Of the four wars in my lifetime none came about because the U.S. was too strong."

"I have wondered at times about what the Ten Commandments would have looked like if Moses had run them through the U.S. Congress."

"The taxpayer: That's someone who works for the federal government but doesn't have to take the civil service examination."

"Government is like a baby: An alimentary canal with a big appetite at one end and no sense of responsibility at the other."

"If we ever forget that we're one nation under God, then we will be a nation gone under."

"The nearest thing to eternal life we will ever see on this earth is a government program."

"It has been said that politics is the second oldest profession. I have learned that it bears a striking resemblance to the first."

"Government's view of the economy could be summed up in a few short phrases: If it moves, tax it; if it keeps moving, regulate it; and if it stops moving, subsidize it."

"Politics is not a bad profession. If you succeed there are many rewards. If you disgrace yourself you can always write a book."

Ronald Reagan

"I believe it was divine intervention that saved us for an important job to finish." – Ronald Reagan when he met with Pope John Paul II after each survived assassination attempts. Reagan went on to make a secret pact with the Polish Pope. They formed an alliance and exchanged information about Communist governments. Reagan secretly sent aid to the Solidarity movement in Poland to help them throw off the shackles of Communism.

INTERESTING FACTS

The paw paw tree is the only tropical fruit tree native to Illinois. The small town of Paw Paw, Illinois, has the **largest modern windmill farm in the state**.

Gretchen Wilson - courtesy Sony Music

Glass blocks became popular with architects and homeowners after Owens-Illinois of **Alton** used them in their building at the Chicago World's Fair of 1933.

At one point in earlier geological history the Rock River flowed southward and met up with the Illinois River at **Hennepin** instead of emptying into the Mississippi River. Glacial action about 12,000 years ago diverted its stream to the Mississippi.

Jill Gulseth – Miss Illinois - made the final cut in a copycat 2005 Miss USA contest in Baltimore and, along with Miss North Carolina, was one of five finalists. She goofed in her informal Q & A with the show's hosts near the end by responding to a simple question with "Uh, yeah!" In a cruel twist of fate Jill lost the title to Miss North Carolina, a big Tar Heels fan.

Illini coach Bruce Weber's brother (Dave) coaches the **Glenbrook** North High School basketball team. Glenbrook won the 2-A IHSA prep tourney championship just a few weeks before Illinois went to the Final Four.

Jewel Tea of **Melrose Park** started as a home delivery service. Frank Skiff started his first route in 1899 delivering coffee, cereals, tea, extracts, spices, graham crackers condiments, soap products, etc.

Many of the steam shovels that dug the Panama Canal were later bought by Illinois coal companies to dig strip mines.

Significant Illinois-based companies omitted from previous books include Piggly Wiggly, National Tea, and Spiegel Catalog.

David Richards sculpted the statue of Chief Blackhawk at Spencer Square in **Rock Island**. The legs are thicker than they should be. This was done on purpose so that vandals might not easily break them.

The nation was shocked in February of 2005 when a distraught Bart Ross broke into a Lakewood-Balmoral home on Chicago's north side and murdered Judge Joan Lefkow's husband (Michael) and her mother, Donna Humphrey. Lefkow had been the judge in a cancer medical malpractice case involving Ross. Ross committed suicide after being pulled over for a broken tail light by an officer in Wisconsin, not long after the murders. Ross was a Polish immigrant who came to this country back in 1982.

Lefkow dismissed a medical malpractice suit filed by Ross, who was an electrician. DNA from a cigarette butt found at the murder scene linked Ross to the killings. The judge and her daughters were taken into protective custody shortly after the shootings.

At first it was thought that neo-Nazis committed the murders. Lefkow previously had a run in with white supremacists after she declared them to be a hate group and ordered their web site shut down. Matthew Hale, the group's leader, was convicted (April 2004) of soliciting judge Lefkow's murder.

Mike Ditka of Chicago appears in the 2005 soccer comedy film, *Kicking And Screaming*; do I hear Oscar?

World famous soccer star Mia Hamm is married to infielder Nomar Darciaparra of the Chicago Cubs baseball team.

Dennis Hastert of **Aurora** wrote *Speaker*, his 2004 memoirs about forty years as a high school wrestling coach and Speaker of the U.S. House of Representatives.

A black cat ran onto Wrigley Field during a Cub's game in early June of 2005. Experts predict that this unfortunate incident will extend "the curse" by at least another decade.

Some members of the All-Century Basketball Team of the

Engineer Casey Jones in the cab of engine 638

Fighting Illini: Ray Woods, Chuck Carney, Andy Phillip, Johnny Kerr, Eddie Johnson, Bruce Douglas, Frank Williams, Brian Cook, Kenny Battle, Nick Anderson, Kendall Gill

Wabash Cannonball Bridge on Ill-Indiana border by Doc Brasel

At least two mournful songs have been written about the woeful state of affairs in Cub Country. One is titled *The Land of Wrigley*, sung to the tune of *Stormy Weather,* and the other is called *A Dying Cub Fan's Last Request*, performed by Steve Goodman. There is also an item going around on the internet that tells how many centerfield flagpoles have rusted away, how many presidents we've had, and what things have been invented since the Cubs last won the World Series, nearly 100 years ago.

The first train to travel from **Chicago** to the Mississippi was pulled by a Rock Island Railroad steam engine called the *Rocket*. It reached **Rock Island** in 1854.

Confederate prisoners during the Civil War were housed at Arsenal Island at **Rock Island**. It was only when one soldier in captivity gave birth to a baby that authorities discovered *he* was a *she*.

On October 5, 1937, President Franklin D. Roosevelt came to **Chicago** to dedicate the largest bascule bridge in the world, spanning the Chicago River. On a bascule bridge one or two sections are lifted vertically, but they always remain in a horizontal position. The London Tower Bridge is an example of a bascule bridge. Roosevelt used that occasion to give a famous speech. He was trying to move the country away from its position of neutrality by calling attention to disturbing events in the world. He called war a contagion and called for a "quarantine" of aggressor nations by peaceful ones.

The prominent and influential Daniel Webster came to **Chicago** via the Illinois River and Des Plaines portage in June of 1837 after buying a farm near **Peoria**. He declared, "Chicago is the seaport of Illinois." He promised to support a bill in congress to improve the

144

river and harbor at Chicago.

Eugene Debs, **Chicago** labor leader and five-time Socialist candidate for U.S. President; spent six months in the **Woodstock**, Illinois jail for violating an injunction during the contentious Pullman Strike in 1894. Imprisonment was 55 miles outside of Chicago to avoid mass protests against the perceived unfair punishment of the charismatic Debs. (from Jeff Ruetsche of **Crystal Lake – look for his book, *On This Day In Illinois History* by Emmis Publishing, soon to be released**)

In 1893 the Illinois legislature passed a bill authorizing the establishment of a new teachers college in northern Illinois. **Rockford, Freeport, Oregon, Dixon, Polo** and **Fulton**, all on scenic Rock River (except Fulton on the Mississippi), were competitors for the prize. Yet the economic windfall went to **Dekalb** on the less impressive Kishwaukee River.

Dekalb won through hard civic work and some clever deception. Before the award committee arrived in Dekalb, special dams were built downstream so that water levels would rise and the place would look more scenic. The whole town went without water for a week just to make sure. (from Jeff Ruetsche of **Crystal Lake**)

How did the Sag near the Calumet River in Chicago get its name? This area was mostly a swamp given the cumbersome Indian name Auso-gananashkee. Descendants of early pioneers made quick work of it by shortening the polysyllables to Sag.

The first AP poll in 1949 had four Illinois basketball teams ranked in top 20 – U of I, Bradley, Loyola, and DePaul.

The 2005 Chicago White Sox set a major league record for having the lead at some point in all of their first 31 games to start the season.

Dorothy Schroeder, a native of **Sadorus**, Illinois, was the only woman to play all twelve years in the All-American Girls Professional Baseball League – 1943-54.

In 1948 the Northwestern Wildcats, who won only three games the previous season, secured their first bid to the Rose Bowl by defeating Illinois, 20-7. They went on to defeat the California Bears 20-13 at Rose Bowl Stadium.

The 1906 Cubs had a 116-36 season record. Their .736 winning

percentage is still the best ever in the major leagues.

Pyramid State Park (near **Pinckneyville**), with 19,000 acres mostly bought from Arch Coal Co. in 2000, is the largest in the state. Prior to that Pere Marquette Park near **Grafton** held the title with 8,035. (from Roger Schlueter: *Belleville News-Democrat*)

Colonel John O'Fallon, a famous railroad developer who had the town of **O'Fallon** named for him, was a nephew of explorer William Clark of the Lewis and Clark expedition.

Parody of Florida Land Boom of the early 1920s

In June of 1924 **Roundout**, Illinois, in Lake County near **Libertyville**, was the scene of the **biggest train heist in U.S. history**. The Newton boys – Willis, Joe, Jesse and Dock – were Texans who had grown weary of working on their father's farm and embarked instead on a life of crime in 1919. They turned to robbing banks and had an affinity for using nitro to blow open the door of bank vaults. Despite their lawless ways, they prided themselves on having never killed anyone.

A couple of armed members of the gang boarded a U.S. Postal Train in Chicago disguised as postal employees. The others waited in ambush near Roundout. The boys made off with nearly $3 million in sacks of cash and securities. Unfortunately for the Newton boys, the Roundout robbery proved to be their downfall.

The 1998 lighthearted film, *The Newton Boys*, (starring Ethan Hawke and Matthew McConaughey) was loosely based on their exploits.

Jim Journell, An electrifying pitcher for the University of Illinois, signed with the St. Louis Cardinals. He immediately required Tommy John surgery on his pitching arm and did little for the next two years. By the 2005 season he was fully recovered and throwing 94 mph baffling fastballs at opposing batters in relief.

With four dozen plants and factories, **Belleville** was once the stove capital of America. Belleville is thought to have the longest Main Street in the state. The town was also famous for its production of white asparagus. Belleville Township also won the state's first

Freshman Number by John Held Jr.

prep baseball championship in 1940 defeating **Champaign** 8-3.

Cahokia and **East St. Louis** in 1,000 A.D. boasted what is believed to be the largest prehistoric city in North America near the site of Monks Mound on present-day Route 40. Roughly 20,000 Mississippians once made their home in the area. It is not known why their civilization disappeared.

Pyramid Mound at **Lewistown** – tunnel entrance in right foreground

The town of **Madison** had the state's first Bulgarian Orthodox Church, built in 1907. Many immigrants who settled there were descendants of Russian-born coal miners.

Although he never lived in there, Civil War general William Tecumseh Sherman once owned 98 acres of land in **Collinsville**.

The town of **Shiloh** (in Southern Illinois) claims to have had the first Christmas tree in the state of Illinois.

Why do many Illini fans have unused tickets to the 1963 Illinois-Michigan State football game at East Lansing? It was cancelled due to John F. Kennedy's assassination the day before. (from Dan Oberle of **Geneseo/Edwardsville**)

Despite losses in the first round of the Final Four in 1949, 1951, and 1952, what else did the Illini basketball teams accomplish? All of them won their next tournament game and finished in third place.

The great sculptor Lorado Taft of **Peoria County** was commissioned to execute two groups for the Horticulture Building at the 1893

Columbian Exposition in **Chicago**. Taft asked the fair's lead planner, Daniel Burnham, if a few of his female students could help with the project to insure its completion on time. A worried Burnham replied, "Hire anyone – even white rabbits if they'll do the work." From that reply was born a group of pioneering women sculptors, "The White Rabbits." (from Jeff Ruetsche of **Crystal Lake**, author of *This Day In Illinois History*)

The 2004-05 University of Illinois basketball team finished first in the Big Ten with a record of 32-1. It won the number one overall seed in the March NCAA Tournament. Guard Dee Brown was voted Big Ten Player of the Year, and their center (James Augustine) was voted MVP of the Big Ten Tournament, also won by Illinois. They set a Big Ten record for number of wins in a season with 37. They tied the NCAA record for most wins in a season. Luther Head set a single season record for three pointers with over 100. Coach Bruce Weber won the Adolph Rupp Award as the national coach of the year. After defeating Louisville in the Final Four semi-final game, Illinois reached the championship game for the first time in school history. They would face North Carolina, a team that had produced Michael Jordan and made it to the Final Four sixteen times.

Illinois held the number 1 spot in the AP poll fourteen weeks. They took the number one spot away from Wake Forest early in the season by handing them a crushing defeat at Champaign. Before coach Weber sent in the reserves, the Illini led the number 1 ranked team in the nation by 32 points.

Starting Five – U of I 2004-5 (*St. Louis Post-Dispatch*)

All season long the pundits talked about how weak the Big Ten Conference was and how good the Big East and ACC was. Yet Illinois, Wisconsin, and Michigan State all made the Elite Eight while the only team to survive in the East was North Carolina. Michigan State and Illinois also made it to the Final Four.

As the team bus drove down Interstate 55 to get to St Louis for the NCAA finals, Coach Weber had the driver stop at Camelot Bowl in **Collinsville** where the team relaxed with some friendly but competitive bowling.

The dream season finally came to an end with a 75-70 loss to North Carolina. Illinois, after being down 13 points at the half, fought back to a 70-70 tie, but couldn't connect after that.

Isn't it amazing that it was an Illinois IHSA official in 1939 who first coined the phrase, "March Madness?" The 2005 NCAA regional Midwest final was insanity taking a quantum leap. Illinois was part of an awe-inspiring tournament weekend that has been called the *greatest ever* in college basketball history. Two regional finals went into overtime, and the Michigan State/Kentucky game wasn't decided until the end of double overtime.

Yet none was more exciting than the frenetic Illini contest. Be still my furiously beating heart. Illinois fought its way into their fifth ('49, '51, '52, '89) Final Four with a stunning, un-FOUR-gettable overtime 90-89 victory against Arizona before 16,957 hysterical fans.

Was that some kind of game or what? When Arizona's Hassan Adams missed a 17-foot shot with seconds to go in heart-stopping overtime, orange-clad fans went nuts with jubilation. It was like watching a CBS episode of *Survivor Rosemont*. On the day before Easter Sunday, the sports world witnessed another miraculous resurrection of sorts.

The Orange and Blue trailed most of the second half, and at one time they were down by fifteen points before making the most scintillating comeback in the school's 100-year history. Furthermore, it was one of the craziest comebacks in NCAA tournament history. The Fighting Illini were down by 15 with just FOUR minutes to play. They had suffered through a 5:32 drought without making a basket. Arizona 75, Illinois 60. They were down. Done. Hopelessly out of it. Dead team walking.

The magical season was going up in smoke. The last moments were fading fast with a decidedly cruel ending. It was about to be a loss that would tear at your guts for weeks and weeks. Illinois was on the verge of becoming the third number one 2005 tourney seed to bite the dust, following in the bitter wake of Washington and Duke. It was about to become an embarrassing loss to the number three regional seed. It was Illinois' largest deficit all year. And what made it all seem hopeless for this vertically challenged team was that their tallest starter, and in-

the-paint mainstay, James Augustine, was out of the game with five fouls. Moreover, Arizona was shooting over fifty percent from the field with Frye and Adams running wild and scoring at will.

Passionate Illinois fans crossed their fingers, chanted D-E-F-E-N-S-E, closed their eyes, and prayed for an improbable miracle. Then the hoop gods smiled on the team that had been to the Final Four only once in the last 53 years. It was Luther Head's three-pointer from another zip code with 3:08 left that brought the stunned crowd back to life. After that, it sounded as if the airplanes at O'Hare air-port had been diverted to the Allstate Arena (better known as Assembly Hall North). The television cameras zeroed in on comedic star Bill Murray who was going berserk with delirium in the stands behind the Illini bench. It was fast and furious after that. A steal by Luther Head; a rebound putback by Dee Brown; a drive to the hole by Williams; a steal by Jack Ingram; a dunk by Roger Powell. Wham! Bam! Pow! Shock and Awe!

The Illini were still down by eight with 1:03 left on the clock. The Wildcat meltdown began with 6:03 left on the clock in regulation. From that point until the end of the game they failed to score a single basket – only free throws. Deron Williams, who along with Head was named to the All-Tournament Team, tied the game in regulation at 80-80 with a three-pointer. Illinois went on to win by a single point in overtime.

Williams was a defensive standout, hanging all over Arizona star player Salim Stoudamire like a second jersey. Stoudamire was just 2-13 shooting and scored a total of only nine points.

Illinois survived by making a school record 16 three-pointers on 16-35 shooting.

Luther Head had a spectacular game scoring 20 points while nursing a bad hamstring, most of them in the critical second half.

"You can see why they're 36-1," Arizona coach Lute Olsen said. "They just don't give up."

An emotional coach Bruce Weber, who had just buried his mom less than a month ago, broke down and cried after the game. "My mother was looking down on me tonight," Weber said. Weber's record in tournament play now stands at 8-3.

"Not only was it the greatest game I've ever played in, it was the greatest game I've ever watched." – Jack Ingram.

"It was just meant to be," Dee Brown said. "See you in St. Louie."

The Stun-back Kids, with the best three-guard attack in the nation, continued their relentless drive, their March to the Arch.

Southern Illinois University at **Carbondale** (26-7) made the 2005 NCAA tournament with a 7th seed, its highest ever.

Kathy Reichs, best-selling author of seven forensic novels and creator of heroine Tempe Brennan, is a native of Chicago. She received her Ph.D at

Illinois v. Arizona 2005

ARIZONA

	min	FG	FT	reb o-t	a	pf	pts.
Adams	37	9-13	2-3	4-8	5	3	21
Radenovic	29	4-6	4-4	1-5	2	2	13
Frye	44	11-14	1-2	3-12	1	1	24
Shakur	37	4-6	2-2	1-2	4	1	12
Stoudamire	39	2-13	4-4	0-5	7	1	9
McClellan	24	2-7	5-6	2-4	1	1	10
Rodgers	14	0-2	0-0	0-0	1	1	0
Walters	1	0-0	0-0	0-0	0	0	0
Totals	225	32-61	18-21	11-36	21	10	89

▶Percentages: FG .525, FT .857.
▶3-Point Goals: 7-18, .389 (Shakur 2-3, Frye 1-1, Radenovic 1-1, McClellan 1-2, Adams 1-3, Stoudamire 1-7, Rodgers 0-1).
▶Team Rebounds: 1.
▶Blocked Shots: 8 (Frye 6, McClellan, Radenovic).
▶Turnovers: 17 (Shakur 5, Adams 3, Radenovic 3, Frye 2, McClellan 2, Stoudamire 2).
▶Steals: 11 (Radenovic 4, Shakur 2, Stoudamire 2, Adams, McClellan, Rodgers).
▶Technical Fouls: None.

ILLINOIS

	min	FG	FT	reb o-t	a	pf	pts.
Augustine	31	1-3	2-4	3-6	1	5	4
Powell Jr.	30	6-11	3-3	4-5	0	4	16
Head	39	7-18	1-2	0-3	2	0	20
Williams	44	8-15	1-2	0-3	10	3	22
Brown	42	6-14	0-0	2-5	7	2	15
McBride	8	1-2	0-0	0-1	0	1	3
Carter	3	0-0	2-2	1-2	0	0	2
Ingram	28	3-8	1-2	2-3	1	3	8
Totals	225	32-71	10-15	12-28	21	18	90

▶Percentages: FG .451, FT .667.
▶3-Point Goals: 16-35, .457 (Williams 5-9, Head 5-12, Brown 3-8, Ingram 1-1, McBride 1-2, Powell Jr. 1-3).
▶Team Rebounds: 4.
▶Blocked Shots: 2 (Head, Powell Jr.).
▶Turnovers: 13 (Williams 6, Brown 5, Head, Powell Jr.).
▶Steals: 12 (Head 4, Brown 3, Augustine 2, Ingram 2, Williams).
▶Technical Fouls: None.

Arizona	36	44	9 — 89
Illinois	38	42	10 — 90

147

Northwestern and currently works for the State of North Carolina as a medical examiner. The new Fox network TV program "Bones" is based on her works.

March of 2005 – Officials announce a proposed takeover/merger with Sears by the K-Mart Company.

The Revell/Monogran Company, maker of plastic kit model ships and airplanes, is located in **Northbrook**, Illinois.

Poor Gary Maddux! The Cub star pitcher has 300 victories, 3,000 strikeouts and four Cy Young awards but is still overshadowed by Roger Clemens in the national media.

"God must have loved the common man for he made so many of them." – Abe Lincoln

Dozens of people in **St. Clair County**, including several policemen, report seeing a UFO-type phenomenon in the year 2000. Eyewitness near **Belleville** said they saw lights, like those on a spacecraft, hovering low in the sky over the area.

Young Abe Lincoln

Eliot Ness

In June of 2005 the American Film Institute selected a Ronald Reagan movie quote as the 89th best out of the top 100 of all time. Reagan's famous line, "Win one for the Gipper," from *Knute Rockne All-American*, made the prestigious list.

In June of 2005 Illinois Senator Dick Durbin, the Democratic Minority Whip from **East St. Louis**, was forced to make a tearful apology to the nation for having made an incredibly stupid and hateful remark about America. He had earlier accused the U.S. soldiers at Guantanamo, Cuba, of mistreating Islamic prisoners in a vein similar to the evil regimes of Pol Pot, Stalin and Hitler. The American public was so incensed that there was talk of removing Durbin from his leadership position in the senate.

In July of 2005 Chicago passed an ordinance making it unlawful for drivers under the age of 18 to converse on cell phones while on the road.

MIKE KRIEGAN & THE CAPONE WARS

A historical novel suggested by actual events, Eliot Ness and Oscar Fraley memoirs, and *The Untouchables* television series.

Chicago 1929 – Al Capone, at the pinnacle of his power, rules the Windy City with an iron fist; no one can touch him. What starts out as a friendly reunion with a college roommate turns out to mean a great deal more – none of it peaceful, but all of it thoroughly dangerous and exciting.

East St. Louis native Mike Kriegan joins a small force of men who swear to bring Capone down, despite impossible odds. Kriegan and his team soon learn that it is going to be an all-out war because Capone not only has muscle and firepower, he also has numerous police and judges in his pocket.

Things get up close and personal when "Machine Gun" McGurn, Capone's heat, goes after Kriegan in an effort to protect the mob's empire.

The brutal murder of Kriegan's landlady (by a bomb that was meant for him) clouds his mind with anguish and sets him off on a dangerous quest for revenge.

Things get even more complicated when Kriegan meets, and falls for, the girlfriend of Murray Humphreys, one of Capone's top lieutenants. Can their love overcome the obstacles life has put in its way?

More important, a lingering doubt begins to creep into Kriegan's mind. Does Ellen really love him, or is she just a plant in an insidious plot by Capone to destroy The Untouchables?

FOREWORD

Most people's knowledge and information about Eliot Ness and the Untouchables group comes from either the television series, starring Robert Stack, or the Kevin Kostner/ Sean Connery/ Andy Garcia/ Robert DiNero/ movie, *The Untouchables*.

There are numerous myths that have gained currency due to the Hollywood version. Many are unaware that the film departed from the facts in a number of significant instances. I have no quarrel with that because a movie is not supposed to be a documentary. The medium of the motion picture lends itself to artistic interpretation for the purpose of entertainment, and I found it very entertaining.

However, it might be useful at this point to examine fact and fiction and separate and delineate the two. The movie depicts Ness forming his special unit in the year 1930 and in reality it was organized in 1929. It shows Ness as being married, yet he did not marry until after Capone went to prison in Atlanta. The Ness autobiography and the Kostner movie also fail to deal with a startling reality that did not come to light until another member of the Untouchables wrote his memoirs. There were two original members of the Untouchables who had to be quietly fired because it was discovered they were on the take.

Director Brian de Palma's version has the "Untouchables" unit consisting of four people when in reality there were ten.

Both Sean Connery and Charles Martin Smith are killed in the film. In a remarkable turn of events, only Ness' driver, Frank Basile, lost his life fighting the Capone mob.

The movie shows the Untouchables breaking into a brewery with a snowplow. In fact, it was merely a large truck with a specially fitted bumper that served as a battering ram.

The Kevin Costner character was depicted on screen as being adverse to publicity. The real life Ness thrived on publicity and often informed the press in advance when a brewery raid was in the works.

The biggest departure from the facts is in one of the final scenes where Eliot Ness throws Frank Nitti from the rooftop of a building. No such melodrama ever occurred. Nitti committed suicide long after Ness left Chicago.

Finally, the film shows Ness being the moving force behind the prosecution and charges being brought against Capone. It was Internal Revenue agents who built the tax case against Capone while Ness concentrated on making raids on breweries and speakeasies.

There is a dramatic scene at the end of the film where Capone is forced by circumstances to change his plea from not guilty to guilty. Actually, it was the other way around. He originally pleaded guilty, thinking a bargain had been struck with the prosecution that would let him off with a fine and a short jail sentence. When the judge made it clear he would not be bound by any such agreement, Capone changed his plea to "not guilty" and the trial proceeded.

The celluloid version pretty much stuck to the facts in the following: The banquet scene where Capone bashes in the

Rocco Fanelli – Capone bodyguard

skulls of three turncoats; Ness insisting that his men be unmarried; Capone being a lover of Italian opera.

Whatever else may be said about Eliot Ness, most of those who knew him considered him to be determined, fearless and intelligent. As good as his work was in Chicago, he surpassed it in the mid 1930s fighting the Mayfield Road Mob and the "Torso" serial killer in Cleveland.

During World War II Ness was the Federal Director of the Division of Social Protection for the Office of Defense, stamping out prostitution and venereal disease in the vicinity of military establishments. His outstanding work in this field earned him the Navy's Meritorious Service Citation in 1946.

In later years after he went into private business, Ness refused to keep a gun in his house. Nor would he go hunting with his friends for the sport of it, complaining that he had been shot at too many times and that he had seen too many men die from gunshots.

If Ness had one fear that he failed to conqueror, it was flying in an airplane.

There is also some controversy about the role of Ness in putting Al Capone out of business. Some historians give Ness short shrift and dismiss him as merely an inconvenience to the Big Guy. Yet Dwight Green, who later became governor of Illinois and was one of the prosecutors on Capone's tax case, said it was Ness who actually nailed Capone.

Ness died from a heart attack in 1957 at the age of 54. He had just finished reading the final galleys of *The Untouchables*. He was a tireless worker; his driving ambition was to enforce law and order. Whatever heroes emerged from the prohibition era of the 1920s and the lawless decade of the 1930s, Eliot Ness must surely be included in that group.

Al Capone

The city of Chicago in 1929 was a cesspool of crime, resembling one of those lawless Caribbean pirate islands of the 1700s. A deadly concrete jungle with human gorillas sporting guns, it was overrun by mob-controlled gambling manipulated by the iron fist of the Scarface Mob. Gangsters swaggered through the streets and rode in bulletproof automobiles with full knowledge that they had little to fear from the authorities because so many of them were in their pocket. The Mob even seemed to be interwoven with Chicago's social life.

Every large city in America suffered a similar fate. Detroit had its Purple Gang. St. Louis had the Egan Rats, Cleveland had the

Mayfield Road Mob, New York had the Broadway Mob, Pittsburgh languished under John Larocca, and Los Angeles was home base for Jack Dragna.

Prohibition was made-to-order for those who sought to circumvent the law and get rich making an easy buck. Premium prices could be charged for illegal liquor served to a parched citizenry. Most of the illegal sources of income for Capone's Outfit still came from beer and hard liquor, but organized crime was beginning to move into other areas as they saw that public sentiment would soon put an end to Prohibition. The take from the numbers racket brought in huge sums. The community was paying through the nose due to scams in the charity business.

Rat-a-tat-a-tat city would soon be in the grip of ruthless labor racketeers, particularly in the building trades. Prostitution and bootlegging was doing a land-office business. There was no question, for those with eyes to see, that the Chicago police department was riddled by graft and corruption. Mobsters paraded openly; betting parlors did everything but advertise in the newspapers; street-walkers operated brazenly even in the better sections of the city.

The rented ambush and the one-way ride were almost as frequent as they had been during Capone's feud with Dion O'Banion and Hymie

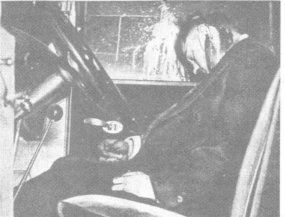
A very dead John "Dingbat" Oberta

Weiss. The arrogant manner in which the underworld publicly displayed its brass knuckles without police retaliation indicated plainly that political pollution and police department chicanery were hastening the disintegration of public safety.

Hopefully, this story will give new meaning and better understanding to important past events that have shaped our lives.

CHAPTER I

Through the efforts of Frances Willard and the Women's Christian Temperance Union, countless Protestant sermons denouncing Demon Rum, Carry Nation, and the Anti-Saloon League, Prohibition went into effect January 16, 1920. More than anything else, this well-intentioned law was responsible for the growth of

Frances Willard – WCTU/**Evanston**

organized crime and the formation of the Mafia.

During World War I many of the prostitution houses, long controlled by street gangs, were closed by authorities to cut down on the VD rate of servicemen. After the war, most of the gangs in places like New York and Chicago were in recession. But Prohibition, the dry, lawless decade, turned everything around. More than 200,000 speakeasies sprang up overnight. The production of illegal booze became a cottage industry nationwide. In the larger cities production often centered in Irish and Italian neighborhoods where drinking was sanctioned by the Catholic Church.

The Jewish Purple Gang from Detroit controlled much of the hard liquor that came in from Canada. Capone dominated Chicago, Frank Zito ran Springfield, and Charlie Birger and the Shelton gang vied for control of Southern Illinois. Police, judges and public officials were corrupted by huge handouts. The pay-off was as regular as the paycheck. Even President Harding served alcohol at his White House poker games. Prohibition was not repealed until December of 1933.

September, 1929

It was an unseasonably warm, breezy day in late September, an Indian summer hiccup. I was waiting in the anteroom of an office complex in Chicago, that modern Sodom and Gomorrah, that haven of mobsters, bootleggers, killers and salesmen of every sin. I was there to see my ex-college roommate about something he claimed was very important.

I absentmindedly flicked a piece of lint from my gray three-piece flannel suit. With fedora in my lap and staring blankly at the ceiling, I wondered if coming all the way to the Windy City was a big waste of time.

I found myself thinking about the similarities of Chicago and my birthplace. Chicago was the largest city in the state (and the second largest in the nation) while East St. Louis, with a population of 80,000, was the third largest city in Illinois, slightly behind Peoria. East St. Louis was a raucous town known as Sin City, while Chicago was a place ruled by knife, pistol, shotgun, Tommy gun and "pineapple" (bomb) of the underworld. Both were jungles of steel and concrete – one dominated by the Capone mob and the other was under the thumb of the notorious Shelton gang. In nearby St. Louis, just across the historic Eads Bridge, there were the Egan Rats, the Hogan Gang, the

Cuckoo Gang, the Green Dagoes, and the Pillow Gang.

Chicago's antecedents went back to 1784 when Jean Baptiste du Sable, a French mulatto from Santo Domingo, built a cabin and a trading post on the north bank of the "Checagoe" River. Captain James Piggott, a Revolutionary War veteran who had fought in George Washington's army at Germantown and Brandywine Creek, established the town of East St. Louis.

A soft voice broke my train of thought. "You can come in now," a pretty brunette with Clara Bow eyes said.

I nodded politely. "Thank you, ma'am."

Pushing open the pebbled glass office door, I spotted a lean six-footer with Nordic good looks and friendly Norwegian blue eyes. He had a scar on his chin that looked like a dimple. The serious-looking man with a determined jaw was engrossed in a mountain of paperwork. It had been three years since I last saw him, but he hadn't changed a bit. He still parted his medium brown hair in the middle and exuded boyish good looks. He once told me his parents had named him for the writer T.S. Eliot.

He looked up, spotted me and jumped to his feet. "Mike, you old dog; how has the world been treating you?" he said as he rushed to shake my hand.

His firm grip was similar to the way he held a tennis racket when he was number one singles player for the University of Chicago. He pumped me hard and nearly tore my arm from its socket.

"Every day, in every way, I'm getting better and better."

He stepped back with a perplexed look. "Have you fallen for that gibberish the Frenchman Emile Coué puts out?"

I laughed. "No, but I'm fine . . . can't complain. How about you, married yet?"

Frenchman Emil Coué and Lady Pearson

He tugged at the collar of his pongee shirt and looked me straight in the eye. "Nope, but I'm courting a pretty lass from a fine family, and it's starting to get serious. You?"

"No, I'm so busy with my job I'm afraid it hasn't left much time for a social life."

He flashed that collegiate smile I remembered so well.

"Great, that's exactly what I wanted to hear. Hang your hat on that hook over there and have a seat, old pal." He motioned to a worn leather chair and ambled behind his desk.

I wonder why he cares whether or not I'm married?

"How are your mom and dad?"

"They're doing well," I replied, anxious to get to the meat of the conversation. "Dad's still a foreman at Aluminum Ore and mother keeps busy with her church activities. How is your family?"

"They're fine. Believe it or not, dad's still in the bakery business."

I had met Eliot's family once during homecoming weekend at the university. He was the youngest of five children.

"Are they still unhappy that you didn't pursue a business career?"

He shrugged. "They were at first, but they've come to realize that everyone has to lead his own life."

"Whatever happened to that real serious Jones kid we used to hang out with at the Sigma Chi fraternity?"

"You mean Indiana Jones, the one who was majoring in archaeology and his dad was a professor of medieval studies at Princeton University?

"Yeah, that's the one," I said.

"The last I heard he was somewhere in the Middle East looking for the Holy Grail . . . or maybe it was the lost Ark of the Covenant."

"He was kinda strange sometimes, wasn't he?"

"You can say that again."

"Did you ever finish your masters degree in criminology?"

"Yes. It took me another year at the University of Chicago, but I really enjoyed taking courses from the renowned August Volmar."

Eliot's mention of the University of Chicago conjured up an odd memory for me. I had once taken a philosophy course and sat next to Nathan Leopold in class. Leopold and his friend Richard Loeb would later be convicted of killing 14-year-old Bobby Franks, merely for the thrill of

151

seeing if they could commit the perfect crime. I quickly pushed the morbid thought from my mind.

"Still an avid fan of Arthur Conan Doyle?" I asked.

"Oh, yes. I have all of his books."

I decided to go to the heart of the matter. "What is this all about? You were pretty tight-lipped on the phone."

A curious grin spread across his face, and then he dropped some startling news on me.

"I brought you here to offer you a job."

I leaned my 185-pound body forward, placing my hands on the edge of the mahogany desk. "You can't be serious. I'm making $3,600 a year plus bonuses with the phone company. Besides, you're with the Department of Justice. I don't have any investigative training or anything like that."

"None of that matters," he said, waving a hand dismissively. "You were a defensive back on the university football team, and you know how to take care of yourself."

"Yeah, I was a quarterback in high school at East Side High, but I couldn't beat out Randy Kramer for the college job . . . and I didn't want to collect splinters riding the bench." I cocked my head at an angle. "Say, wait a minute, what does knowing how to take care of myself have to do with anything?"

He ignored my question. "Do you still know how to use jujitsu?"

"Sure." I was becoming slightly irritated. "But what does any of that have to do with the price of bread?"

He grew serious. "A lot! I want you to join a team I'm putting together."

"A team to do what?" I asked in near exasperation.

He leaned back and laced his fingers across his chest. "To enforce the prohibition laws here in this town."

I shot my former roommate an incredulous look. "I hear that the 932 square miles of Cook County are already crawling with 300 agents."

Once again he turned serious. "Correct."

We were interrupted by a knock at the door. "Yes, what is it?"

His secretary came in with a tray that held two steaming cups of black coffee. "I thought perhaps you might need a pick-me-up," she said.

Home (3312 N. Keystone) of Marillyn Watts, Eliot's secretary

"Thank you, Marillyn," Eliot said. She placed the tray on the desk, pivoted and went back through the door.

"If I remember, you take a little cream and sugar," he said. "Help yourself."

1920s Route 66 house in **Lincoln**, Illinois – Dan Oberle collection

In plopped a sugar cube. I poured a smidgeon of cream and stirred it slowly with a spoon. "So what do you want a special crime busting team for if this tenth level of hell is already crawling with feds?"

"The system we have now isn't working." His voice gathered momentum. "Along with 6,000 Chicago police, very little has been accomplished against the criminal combine the last three years." He waved a spoon at me. "I was getting so frustrated, I was ready to quit. The first raid I ever went on was assisted by Chicago policemen."

"What happened?"

It was a fiasco. "One of the policemen tipped Capone off, and the place was as empty as a bank vault after Butch Cassidy and the Sundance Kid rode out of town. When we broke open crates that were supposed to be full of hard liquor, all we found inside were carnival teddy bears."

"So there you were with egg on your face," I said sympathetically as I sipped my coffee.

His face was a study in Norwegian gloom. "The 32 page edition that rippled off the *Tribune's* presses was emblazoned with an embarrassing headline. See for yourself."

He pulled a newspaper from the bottom drawer of his desk and pushed it toward me. ***Wuxtra! Wuxtra! Read alla bout it!***

CRUSADING FED STRIKES OUT!

The piece made Eliot Ness out to be a bumbling buffoon. To many, honest law enforcement was an oxymoron, but Eliot was one of those principled straight arrows.

I blew across the lip of the cup and took another sip. "So," I shrugged, "why didn't you quit?"

Eliot rose and paced back and forth behind his desk, twiddling with the suspenders that held his trousers. He tapped on his noggin with his index finger. "I got this idea?"

"Idea?"

"Yeah. I went to see George Q. Johnson, the United States District Attorney. I proposed the creation of a special squad of men who would cut through all the red tape and put Al Capone out of business by closing his breweries and raiding his speakeasies. I told him I was sick of Chicago being called 'the gangster capital of the world.' These would have to be men whom I could totally trust to be honest and above board . . . and willing to do a dangerous job."

"What did he say?" I queried.

"He liked the proposal. Said he had just had a meeting with Chicago banker Charles Dawes."

"*The* Charles Dawes, our former U.S. Vice-president?"

"One and the same. Dawes told him Chicago needed cleaning up. His friends on Wall Street were beginning to worry whether their money was safely invested here."

I scratched my chin. "Yeah, I can see where Capone and the boys might make the money crowd a little nervous."

"Dawes was also one of the movers and shakers behind the upcoming World's Fair." Eliot paused, then continued.

"I told George that since the special squad was my idea, I wanted to be one of the agents picked to do the job. I almost fell off my chair when he said I could lead the team and gave me *carte blanche* to pick my own men."

"Why not use Chicago people who know all the ins and outs?"

"Good point, except I need outsiders who are free to investigate without being smothered by old alliances or checked at every turn because they are too well known."

"Well, what makes you think *I* might be qualified for the job?"

"Mike, I want you to be my right hand man. I know you're honest as the day is long, and you're dependable."

"Even if I did agree to jump in front of bullets, which is highly unlikely, what skills or talent could I bring to the team?"

"I need a telephone man. I remembered you worked summers as a lineman to help pay your college tuition. I need someone who can tap a phone with speed and precision. I asked you if you're married because it's going to be a dangerous job, and it's my personal conviction that someone with marital responsibilities shouldn't be in on it."

I sat there silently, turning what he had just said over in my mind.

He pressed on. "Can you handle a gun?"

"Oh, I've hunted squirrels and jackrabbits near Jackass Flats on the outskirts of East St. Louis, but I'm not a very good shot."

"Don't worry, I can give you more training on the firing range."

My head was tilted down as I stroked the cleft in my chin, trying to absorb everything Eliot had just told me. I looked back at him. "If I did agree to come on board and join your intrepid crew of spoilsports, what's the salary?"

Eliot leaned his elbows on the desk, folded his athletic hands, and looked over them at me. "Every man on my detail gets the same amount - $2,800. That's slightly more than what a Chicago police sergeant makes."

I cocked an eyebrow. "You realize, Eliot, that would mean a hefty cut in salary for me. I'd have to be daft in the head to say *yes* to a job that could result in an early funeral and paid out in peanuts."

"I know it's asking a lot Mike, but you would be doing something really important for your state and for your country – good versus evil, the age-old battle."

"What makes you think our group would succeed where others have failed? It would be . . . what, ten or twelve of us against hundreds of men in the Capone mob? Wouldn't that be like King Canute trying to push back the ocean?"

"We'll have the full backing of the authorities, and they've promised every arrest we make will stick. Come on, Mike, you're an idealist . . . and you know this is going to be a lot of fun."

"Sure, sure, I can't wait to take on the likes of Scarface Al, Frank Nitti, and trigger-happy Machine Gun Mc-Gurn with our .38 peashooters. It sounds like a recipe for a nervous breakdown or an early grave."

He assumed the demeanor of Loci, that Norse trickster. "You wouldn't want it to be too easy, would you? We'll also have the backing of the Secret Six. Believe me, they have a lot of political clout."

"Secret Six?"

"Yes. It's a group of top business leaders in the community who are dedicated to using their influence to get things cleaned up."

"What kind of clout?"

"Well, it doesn't leave this room. . . ."

I rolled my eyes to the ceiling and crossed my heart and zipped my lips.

"The leader of the group is Robert Randolph McCormick, head of the *Chicago Tribune*."

"Yeah, ok, I'll bet the others are guys like Insull, the utilities giant, Wrigley, the chewing gum mogul, Colonel Knox of the *Daily News*, Palmer, the hotel entrepreneur, etc. – right?"

"I can't say; I've told you too much already, but . . . those are the kind of men we're talking about. For their own protection only a handful of people know about the Secret Six. My brother-in-law, Jamie, left the Department of Justice to become chief investigator for the Secret Six."

I took a deep breath, ran my fingers through my hair and rested my head on the back of the chair, trying to collect my thoughts. This was almost too much for me to comprehend, a small group of idealistic men pitting themselves against a harsh and hostile universe; doing battle with Satan's spawn. I knew Eliot was going to be pushing for an answer before I left the office. I stared down at my coffee, looking into the cup like someone trying to read tea leaves.

"Before I say yes or no, I need you to give me a quick rundown on what we're really up against, and no sugar coating it."

Eliot could see that I was hooked, like a large mouth bass on a ten-pound test line. He began to reel me in.

"Okay – here it is, buddy-boy. Capone is the *de facto* mayor of Chicago. We figure that last year alone the Capone mob is estimated – and it's probably a low estimate – to have raked in an income of close to a hundred and twenty million dollars."

I put my lips together and blew out a loud whistle. Then I took another drink of my coffee and digested those figures.

"Of that incredible amount, we think they took in twenty-five million from dog tracks, slots and dice games, another ten million from dance halls and prostitution, and ten million from labor racketeering. By the way, you have any dog racing tracks down in your neck of the woods?"

"Yeah, there's one near Route 3 near Dupo, another one on Collinsville Road, and a third one on Choteau Island by Route 66 near Granite City. And four years ago, the Fairmount Jockey Club opened for

horse racing."

"So you probably have some of the same type of problems that we do."

"Oh yeah, Carl, Earl, and Bernie Shelton have had a firm grasp on things ever since Charlie Birger got himself hanged."

"Birger?"

Congressman Andrew Volstead

"Uh huh – Charlie Birger, the Scourge of Little Egypt, they used to call him; the Sheltons' nemesis until he was convicted of killing the mayor of West City, down near Marion."

"Oh, yeah. I remember reading about it. Wasn't he the last man hanged in the state before the legislature decided to give 'em the juice with 'Old Sparky' instead?"

"Yep. That newfangled machine put Carmi's Phil Hanna, the 'Human Hanging Machine,' flat out of business. By the way, you didn't say how Capone obtained the rest of his money."

Eliot nodded and then paused, as if to place special emphasis on his answer. "When you add things up, that means from beer and hard liquor alone they take in over seventy-five million."

I shook my head in disbelief. I knew Capone and his men were making big bucks, but hearing the actual figures of criminal capitalism was mind-boggling. "How many stills or breweries do you figure Capone has in operation?"

"It's our estimate that they have at least twenty breweries percolating."

"What's the capacity?"

"Each of Capone's breweries has varying capacity, but the average is probably one hundred barrels of beer a day – each sells for fifty-six dollars. That's a hundred twelve thousand daily, working three hundred sixty-five days a year."

Curious, I asked, "What about the hard stuff – the White Mule, Applejack, Jersey Lightning, or whatever they call it?"

"They buy it directly from the Mafia." He was waving his spoon at me again. "We figure the Capone mob's weekly sales volume exceeds one and a half million dollars."

"Some people think the Capone boys and the Mafia are the same thing."

"No way – they're two different organizations. Capone can never become the head of the Mafia because he's a Neopolitan – from Naples, Italy. Mafia figures are always Sicilians."

Gramaphone with pleated speaker

154

"How come nobody seems to lay a finger on them?"

"I'll tell you why," he bridled. "Too many people are being paid off. Every time we try to pull a raid we don't find anything because someone has tipped them off. And if we do somehow luck out and make a pinch, the case never comes up in court. Out of 3,465 liquor related cases from 1925-1928, only 300 resulted in convictions. Arnold Rothstein, the Fixer, made sure the case either never went to trial or was dismissed on some technicality. They're greasing all the right palms – policemen, commissioners, magistrates . . ."

"Isn't Rothstein the one who 'fixed' the 1919 World Series, resulting in the Black Sox scandal?"

"One and the same. Fortunately for us he was murdered last year, killed for welshing on a big bet."

"Why do they do it . . . you know, take the money?"

Ness' eyes narrowed. "Because Capone is smart. He doesn't bother with penny ante stuff. When he offers bribes it's big money. Probably a third of what he takes in goes for graft. Those on the take are doubling or tripling their annual salaries."

I nodded. "That's a lot of dough. And that makes too many rotten apples spoiling the whole barrel."

"Yeah," he said disgustedly.

"So you're looking for a group with no rotten apples, and you think you can hurt Capone's business."

Eliot slammed a clenched fist into an open palm. "Look, Mike – I don't just want to hurt Capone's business, I want to put him *out* of business, once and for all. And you can be a part of it! What do you say?"

"I don't know, Eliot. I just don't know. I like what I hear, but the odds are impossible. You want me to help you with the Herculean task of cleaning up the muckiest Augean stable on earth. And I'd have to give the phone company six weeks notice. . . ."

"We can do this Mike, I know we can – I can feel it in my guts."

I let out a long sigh. "I'll tell you what." At that fateful moment my carefree and optimistic outlook on life, inherited from my father, kicked in. "Do you have a coin? Flip it in the air and let it land on the floor. If it comes down heads, I'm with you. If it's tails, I go back home and forget the whole thing."

He scratched his chin. "Whatever you say, Mike." Eliot reached into his pants and fished out some change. He kept a quarter and slipped the rest back into his pocket. The coin flipped into the air; it bounced a couple of times and finally came to rest on the floor . . . with Lady Liberty looking me straight in the eye.

I shrugged my shoulders and shook my head. "See you in six weeks, Eliot."

CHAPTER 2

NOVEMBER 8, 1929

The music of the twenties, reflecting the theme of the Jazz Age, was often hot and hyperthyroid. A place in New York called Tin Pan Alley (because of the racket by musicians) became famous for cranking out songs. And right behind New York was Chicago with its musical geniuses.

Some of the hits of the Twenties include: "Swanee" by Al Jolson, "A Good Man is Hard to Find," "Broadway Melody," "Lovin' Mike (The Sheik of Alabam')," "You're the Cream in my Coffee," "My Heart Stood Still" by Rodgers and Hart, "Whispering" by Paul Whiteman, "Charleston," "Kitten on the Keys," "Ain't We Got Fun?" by Gus Kahn, (F. Scott Fitzgerald used this song in *The Great Gatsby*), "Stumbling" by Ray Miller, "With A Song in my Heart" by Rodgers and Hart, "Ol' Man River" from *Showboat*, "Black Bottom," "Absolutely, Mr. Sheen," "Lady Luck Blues" by Bessie Smith, "Snake Hips," "I Can't Give You Anything But Love" (inspired by a poor couple hopelessly window shopping at Tiffany's), "East St. Louis Toodle-O," by Duke Ellington, "Birth of the Blues" by Harry Richman, "It Had to be You" by Gus Kahn, "Rhapsody in Blue" by George Gershwin, "The Loneliest Gal in Town," "All Alone," "California Here I Come" by Al Jolson, "I Want to be Happy" from *No, No, Nanette*," "Roll 'Em, Girls, Roll 'Em,"* (roll your stockings and show your knees), "I'll See You in my Dreams" by Gus Kahn, "Can't Help Lovin' That Man" from *Showboat*, "Sweet Georgia Brown," "Bye, Bye Blackbird" by Florence Mills and Mort Dixon, "The Sheik of Araby," "Chicago, Chicago" (that toddlin' town) by Paul Fisher, "You Do Something To Me," "Yes We Have No Bananas," "It Ain't Gonna Rain No Mo'," "I'm Just Wild About Harry," "Tea For Two," "Baby Face," "Sometimes I'm Happy," "Barney Google," "I'm A Little Blackbird," "Indian Love Call" (from the musical *Rose Marie*), "April Showers" by Al Jolson, "Secondhand Rose," popularized by Fanny Brice, "Five Foot Two, Eyes of Blue," "If You Knew Susie," "All By Myself" by Irving Berlin, "Toot, Toot, Tootsie" by Al Jolson, "Margie," "Tiger Rag" by Bix Beiderbecke and the Wolverines, "Ray And His Little Chevrolet," "Ukulele Lady," "By The Light of the Silvery Moon," "Blue Skies," "How Are You Going to Wet Your Whistle?" (when the whole darn world's gone dry), "Painting the Clouds With Sunshine," "Give Me a Night in June," "Carolina in the Morning," "Muskrat Ramble," "Avalon" by Jolson, "Twelfth Street Rag," "Someday Sweetheart," Yes Sir, That's My Baby," "Tip Toe Thru the Tulips With Me" by Gene Austin, and "When my Sugar Walks Down the Street."

Some songs gave an indication of the new morality that was evolving: "There's Yes! Yes! In Your Eyes," "Shake It And Break It," "Runnin' Wild," "Where'd You Get Those Eyes?" "Let's Do It" by Cole Porter, "Gimme a Little Kiss, Will Ya Huh?" "Oh, Mother I'm Wild" by the Original Dixieland Jazz Band.

Six weeks later I returned to Chicago. I was nearly hit by a car crossing the street on the way to Eliot's office. I'd forgotten that challenging Chicago traffic was a jaywalker's

Dancing the Black Bottom

CHICAGO
and
ENVIRONS
Circa 1924

DION
O'BANION

BUGS
MORAN
GANG

TOUHY
GANG

CITY

LIMITS

CHICAGO RIVER

ASHLAND AVE.

MICHIGAN

NORTH AVE.

O'BANION'S SHOP

CHICAGO

GUILFOYLE GANG

MADDOX CIRCUS GANG

KLONDIKE

O'DONNELL GANG

DRUGGAN LAKE GANG

GENNAS

THE LOOP

FOUR DEUCES

METROPOLE HOTEL

HAWTHORN HOTEL

Cicero

HAWTHORNE RACE TRACK

OGDEN AVE

SHIP CHANNEL

SALTIS GANG

UNION STOCK YARDS

CAPONE

CAPONE BROTHELS

RALPH SHELDON GANG

CAPONE

LAKE

CAPONE

CITY

LIMITS

SPIKE O'DONNELL GANG

ASHLAND AV.

CAPONE HOME

TORRID HOME

CAPONE

CAPONE EMPIRE

KEDZIE

LAKE CALUMET

CALUMET RIVER

LITTLE CALUMET RIVER

CAPONE

CAPONE

ILLINOIS
INDIANA

map by
P.J.Meketa

version of Russian roulette. It was early November and the weather was cold and windy. The phenomenon known as the "lake effect" had kicked in. It had snowed six inches the night before, but Chicagoans considered anything less than eight inches a mere dusting.

The first thing we did was to begin the interview process and handpick eight other men. Eliot had already scanned the dossiers of available prohibition men who had expressed an interest in the job. He pored over their files looking for any Achilles heel that would disqualify them. They were put under the microscope vis-à-vis their personal and professional life. Several were eliminated because they were flashy dressers and seemed to have fancy cars and more money in the bank than was warranted for an annual salary of less than $3,000. A few more were nixed because they spent too much time enjoying the nightlife. One had a reputation that was above reproach but he was a compulsive pony bettor. Eliot felt that he might be vulnerable by becoming indebted to a loan shark or someone who was passing out hot tips.

Unquestioned integrity was his first criteria, but there was much more. Ness had established certain parameters: no one over thirty; unmarried; impressive arrest records; mental and physical stamina – something beyond mere muscle men; courage and ability to use both fist and gun.

To top it off, he was looking for a special training or skill that would come in handy. They would have to be fresh faces – someone from other than a Chicago unit so the mob wouldn't recognize them.

Ironically, the first man we brought in for an interview was an ex-con.

"Why on earth are you looking for someone with a record?" I asked.

Eliot was chewing on his lower lip. "I want someone with experience as a wheel man – someone who's considered a genius as a driver. I want a man who can turn a corner on two wheels, someone who is as good at driving in reverse as he is driving forward in first, second or third gear."

John Kaufman seemed the perfect man for the job. He was Dion O'Banion's former driver and had taken him on numerous safe-cracking jobs. His skill as a driver prevented them from being caught on numerous occasions. After leading the cops on one merry chase that led to escape, Officer O'Malley, one of the pursuers, made the comment, "That bird sure can drive."

Lon Chaney as the Hunchback– Library of Congress

After serving a two-year stint at Joliet, Kaufman was paroled early for good behavior. He had taken some mail order courses in prison and was currently employed as a bookkeeper. He met a girl, fell in love, and promised to marry her when his tour of duty with our group was over.

John walked into the office for a final interview. Eliot was seated behind his desk and I was standing next to it, just to his right. Eliot was willing to gamble that John had the motivation to go straight. Also, John hated Al Capone because his triggerman, Machine Gun McGurn, had rubbed out his brother back in 1926.

Eliot introduced us and told John to take the seat located in front of his desk. John was solidly built with bushy eyebrows and a blank expression on his face. His hair was a sheaf of porcupine quills. A burly guy, he had flecks of scars here and there on his face. His formidable visage reminded me of Sandow, the European strong man. John settled what I guessed to be a 210-pound frame into the chair.

"What is your secret – how did you get to be so good?" Eliot asked, drumming his fingers on the desk.

A sly smile crossed his lips. "When Prohibition first began back in 1920, I lived in the hill country of East Tennessee. Me and my brother, we made moonshine and delivered to all the local stores and taverns. Them revenuers chased us all through the back woods, but we never got caught. I knew all the side roads and dead-enders by heart. Plus I had an advantage. I was willing to take risks they weren't."

"But this is Chicago. How did you make the transition?" I asked.

He pulled a street map from the breast pocket of his blue serge suit. It was dog-eared, creased and stained. "I pored over this thing like fleas on a coon. Then I drove all over and memorized buildings, construction sites and alleys." His eyes grew bright. "I know this place like the back of my hand."

1921 Lincoln Brougham

Woman with marcelled hair

Eliot nodded in satisfaction. "What's the secret of tailing someone without getting caught?"

Kaufman leaned forward. "That's the easy part. First you have to stay far enough behind that they don't spot you in the rear view mirror. But even that isn't enough because some guys have scout cars looking for tails. You have to be willing to make an occasional turn off and hope you can pick them up again several blocks down the street."

"But how do you keep from losing them if they take a circuitous, precautionary route to their destination?" I asked.

"I have good hunches and instincts," he said, pointing to his forehead. "Kind of a sixth sense about what direction and what route the quarry is taking."

"But how can I be sure you're a changed man? I need someone with unerring loyalty to me," Eliot remarked.

"This gal that I plan to marry, me and her go to church three times a week. I got religion and there ain't no way I'm going to give her up. She's the best thing that ever happened to me."

"I believe you," Eliot said. "I had a talk with your pastor at the Nazarene Church, and he said your conversion was totally amazing. He claims there isn't a more dedicated, hard working man in the entire congregation." Ness stood up and walked around the desk. "Welcome to the club."

We shook his hand.

After Kaufman left, Eliot turned to me and said, "We need a gunman - someone who is an expert on guns, ammo and weapons. He must also be an expert marksman."

In walked a handsome brown-eyed fellow named Paul DeWitt - thin and wiry - only about 160 pounds. Eliot, in a lightning-fast move, tried to surprise him by tossing a rifle in his direction. With cat-like reflexes, he caught the ten-pound weapon with one hand, as if it were a toy. My eyes bugged out as I watched him toss it up in the air and balance it on the open palm of his hand in vertical fashion when it came down, like it was some kind of circus trick. Frank Butler, Annie Oakley's shooting rival, certainly didn't have anything on him.

DeWitt would become the oldest member of our group. He had served in World War I with Alvin York's outfit in France, winning the prized Croix de Guerre from the French government for his bravery. On the shooting range he was the only man in the outfit who had posted a higher score than York.

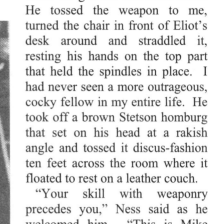

Frank "the Enforcer" Nitti

DeWitt had been with the New Orleans FBI division when he got the call from Ness. He tossed the weapon to me, turned the chair in front of Eliot's desk around and straddled it, resting his hands on the top part that held the spindles in place. I had never seen a more outrageous, cocky fellow in my entire life. He took off a brown Stetson homburg that set on his head at a rakish angle and tossed it discus-fashion ten feet across the room where it floated to rest on a leather couch.

"Your skill with weaponry precedes you," Ness said as he welcomed him. "This is Mike Kriegan, one of the team and my right hand man."

I quickly learned that Paul wasn't much for protocol. As I moved to greet him, he froze me by throwing his hand to his forehead and giving me a semi-military salute. I simply nodded and said, "Pleased to meet you, Paul."

"Same here," he replied.

"I hear you're one of the best there is when it comes to gunplay."

Paul shot Ness a frown. "One of the best?"

"OK, *the* best," Ness replied. "But I need more than a skilled shootist; to make this team you need street smarts."

"Try me," DeWitt boldly insisted.

Funk's Grove at **Shirley**, Illinois, on Route 66 – Dan Oberle

"How do gangsters make dumdum bullets?"

DeWitt shook his head and gave an orbital roll. "Hah - that's easy. They take a Barlow knife and mark an "x" on the soft lead on the nose of the bullet. The bullet spreads open when it strikes soft flesh, causing more damage and making it less likely the victim will survive. The smart ones order their ammo from the Winchester-Western plant in East Alton, Illinois, because they have superior quality control and their bullets seldom misfire and cause jams."

"Very good," Eliot said. "How did garlic come to be part of the gangster's arsenal?"

Dewitt's eyes grew big. "Keep in mind that these plug-uglies aren't very bright. They somehow think that rubbing their bullets with garlic before inserting them in the chamber will cause wounds in their victims to become infected. Some journeyman thug named Frankie Vaschetti, with Detroit's Purple Gang, heard this old wife's tale in the Old Country and started the practice. His idea caught on like wildfire. But it's 99 and 44/100 percent pure bunk. Garlic might keep the mosquitoes away, but it doesn't cause infection. Bullets cause infection and the best way to treat the wound is to cauterize it."

I thought Paul DeWitt was much too brash and a glory-seeking individualist, but later events would prove me dead wrong. He was the bravest, most dedicated man on the team. He hero-worshiped Ness and followed his instructions to the letter. And boy could he shoot!

The next man who came in was Gary Tesson, an Irishman with a perpetual devil-may-care grin, bright blue eyes and brown hair parted in the manner of Bix Beiderbecke.

You could tell he was a ladies man because he smelled like a Lifebouy/Vitalis cocktail. His flamboyant tie was a geometric abstraction, doodlings in yellow and sienna.

"I'm not sure we want a Wild Man of Borneo on our team," Eliot said in mock seriousness.

Tesson flashed a vast smile. "You could use a vulgar rowdy to liven up the place."

In a few seconds they were unashamedly embracing like the old friends they were.

Gary was a genuine sports nut who memorized the baseball standings, could quote batting averages, football scores and fight results by the hour if necessary. He carried his love of sports over into his everyday living, maintaining a trim and fit body with rope skipping, push ups and pounding a body bag at the local gym. He also knew jujitsu, and he and Eliot had had many a long bout together on the mat. He was energetic and seemingly tireless.

Eliot said when Gary was around you could always count on the unusual or the unexpected. He told me of a time when they worked a case together and they raided a combination speakeasy and bordello. The patrol wagon was an old-fashioned Moon, built in St. Louis, which sat high off the ground. They made their arrests and placed the women inside. When some of the inebriated ladies started doing the Charleston on the way to the station house, the paddy wagon tipped over. Gary and Elliot had to sit down on a curb because they were laughing so hard.

He told me about another time when they received an anonymous tip that illegal bootleg booze was being brought into the Shakespeare Avenue police station. Ness had Gary arrested and booked on some trumped-up charge so that he could stay overnight in jail, awaiting his arraignment scheduled for the next day.

That night, by waving around the

Curbside gas pumps

proper amount of money, he was able to purchase two pints of liquor from the jailer. With evidence in tow, they were able to obtain search warrants – probably the first ever for the purpose of searching a police station. After finding and confiscating a large amount of "hooch" on the premises, the police captain at the station pooh-poohed the charge, claiming it was merely evidence in cases that they had handled. They traced the liquor back to the bootlegger who supplied the station, proving once again that there is no honor among thieves.

Movie Star John Boles

My train of thought was interrupted when Eliot introduced us and got down to brass tacks.

"I assume there's some really important reason you wanted to see me," Tesson told Ness.

"Right," he replied. "I'll get right to the heart of the matter. I'm going to take Al Capone down, and I'm hoping you'll want to be a part of the group responsible."

Tesson let forth a long, loud whistle. "Well I'll be a monkey's uncle. You're really serious about this." His eyes lit up excitedly when Eliot explained exactly how he planned to go about doing it.

"Count me in, Chief," Tesson exclaimed, coining a nickname that caught on and was used by everyone except me.

"It looks like my uncle was right," Tesson said.

159

"How so?" I asked.

"Well, my uncle is a captain in the department over in Des Plaines. He constantly nagged me about taking the examination to qualify as a special agent in the Prohibition Bureau. He told me to stay the h--l out of the Chicago police because so many of them were on the 'take.' But he also said the Tessons were a special breed of cops. So finally, looking for excitement, I guess, I took and passed the test."

"Your uncle was right about far too many of the Chicago police," Ness said. "Everyone remembers Capone's famous quote – 'I own the police.' But God help the man on my detail who takes a bribe – I'll break his neck."

Tesson's voice lost its lightness. "You don't have to worry about us Tessons; we're honest to the core."

"I know that, Gary." Eliot stood up, and the three of us shook hands. "Glad to have you with us," I said.

I later learned that Tesson was a confirmed bachelor who lived in an apartment with eccentric and haphazard décor that would incite an interior decorator to suicide.

"Well, you've got a phone man, a driver, a sharpshooter, and someone good with his fists. What next?" I asked.

"Now we need a gray man," Eliot responded without pre-amble.

"Come again?"

Ness buzzed his secretary. "Please send in the next candidate, Marillyn." Eliot glanced over at me. "You'll see."

The prospect who came through the door was a Jewish fellow named Wes Bokal, a rawboned, hard faced and dead eyed man. He was an ex-prison guard who moved like a cat as he lowered his five foot, ten inch, 180 pound frame into the chair. His nose splashed over his face like confused disaster. Wes was wearing a non-descript suit that seemed somehow to blend in with his coloring. He was the type of man that if you walked into a room of people, he would be the last one you noticed. All of a sudden, it hit me. Ness planned to

use this guy as a fly on the wall – hang out unobtrusively in various places and keep his eyes and ears open. He would listen in on the latest scuttlebutt and keep the group informed on what was happening in the streets.

Jackson Historical District in Chicago - Dan Oberle Route 66 collection

Eliot later told me that Bokal liked to read westerns and was an avid fan of a new craze sweeping the nation – crossword puzzles. He said Wes was fearless except for one thing. When he stayed at a hotel and came to the bathroom, he wouldn't think of getting near the sink or tub without scrubbing them down with carbolic acid. He always carried a bottle of the solution in his suitcase for that

very purpose. Wes had once read a book about microbes, and it shook him up pretty good. He would go up against the toughest gangster or take on the meanest gunman, but he was scared to death of germs.

Eliot went over in detail the reasons why he had asked Wes to come. He listened intently and didn't say a word. When Eliot was finished, Wes sat quietly for a few moments and then began to speak in a firm, husky voice.

"It makes me feel pretty good, Eliot, that you picked me. When I quit the death house at Menard prison in Chester and joined the Prohibition Bureau, I thought I was getting into a high-class outfit. But I saw things go on among our agents that turned my

stomach. It made me want to puke."

"I felt the same way," Ness interrupted.

His voice was a growl when he answered. "You're da—ed right! I'll be proud to help you guys clean up vermin like Capone and the rest of them."

After Bokal left, I asked Eliot how we were going to put Capone away. It would be difficult to prove Capone was running these businesses, and witnesses would clam up, fearful of being killed before they could testify.

"We've got that covered, too," he replied. "We're going to help treasury agents collect

160

information that will lead to his arrest and conviction for failure to pay income taxes to the Internal Revenue Department on all his money."

"But I hear Capone doesn't write checks and makes all payments in cash. That doesn't give us much of a paper trail to follow," I argued.

Eliot got up and paced. He shook his head and frowned. "I know. That's going to make everything tougher. He even places property he owns in his wife's or mother's name. And he has no bank accounts. We'll try to get him on conspiracy charges and prohibition law violations and give the data we collect on his operations to the T-men.

"The next thing we need is someone who is good at shuffling papers, sees facts and figures, credits and debits as real interesting challenges," Ness said.

In walked a man named Dan Mizell, a wiry medium-sized man from Murphysboro in southern Illinois. His parents were persecuted French Protestant Huguenots who migrated to America from the Alsace-Lorraine area. He had minored in psychology and spent a lot of time studying the criminal mind – what made them tick, what motivated them, how they were likely to react to certain pressures, and so on. He was extremely bashful around women, liked to play chess, and gloried in the anonymity of working long hours behind a desk.

His piercing hazel eyes watched attentively as Eliot described in detail the job we were all about to tackle.

"I don't have to tell you it's a job that really needs doing," he concluded.

"You don't have to sell me on it, Eliot," he said. "Doing this job would give me more satisfaction than you can imagine. I'm thorough, pay attention to detail, and make sure all the i's are dotted and t's are crossed on any reports I turn in."

"Glad to have you aboard," we said in near unison.

"Next we need an Italian who doesn't look Italian," Ness chirped as Mizell walked out the door.

"I'm afraid you have me stumped this time, pal. I have

no idea why we need a team player who is Italian but isn't swarthy."

Ness gave me that boyish 26-year-old grin he was famous for. "Think about it, Mike. Let's say we walk into a hotel room and have a conversation with some of Capone's men. You know how it is; sometimes when they want to say something to each other and they think it's safe, they lapse into using Italian. If we can have some guy with us who looks Irish but knows Italian, that could come in pretty handy if we ever get in a tight spot."

"That's a great idea, Eliot. It's probably why you're the most logical choice to head this unit."

Eliot's pick for our surreptitious interpreter was Sal Martino. Sal was from Florence, but his mother had been an Irish woman from whom he had inherited most of his physical traits. He was five-foot eleven, with light complexion and red hair. He was energetic - full of fire and vinegar. The last thing anyone would guess was this agent from Cleveland, with a firm grasp of the chemistry involved in the art of brewing, and an expert on explosives, was bilingual.

We changed his name and told the rest of the group he was Mike Gillespie. We never told anyone else his real name. We didn't want anyone to slip up and call him Sal in front of any mob figure.

"Aren't you going to need someone who knows the exact letter of the law and can write out reports that we will rely on to prove the basis for indictments and, ultimately, convictions?"

Leaning back in his chair, Eliot fashioned a tent with his fingers, pursed his lips and said, "Mike, you must have read my mind."

In strutted a bantam rooster of a man named Steve Strohman. He had been a lightweight on the St. Louis University boxing team and was a championship debater. Eliot informed me that not only did he have an itch for action, he was also an inside man

The Tropics at **Lincoln**, Illinois (Route 66) Dan Oberle collection

extremely adept at doubling as a "pen and pencil detective." It would be his responsibility to track down every clue we could uncover during our raids, digging out information concerning who had rented the buildings, who had purchased the trucks and supplies we confiscated and a thousand other details. He would need the patience of Job to check and double-check such details and file and cross-file reports. In contrast to the others, Strohman told Ness he was good at logistics and was happiest when working on a difficult office problem.

"How did you get into this line of work?" I asked him.

His eyes lit up. "I once started a thesis on law enforcement." "Before I knew it, I couldn't resist the urge to get on the inside and see a bit more of it. There was a time, Mike, when I was torn between becoming either a lawyer or a writer. This assignment will satisfy both impulses."

"He's a small man but packed with guts," Eliot told me after he left.

"I really like what we have so far," I responded.

"Now we need a good undercover man. Someone who won't be seen with the rest of us. Someone who stays in a hotel room and never comes to our office. He'll also act as our 'tail,' staying several blocks behind us to keep an eye on things when we go to a meeting or on a raid. He will be someone completely unknown to the mob and he will use an alias and have false credentials and a fake passport. I asked him to check into a hotel under an assumed name. He confirmed his arrival by a telegram he sent me."

Eliot handed me the wire. It read: "The Dixie Flyer has arrived on track number nine." It was signed, "Al Brown."

"Who is Al Brown?" I wondered out loud.

"It's an alias Al Capone uses on a business card he hands out that says he's a used furniture dealer. The wire is really from Tom Bischoff."

"Tom Bischoff . . . Tom Bischoff." My eyes lit up like a Christmas tree. "You don't mean *the* Tom Bischoff who played alongside George Gipp for Knute Rockne's Notre Dame team?"

Ness was a tennis and golf man and didn't pay much attention to other sports. "I know he played football there, but that's all."

I threw my hands up in the air. "Played . . . this guy was a legend. Haven't you read *Collier's* this week?"

Eliot admitted that he hadn't, and I almost snorted. "Knute Rockne picked his all-time All-American team in this week's issue. And you know what? He

Actress Ina Claire by John Held Jr.

John Barrymore

nearly picked Bischoff as one of his ends. Right along with such guys as Jim Thorpe, Walter Eckersall, and Notre Dame's Four Horsemen." I was giddy. "Boy, imagine having him with us."

All of a sudden, Eliot's face froze. "His picture wasn't in the magazine, was it?"

"No, he was honorable mention. The only ones pictured were those who made the first team."

He heaved a sigh of relief. "Thank goodness. Well, he's checked in at the LaSalle in the Loop, so let's go on over and see him."

I was on pins and needles and couldn't wait to see one of my sports idols. We left the building, hopped in Ness' year-old Cadillac, and drove to the LaSalle.

"He's registered under the name Henry Schlitz," Eliot told me.

But when we inquired for him at the desk, the clerk checked the records and found no such name listed.

"This guy's six-foot one," I told Eliot. "There isn't any way a tall, blonde German could have checked in here without somebody noticing him. Let's take the elevator to the top floor and work our way down, asking the desk clerk assigned to each floor."

"Good idea, Sherlock," Ness said with a gleam in his eye.

We had worked our way down four floors when we were stopped by a house dick. "What are you two birds up to?" he asked skeptically.

We identified ourselves and told him our problem.

"Come on down to my office," he instructed.

There he told an assistant to obtain the hotel's daily listing of outgoing calls. Then he jotted down Ness' office telephone number and swiftly began going through the slips.

"Here's your answer," he grunted with a look of disdain. "Your man is in room 312, and his phony-sounding name, for your information, is Pabst - not Schlitz."

Eliot turned six different shades of red.

A tall powerfully built man opened the door. Bischoff moved with the unmistakable grace of an athlete. Eliot went over the details of his assignment step-by-step. He then informed him that he would work alone and wouldn't participate in any group meetings, after the first one, and might miss out on the camaraderie of what we were doing. Bischoff assured us that he could handle the solitude. His satisfaction, he dryly explained, would come with the end result.

* * *

The next day we met with all the agents, and Eliot began to build the *esprit de corps* necessary for such an undertaking. He was a natural born leader and I admired him greatly. He began to forge a fraternal bond that was essential if we were going to succeed in the coming months and years ahead. Knowing Eliot, I figured it would be Shakespearian, something like: "We few, we happy few, we band of brothers . . ."

"Welcome aboard, men. I want you to take a good look at everyone; get to know each other. You'll be working alongside the finest group of highly skilled men in the country. I picked each of you because I knew you were dependable, dedicated, impeccably honest men. You can proceed with this assignment knowing that you can depend on the others with your very life. You're the *crème de la crème*, the best and the brightest. Right now Chicago is the black spot on the map of America. You're going to help stem the tide of crime, graft and corruption in this city. You'll help turn back the clock to a time before we became a nation of scofflaws. You're going to bring back respect and honor to those who accept a badge and swear to uphold the law."

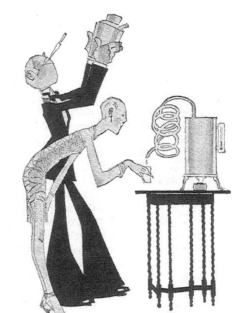

Mae West

Ness' words flowed smoothly on as I leaned forward in my chair and listened intently.

"One day you'll look back on this assignment and tell your children and grandchildren, I was there; I was part of the team that helped bring America back to what it stands for: truth, fairness, honesty and justice. You can say I helped play a major part in restoring confidence to the credos established by the Founding Fathers.

"I won't insult your intelligence by telling you this is going to be easy or without sacrifice. Capone is at his zenith. He's the king of Chicago. Some of us may be killed. But I can tell you that if we stay the course and remain dedicated to our mission and true to ourselves, when it's over, it will have been well worth it.

"I don't plan to be a desk jockey, issuing orders from the cozy confines of a plush office." He pointed to himself with a thumb. "I'll be with you in the heat of battle; I'll be there to back you up. I want you to depend on me just as

much as I'll depend on you. To accomplish our goal we must think and act like a team – like a well oiled, complicated machine. If we do that, and trust in God, then the sum will be greater than the individual parts.

"There will undoubtedly be dark days ahead, full of setbacks and disappointments. Remember the example of George Washington. During his darkest and bleak hours, those bitter days at Valley Forge when the naysayers were trumpeting 'quit,' or 'we're beaten,' he never once gave up hope. As individuals we can do the unlikely . . . together we can accomplish the impossible."

Elliot's pep talk was better than any I'd ever heard from Amos Alonzo Stagg, my football coach at the University of Chicago. It took me back to the rah! rah! college days when we would lustily sing the school song.

Wave the flag of old Chicago,
Maroon the color grand;
Ever shall her team be victors,
Known throughout the land.

I looked over at several of the men, and they had tears in their eyes.

"If anybody wants to quit, now is the time to say so. I won't hold it against you, and no black mark will be placed by your name in the personnel files."

It was a tense moment, my eyes darting back and forth to see if anyone would back out.

"I'm in it to the end," Steve Strohman yelled.

"You can count on me, Chief," Gillespie shouted.

"Me, too," DeWitt boomed in a rich bass voice.

A big cheer went up and someone else yelled, "All for one and one for all . . . hip, hip, hooraaayyy."

The hairs on the nape of my neck were standing on end as I shook Eliot's hand and congratulated him. I alone was privileged to see a dampness that welled up in his eyes as he gave me a big hug.

"Now we are ten," I said.

"Now we are one, he corrected. "Let's do this; let's roll, Mike," he whispered as he gave me a bear hug.

CHAPTER 3

NOVEMBER 13, 1929

The St. Valentine's Day Massacre: The mass killing of six men in Bugs Moran's Irish North Side gang took place on February 14, 1929. Moran inherited leadership of the gang when Dion O'Banion and Hymie Weiss were previously gunned down in separate incidents. The murders were planned by Machine Gun McGurn with Capone's full

knowledge. Capone was at his Florida retreat at Palm Island so that he would have an alibi.

Moran, Capone's archenemy, was set up by having a Detroit mobster offer him a load of hijacked booze. Moran agreed to take delivery at the gang's headquarters, a garage at 2122 North Clark Street. The sign on the building read S.M.C Cartage Company.

Capone's men arrived on the scene in a dark blue Cadillac touring car with a police gong mounted on the running board. The men inside were dressed as Chicago policemen. Moran arrived late for the meeting, thought it was a police bust, and walked away from the scene of the slaughter. The seven men inside were disarmed, lined against a wall, and viciously machine gunned. So many bullets were fired that several arms and legs were nearly dismembered.

Knocking off six rival gangsters in one fell swoop was considered a noteworthy coup, despite Moran's incredible luck in escaping the carnage.

One of the unfortunate victims was Dr. Rinehardt Schwimmer, an optometrist and gangster hanger-oner who just happened to be there.

"You know, Eliot, I'm afraid I'm going to feel like a fifth wheel with the rest of the men."

Wrinkle lines shot across his forehead as he frowned.

"Why is that, Mike?"

"Because it won't be that often my telephone tapping skills will be needed."

"But you'll be right next to me every time we go to a meeting or on a raid."

"I know, but I wish I could do more, contribute more."

"Well, maybe something will come up once we really get into this thing. We'll just play it by ear."

"I hope we both know what we're doing."

"Let's go on over to the firing range and see if you can hit the broad side of a barn."

We went. I couldn't.

We drove back through a tangle of traffic to Eliot's office.

The jousting cars reminded me of dogfights in the recent Great War.

He had kind of a worried look on his face, like he was going to fire me but hated to break the news.

"I'll make it easy for you, Eliot. I'll be happy to resign. It will save you the embarrassment of having to fire me. Don't worry. I didn't burn any bridges back home. I won't have any trouble landing another job."

He looked at me like I was crazy. "What are you talking about? I have no intention of firing you. I was just trying to figure out how we're going to solve your weaponry problem."

"I know — pretty hopeless, huh?"

"I think I've got the solution." He walked over and pulled something out of a closet. His back was to me so I couldn't see what it was. "We need to get you something that makes a loud enough noise to scare people."

He turned and tossed it to me. I caught it with the same aplomb as my pass interception that beat Michigan at Ann Arbor before 60,000 stunned fans

back in 1925.

It was an odd looking piece of artillery. I arched my eyebrows. "What am I supposed to do with this antique blunderbuss?"

Fred Burke, a massacre killer suspect

He laughed. "That's not an antique. It's a special-made Winchester."

John Thompson – gun inventor

I looked it over more carefully. "How is this supposed to improve my aim?"

He laughed again. "Don't worry; you just point it in a general direction. That little baby has a short fifteen-inch barrel, lever action and a rosewood pistol grip."

"Can I hurt anybody with this toy?"

"Are you kidding? It has four shots, three shells in the magazine and one in the chamber. Loaded with OO buckshot for maximum effect, it's roughly the same thing as shooting a Tommy gun 36 times."

"Hot diggety! That's pretty amazing. Is it legal?"

Eliot winked. "For you it is."

I immediately christened my piece of hardware "Little Big Man."

Spike O'Donnell – C.H.S.

The next day, Ness held an informational pow-wow to introduce everyone and explain what his function was in the organization. Then he launched into a statement of our goals and objectives, along with an outline of what procedures he expected everyone to follow.

"The job ahead of us is going to

be difficult," he announced. "We are in the awkward position of trying to enforce a law that a substantial portion of the citizens don't seem to want. Al Capone is probably at the height of his power. Capone and his men have blasted a lot of mugs out of the beer and alky rackets into shiny new coffins. Johnny Torrio – Al's mentor - had his men rub out Dion O'Banion, his Irish competitor, with the famous 'handshake murder' in his own flower shop back in 1924. In retaliation, O'Banion's boys pumped five bullets into Torrio in 1925, but he somehow miraculously survived. Then he got cold feet and left for the sunny climes of Italy, turning everything over to Capone, lock, stock and barrel.

"Hot-headed Hymie Weiss rose to replace O'Banion and he, in turn, was on the receiving end of a dozen slugs in front of Holy Name Cathedral on State Street, near O'Banion's poesy shop."

"Didn't a bunch of other guys get it with him, Chief?" Paul De-Witt asked.

"That's right. A group of Capone's men rented a room next to O'Banion's old flower shop and shot through an open window, gunning five of them down in the street. Weiss and a guy named Peller were hit by over ten bullets each and were sent to that oblong hole in the ground. Three others were wounded but eventually recovered. That's now known as the 'rented ambush.' "

"Didn't Bugs Moran take control of the Irish gang afterward?" Steve Strohman inquired.

"Yes, he and Schemer Drucci ran things jointly for a while," Ness said. "Then they got together with Capone and agreed to what was called the Hotel Sherman Treaty. Territories were parceled out to every gang, and each promised not to make raids on the others. Killings were denounced as a way of settling disputes."

"I'll bet it didn't last long," Gary Tesson interjected.

"You're right," Ness said.

Joe Aiello – Chicago Hist. Soc.

Hymie Weiss – Chicago Hist. Soc.

Mrs. Joe (Catherine) Aiello in mourning

"Didn't Joe Aiello put out a contract on Capone?" Wes Bokal asked.

Ness nodded his head. "Yes, and four torpedoes came to town to try and collect the $50,000, two of them from St. Louis, Tony Russo and Vincent Spicuzza. But Capone has plenty of 'eyes' and 'ears' and Machine Gun McGurn got to them first. Then they gunned down Aiello as he walked out of a West Side flat where he had been holed up like a rat for ten days. Ouch, what Joe got. Thirty .45 hot sizzling slugs between his chin and his privates!"

"Didn't that set the stage for the St. Valentine's Day Massacre?" John Kaufman inquired.

"February 14 – earlier this year, 1929," Ness said. "Capone was at his villa in Key Biscayne, Florida, but he kept in close touch with McGurn who orchestrated the whole thing."

"How many men bit the dust, seven or eight?" someone asked.

Ness held up one hand plus two fingers. "Seven men. Bugs Moran was the main target, but he was late to the meeting and headed the other direction when he saw the killers pull up in a police flivver, dressed like cops."

"Lucky him," Strohman said.

"Capone isn't even in Chicago right now; he's doing time in a Philadelphia prison."

"That'll make our job a lot easier," Gary Tesson remarked.

"Don't kid yourselves. Capone may be in prison, but he's still running things. Capone went to Atlantic City, New Jersey, in May of this year to a big gangster conference. On the way back he was arrested on a concealed weapons charge, and the judge threw him in the klink for a full year, the maximum. My best guess is that he'll get out in March of next year."

"So, what's our first move, Chief?"

A serious look crept over Eliot's face. "There are over a dozen stills that have been marked and identified over in Chicago Heights. We're going to move against them tomorrow night."

CHAPTER 4

NOVEMBER 15, 1929

Tidbits about alcohol and Prohibition:

"I was a teetotaler until Prohibition." – Groucho Marx

"The country accepted Prohibition not only willingly, but almost absentmindedly." – Paul Lewis Allen

In colonial days rum was currency and an item of barter in the slave trade.
While our Puritan forbearers lashed out against pleasures of the flesh and drunkenness, they did not forbid drinking the extract of the grape.

The campaign against alcohol in America began around 1840 and it was a religious crusade started by the Methodist Church.

Prohibitionists scrutinized the Bible and began publishing versions that left out (bowdlerized) all references to wine.

The first states to pass their own prohibition laws were Bible-thumping rural entities such as Georgia, West Virginia, Mississippi, and Tennessee.

World War I gave impetus to the prohibition movement because it was easy for proponents to argue that sober doughboys and sober factory workers made good sense. It also helped create a climate of crusade and reform that resulted in women getting the vote.

It was widely thought that once the consumption of alcohol became illegal, the masses would flock instead to ice cream parlors and penny candy confectioneries.

Within a year after the passage of the 18th Amendment, bootlegging became the nation's largest industry, amounting to an estimated $4 billion a year.

The cocktail was invented by bartenders at speakeasies who came up with pieces of fruit, spices and other flavorings to disguise the foul taste of the alcohol they were selling.

It is estimated that by 1927 deaths from alcoholism had risen 600 percent.

By 1932 approximately 2,000 civilians (mostly gangsters and bootleggers) had been killed in Chicago warfare.

Liquor lovers were so desperate for the taste of spirits that there were instances where party-givers served wine laced with formaldehyde.

The next day, Ness had the group get together to take a tour. He wanted everyone to get a feel for the Chicago streets and see the landmarks— gangster landmarks, that is. He drove one group in his shiny ostentatious Cadillac (a 16 cylinder, seven passenger sedan). I drove the rest in my Hudson Terraplane. Having attended the University of Chicago for four years, I still pretty well knew my way around town. Eliot merely filled me in on some of the new landmarks that had sprouted during the three years I had been gone.

We drove by Capone's two-story brick house on Prairie Avenue, Dion O'Banion's flower shop, Frank Nitti's Capri Restaurant on North Clark Street, Johnny Torrio's house, the Green Mill, the Metropole Hotel on Michigan Avenue,

Mr. Prohibition by Rollin Kirby

Young Al Capone with acne

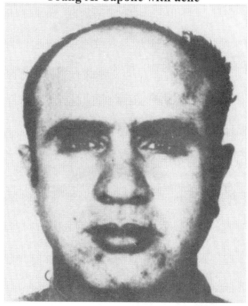

Eliot Ness I.D. (*Chicago Sun-Times*)

the Clark Street garage - site of the St. Valentine's Day Massacre - the Pershing Hotel (Capone's original headquarters), and the Hawthorne Racetrack.

"Who was the driver the day of the St. Valentine's Day Massacre?" Tesson asked.

"Nobody was ever convicted of the crime, but they're pretty sure Fred 'Killer' Burke was one of the triggermen and George 'Devil Driver' Moore was at the wheel." I responded.

"Devil Driver?" Strohman remarked.

"Yes, it's another one of those stupid nicknames. He supposedly can drive like the devil."

I hated to admit it, but it was kind of fun driving around and soaking up the local color.

The stills in Chicago Heights had been located during a small reconnaissance mission that Eliot, his driver John, myself, and Paul DeWitt went on. As an opening gambit, one of the stills was seized, and we waited for an expected reaction. A Mafia representative, Johnny Giardelli, quickly approached our group. He was slim, dark and a fancy dresser, wearing a diamond stickpin big enough to choke a mule. He seemed to come out of nowhere shortly after we smashed the equipment and arrested one of the still operators.

"Listen, youse guys," he said out of the corner of his mouth. "Ya don't want-a go around making trouble for a lot of people. We can work this thing out. We'll make it worth your while."

Eliot played it coy and pretended we were interested. I guessed he wanted to go along with the scheme, build a bribery and conspiracy case and go after bigger fish. We all acted like we were receptive to payoffs.

"Fine, meet me at the Toddle Inn Saloon tomorrow night at eight o'clock," he said, shifting his eyes.

"We'll be there," Ness said, while the rest of us all nodded.

The next night we all piled into Ness' government-issued Cadillac, and John Kaufman

166

drove us to the Toddle Inn at Chicago Heights. *Toddle Inn and wobble out*, I thought.

The Heights were located about thirty miles outside of south Chicago. Kaufman parked right in front of the place.

I could feel my pulse quicken. For the first time we were going into enemy territory. We went inside and proceeded to sit down at one of the tables. I took a good look around the dimly lit interior, trying to read faces. There was a lively crowd on hand, and they were three deep at the bar. A skinny man with rolled up sleeves sat at a honky-tonk piano in the corner and played broken threads of "Happy Days Are Here Again." There was a policeman standing at a highly polished mahogany bar, drinking something amber that looked like straight whiskey. He watched us in the long mirror behind the bar as we came in, but grew disinterested and went back to his booze.

Ness went over to the barkeep, a beefy fellow with beamed shoulders, and whispered, "Tell Johnny Giardelli we're here."

He nodded. "Sure thing. What do you want while you're waiting?"

"I'll have a boilermaker and the other guys want gin rickeys," Ness said.

I watched the barkeep with a certain fascination. He had a nose that looked like it had been broken several times. A whirlygig of activity, he worked quickly and efficiently. Drinks were mixed with a dash of this or a splash of that while the bottle was adeptly held a foot high from the glass without spilling a drop. If a patron wanted a beer he positioned a glass under the tap and pulled on a porcelain handle that released a frothy stream of suds. The excess head was skimmed off with a scrimshawed foam stick. Between pouring drinks he washed glasses, wiped his rag over wet stains on the bar, and chatted with customers, responding with a big toothy grin to comments flung at him.

When a lady patron began to laugh loudly in giddy fashion, he nodded to a waiter who escorted her to a table in a far corner behind a potted palm. He was like a ringmaster at a three-ring circus, presiding over the festivities, keeping obnoxious drinkers in tow, and awing noisy customers into quiet.

Capone rival, George "Bugs" Moran

Hawthorne Smoke Shop in Cicero – Chicago Hist. Soc.

Frank Gusenberg – killed in St. Valentine's Day Massacre – Chicago Hist. Soc.

A waiter delivered our drinks. I thought the mixture tasted like something akin to radiator fluid, but everyone else seemed pleased with what slid down his gullet.

Paul DeWitt took a long drink and rolled the alcohol in his mouth before swallowing. "Aahh . . . not bad for battery acid. Who says this job doesn't have any fringe benefits."

Eliot looked at him, shook his head and rolled his eyes in a look of mock disgust.

After we slaked our thirst, the barkeep led us to a room in the back. Giardelli was sitting at the table with a couple of men, and another was standing nearby.

He splashed some hard liquor from a shot glass against the back of his throat before speaking. "Well, well, glad you men showed up. And I'm happy you guys are willing to be reasonable about this whole thing."

"We haven't agreed to anything yet," Ness said.

Giardelli—born in Milan in 1888, parents came to Chicago's Little Italy in 1894, served a year at Joliet for robbery and assault, burglar and hijacker, suspected killer—eyed us suspiciously.

"Listen, we have a pretty good thing going here. Everybody works together, the cops, the magistrates and the prohibition boys."

I had a queasy feeling in the pit of my stomach and couldn't tell whether it was from the drink or my nerves.

Eliot leaned back in his chair and said, "That's fine Johnny, but what we want to know is what's in it for us?"

My knees started getting a little weak because I thought Ness was sounding as if he was going to be greedy and unreasonable.

Giardelli reached inside his wide shouldered, double-breasted coat pocket and drew out an expensive-looking leather wallet. It was the fattest bill case I had ever seen. His fingers pulled out three C - notes and he spread them on the table. "Here's three hundred bucks, and there's

167

more where that came from. All we want is a little cooperation. That comes to seventy-five bucks apiece. Whatta ya think?"

Ness looked down at the money but didn't reach for it. "That might be enough and it might not. It all depends on how bad a case of amnesia we're all supposed to get."

Take the money; take the money, Eliot, I thought. I had one of those little flashbacks and remembered that the mob killed a reporter in June of 1927 because they thought he got too greedy.

"Well," Giardelli responded, "things are kind of quiet right now, and this is about all that's going on. We're offering you a fair amount."

"That's fine for now," I said, reaching for the money. "When do we get our next payoff?"

Giardelli's eyes hardened a bit. "You can expect this same amount on a monthly basis as long as there isn't any trouble."

"We'll be back," Ness said calmly, displaying nerves of steel. "Let's go, men," he said to us.

Steve Strohman carefully recorded the serial numbers and filed a complete report for us the next day with the United States District Attorney.

The following night we drove back to Chicago Heights for an inspection tour. As we approached the area where the stills were located, two cars began to tail us.

"We've been made," DeWitt commented.

"Nothing to worry about; they're just watching us for now. It's much too early for gunplay," Ness said.

When we returned the next night, the same thing happened. Apparently the Chicago Heights thugs made a habit of cruising the streets, following any strange cars that drove around through their territory.

"That place we went to a couple of nights ago, the Toddle Inn, had a second story to it. I wonder what was going on up there," I said.

"Probably craps tables, chuck-a-luck, roulette wheels and poker tables," DeWitt replied.

Ness decided new tactics were in order the next night. We left his Cadillac at the office and took my Hudson

Bel-Air Drive-in at **Mitchell** on Route 66 – Dan Oberle Collection

Teraplane. Instead of dressing in suits, we wore dungarees and chambray cotton work shirts. When we approached our target area, we parked the car in an isolated spot and fanned out, agreeing to meet at a prearranged rendezvous spot in a darkened, secluded alley.

We were like commandoes on a reconnoitering mission. I labeled it "Operation Mongoose," and it was a complete success. It wasn't difficult locating fifteen different stills. All we had to do was follow our noses, picking up the sour stench of fermenting mash that hung like a miasmic pall over the neighborhood. The distinct odor could be picked up as many as four or five blocks away.

The next night we went on "Operation Shakedown," a return trip to the Toddle Inn. This time we brought along Martino/Gillespie, the non-Italian Italian.

That same barkeep, the big, burly, bald guy with one of those odd-shaped heads loved by phrenologists, gave us a hearty welcome and brought over some drinks.

"Anything else for you boys?" he cheerfully asked.

"Never mind the idle chatter," Ness told him tersely.

"Tell Giardelli we're here for a serious palaver."

"Sure, sure . . . right away." He scooted off towards the back room and came back in less than a minute.

"Johnny sez , 'come on back.' "

Giardelli was slowly chewing on a ubiquitous toothpick as we sauntered into the room with a slight touch of braggadocio.

"Have a seat. What's on your mind?" he said, leaning forward.

Eliot was the consummate actor, and he added a touch of arrogance to his tone. "What do you take us for, a bunch of pikers?"

He frowned. "Whatta ya mean?"

"We combed this section of town last night and located fifteen stills. And you

168

tried to make us think this was a two-bit operation. We got a lot more money coming to us for looking the other way."

Giardelli's voice hardened. "Well, now I'd hafta talk to the rest of the boys about that."

"I'll tell you what, Johnny," Ness said in a more congenial tone. "Why don't you get the owners of these stills together, and we can all sit down and work it out."

There was a pulse beating in his neck as he toyed with his toothpick then nodded. "Okay. I'll make the rounds and see everybody, and then we can all meet at eight o'clock tomorrow night in Pete Falcone's joint on State Street."

I could hardly contain my enthusiasm. This was a good way to build a conspiracy charge, and if we put the hoodlums in a vise they might cough up corrupt police, judges, city officials and even prohibition agents.

"We'll be there," Ness said in a steady, level voice.

Giardelli sat motionless, watching us with snake-like eyes as we left. Out front, as we piled into Eliot's car, DeWitt observed: "We still have that dark blue Pontiac that's been tailing us."

Tinker Toy Wonder Builder

The next night, we purposely arrived five minutes late just to make Giardelli's men think we were pretty blasé about the whole thing.

Falcone was waiting for us at one end of the bar, a massive hulk who was well over six feet with a raspy voice.

"The guys from the Heights are already here; let's go into the back room," he said.

A half a dozen patrons watched us as we marched Indian file past the length of the bar and followed Falcone into the back room.

"Keep a close watch on things," I whispered to Martino/Gillespie.

He nodded.

The first thing that caught my eye was a Stiletto-thin Italian guy over in the corner with his chair tilted back

State Farm Insurance Building at **Bloomington** on Route 66 – Oberle

against the wall. He had a Jack Frost pointed nose and a swarthy complexion. A fancy Sweet Caporal cigarette dangled from the corner of his mouth. His hair was slicked back, Valentino-style, and he wore a gaudy red candy-stripped shirt and green tie. His piercing dark brown eyes gave us a menacing once over, and he kept a riveting stare on us the whole time.

Giardelli, dressed all dapper in a chalk-striped suit with a Dion O'Banion-like carnation in his lapel, tried to allay our fears. "Don't worry 'bout that greaseball; he works for me, and he don't speak no English."

Giardelli sat behind a round poker table. Falcone was next to him. A bulb with a green metal shade hung from a wire over the middle of it, reminding me of a hangman's noose. The walls were dark paneled and the windows were covered by dark green shades. My nose flinched at the smell of stale air, alcohol and unwashed bodies. There was a pockmarked-faced man standing next to Giardelli and another bruiser who stayed behind us near the door.

Giardelli took out a cigarette and put it between his lips. He flicked a gold-plated lighter and it flared brilliantly. He touched the flame to the tip of the cigarette, flipped the lid closed and returned it to his breast pocket.

"This is Louie Bartilino," Giardelli said, waving his thumb at the man next to him. Bartilino was nervously chewing a stick of gum. "He's the head of the Chicago Heights organization."

"Where's everybody else?" Ness asked.

Giardelli's eyes grew hard. "This is all that'll be here. Don't worry. The others have agreed to accept

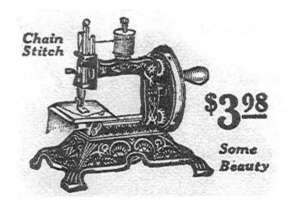

Chain Stitch

$3.98

Some Beauty

what we decide here tonight. Me, Louie and Pete will do the talkin' for 'em. Now let's get at it."

"Based on what we saw the other night, we think we deserve a lot more than seventy-five bucks a man," Eliot said in a harsh manner.

"Giardelli's face slowly grew red. "It sounds like this is gonna be some *#!@# kinda shakedown."

Eliot held out a palm-forward hand to calm him down. "It's nothing of the sort. We've got a pretty good idea what others are getting paid, and we only want what's fair."

Giardelli was still fuming.

"We're reasonable men. How much are you paying the cops in the Heights?"

"Well, let's see . . ." Bartilino volunteered. "We're paying off about—"

"Shaddup, Louie. It's none of their business," Giardelli interrupted.

Giardelli threw us a murderous glare. "You guys must think we're made outta money. There are so many hands in the cookie jar, you guys are making more money than we are. I could have you knocked off for half of what you're asking."

Ness remained calm and poised. "Don't try to intimidate us, Giardelli. We don't play that game. What your overhead costs are don't concern us. But don't take us for a bunch of suckers by low-balling us."

Giardelli paused and regained his composure. "Hold on a minute." Three of the men gathered around in a huddle in a far corner. Their voices rose and fell in heated discussion, held in Italian.

Martino/Gillespie leaned over and whispered to me: "They're arguing over whether to go as high as $500." I passed it on to Eliot.

They came back to their original positions. Giardelli straightened his silk tie and harrumphed, "Four hundred is as high as we can go – take it or leave it."

My heart leaped to my throat as Eliot put the pressure on and insisted on five hundred.

"If you're not willing to be reasonable, this can be settled in other ways," Giardelli said with sinister overtones.

Take it, Eliot, please take it.

"Don't threaten us, pal, or it'll cost you even more. We said $500 – not a red cent less."

Bishop Motors at **Staunton** on Route 66– Dan Oberle Collection

Poor roads in Illinois – 1923 – I.S.H.L.

They went back into their huddle. The one in the red shirt stood up and said something to them in Italian.

Martino/Gillespie leaned forward and whispered to Paul DeWitt: "That slimeball over there just asked Johnny if he should stick a knife in Eliot's back. He's got his knife out now, and he's inching toward the chief."

"Okay, I'll take care of him," DeWitt murmured.
Paul slid his hand under his coat and stealthily pulled the gun out of his shoulder holster and slowly turned around, revealing the business end of his blue steel .45.

I breathed a sigh of relief, thanking God that Ness had seen the wisdom of bringing the non-Italian Italian along with us. I felt like I'd be a lot safer if I pulled my gun out of my shoulder holster, but I followed the lead of Eliot and Gillespie and left it alone.

Giardelli, seeing the possibility of what might transpire, shouted, "No! Wait!" The situation remained tense as Giardelli calculated the odds and looked around the room. Then he stuck out his arm and waved the Mafia killer off. The man clicked a button and the blade slid back into the handle. He slowly backed away.

"Okay, five hundred it is," he said, muttering in Italian under his breath.

Ness remained cocky. "That's being downright sensible of you gentlemen." He extended *my* arm and opened *my* hand palm's up. "That means you owe my bagman a little matter of a couple hundred more bucks."

I had visions of Giardelli whipping out his knife and pinning my hand to the poker table.

Without a word, but with veins popping in his forehead and muscles twitching in his jaw, he took out his wallet and slapped four fifty-dollar bills in my hand.

"Thanks, Johnny. It's been a pleasure doing business with you. Just make sure the money keeps coming on a regular basis. We'll see you a month from now."

I couldn't wait to get out of there as we turned and slowly made our way to the door. Paul DeWitt protected our rear with a hand inside his coat as he nimbly backpedaled, keeping a steady eye on the Mafia goon until we were safely out the door.

No one said a word until we were back in the car, and John Kaufman smoothly sent us out of harm's way. My heart was still pounding so loud I was afraid the others would hear it and start ribbing me.

"Wow! That was really something," DeWitt howled. "I can't believe Giardelli took all that lip from the Chief."

Eliot let out a loud whistle. "I really owe you one, Paul. I could almost feel the knife sticking in my ribs."

I tried to think of something brave or witty to say, but couldn't. I felt more like we were a bunch of clay pigeons than some tough-guy feds.

And this is only the beginning, I reminded myself.

The next morning all ten of us gathered in Eliot's office, listening to him explain how we were going to fire the first shot in the war against Capone. I had barely gotten over my case of jitters from the night before.

Lon Chaney and Mary Philbin in *Phantom of the Opera*

"Hey, Chief, we're dying of boredom sitting on our keisters," Mizell complained.

"Don't worry, you'll get a chance for some action. Tonight we're going to raid over a dozen stills."

I searched the faces of my fellow men in arms. They were eager . . . and ready. Gary Tesson, a delighted Boy Scout grin on his face, nudged Wes Bokal and sparked a set of murmurs that went around the room.

"Four of us went out and located fifteen stills the other night in Chicago Heights. Then we met with a thug named Giardelli and accepted a "bribe" to lay off the stills. Just in case some of you think this is going to be a picnic, let me remind you that some punk in a fancy silk shirt tried to stick a knife between my ribs at that meeting. Gillespie's quick action prevented it from happening. I'm pretty anxious to meet up with Giardelli and his boys one more time…"

Actress Norma Talmadge

Another set of stage-whispers floated around the room.

"Gary Tesson has secured some search warrants for us and our first order of business is to knock off those stills. After that we go after Capone's breweries."

"What about the speak-easies?" Strohman asked.

Ness nodded. "There are roughly two hundred speak-easies in Chicago. We could go after them but as soon as we closed one down, another would pop up somewhere else. That wouldn't be very productive. The solution is to go after the source. If we can take them out, we'll dry up the town, and cotton-mouthed Chicagoans will have to go back to drinking soda pop."

"How do we locate the breweries?" DeWitt wanted to know.

"The beer is shipped in stave barrels. We'll locate large quantities of barrels, and we know they get used over and over again. We'll follow them back to the breweries."

"Then we hop on the hops, right, Chief?" Bischoff added.

I knew a little about brewing because Heim's Beer was located less than a block from my old high school in East St. Louis. Hops are used as the flavoring ingredient for beer. Hops are to beer as grapes are to wine. The flavor from the plant dries out the sweet flavor imparted by the malt used in the brewing process. Hops are a member of the hemp family of plants, the same family that claims marijuana.

Ness gave an easy smile and nodded. I could tell he was pleased at the group's enthusiasm.

Wes Bokal, "the Fly," put forth a question. "Chief, how do you figure that only ten of us are going to be able to knock over fifteen scattered stills without letting the cat out of the bag and the word getting out after we've hit the first two or three?"

"We might not be able to take all of them out in one night, but we can get at least ten of them. The others we'll just catch as catch can. I've asked the prohibition unit to loan us some men. Each of you will be in charge of four of those men to form an independent raiding party. Hopefully, we'll take out quite a few stills and round up a few of the mugs who are operating them."

Eliot turned to me. "Anything you want to add to this, Mike?"

Eliot caught me completely off guard. For a second or two I didn't know what to say. I was nervous and dry-mouthed.

"I, uh, shouldn't need to remind you of, uh, the utmost need for secrecy as we prepare for this mission. Once we assemble with the other agents and the assignments are given out, absolutely no one is to get to a telephone. And make sure that everyone in your group knows that you are in complete charge and that they are to follow your orders to the letter."

Eliot looked at me as if I was supposed to say more.

I flashed everyone a V for victory sign with two fingers.

"*Semper Paratus* – always ready. The Coast Guard motto is apropos to our situation."

My heart was pounding again. I had conducted dozens of meetings as a telephone executive without the slightest qualm, but somehow this was different.

The rest of the morning and afternoon we began poring over the details of our plan of attack and made ourselves thoroughly familiar with a map of Chicago Heights. In the early evening we gathered at a large garage that was under government contract to house and inspect the cars we were going to use on the raids. As darkness began to close in, the other prohibition agents began to arrive. Ness had us all meet in a large glass-enclosed office, but even so, the room was jam-packed. Eliot nimbly hopped on top of the desk, and the crowd grew hushed.

"We've an important mission to undertake, men," he said. "Follow the orders of your leader and work as a team. We're not looking for any prima donnas or cowboys. Just do as you've been trained."

Then each of the leaders stepped forward and picked out four men. Eliot and I settled for the eight that were left.

"Is it all right if I make a quick trip to the rest room?" an angular fellow with a bobbing Adam's apple inquired.

"Sure, Steve will show you where it is," Eliot replied. He intended to let everyone know that nobody was getting out of our sight, not even for a trip to the bathroom to give the mob a tip-off that the raids were going to take place.

I took a good look at the man to make sure he wasn't going to be included on any more of our raids.

Eliot gave some last minute instructions. "Look at that clock on the wall and synchronize your watches. Remember, nine-thirty on the dot is when we strike. That way we'll hit them simultaneously, and maybe some of you will be able to get to a second target before word gets around."

We started loading into the cars as the two large garage doors were raised. Surprisingly, Eliot told me that my target was to be the Toddle Inn Saloon. He said he was afraid it might get too personal if he picked that target.

I was happy to get the assignment because further investigation by Wes Bokal, our fly on the wall, revealed that it was the brain center of the Chicago Heights operation. It also happened to be a pickup depot for most of the illicit alcohol trade in the entire Midwest. We later learned that one of their sources was a place in Kentucky near Eddyville called the Land Between the Rivers. This stretch of land between the Tennessee and Cumberland Rivers, near a point where they emptied into the Ohio River, was a hotbed of still activity with a small landing strip. The stuff was being flown back to Chicago at night in planes.

Ad for the Jordan automobile – especially made to appeal to women

"Frozen alive" stunt at a typical walkathon – George Eells collection

We learned that rumrunners from Iowa, southern Illinois, St. Louis and even Kansas City used the Toddle Inn as their

Chrysler "70" Royal Sedan
$1795, f. o. b. Detroit

base. They would leave their cars with the bartender to be driven away by the members of the Chicago Heights alcohol mob, while they waited at the bar.

By nine-fifteen our car was parked on a secluded road on the outskirts of Chicago Heights, poised to make the strike. "Operation Cobra," as I termed it, was about to be launched. As I sat there I could start to feel my pulse in my ears, a sure sign that my adrenalin had kicked in, priming me for action. I knew the others had arrived at their destinations and were fanning out all over the area.

I wondered about the fear that settled in my gut . . . wondered whether the other men on the team had the same tightness. I remembered that Mark Twain had once said courage was resistance to fear, not absence of fear. Cradling my lever-action sawed-off shotgun in my lap, I leaned down into the glow of the dash light to check my watch.

"Okay, boys, it's time to fish or cut bait." The nervous high pitch in my voice irritated me. "Let's go catch some mackerel."

I edged the car to the curb and we slid quietly to a stop in front of the Toddle Inn. I stretched and rolled my shoulders in a vain effort to remove a knot in the back of my neck. Another quick look at my Elgin confirmed that we were right on schedule. I crooked a finger at two of the men and waved them around the corner of the building so they could gain entrance by the rear. I led a charge through the front entrance into the barroom.

Four men drinking at the bar raised their hands quickly when I barked: "Nobody move, this is a federal raid. There are other agents coming in the back door."

A coin-operated player piano was playing a brassy tune. The same lumpy headed bartender was still there, swabbing the top of the bar. His stubby cigar fell out of his mouth. His eyes looked like Moon pies when he saw us barge in.

"Where's Giardelli?" I sharply asked.

He shook his head, unable to speak. "He, he's . . . he's not here."

We frisked the four men at the bar and relieved them of

their revolvers. My partner placed all four guns into his belt. Their heads jerked to the side as our other men crashed through the rear door and made their way into the barroom.

"There's nobody back there," the first agent said in a disappointed tone.

"Well, we caught a few fish," I said.

"Give those guns to Augie," I told my partner, "and you and I are going to take a look upstairs. "Plug anybody that makes a false move," I ordered the other two.

We raced up the wooden stairs, making a tremendous clatter, and emerged into a long narrow hall that ran the length of the building. A series of rooms faced the corridor on one side. From behind the nearest door we could hear the blare of a radio.

I grasped the knob and flung the door open. "Hold it, this is a federal raid," I brashly announced.

My mouth fell open. We had barged into a gaudily decorated parlor. There were four women. Two were wearing filmy negligees while the others wore the kimonos fashionable to their profession. One was sipping a grape Nehi. Two buxom brunettes were sitting at a table with mah-jongg tiles scattered on its top. Another, startled by our abrupt entrance, dropped a *True Confessions* magazine from her lap. The fourth was sitting at a small table in a straight-backed chair, applying bright red finger nail polish. A striking blonde, she didn't even bother pulling the front of her kimono closed. She stared in disbelief at the two of us, me with my shotgun and my partner with his .45.

"W-e-l-l . . . look what we have here," she boldly announced. "It's Tom Mix and the Boy Scouts, here to rescue damsels in distress."

I felt a big lump forming in my throat and a quick glance at my partner revealed a face red with embarrassment.

"Pull up a chair and let's talk this over," she said with coquettish inflexion. "I'm Angie – what's your handle."

"Sorry, uh, ladies, but we're, uh, busy r-right now," I nervously said, backing up.

173

We wheeled and got out of there as fast as we could.

"Come back and see us when you can stay longer Mr. Mix," she said. "Toodle-O, and don't forget to bring Big Boy with you."

When we got back in the hall, several other women were standing there with curious looks on their faces. We quickly checked the other rooms, but they were empty, except for a bed, washbasin, towel and a small lamp with a beaded shade on a small table.

My partner and I exchanged embarrassing grins as we headed back down the stairs. "Do you think we should notify vice?" my partner asked with a ribald wink.

I shook my head. "No, why bother."

I was deeply disappointed that the red-shirted Mafia torpedo and Giardelli weren't there. But when we dropped off our catch at a local police station and got back to the garage, I was elated to discover that the other raids were a complete success. All fifteen of the stills were found and smashed, and thirty-eight operators were arrested.

CHAPTER 5

NOVEMBER 20, 1929

Capone's custom-built 1928 Cadillac featured a 40 h.p. V-8 engine and cost a small fortune. It weighed four tons, this being attributed to an armor-plated body, a steel protected gasoline tank, and windscreen (windshield) and other windows of bulletproof glass one and a half inches thick. The behemoth was also equipped with a removable rear window for a tail gunner, a police siren, and a secret gun locker hidden behind a rear seat panel.

"Mike, you're not normal," she in-toned in a high-pitched voice.

We were sitting at the supper table, finishing a meal. It had been a boring day. Eliot didn't come to work at the office. Marillyn, his secretary, said he was home in bed, sick with the grippe. I was somewhat concerned because I remembered more civilians lost their lives here in the states from the flu than the number of doughboys killed overseas during the Great War.

"What?"

Cartoon – Bull Durham is discouraged

Capone's heavily armored Cadillac

"The life you lead, it's unhealthy," she reiterated, her eyes slightly stern and her ruddy cheeks aglow.

This slightly plump and usually pleasant woman had apparently decided late in life to go into the field of psychiatry. Until now, I had assumed she was merely a seamstress and landlady who collected rent from me on a weekly basis.

Thor, the Norwegian forest cat who held dominion over the house, was rubbing his cheek against my leg. I reached down and petted him. "Nonsense, I'm fit as a fiddle," I retorted.

"That isn't what I'm talking about and you know it, young man."

There were just the two of us; her husband, I learned from Eliot, had passed away three years ago. I pushed my plate away.

"All I know is that if I eat one more bite of this lasagna, I'm going to pop. I haven't tasted anything this good since my mother made me some for my birthday last year. If I had to choose, I'd have to flip a coin."

Her face squeezed into an irritated frown. "You know what I mean," she said, wagging a finger at me.

"If I did, then I'd qualify as a mind reader," I replied in a slightly aggravated tone.

I had only known her six weeks. Eliot told me when I first agreed to join him that his aunt had a duplex apartment for rent, located in a quiet middle class neighborhood. She and her husband lived in the other half.

"You're on the verge of middle age, and you're not married. Not only that, as far as I can tell, you don't even have a lady friend. Your mother must be terribly disappointed."

She rose and began placing dishes in the cast iron porcelain-coated sink.

"I'm only 27, Mrs. Griffin. That's hardly middle age. And you can blame my lack of social life on that nephew of yours; he's a slave driver at work. Besides, how do you know I don't have a steady girl back home?"

As she started running water in the sink, I rose to collect the flatware and glasses. Her back was to me, and she raised a brace of pudgy fingers in the air. "Two things.

174

You forget these walls are paper-thin. I can hear everything you say on the telephone, but, er, uh . . . most of the time I don't bother."

"It's so nice to learn that my constitutional right to privacy is being violated by a surrogate mother. And what is the second, pray tell?"

"Well . . . I'm also the one who checks your mailbox everyday – you know – just to make sure none of it has fallen out."

I was standing next to her now, with dishtowel in hand. She shook a dash of Ivory soap flakes into the water.

"I hope you realize that you're probably going to be fined for violating city ordinance #5744, snooping without a license."

She handed me a glass to dry. Although I had only known Mrs. Griffin a short time, I had grown very fond of her. When she learned that I had handyman skills, she offered to cook me one hot meal a day in return. Figuring that was a bargain, I readily agreed, although my job downtown often kept me from taking full advantage of the meal offer.

"I think I know just the girl for you," she said.

"Are you going into the marriage broker business? You need a license for that, too," I chided.

She handed me a plate. I dried it and rubbed my finger across the surface. It made a mournful sound. She reacted by squinching her blue eyes. "Squeaky clean," I teased.

Mrs. Griffin shook her head. "One of my friends has this niece. She's a lovely thing. Teaches high school."

"If she's so *lovely*, why hasn't anybody dragged her down the church aisle yet?"

"She's shy."

"Probably homely."

"But, I promised."

I blanched. "Promised what?"

"That I would fix the two of you up on a blind date."

"You what!!!"

John Scalise – Chicago Hist. Soc.

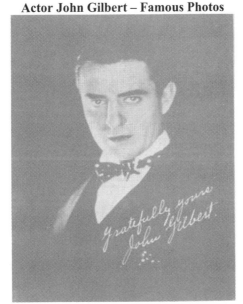

Actor John Gilbert – Famous Photos

Gangster photos on Eliot's wall (Courtesy Dell Comics)

She handed me a bowl. "You need a little female company. It'll do you good. You've been edgy lately."

"Yeah, thanks to you." I gave her a devilish wink. "How do you know I won't seduce her?"

She turned and looked at me, hands on hips. "How . . . oh, Mike, you're such a great kidder."

"I'll need to see her picture first."

"It's on the table in the parlor."

After finishing the dishes, we went into the parlor and I scrutinized the young lady's picture. She wasn't bad looking.

"I bet she has the personality of a witch, dealing with rowdy kids all day long."

"Well, young man, my friend said she has qualms about you, too."

"Fine, let's call the whole thing off."

"I promised that you would at least give her a ring."

I widened my eyes in mock surprise. "You've practically got us engaged?"

"No, smarty pants. I mean you're supposed to call her."

I was piqued, but I didn't want to hurt her feelings. "Okay, Mrs. Griffin. I'll do it, just this once – but you owe me big. I've got a birthday coming up in two months and the quid pro quo is a two-layer chocolate birthday cake."

A mischievous smile crept across her face. "Deal!"

I called the niece of Mrs. Griffin's friend the next evening.

"Hello, this is Ruth Ann."

"Yes, this, uh, this is Mike Kriegan calling. I believe you were expecting my call."

"No, I've never heard that name before. By the way, do you realize that you repetitively used the words call and calling in both of your brief sentences."

"My mistake. I assure you, I'm a reasonably well-educated man, Miss. I normally don't commit such an unforgivable social *faux pas*. Chalk it up to nervousness."

"I didn't mean to be rude. I'm a grammarian, and I was merely trying to improve your oral presentation. Who did you say you were?

"Are you sure it's not supposed to be *whom*?"

"Pardon?"

"Never mind. I'm the renter who lives in Mrs. Griffin's duplex."

"Yes."

"Well, she said you were expecting my call – something about a date."

"What date?"

"I, uh, you know, a date . . . between a man and a woman."

"What man? What woman?"

"Us."

"I don't even know you!"

"Mrs. Griffin said it's supposed to be a blind date. That's the whole point."

"Oh, I don't know. I haven't been on a date for over a year."

A real social butterfly.

"Do you like opera?"

"It's all right."

Don't knock yourself out with enthusiasm.

"Well, the Chicago Opera Company is doing Wagner's *Flying Dutchman* this Saturday."

"It's not gory is it? You know how those Germans are."

"I don't think so."

"And I won't like it if the heroine dies in the finale, victim of an ill-fated relationship with some crumb of a man. It's not like *La Bohème* or *Carmen*, is it?"

I shrugged. "I don't know; I'm not familiar with the story. My landlady highly recommends me so would it be all right if I pick you up around seven?"

"P.m. or a.m.?"

"P.m."

"We wouldn't be out really late or anything?"

"I'll have you home in bed before midnight."

"In bed?"

"Uh, I mean, I'll walk you to your front door before midnight."

"Well . . . I guess that would be all right."

"Where?"

"Where?"

Good grief!

"Where do you live?"

"Oh, 2404 Melrose."

"Is that out in Cicero?"

"Yes."

"Maybe I should pick you up at quarter to seven."

"Why so early?"

"I thought I might introduce myself to your parents."

"Oh, yes, that would be nice."

"I'll see you Saturday."

"*This* Saturday?"

"Yes. ***This*** Saturday, the day after tomorrow."

"That will be fine."

"See you then. Good-bye."

"Wait . . . what did you say your name was?"

"Mike, Mike Kriegan, K-r-i-e-g-a-n."

"Oh, that's right. Now I remember. Well, good-bye"

"Good-bye."

I shakily placed the phone back on the receiver. That was about the most futile, exasperating conversation I had ever had with a member of the female species. I nearly hung up on her in the middle of the conversation, but I stuck with my promise to Mrs. Griffin.

* * * *

I was dressed quite the sheik in white tie and black tails as I arrived at Ruth Ann's house promptly at the appointed time and presented her mother with a half-dozen yellow roses and a white violet corsage for her daughter.

"They're lovely," her mother said.

Ruth Ann came into the room, reached out, and brushed a piece of black lint off my white piqué dress shirt. She looked like a Sheba, wearing an outlandish red satin gown featuring outsized fur-trimmed sleeves and a turban wrapped around her head.

"Your outfit – it's beau-, uh, er, quite unusual."

"Thank you."

I was so nervous trying to pin the sprig of flowers on Ruth Ann, I stuck my thumb with the pin.

I was pleasantly surprised to discover that my date was nicely proportioned and had a great looking set of gams. I also noticed she had a leatherette case that seemed to be bulging with something.

"Why are you taking that along?" I asked.

"Oh, you'll see," she said nonchalantly.

We arrived at the ornate opera house and were seated near the orchestra pit.

"I'm so glad we're near the strings," she gushed.

"Why is that?"

"I love music. I play cello for the city orchestra during the summer when school is dismissed."

As soon as the orchestra began to play, she donned a pair of pince-nez glasses. I was dumbfounded when she pulled

176

out a stack of papers from her folio and began correcting them with a red pen.

Harold Lloyd in *Safety First*

"Aren't you going to watch?" I asked incredulously.

"No need. The entire production is in German and one can't understand a word they're saying. Besides, I read the synopsis and I can still hear the music. That's the best part anyway."

"But—"

She reached over and touched my hand. "Look, I know it's rude, but I promised my students I'd have these themes graded to hand back on Monday."

"Sure, okay," I said numbly.

I had never been to an opera before and quickly became immersed in its ambience and trappings. The great classical hall, richly decorated in maroon and gold, seemed to have perfect acoustics. Many of the "Garden City's" elite were there, dressed in their finest. The women wore opulent gowns of extravagant hues – violet, heliotrope, carmine, aquamarine. Harold and Edith McCormick née Rockefeller were in attendance. I glanced to my left and spotted Mike

Insull, the utilities mogul, talking to Mayor "Big Bill" Thompson. I overheard writer Ben Hecht saying that Enrico Caruso had performed *Pagliacci* a few weeks earlier at the opera and was fantastic.

Mary Garden, the middle-aged soprano, had a pure and pearly voice, every word meticulously pronounced and carefully pitched. What amazed me was the amount of emotion with which she loaded every note. She sang her heart out and was richly rewarded by enthusiastic applause. The music was fantastic and the text richly antique. The maestro, handsomely dressed in a black swallowtail coat, managed somehow to fuse the cast of many into an organic, viable whole.

Ruth Ann seemed to be ambidextrous of the brain. She was deeply engrossed in correcting the papers with markings and pithy comments in the margins. Yet she also bobbed and weaved with her head and occasionally gesticulated, waving her hand as if she were conducting the music.

She finished with her papers a few minutes before it was over. As we rose together and clapped and shouted "Bravo!" she leaned over and whispered: "That finale was a *tour de force*, don't you agree? Old Wagner could really write music – all those great chromatic changes in the downward tetrachord. And he's the one who invented the leitmotif technique."

I nodded in agreement although I didn't know the difference between a bass clef and a treble clef.

"I thought Mary Garden was wonderful," I said. "The playbill says she once performed the Dance of the Seven Veils in *Salome*."

"Yes," she answered. "That version of Richard Strauss' play was so scandalous, the authorities shut it down."

The cast enjoyed three thunderous curtain calls. Enthusiasts from the audience cheered wildly, threw flowers, and clapped until their gloves split.

There wasn't much conversation on the way home. I did notice that her hair, what little I could see under that ridiculous turban, looked soft, and her voice was gentle.

Out of the clear blue sky she asked, "You don't have any odd or unusual habits, do you?"

"I don't think so," I said without much thought.

Mary Garden

"Please, don't hedge. Everyone has at least one quirky mannerism."

"Well, let me see. I, uh, I take an ice-cold shower every morning."

Her hand flew to her chest near her throat. "You mean you have sexual frustrations?"

"No, no, it's nothing like that."

"Well, then, what is it?"

"It's nothing Freudian. A refreshing cold plunge stimulates the body, puts you on your toes, clears your head, prepares you mentally for daily challenges."

Chicago jazz musician "Baby" Dodds

"How on earth did your body get accustomed to such a shock?"

Chicago's Michigan Avenue 1929 (Chicago Historical Society)

"Each day when I took a shower, I mixed less and less hot water in with the cold. After about a month, I didn't need any more hot water."

"Where in the world did you come up with such an idea?"

"From my college roommate. His heritage is Scandinavian, and he said it was quite common for Nordic people to take a dip in a near-frozen lake in the midst of winter."

She wore a perplexed frown on her face as I walked her to the door. I was expecting a thank you and a handshake. Instead, she kissed me passionately on the mouth and invited me to her parent's home the next Sunday to listen to her group practice music. I was going to say no, but thought **why not**? Wasn't music supposed to soothe the soul of the savage beast?

It was a decision I came to regret. I fretted about it all week, hoping something would come up. But there were no urgent messages from home. I didn't get sick. There were no weekend assignments from Eliot. And Mussolini didn't launch an invasion of America.

Since there was no dramatic intervention by fate and I had no believable excuse, I found myself standing in front of the door at 2404 Melrose with another bouquet of roses for Ruth Ann's mother.

Her father opened the door. "Hey, Ruth Ann," he yelled back inside. "It's that nice young man again, and he brought me some flowers."

What have I gotten myself into?

He put his arm around my shoulder and pushed me inside a large room. "Ruth Ann and the others are getting ready to practice."

There were about eight musicians in the room, most of them dressed in casual clothes. I felt a little uncomfortable in my three-piece suit. The room was filled with pleasant chatter and the discordant sounds of eager musicians tuning their instruments. Some of them were clowning around with some jazz improvisations.

My thoughts drifted to Capone. I knew he was an ardent lover of jazz. "It's got guts, and it doesn't make you slobber," he once enthusiastically exclaimed.

Ruth Ann was grading another stack of papers. She briefly looked up and waved at me. She paused long enough to come over and introduce me collectively to the group. They either waved or nodded at me with their instruments. She then guided me to an overstuffed chair and plopped me into it.

Once they started, I'll have to admit they played some pretty good music. Some of it I even recognized. Now a segment from Beethoven's "Fifth Symphony," then a Stravinski, now Sibelius' "Finlandia," then an obscure piece by someone I never heard of - Georg Philipp Telemann. After Telemann came a haunting piece by Rachmaninoff, then some delicious sauerbraten, with sides of red cabbage and potato pancakes.

I was somewhat puzzled, expecting something more kosher. "Isn't Eisenstein a Jewish name?" I asked.

"Yes, but we're all non-practicing Jews," Ruth Ann explained.

I couldn't hide my astonishment. "How can you deny your Jewish heritage?"

McKinley Bridge on Route 66 (**Harold Zeigler** {Granite City} col.)

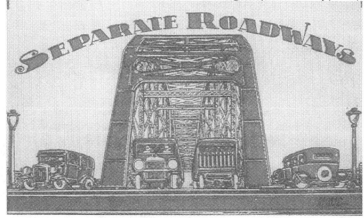

"Oh, we don't deny our heritage," her mother explained. "We just don't go to the synagogue on Saturday."

Ruth Ann nodded. "It's very fashionable nowadays. Dr. Freud says people use religion as a crutch."

During the food break, Ruth Ann's brother, David leaned over and whispered, "Is it true you work for the government?"

"Yes, but I mainly sit behind a desk and push a pencil." Her other brother Seth looked disappointed. "I thought maybe you were one of those G-men."

"Naw, about the most exciting thing I do is occasionally work on phone lines."

"You must be terribly bored," Ruth Ann intervened. "My family must be driving you nuts."

"Nonsense," I replied. "I'm actually enjoying myself." I reflected a bit on that comment, and it suddenly dawned on me that it wasn't a lie. It was a harmonious, happy family and an eclectic group that seemed to be genuinely enjoying what they were doing. I found the music to be interesting, and the kibitzing was stimulating. I relished their conversation and found it intriguing the way they complimented one another on the execution of a tricky passage. It was far different from the football jocks in my group at the University of Chicago who would psych themselves up by pounding on the lockers and look forward to trampling the opposition.

After dinner, they were nearing the finale of Tchaikovsky's "1812 Overture," and I eagerly anticipated the rousing conclusion, wondering what was going to make the sound of the canon when suddenly the guns went off.

Actually, it was the fist artillery pounding on the front door.

"Open up!!!" a strong *basso profundo* voice thundered from the other side.

East St. Louis jazz musician Lonnie Johnson (1899-1970)

"What the #!*%# are youse makin' all dat racket for again? I have ta do dis every month. Cut out the noise!"

I glanced around the room. Despite outnumbering him 12-1, everyone was cowed. I took a good look and saw a heavy-set, sub-human-looking man in his undershirt, with hair all over his arms and shoulders.

"But we always end by seven p.m., Mr. Romanowski."

"If I hear any more of dat garbage, I'm coming in there an' bending dat horn 'round your ears."

The two young boys, clearly frightened, moved to join their mother.

"Don't you Jew people know enough not ta violate the *!##@! law?"

"Excuse me, Mr. Romanowski, but I think *you're* the one who's violating people's rights."

I had somewhat surprised myself, having left my seat and moved toward the door.

He looked hard at me from beneath his jutting brows. "Well, well. Whatta we have here, a regular buttinski. What's your problem, punk?" I used my arm to push Mr. Eisenstein behind me, and now I was staring the monster in the face.

I decided on a bluff. "Have you ever heard of section twenty of the Criminal Code that deals with trespassing?"

He just looked at me, veins popping out on his neck.

"Or section twenty-two – threatening bodily harm? Or section —"

"You – some kinda Jew lawyer?" he grunted. He flexed his muscles. There was a naked lady tattooed on his right arm and when his biceps moved she did a suggestive jiggle.

"Step out here an' let's settle dis, man to man, or are ya a fruit?"

"Now I don't think we should bother these nice people with a public brawl." I pulled my suit coat open just enough to let him see the butt end of my .45. "I would hate to have to tell my cousin Tony Napoli that you've been bothering my friends."

A look of terror flashed across his face. He began backing off the stoop. "Excuse me, I've got somethin' cookin' . . . on the stove I hafta check on. Sorry, uh, sorry to have bothered youse nice people."

After the intruder beat a hasty retreat, I buttoned my coat

"Police?" I asked Ruth Ann, who had rushed over to my side.

"The police don't bother anybody in Cicero," she smiled.

"It's Gargantua from the apartment next door. His real name's Robert, and his mission in life is to make everyone as miserable as he is."

"Open up, I said," the voice repeated as the pounding continued.

"What does he want?"

"He harasses us all the time, complaining about the music."

Mr. Eisenstein timidly opened the door.

and turned around. Everyone was standing there slack-jawed.

"What?" I said.

"Are you really related to Tony Napoli, the hit man?" one of the musicians asked in utter disbelief.

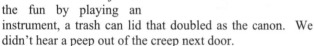
Roger Touhy being arrested - UPI

"No, of course not," I assured them. "It was just a bluff. Most bullies are cowards at heart. My father taught me that a long time ago."

Everyone breathed a sigh of relief. The orchestra then voted to replay the last movement of the "1812 Overture," louder than ever. I joined the fun by playing an instrument, a trash can lid that doubled as the canon. We didn't hear a peep out of the creep next door.

"Come back and join us any time you like," they said as I left.

I can't explain it, but that was the last time I ever saw Ruth Ann.

CHAPTER 6

NOVEMBER 24, 1929

BEER BREWING IN PROHIBITION DAYS

The brewing process usually started in a large copper vat, called a tun, where the ingredients were mixed with water.

Sacks and barrels of corn, sugar and malt (Chicago Library)

The ingredients consisted of grain (rice or malted barley), hops (a flower usually grown in Oregon or imported from Germany), creating a mixture (the solid ingredients are known as mash) that was then cooked or brought to a near boil for about two hours. Malted barley is different from regular barley in that it has higher carbohydrate/starch content.

The malting barley was often placed in shallow pans and roasted in an oven. The amount of time you roast the barley affects the flavor and color of the beer. During this process

the hops provide the flavor and the starch is converted into sugar and dissolved into a solution. This mixture is allowed to settle and the liquid, called wort, is taken off through a filter and placed in a cooling vat. These vats were made of wood (usually white oak or ash) and had either cooling coils or cooling jackets that held cold water.

Generally speaking, the higher the starch/sugar content, the higher the alcohol content. Good beer generally ran from about four to six percent in alcohol content.

After the wort cooled, the yeast was added. It was the yeast that started the fermentation process. Back then, breweries worked in conjunction with bakeries. Bakers either bought their yeast from breweries or vice versa. Yeast is actually a living plant that reproduces or multiplies by consuming sugar. Some housewives keep what they call a Herman in a Tupperware-type container that produces a constant supply of sour dough. To keep it alive and growing, simply add flour and sugar.

The yeast ferments the sugar by converting it to ethyl alcohol and CO_2 (carbon dioxide) in a procedure that takes about six days. During this process, the carbon dioxide had to be vented off and this unique sour smell is what gave the location of most illegal breweries away to prohibition agents.

The fermentation process stops when the alcohol concentration reaches about 12 percent because at that point the yeast stops growing. Brewers control the final alcohol content by the amount of water or the amount of starch/sugar.

British writer H.G. Wells

This mixture is filtered once again (to remove the yeast) into what is called a bright tank. In the bright tank, there is still a trace of yeast. From this tank the beer is bottled. A small amount of sugar syrup was sometimes added and the mixture was trapped by capping. This slight chemical action inside the bottle is what creates the carbon dioxide bubbles that you see when you take the cap off and pour it into a glass.

The beer was usually placed in dark brown bottles to prevent sunlight from oxidizing the brew and causing it to degrade.

Many breweries stored the final product in caves because a temperature of about 72 degrees or less stopped the fermentation process. It was not uncommon for breweries to also have ice plants. Selling ice and soda pop was a way many breweries survived the 1920s until Prohibition was repealed in 1933 by the 21st Amendment.

Back then, people often bought beer from taverns in ¾ gallon tin pails. Some customers, in order to get less of a "head" and more actual beer, would grease the bucket with a light coating of lard. This reduced the surface tension of the carbon dioxide bubbles, making it difficult for them to form.

"Follow the barrels!" Eliot had said that if we could locate a large supply of cooperage, then we could trace them back to wherever they were being sent to help us locate the breweries. It was ironic that our first big break came from Colosimo's Restaurant, the ill-famed den of the late "Diamond Jim," which had been the hub of the Chicago underworld since 1895.

Bischoff had spotted a large storage area for beer barrels behind Colosimo's place and we called a meeting in Ness' office in the Transportation Building to formulate a plan.

"I think I have an idea how I can contribute more to the team," I eagerly told Eliot.

"How is that?"

"I've been reading a German fellow named Von Clausewitz who wrote a book about strategy and tactics in war."

"I'm not sure that will be useful," Eliot kidded. "Remember, the Germans lost the war."

"But he had something important to say about understanding your enemy. I think it makes sense. I plan to read everything on these guys I can get my hands on. The more we know about them, how they operate, who their friends are, who their enemies are, the better off we'll be in the long run."

Ness grew more serious and nodded in agreement. "You just might have something there, old pal."

"Don't forget, most of our men are from other states and they're here in sort of unfamiliar territory. Are you acquainted with pointillism?"

He gave me a palms up gesture. "I haven't the foggiest notion."

"Well, it's a new art technique where the painter places a group of dots on a canvas. At first, it looks like a mish-mash because there aren't enough dots on the fabric. But as more and more dots are transferred, the true picture begins to take shape."

"So you're going to be my dot expert?"

I tilted my head at a cocky angle. "Yeah, something like that." *Know your enemy – know the game*, I thought.

"You might want to check with Archie Martin, a local Internal Revenue agent. He's trying to build the tax fraud case against Capone and he's reputed to have an encyclopedic knowledge of Chicago's underworld."

"I'll be sure to do that."

Eliot Ness handing out assignments (courtesy Dell comics)

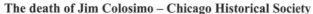

The death of Jim Colosimo – Chicago Historical Society

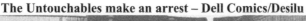
The Untouchables make an arrest – Dell Comics/Desilu

At our next meeting, Ness let me fill everyone in with a mini-lecture.

"Colosimo was born in Italy but migrated to Chicago with his father," I told them. "He worked at various jobs including newsboy and bootblack. But he soon started looking for easier ways to make a fast buck and became adept at pick-pocketing. From there he became a collector for two notorious aldermen, Mike "Hinky-Dink" Kenna and "Bathhouse" John Coughlin. They ran the First Ward, located down by the lake.

"In 1902, while making the rounds, Big Jim met a madam, fell in love, and they were married. Now he was in the brothel business. He bought a place on South Wabash and named it Colosimo's Café. It became a favorite watering hole and entertainment spot for such notables as Enrico Caruso, Al Jolson, Sophie Tucker, George M. Cohan and John Barrymore.

"His success attracted the attention of the Black Hand, a murderous group that threatened him with death unless he paid protection. Colosimo fought back by importing his nephew, Johnny Torrio of Brooklyn. Torrio came over in 1909, set some traps for the rat extortionists, baited them with green cheese, and the vermin were exterminated.

"Torrio was shrewd enough to realize that Prohibition was going to provide him and his associates with enormous opportunities. But he couldn't get Colosimo to listen. Colosimo was satisfied running his nightclub and prostitution houses. Torrio invited his old buddy Capone from Brooklyn to come join him in Chicago, and the two of them plotted a takeover.

"Meanwhile, Colosimo had decided to divorce his wife because he went crazy over a beautiful young singer named Dale Winter. Word got around that Colosimo had gone soft."

"So it was like sharks smelling blood in the

181

water, right Mike?" Paul DeWitt commented.

"Exactly," I replied.

"That's why I was so tough with Giardelli last week," Eliot said. "These guys exploit weakness but respect power."

"So what happened to Colosimo?" Gary Tesson asked.

"Exactly what you think," I said. "Colosimo was killed in the vestibule of his own café in May of 1920. Torrio imported Brooklyn gunman Frankie Yale to do the job so that he and Capone would have alibis. Then they blamed it on Colosimo's old enemies and even hinted it might have been revenge by his ex-wife."

At the office planning a raid – Dell comics/Desilu

"So who runs Colosimo's now?" Strohman asked.

"After Bugs Moran and his men put some bullets in him, Torrio, with a net worth of about $30 million, turned things over to Capone and fled to Italy. Capone's men run the place."

"Bischoff, will you come up front?" Ness requested.

Bischoff rose and joined Eliot.

"Bischoff is the one who deserves the credit for finding out the location of our first raid," Eliot said in a congratulatory tone. "He spotted the cache of barrels behind Colosimo's and did a 24-hour stake-out. When the barrels were finally picked up, they were taken to an old factory on Thirty-eighth and Shields."

Mike Kriegan – Dell comics/Desilu

Eliot patted him on the back. "Great work, Tom."

"Bischoff has rented a room overlooking the place and we're going to conduct some more surveillance to make sure this is the right target. Meanwhile, keep your eyes and ears open to help us locate more breweries. As soon as we're ready to move, we'll let you know."

The next day, Eliot and I drove to within a couple of blocks of Bischoff's location. The eighteen hundred block of Shields was a monument - a monument to destruction by age. The buildings sagged; myriad cracks shot through the sidewalks. Assorted clapboard tenements were shabby and grimy. We walked the rest of the way to a small red brick house with a sign in the window that said ROOMS TO RENT. Bischoff met us at the door and led us upstairs. The place was dirty, smelled vile, and had a threadbare carpet on the floor. On one side of the room was a rumpled bed and a wicker chair. The ceiling plaster was cracked and the floral wallpaper had stains.

"So this is what you've been calling home the past two days?" I asked Bischoff.

"Yeah, not much to look at, is it?"

We stayed there for several hours, hoping to catch a glimpse of something significant going on. But the whole time we were there, except for a few more barrel deliveries, there wasn't a great deal of activity.

"Well, we have to start somewhere," I said with a shrug.

"Okay," Ness said. "We'll go in with the team tonight and start applying the federal lash to the back of the Chicago Syndicate."

Armed with .45 automatics, axes, crow-bars, sawed-off shotguns and sledgehammers, we surreptitiously drove up in front of the building at 7:00 p.m. There were a few lights on inside, but the windows were either high off the ground or boarded up, making it impossible to know what was going on.

No one said much during the entire trip. This being the first big raid, I think most of the men were reflecting on what it was going to be like, bursting through doors, not knowing quite what to expect. There was a good chance that we would meet with resistance and might have to use our weapons and injure or kill another human being who had a wife and kids back home. The other

The Untouchables making a raid – Dell comics/Desilu

182

possibility was that one of us might be badly injured or killed. And that, too, was a sobering thought.

We took two cars. Team A consisted of Eliot, DeWitt, Strohman, Kaufman and I. We were to go in the front door. Team B contained the other five – Martino/Gillespie, Tesson, Bokal, Bischoff and Mizell.

Our watches were once again synchronized and we went in at 9:30 p.m. "Everybody put your hands up!" Ness announced as we burst through the flimsy doors. "This is a federal raid."

The B team came through the back door just a few seconds after we entered. We all stood there with our mouths open. There were four disbelieving workers who looked scared to death.

I looked around, trying to locate the vats, storage tanks and other brewing paraphernalia. All I saw were stacks and stacks of 31 gallon wooden barrels, huge 155-gallon kegs, scattered hoops and staves, a conveyor belt, and assorted cleaning equipment, including a final rinse tank. And there was a parbuckle, an antique-looking rig that was used to pull heavy barrels into the back of a flatbed truck.

I walked over to one container, wondering what it held, but found the sticky contents inside to merely be brewers pitch, used to form a seal between the compressed staves.

We lowered our weapons and stood around with pained looks on our faces. When Ness questioned the men, they played dumb and said that they just cleaned and loaded and unloaded barrels and had no idea where the refurbished ones were taken. Ness didn't even bother arresting them.

"What would be the charge?" he shrugged.

"Laundering dirty barrels," I said, tongue in cheek. Everyone was feeling kind of low and defeated. Our first big raid had been a bust. But then Wes Bokal perked everyone up by saying that he was pretty sure he had located a brewery.

"How do you know it isn't just another barrel cleaning operation?" I asked.

"I watched the trucks pretty closely as they came in and out. The ones coming out sat pretty low on their axles from

Fingerprint technology at the **Northwestern** University crime lab – Dell comics/Desilu

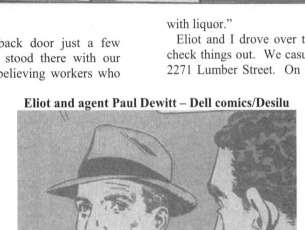

Eliot and agent Paul Dewitt – Dell comics/Desilu

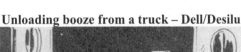

Unloading booze from a truck – Dell/Desilu

the weight of the barrels. I'm pretty sure they were loaded with liquor."

Eliot and I drove over to the place the next morning to check things out. We casually drove by a large building at 2271 Lumber Street. On the closed wooden double doors was a painted sign that read Forquer Storage Company.

Bokal had told us that the trucks came in on a regular basis around ten. We both agreed that was the best time to stage a raid for maximum effect.

Our same two teams, armed with the usual weapons and brewery-smashing equipment, drove quietly into the neighborhood that night. The A team would break into the front while the B team attacked from the rear alley.

Our car rolled to stop, and we doused the lights, waiting and biding our time in the dark. We watched as several trucks approached the building, gave three blasts on their horn as a prearranged signal, and pulled inside when the doors swung open.

"Let's get ready to do some good," Eliot said.

I had to admit I was nervous. I tossed a couple of Sen Sen in my dry mouth. The thought of the other guys slinging hot lead in my direction was unsettling. "If I had my druthers, I'd just as soon be watching a Harold Lloyd comedy at the Tivoli right now."

"Wait and see. This will be a lot more fun," Kaufman chimed.

At exactly ten-fifteen we approached the locked doors.

"Let's hope we find more this time than the last," Strohman said in a deadpan manner.

I scratched an itch on the side of my cheek while awkwardly trying to hold on to my trusty firearm, Little Big Man. I could feel the tension starting to build.

"I want to get inside before those guys figure out they're being raided," Ness said.

Ness heaved the big ax with full force against the lock on the door. The wood made a loud splintering sound. Then Paul DeWitt used a crowbar to pry the hasp away from the door, and it swung ajar.

We stood there dejectedly with slumped shoulders. Behind the wooden door was a steel door with another lock. Eliot swung the ax again and it made a sharp ringing sound as metal clashed against metal.

"That ought to wake up the dead," Strohman said.

Robert Stack as Eliot Ness on *The Untouchables* – Desilu

After several futile efforts, Ness took out his .38 Colt revolver.

"Stand back boys," he said as he took dead aim at the

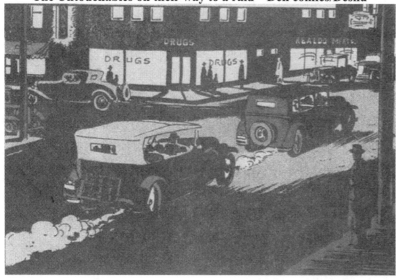

The Untouchables on their way to a raid – Dell comics/Desilu

lock.

A nervous sweat popped out on my forehead as I wondered whether the B team had already gained entrance and was battling it out by themselves. But I didn't hear any gunfire, so that was reassuring.

The lock remained intact after Ness fired the first round. A second slug found its mark, and the lock fell open. We shouldered our way inside and found ourselves standing in a large, well-lighted room with a concrete floor.

Our olfactory senses were assaulted by the sour smell of fermenting mash. Several large trucks were parked inside, both of them nearly full of loaded barrels. But

Up the stairs during a raid – Dell

whoever had been inside was gone, somehow having fled the premises.

From the back of the cavernous room came the sound of the B team still trying to batter their way inside. Eliot waved to me and said to go to the back and let them in. His enthusiasm had clearly wilted.

"Let's see what we have here," he said as everyone gathered around.

Kaufman raced up a wooden set of stairs and searched the upper portion of the brewery. "Our birds have flown the coop and you don't have to be a genius to see how," he said.

The wooden flight of stairs led to a door that opened onto a roof. When the truck drivers and operators heard us pounding away at the door, they simply fled the premises, bridged the gap between the adjoining building with a homemade catwalk of double 2x12s, and escaped by a pre-planned route.

There was no telling where they were by now, probably fanning out and spreading the word that the law was finally getting out of Capone's grasp.

Yet it wasn't all for naught. We confiscated nineteen 1,500 gallon copper vats, two new trucks, and 140 barrels of beer that were getting ready for shipment. Five of the vats were cooling tanks where the liquid was drawn off and cooled down in preparation for shipment. The others were filled with mash. We poured the beer down nearby storm sewers. Then we called in Greg Weiss and his wrecking crew to come in and tear everything apart. Junk dealers bought up all the iron and brass. The barrel staves, mostly made from white ash, were sold for firewood. The vats were offered for sale as cisterns.

Subsequent investigation set the value of the plant at $75,000 with a capacity of 100 barrels a day.

"Well, it's a start. We made a dent in their operations," I said trying to generate some enthusiasm.

"Yeah, Chief. At least we put a brewery out of business," DeWitt quipped.

Ness allowed a slight smile to creep across his face.

"You're right, men, but the next time we draw up a better game plan to make sure we cover all the escape routes so that we bag the whole lot of them. It will hurt Capone even more if we can put his brew meisters behind bars.

* * * *

Western Auto Supply – 54 stores by 1929 – Library of Congress

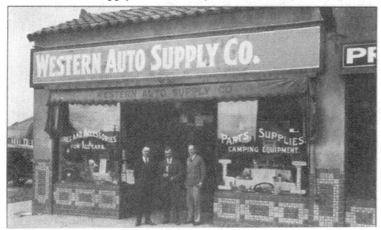

"The clientele leaves a bit to be desired, but the food is great," he said. Eliot and I were at the Monadnock Restaurant. The place was moderately filled with the late-lunch crowd. We were sitting together at a small table facing the street windows, leisurely drinking cups of coffee, only a table away from two of Capone's henchmen, Frankie Lombardo and Tony Larussa. They were ogling the women on the sidewalk and talking loudly. The subject of their conversation revolved about the physical attributes and the speculative bed skills of women walking past outside.

The subject of our conversation was Chicago politics. "Do you think anyone can defeat Big Bill Thompson in the next election?" I said.

Eliot was slowly stirring his coffee with a spoon. "Thompson is still popular, but he's a Republican, and if Hoover doesn't do something quick and dramatic to get the economy turned around the Democrats could carry the White House."

I raised an eyebrow. "And you think the Democratic landslide could be big enough to allow Thompson's opposition to ride in on their coattails?"

He nodded.

"Who do you think will get the nomination for the Dems, Al Smith or Franklin Roosevelt?"

Eliot took a sip of his coffee and gave me a long thoughtful look. "Hard to figure. Roosevelt is the one who gave Smith's nominating speech to the convention back in '28."

"Yeah, and then Smith lost in a landslide to Hoover."

The Boston Daily Globe

ELECTION OF HERBERT HOOVER INDICATED IN EARLY RETURNS

"Do you think it was because Smith was a Catholic?" he asked.

"Nope. I think it was the economy. People are calling the Twenties the Prosperity Decade and no one wants to change horses in the middle of a stream," I replied, borrowing a line from Abe Lincoln.

Out of the corner of my eye, I saw a string of three identical black Pierce-Arrow sedans coming toward the restaurant. That alone was enough to pique my interest, but I slid my hand to Eliot's arm when I spotted the dark snout of a Thompson sticking out of one of the windows. The quiet afternoon was shattered by the sudden chattering of several machine guns.

Terrified and without stopping to think, the restaurant's patrons flung themselves to the floor. An instant later, the front window exploded under a hail of submachine slugs.

One slug passed within inches of my head and the breeze created by its passing ruffled my hair. I dove and wrapped my arms around Eliot, gaining leverage with a bent leg and we rolled to safety under the cover provided by the section of brick wall beneath the window frame.

Dishes, glasses, table settings, coffee urns and shelves

Al Smith NYC caricature

disintegrated under the heavy stream of .45 caliber slugs pouring into the restaurant.

The angry guns clattered steadily. Women were crying. Clouds of plaster and brick dust rose from facades and walls; ricocheting bullets screamed – walnut woodwork splintered.

Eliot and I drew our weapons, but we knew they were no match for the firepower outside, so we stayed down. There was a brief lull in the shooting, and I sneaked a quick peek. One of the men was getting out of the car. It was James Clark, one of Bugs Moran's men.

Eliot nodded toward the overturned table where Lombardo and Larussa had been sitting. Lombardo was sprawled on the floor, face down, a large pool of blood forming beneath his body. Larussa was crumpled over the legs of a chair, his body riddled with numerous bullet wounds. He uttered an agonizing moan.

A few seconds later Clark's gun let loose with another burst that gouged the walls, shredded a pair of rubber plants, and demolished a wooden stand where extra menus were kept.

185

The distinctive gong of a police car sounded in the distance. Then a car horn blared three times. "That's their signal to get going," Ness said excitedly.

Pieces of glass fell to the floor as we stood up. Clark had his back to us and was getting ready to climb back into the third car. The first two had already pulled away, tires screeching.

Eliot and I opened up and let loose with a hail of lead from our .38s. Clark arched his body and reached for his back as our slugs found their mark. His Thompson clattered to the street as he fell.

"Go! Go!"

We ran out the door and emptied our guns at the fleeing car as it picked up speed, crossed Cicero Avenue, then disappeared. Ten seconds later the police car arrived, and we shooed them on, pointing in the direction of the fleeing car.

A dazed public slowly came out of hiding. Excited, babbling groups formed on the sidewalk. Several persons stood in silent shock, staring at the ravaged storefronts.

I ran my hand over my head, feeling for a crease in my skull.

"Those guys almost gave you a new look," Eliot said.

"That's okay. I always wanted to part my hair on the other side," I said with a smirk.

Eliot and I went back inside and he dialed MAin oh-four-four-four for an ambulance.

Above: Courtesy Dell comic books/Desilu

cross-country team in the spring. I had recently read an article by Dr. Freud where he talked about the concept of therapy. The human mind was a complex organism, he argued, and if placed under too much stress, could break down, leading to insanity. Vigorous exercise, he insisted, was one way to deal with this dangerous stress.

Feeling the strain and stress of working with Eliot and the rest of the men, I decided to get back to running, but more for relaxation than trying to build up endurance.

CHAPTER 7

MARCH 27, 1930

PROHIBITION VERSE:

**Prohibition is an awful flop,
We like it.
It can't stop what it's meant to stop.
We like it.
It's filled our land with vice and crime,
It's left a trail of graft and slime,
It don't prohibit worth a dime,
Nevertheless we're for it.**

When I was at the University of Chicago I played football as a backfield defender. To help stay in shape, I ran for the

CLOSED

FOR VIOLATION OF

NATIONAL PROHIBITION ACT

BY ORDER OF

UNITED STATES DISTRICT COURT

———— DISTRICT OF ————

All persons are forbidden to enter premises without order from the UNITED STATES MARSHAL

Jackson Park, near Lakeshore Drive, was the perfect place to do my running. An island of serenity in an ocean of concrete and steel. It was a veritable paradise of oak, elm, maple, bulrush, sweet peas, Jimson weed, sunflowers and morning glories. Queen Anne's lace listed in a slight breeze. Jackson Park had been the site of the 1893 Columbian Exposition extravaganza in Chicago – the great white neoclassical city.

I was pleased to discover that athletes from DePaul, Northwestern, and the University of Chicago also frequented the place.

My first time out I met Ed Wood, an athlete wearing the maroon of the University of Chicago, and we chatted amiably about university life, past and present. We agreed to run together and keep company, but I soon developed an ache in my side and had to slow to a trot.

"Hey, buddy, you go ahead without me." I said, my lungs wheezing like the bellows on a pump organ.

After a month of exercising every weekend, I seemed

Stagg Field where Mike Kriegan played football

to finally hit my stride. One day, while out on the path, I spotted someone ahead of me wearing a blue sweat suit. I had been running a while, and my vision was blurred from the sweat trickling down my forehead and into my eyes. As I drew nearer I could see by the flowing blonde hair that it was a young woman. I figured I would show off a little and pass her. I shifted into high and passed by without either of us saying a word.

I was cruising along when a figure passed me in a blur. At first I thought it might be some high school athlete showing off, but further scrutiny revealed it was that young woman again.

I was quite impressed with her physical prowess and decided to catch up to her. She had lovely long legs and trim thighs. A sailor blouse and shorts showed off her athletic but distinctly feminine figure. After considerable effort, and much huffing and puffing, we were abreast.

I didn't know what to say so I resorted to an old line. "Excuse me, Miss. Could you please tell me what time it is?"

She skidded to an abrupt halt and turned to face me, hands on hips. Then she launched into a soliloquy that left me speechless.

"I am greatly embarrassed and deeply humiliated that due to unforeseen circumstances over which I have no control, the inner workings and hidden mechanisms of my chronometer are in such accord by which time is ordinarily reckoned, that I cannot with any degree of accuracy give to you the exact time." She glanced at her watch. "However, without fear of being too far off I will tell you that it is

approximately 4:05 p.m."

Without saying another word she spun around and took off down the path, leaving me totally stunned. It took me a few seconds to gather my wits, and then I took off in hot pursuit. After great exertion on my part I finally caught up to her again.

"Hey, are you the state cross-country champion or something?" I asked.

She was running with grace and ease, and when she looked over at me without breaking stride, I was astonished by her clean good looks.

"What makes you think that?" she said breathing free and easy.

Her strawberry blond tresses bounced attractively in carefree fashion. She had that stunning fair Florentine complexion that showed up so often in Botticelli's paintings.

"I can't believe how easily you passed me."

"You weren't really going all that fast."

Ouch, that whiplash retort cut to the quick.

My mind futilely tried to think of a clever rejoinder. Couldn't!

I don't think a young woman had ever talked to me in such a brash manner – cocky, bordering on insulting. Whatever happened to mellow and warm? I was determined to hurl the last stinging barb in this conversation.

"I was merely trying to pay you a compliment, Miss . . . whoever you are."

I was drawn to her supple form and grace. All of the female athletic types I had known in my life were built like trucks, but she was different – very different.

If only she didn't have that smart-alec attitude.

She tossed me a look of reproof. "Sorry, I thought you were a masher, approaching me in such a bold manner without a formal introduction."

She had incredible hazel eyes that danced when she spoke. And even though her face had a disquieting smirk, I found it irresistible.

"Well, I was just trying to be friendly. I thought your response bordered on snobbish."

"Sorry, you must have one of those fragile egos Dr. Freud is always talking about."

"Quite the contrary," I retorted. "My confidence is rock solid."

"I find you a very difficult person to talk to," she haughtily said. "Would you rather run by yourself?"

"That would be fine with me," I replied, slowing down my pace and allowing her to take a lead of about thirty feet.

She sure got the best of me in round one of the battle of the sexes.

Ellen had one of those Pepsodent-bright smiles

I put on a burst of speed and soon came along side of her. She looked over at me, somewhat surprised.

"Hello, again," I called to her.

"I thought you wanted to be alone."

My breath was getting short, so I kept the dialog brief. "I felt like we got off on the wrong foot back there."

She didn't mince words. "Is that your idea of an apology?"

This woman was simply exasperating. "Apology? I thought maybe you owed me one!"

She shook her head and looked up at the sky.

"Are you good at anything else besides running?"

"Yes – fending off advances from impulsive young males."

"Hey, would you mind if we stopped a minute so we could start this conversation over again?"

There was a park bench directly ahead, and she braked to a stop in front of it. I plopped down and tried to catch my breath. A trio of birds reconnoitered overhead.

I tried not to stare at her legs. They were long, shapely . . . amazing. "I'm sorry if I came off as pushy or rude," I said. "I haven't had a lot of experience talking with women, and sometimes I just say the wrong things."

"Perhaps I judged you too harshly, Mr.—"

"Kriegan, Michael R. And may I know your name?" I said almost apologetically. I was so transfixed by her remarkable beauty that I was having trouble composing my sentences. An irritating awkwardness clamped over me like a bell jar.

"It's Ellen Esposito," she said in soft, melodic tones. She had sat down on the bench at a comfortable distance.

"Do you run here often?"

"Only about twice a week," she said.

"Are you training for the Olympic team?"

She smiled, revealing a cute dimple on her right cheek.

"Hardly, I'm cooped up all day and this gives me a chance to get out and see nature. I'm an accountant for my father and uncle. They run a business, and I help take care of the books. I had two years training at a business college. How about you?"

I thought perhaps it unwise to say I was a prohibition agent so I merely told her that I was a desk jockey working for the government. She let it go at that.

"Do you have any hobbies?" she asked.

"I'm a history buff," I said. "My head is full of all sorts of useless trivia."

"That's a misnomer. There is no such thing as useless trivia. All information is interconnected and all knowledge

is good. You know, I also was pretty good at history in high school," she said.

"Remarkable coincidence."

"Bet I can stump you," she said with a mischievous sparkle in eyes that were captivating.

"I don't think so."

"Try me."

"What are the stakes?"

"Stakes?"

"Sure, it's a lot more fun if there is something at risk."

"Are you rich?" she asked.

"No - why?"

"Just wanted to see how much you could afford to lose."

"How about dinner? The loser pays and the winner picks the restaurant."

"You . . . me?"

"Yes, the two of us."

She threw me a frown. "For a man, that's a winning proposition either way. I didn't just fall off the turnip truck."

"What then?"

"If you win, we dine together. If you lose, you owe me a steak dinner – by myself."

"Agreed. How about five questions? If you stump me on two of them, you win."

"That sounds fair. It's a bet."

188

"Okay, let me see." She cradled her chin with her thumb and pointer finger. "All right. Here goes. First question: What was the name of the ship that tried to rescue the *Titanic*?"

"That's easy, the *Carpathia*."

"Very good. That one was too easy. Hmm. What was the name of the woman that Ivanhoe married?"

"That's a novel, not history, but it was Lady Rowena. *Ivanhoe* is one of my favorite reads."

"You are good. Number three is a tougher one. What was the name of the wild horse tamed by Alexander the Great?"

"Bucephalus. Alexander realized the horse was scared by his shadow so he turned him so he couldn't see it." I thought of what Bois-Guilbert said to Rebecca in *Ivanhoe* . . . *thou hast in me found thy match*. "You owe me a dinner!"

"Not yet, o haughty one; I have two more chances. Who was the only president ever impeached?"

I gave her a smug look because I also knew this one. "We've never had a president impeached. They tried to get Andrew Johnson, but he was acquitted by one vote."

"Wrong! He *was* impeached. The definition of impeachment is 'to bring charges against.' He was impeached by the House but then acquitted by one vote in the Senate."

"Unfair! You got me on a technicality."

"Quit whining. Last question. Hmm. Uh. This needs to be tough but, as you say, *fair*. Let's see . . . uh, what name did Davy Crockett give to his favorite rifle?"

"Oh, I know this . . . it was named for a woman, uh Barbara – no, Brenda – no . . . uh, I think it was Bess— that's it, Bess."

"I'm afraid you're confusing it with Queen Bess – a moniker for Queen Elizabeth I. Crockett named his rifle 'Betsy.' "

"Aughhh!" I slapped myself up side the head. "You're right. But I almost had it."

"Unfortunately, close only counts in horseshoes and pin-the-tail-on-the-donkey."

"You left out hand grenades."

She stuck out her hand. "You owe me three bucks. I think that's the going price for a steak dinner."

"You really plan to eat it by yourself?"

"Of course! Those were the terms. And don't give me that tiresome, sad puppy look men are famous for. I don't fall for that anymore."

—Providence Bulletin

The Score-Keeper

"Tell you what. Let's flip a coin. Heads I win, tails you win. If I'm the winner, that will be a dinner for two. If I lose, you get two steak dinners, and I'll never bother you again."

It took her a few seconds to mull over my offer. "Hmm . . . uh, never bother me again - okay. But let me have the six dollars now so you don't change the terms on me."

"Sure. I fished through my wallet and handed her the money. I pulled a quarter out of the change section and prepared to make the flip.

"Wait a minute. Not that I don't trust you," she said, warily eyeing me. "I'll flip the coin to make sure there are no tricks."

Her eyes grew bright and mischievous. "Are you sure you don't want tails? Statistically, tails comes up 52 percent of the time."

"Yeah, I know the saying: 'Tails never fails.' I'll stay with heads."

"Too bad. Here goes."

She stood up and flipped the coin high in the air. It came down on the trail, kicking up a bit of dust as it landed **heads**.

"Any preference for a restaurant?" I asked haughtily as I took my money back and picked up Eliot's **two-headed coin** as she started trotting down the path.

I was thoroughly confused when she stopped briefly and threw a coquettish look over her shoulder. "The Green Mill," she yelled. "Seven p.m., Tuesday night."

CHAPTER 8

MARCH 28, 1930

189

It was the 1920s that brought about a music revolution that culminated in the Big Band Era. It started with African-Americans pursuing careers in music following the Civil War. The sound, rhythm accents, and beat of their West African music tradition were vastly different from the music of whites, influenced by hundreds of years of European court and folk music.

The first popular trend produced by this blend of African-European synthesis was Rag or Ragtime (1895-1920), led by Scott Joplin. Jazz music started in New Orleans and spread north when Louis Armstrong moved to Chicago. The first jass or jazz record was "Livery Stable Blues" by the white Dixieland Jazz Band.

Many thought jazz to be decadent, but rebellious flaming youth of the Twenties quickly adopted it. Fletcher Henderson, Bix Beiderbecke, Eddie Condon and Benny Goodman were notable performers in Chicago. Clarinetist Good-man went to NYC and formed his own band, and with the help of burgeoning radio broadcasts, ushered in the era of the Jazz/Swing style. Other bands quickly formed, led by the Dorsey brothers, Glenn Miller, Lionel Hampton, Count Basie, Duke Ellington, and the great Harry James. They led the transition from 1920s Charleston-style movements to the new national craze of herky-jerky jitterbug dancing.

"Jelly Roll" Morton

Eliot was frustrated by the degree of difficulty we had encountered in getting past that steel door. As we parked the two captured trucks from the last raid in the huge garage, it came to him.

He reached over and slapped me on the knee. "That's it. I've got it. What we need to smash through those doors is about a ten ton truck."

"That would work," I nodded in agreement. "But it might crush the radiator and put the truck out of commission."

"Yeah. We need some kind of battering ram."

"Why not take one of the trucks and have a blacksmith weld a special steel bumper on it to protect the radiator?"

"Sure, that should work,"

Benny Goodman

Dave Tough – jazz drummer

he grinned.

"Can we convert one of these that we just captured?"

"No, we have to keep them intact as evidence. Besides, our new truck needs to be a flatbed for hauling away some evidence and a rack for carrying scaling ladders to enable us to check out and block escape routes."

"Good idea. Make sure the top edges of the ladders are padded so they won't make noise when leaned against metal buildings. From now on, we'll be ready for anything."

The truck conversion was done at a garage by a man Eliot trusted with utmost confidence. When it was finished, the new front end mimicked the prow of a battleship. Eliot and I christened her *Dreadnaught*. It weighed over 9-tons and even had handles welded in strategic spots for the men to hold on to protect them from the force of impact.

The next day Steve Strohman gave us a report on a barrel cleaning plant at Thirty-eighth and Shields.

"What's up?" Eliot asked.

"I think I finally have this one nailed down, Chief." He looked exhausted from the effects of his vigil.

"I tailed a load of barrels from the cleaning plant to a large garage on Cicero Avenue, adjacent to the Western Electric Company. On this particular trip the barrel truck had a convoy of two gangsters in a souped-up Ford."

"Any idea whose men they were?" I asked.

"Yes. They were all wearing those floral kipper ties and pearl gray fedoras of cavalier breadth with a narrow black band, the trademark of the Capone organization. There's a field full of tall weeds right across the street from the garage. I came in from the other side of that vacant lot yesterday afternoon and kept watch until three this morning."

"What happened?" Eliot asked.

"At that time," he related, "the lights went on in the garage, and an old REO truck pulled out with a load of barrels. Apparently word had gotten out about our first raid. This time there was a convoy of two Nash coupés loaded with hoods, and they were really on the lookout. Naturally I had to lay low because those cars scooted around the neighborhood like a couple of rat terriers. From what I could see, this was only a 'cooling off' spot, not a brewery."

"What do you think we should do?" I asked Eliot.

"I want Steve Strohman to find a hiding spot where you saw that truck disappear with the convoy last night and watch its route without being seen. You'll have to follow it step by step, night by night, until you discover where the convoy leaves it before returning to the cooling off garage."

The next night Strohman continued where he left off, working on foot. He took up the point at which he had lost track of the trucks. Two days later he was back in the office.

"How do you like that?" he growled. "We must have thrown a scare into them the other night."

"What happened? Were you made?" I asked.

"Naw, I wasn't spotted. It's just that after all that surveillance and tailing those trucks, they only moved them a few blocks from the cooling off spot. They merely made a lot of twists and turns in a round about route to get to what must be a brewery at 1632 South Cicero."

"Great!" Ness said. "Any likely spots for us to set up a command post?"

Strohman grinned. "Just our luck, there's a vacant lot right across the street."

Eliot pulled Bokal and Tesson away from other assignments and put them on 24-hour watch from that handy field. They reported back and said the only thing going on around there occurred between 3:30 a.m. and 5:30 a.m. when the trucks rumbled in. About an hour later the trucks would reappear, groaning under the weight of their contraband.

Eliot and I relieved the men for a couple of days and observed the same routine. Convinced we had hit the jackpot, Eliot made plans for the raid.

Meanwhile, Eliot had been sending daily reports to the United States District Attorney's office. He was afraid we might get chewed out for having bypassed the Prohibition Bureau when we made that first raid. But all that happened was the suggestion that we take along one of their agents on the next raid.

Ness called John F. Herbert, and he sent over one of his men. Thinking what we were doing wasn't that important, he sent us a scrawny pipsqueak of a fellow who had never before participated in a raid. We found out later that Oscar had been a desk

clerk in a Chicago hotel and obtained his brand new job through political connections.

A foppishly dressed dandy, Oscar arrived just before the raid. Eliot put him in our car so we could keep an eye on him. He wore thick glasses and looked like the last person on earth who would be involved in such a dangerous mission. For a fleeting moment I saw him as a modern-day Scarlet Pimpernel, his milquetoast manner a cover-up for revolutionary activity.

Hupmobile

Eliot and I had difficulty with the smirk on our faces when he slid in the back seat and was sandwiched by Mizell and Strohman. The bantam-sized man meekly acknowledged the introductions and almost disappeared between the other two men.

"Do you have a gun?" Ness asked.

Oscar's eyes grew big as he nervously flexed his hands.

"Why, no, do you think I'll need one?"

I checked the glove box and pulled out a .38 with a leather shoulder holster and passed it back to Strohman. Mizell lifted the little man forward with one hand and pulled back his coat with the other, Strohman strapped the weapon in place.

We could hardly contain ourselves when he complained about it hurting his ribs. Kaufman drove us to a rooming house not far from the scene of our raid. It was run by a woman who had been made a widow by the Capone mob. We didn't have to worry about her tipping them off. Ness sent Tesson and Bokal to the field as lookouts while we waited for

1920 Illinois farm

The Untouchables on the move – Dell Comics/Desilu

191

the designated time to arrive.

"Anybody for a game of friendly poker to pass the time?" Mizell asked.

"Who brought cards?" Strohman asked.

"I have a deck," I said.

Ness, Kaufman, Strohman and Mizell pulled chairs up to a small table. I wore a sly grin as I tossed a deck of cards on the table.

"What is this?" Ness said as he pulled the cards from the box and stared in disbelief.

"It's a homemade deck," I said, "courtesy of newspaper morgues and police mug shot files."

Ness fanned the cards out on the table and the others looked on, eyes agog. I had hired a local artist to look at the photo collection I furnished him and draw the likeness of the person, along with his name, onto a blank card. Capone, Humphreys, Moran and Guzik were the kings. Four gun molls impersonated the queens, while McGurn, Yale, Frankie Rio and Mike "Golfbag" Hunt were the jacks.

The numbered cards had the faces of lesser known hit men, lieutenants and foot soldiers that operated in the local crime cartel. Among them were Jack Zuta, Joe Saltis, James "Bomber" Belcastro, Tony Volpe, Frank Lake and Peter von Frantzius, who was known as the "Armorer of Gangland," having supplied the weapons for the St. Valentine's Day Massacre.

"I had another set made for the B Team," I said. "I think it's a good way to become familiar with the forty-eight top public enemies in Chicago."

Strohman frowned. "Forty-eight? Are we missing some cards?"

"No, there are fifty-two. I wasn't counting the gun molls. None of them have ever shot anybody."

Ness threw me a questioning look. "What, no jokers?"

"I didn't think about that. We'll see. Maybe that will come later," I replied.

"Perhaps you and Ness are the jokers," Strohman said. Everybody had a good laugh at that one.

During our first card game I tried a bold gambit that I had

Lawbreaker James "Terrible" Genna

Massacre drawing by police

read about in *Police Gazette*. It was penny ante stuff but everyone played like there were thousand dollar pots. I started the game by trying to bluff everyone out of the pot – even if I only had a pair of treys. It wasn't long before my

Making another raid – Dell Comics/Desilu

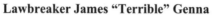

stack of pennies and nickels was smaller than the rest. I could tell by the look on their faces that they thought I was a novice at poker. Then I switched tactics and they couldn't adjust. I started betting smart. When the cards started running in my favor I bet heavily and the whole group stayed in – assuming I was still bluffing. Before they caught on, I had the biggest pile of coins.

The game ended as it was getting late. One of those proverbial light bulbs lit up in Paul DeWitt's head. He had a chagrined smile on his face as he shook his head and threw in his cards.

"We've been had!"

When it came time to make our move, Ness laid it out for the team like a football coach goes over a game plan.

"The B team will meet us there at 4:30 a.m., and they'll take the ladders off the truck just before we ram the door. Two of them will get up on the roof to make sure all the rat holes are covered. They will have exactly one minute to grab the ladders and scramble up on top. The other two will go around the back and come in from behind.

"Kaufman is going to drive the truck right through the door. I'll be with him on the passenger side. The rest of you will follow the truck in. Oscar, our prohibition bureau agent, will stay behind and protect our rear by guarding the hole made by the truck.

"Not a single prisoner has ever been captured in a raid on a Capone brewery. We're going to change all that. Tonight we make history."

South Cicero Avenue, as Kaufman trundled the truck along its cobblestone surface, was deserted. No one was on the streets, and only one car passed us going the other direction. I drove the car that followed the truck and was with Strohman, Bischoff and Tesson. The little prohibition bureau agent sat in the front passenger seat and never uttered a word the entire time. He looked like a scared rabbit.

I looked in my rearview mirror and saw the B team car behind me swing off around a corner as it made plans to cover the rear entrance of the brewery.

A short distance from the double doors, Kaufman glided to a stop and I pulled up right behind the truck. The streets were quiet except for the distant rattling of an elevated. I looked at my watch in the glare of a streetlight. It was 4:28 a.m. The timing was precise.

We all got out of the car and waited for Ness to give the signal. As the big hand swept to the top of my watch, I saw

Eliot point straight ahead and give the *go* order to Kaufman. Ness had one hand braced against the dash and the other arm bent in front of his face in protective fashion. The truck crashed through the door with splintered wood and debris hurtling down on the hood and windshield. One flying fragment caused a spider web crack in the passenger side windshield.

The doors gave way with a thunderous clap, and the rest of us rushed in. I looked around and my heart sank. There was no brewery. I had that same dumb feeling I experienced when my older cousin once took me on a snipe hunt.

Ness scanned the room in stunned surprise. But his countenance changed from shock to a cat-that-ate-the-canary look. He quickly figured out that it was a ruse.

"The back wall has to be fake, men," he tersely announced. "One more time."

Ness and Kaufman hopped back in the truck. Kaufman quickly threw it into low gear and it lurched forward again. The fake wall collapsed easily and once more we rushed into the breach.

The five men inside scattered like tenpins as we crashed through. Two of them had guns drawn. Eliot leapt from the truck before it had stopped rolling and

holding his badge high in his left hand yelled: "Everybody hold it; this is a federal raid! You're all under arrest for violating the Volstead Act!"

One of the men took aim at Ness, but Strohman winged him in the shoulder with a blink-of-an-eye quickness, causing the gun to clatter as it hit the floor.

Another man bolted and started to run up the stairs in an escape attempt. I cocked my Winchester and aimed ahead of him and fired a quick booming shot that reverberated around the room like a cannon going off. Several wooden barrels in front of him were splintered by the impact of the blast, with some of the buckshot hitting him in the leg, bringing him down. Paul DeWitt of the B team quickly came in through the roof escape hatch and took his gun.

The other man with a gun never aimed it at anybody and quickly dropped it to the floor and threw up his hands. Another grizzled man came out a restroom door, ducked, and then made a dash for the rear. But Mizell came in the rear exit, and I heard a smacking sound followed by a moan. A few minutes later Mizell appeared out of the shadows dragging the man by his coat collar.

The man was nursing a swollen eye that was going to turn black and blue in a few days.

Everyone was jubilant as we lined up the suspects and gathered around them. It turned out that one of the armed

Chicago street scene near illegal brewery – Dell Comics/Desilu

men was Larry Williamson, Capone's old assistant. The burly, grizzled man was Ken Hoelker, Capone's top brewer. The other men were all drivers. We learned that they were short-handed the night of the raid, but everyone was well satisfied with the haul. Ness was especially happy that not one person had escaped.

Ness wanted to check out the equipment. He told the diminutive prohibition agent to hold a gun on the men while we searched the premises.

"Keep an eye on these birds, Oscar, and if they make any false moves, let 'em have it."

You could almost hear him gulp as he aimed his pistol at them and moved a step closer. Eliot didn't expect them to give him any trouble since the rest of us were armed and were simply moving around taking inventory.

We figured the brewery was capable of turning out one hundred barrels of beer a day. About 320 gallons of wort, or unfermented beer, were brought by truck in glass-lined containers. One hundred barrels would be filled with beer that had been fermented and "spiked" with carbonated gas. We later found that 100 barrels a day was pretty much a set standard for all Capone breweries.

We then proceeded to destroy the brewing equipment. I could see the prisoners wince as thousands of dollars of equipment was smashed.

"Youse guys are gonna have to answer to Big Al for this," the biggest one threatened.

I walked over to him. "Look pal, we're just doing our job. We're not afraid of Mr. Big Shot. Besides, he's still locked up in Pennsylvania doing time for a concealed weapons charge. He's not due to be released for two more weeks. If he has any problems about this, tell him to give us a call." I shoved Eliot's business card into his hand.

The prisoners were taken to the United States Marshal's office. The three trucks – brand spanking new – were taken to the government garage with the other two previously captured. We were collecting quite a fleet.

When Ness went to see Mr. Herbert to thank him for loaning him an agent, he looked up from his desk and inquired: "What in the world did you do to him?"

Ness was taken aback. "Why, nothing. I didn't do anything to him? What makes you say that?"

Herbert got up from his desk and walked around Ness with the same type of look that a kid at the circus might have in making a close inspection of the Wild Man of Borneo.

"Oscar burst into my office and threw his gun and badge on the desk and said, 'I had no idea this job was going to be that dangerous. Ness and his men are gun crazy. I quit!'"

Ness thought the whole affair was pretty humorous. Mr. Herbert never bothered trying to send us over another agent, and that made our work easier.

But the little man was right in one respect. Things were going to get a lot more dangerous as soon as the word got out about our raid. Word reached us through friendly police sources that the mob had had a meeting to decide what to do about the new threat to their empire. Some wanted to call in outside gunmen. Some wanted to put out a contract on Eliot. But cooler heads prevailed. Killing federal agents would bring unpleasant pressures to bear and unwanted publicity.

For the time being, they simply decided to take more precautions and put more gunmen in the breweries.

The other thing that threw a monkey wrench into a plan of action was the fact that Capone was still in prison. No one wanted to take drastic action and preempt his authority.

Andy Gump cartoon – no chin

Gasoline Alley - a baby on the doorstep

Tom Swift book by Appleton

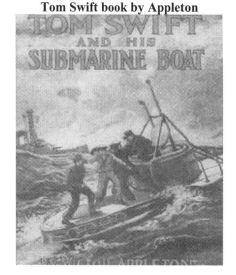

We knew this respite was tenuous and that Scarface Al would be getting out of prison soon. Then the octopus of crime and corruption, with tentacles reaching into all parts of the city, would once again be fully functional. We all realized that we were sitting on a powder keg with no means of determining the length of its fuse.

* * * *

The next aspect of Capone's empire that I became an expert on was the policy racket. Eliot agreed that the more we knew about the trappings and nuances of organized crime, the more it would work to our advantage when we interrogated foot soldiers and lieutenants caught up in our raids. Knowing street lingo and all the ins and outs also came in handy when it came to dealing with stool pigeons or potential stoolies.

Eliot had a clever angle that he played when it came to dealing with street stoolies. This one guy who ran a newspaper kiosk was also a numbers runner. We knew he heard a lot of underworld scuttlebutt, and it was always to our benefit to find out what the mob was planning or thinking.

"What did you hear about the Capone organization's reaction to the raid we made last week, Louie?" Eliot asked him.

I watched as the man broke out into a cold sweat.

"I can't tell you that, Mr. Ness. If I did, then my life wouldn't be worth a plug nickel."

"Well, life is short and then you die, Louie. You either give us this information, or here's what we're going to do. If we don't get it from you, we'll just have to work that much harder and waste a lot of time getting it from someone else. And, believe me,

Louie, we'll get it."

Louie was shaking now. "I swear, Mr. Ness, I haven't heard anything about last week's raid."

Ness turned up the heat.

"There are a lot of people out here on the streets breaking the law. And we sometimes give them a break in exchange for some information. They're happy to cooperate. So when we do get what we need, we'll put the word out that it was you who ran his mouth off. Then how long do you think you'll last?"

That line invariably worked wonders. The stoolie spilled his guts and told us everything we needed to know. After it was over, Ness patted the man on the back, thanked him for being a good citizen and slipped a couple bucks to him.

But, I digress. Back to the numbers racket. Eliot gathered the men in his office one morning and wanted me to explain to them what I had gleaned. I figured I'd break the ice by telling them a joke.

Cook County Hospital – Oberle collection

"Did you hear the one about the father who had a talk with his teenage son about the perils of drinking?" I asked rhetorically. The man figured a demonstration was the best way to do it. He sat two glasses in front of his son. One was half filled with water and the other contained alcohol. He plopped a worm in the glass of water. The worm swam around, content in his new environment. Then the man took the worm and dropped him into the glass of alcohol. The worm shriveled up and died. 'Well, what lesson can you draw from that demonstration, son?' The youngster thought about it for a few seconds, then his eyes lit up with enthusiasm. 'If you drink, you won't get worms!' Gales of laughter reverberated throughout the room.

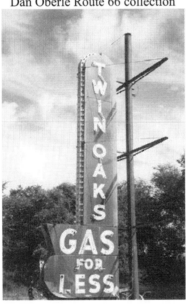

Twin Oaks at **Mitchell**, Illinois - Dan Oberle Route 66 collection

Then I got serious.

"Don't be fooled into thinking that playing the numbers is penny ante stuff. Because there are so many people doing it, the total amount of profit is staggering. Over in New York's Harlem, the profits on this racket are turning Arthur Flegenheimer into a millionaire."

"Don't you mean Dutch Schultz?" Strohman asked.

"Yes, that Brooklyn hood with all the quirky habits. When Ellis Island officials asked newly arriving

immigrants their country of origin, the Germans responded in their native language, 'Deutschland.' Officials took this to mean Dutch, as in the country of Holland. So "Dutch" became a nickname for Germans, and the famed Pennsylvania Dutch are actually of German descent.

"And the Dutchman thought Flegenheimer was much too long so he Americanized it to Schultz."

"The numbers racket is a very lucrative operation for Capone and his men. Bettors can put up anywhere from a nickel to a dollar. Five cents might not sound like much, but in 1929 it buys a loaf of bread and pays your admission to a nickelodeon."

"Why is it sometimes referred to as a 'policy?' Paul DeWitt inquired.

"It first started when policemen stopped the people who were collecting the money. They merely told them that they were insurance salesmen who were collecting the weekly premiums that were due on life insurance policies," I answered.

"How are the numbers determined, and who or what determines the winner?" Mizell wanted to know.

"Bettors are allowed to pick any three digit number they want and the odds range anywhere from 100-1 to 500-1, so the payoffs are pretty good. The winning number is pegged to the last three numbers to the left of the decimal point of the total weekly take of pari-mutuel betting at Chicago's Sportsman Park racetrack."

"Where do people buy their policy numbers?" DeWitt asked.

"For the most part, it's local shopkeepers, barbers, candy-store owners, bartenders, newsmen and shoe shine boys who take the bets. Then runners pick up the money and deliver the cash and slips to what are known as controllers. They, in turn, hand it over to the bankers who are the Capone mob's financial wizards."

"Any idea what the weekly take amounts to in the numbers game?" Ness inquired.

"Yes, it's about $30,000 net a week."

As we began to make more raids and talk to more shady

St. Boniface at **Edwardsville** – Dan Oberle collection

characters, we all began to better understand, almost through osmosis, the processes and inner workings of Capone's empire. More important, I figured that understanding the mores of organized crime would be the key to our survival. The thought preying on my mind was even that might not be enough.

CHAPTER 9

MARCH 29, 1930

The advent of Prohibition ushered America into a new literary age, led by writers who were dubbed by Gertrude Stein as "The Lost Generation." For the first time reading became a popular pastime for middle class Americans. The literature of this age reflected the historic changes in American society as we moved from a predominantly agrarian nation to an urban one.

This new breed of writers helped lead a revolt, marked by spiritual unrest, cynicism, disillusionment and a desire for social experiment. Their ideas would clash with those of the old conservative order, forcing traditional concepts to be redefined.

The literary manifestations of this age expressed a liberal discontent with organized religion, crass materialism, political corruption, the new Puritanism of prohibition, censorship and the moral delinquency of the populace.

Poet Marianne Moore – 1929

Sinclair Lewis railed against the dullness of bourgeois success and small town mentality in *Babbitt* and *Main Street*. Ezra Pound, Ernest Hemingway, and T.S. Eliot left America, headed to Paris and became expatriates.

It is interesting to note that Eliot Ness was given his Christian name in honor of St. Louis-born T.S. Eliot, made famous by his poem, "The Wasteland." And F. Scott Fitzgerald's *The Great Gatsby*, which has never been converted into a *good* movie, showed the tragic consequences of high living and organized crime of this period.

Poet/social critic – Langston Hughes

"So, Mr. Lonely is finally going on another date," my landlady pointedly said. Mrs. Griffin was hunched over an ironing board in the kitchen. Six decades of life had made inroads upon her face – crow's feet and loosened skin.

I glanced over at Thor who was lying over in the corner, washing his face with his paws.

"Yeah, no thanks to you, setting me up with your friend's ditsy daughter, a workaholic who's married to her job."

Young Bing Crosby

"Sure, sure, Mr. Smarty Pants. Look at the pot that's calling the kettle black."

"Well, in any event, it didn't work out." A slow smile began to spread across my face.

"When you smile like that, I know I'm in trouble." She walked to the stove where a second flatiron was heating, switched it with the one she was using, licked her finger and tested the heating surface, then sighed and returned to the half finished house dress draped over the ironing board.

"I just remembered; don't forget, you still owe me a chocolate cake."

"Yeah, yeah!" Mrs. Griffin rolled her eyes. "So who is this princess you're meeting tonight?"

"Her name is Ellen Esposito."

"It sounds like a mob name to me."

"You're way too judgmental."

"Really? Are you picking her up at her house?"

"No. I'm meeting her at a nice restaurant."

She shook her head and threw me her best motherly skeptical look.

"She's hiding something."

"Tsk. Tsk. I'm afraid you're what Freud would call delusional."

"Wait and see; you'll be sorry you didn't stay with that nice Jewish girl."

Thanks to Eliot's two-headed coin I finally got to meet Ellen for that steak dinner. I wore a dark blue flannel suit with wide pinstripes, a bow tie, and a pair of navy and white wingtip shoes. When I arrived at the Green Mill on North Broadway, I told the *maître d'* that I was supposed to meet a young woman.

"Oh, yes, sir." He made a little bow. "Right this way, please." We walked past the huge mahogany bar, through the green velvet-walled, brass and crystal-chandeliered main dining room into an equally opulent overflow room. It had recently been remodeled and looked very posh with thick green carpeting and an interesting mixture of Italianate arches and art-nouveau posters decorating the walls.

A slight chill went through me when I remembered Big Jim Colosimo had been gunned down in a similar vestibule, next to a dining room entrance.

A striking blonde, a slightly plump woman, and a dark-haired girl of about 18 walked past me. It took me a few seconds before I recognized them – Al Capone's wife Mae, his mother, and his young sister Mafalda.

Ellen was already seated at a quiet table on the far side of the room, elegantly dressed. I handed her a long-stemmed white rose. A rose in full bloom is the metaphorical pinnacle of life.

She drew it to her nose and inhaled. "It's lovely. Thank you." She placed it on the table to her right.

"Hmm. Very traditional. I had you pegged as an eccentric – someone who might bring a girl a jar of blackberry jam."

I ignored the remark and paid Ellen a compliment. "You look very chic in that outfit," I said.

She gave me a pleasant smile. "Thank you for those flattering words."

Ellen was "the bee's knees" wearing a crepe afternoon dress decorated with cubist designs in red, gray and black lacquer. A perky roll-brimmed cloche hat had matching painted designs. I had seen one of the female cast members in the movie *Wings* wear something similar to it. Bright red patent slippers accented her charming femininity. She was incredibly beautiful, had perfect posture, and her composure made me feel like yesterday's wilted tossed salad.

"Are you going to have a seat or are you waiting for permission?"

How can anyone so beautiful have such an acerbic tongue?

I sat down.

She had a fancy cocktail glass and was drinking something orange colored.

Probably vodka and orange juice.

"What are you having?" I asked.

She looked up at me with beautiful green eyes. Though mostly hidden by the hat, her hair was short but not bobbed. I guessed that, like most women, she had changed her style.

"Orange juice."

"And what else?"

"Ice. Say, you're not part of the liquor patrol, are you?"

I nearly swallowed my tongue. "Uh, . . . er, no."

Before she could say something else a waiter was at hand. He welcomed us as if we were regular customers.

"And how are we tonight?"

"We're fine." *What's this 'we' stuff?*

He made a slight bow and wanted to know what I wanted to drink.

"Coffee will be fine, thank you."

"Very good, sir."

"Oh, and a little cream with that, please."

"Cream?" He just stood there with an odd look on his face.

"Yes, just a little," I reiterated.

"Very well, if you *insist*, sir."

I shrugged my shoulders and gave Ellen a palms up gesture.

"What was that all about?"

"Anthony thinks everyone should drink coffee the way Italians do—black."

"Anthony . . . you know this waiter's name? Do you eat here a lot?"

Nod.

"It's my favorite place."

I wondered how many other dates she had brought here, but didn't ask. I knew it was none of my business.

"Well, here we are." (It was a line I'd practiced all day.)

"Yes. (She ignored my clumsiness) Did you have a busy day at the office?"

"Oh, the usual. Mine went okay."

Actor Rex Bell

"You?"

"The same . . . numbers, numbers, numbers - you know."

"Yeah, pretty routine."

Ellen removed her hat and set it on the seat of one of the other chairs. Her hair had golden, soft deep waves, styled in the Jean Eagels manner. She took out a compact and patted a loose strand into place.

"Does this look okay?" she asked.

"You look like an angel. Your hair is perfect. But I thought most Italians had coarse dark hair."

She flashed a winsome smile. "My mother was Irish. I guess I take after her."

"Oh, that explains it. Did you say *was*? Is your mother deceased?"

"Yes, my mother and father were killed in a Chicago & Northwestern train wreck."

"I'm so sorry."

"That's okay, I was only six at the time. Ironically, they were on their way to the funeral of my dad's best friend. They left me behind with my aunt and uncle, and they have taken care of me ever since."

Anthony, the stiff-backed waiter, was back with my coffee.

"Are you ready to order, sir?"

"What kind of steak do you want?" I said to Ellen.

"Oh, I'm not really into steak that much. I prefer pasta."

I looked at Anthony. "Is there a house specialty?"

"Yes, sir. It's fettuccini alfredo. Our special butter-garlic sauce is the finest."

I looked at Ellen. "Does that sound good to you?"

"Anthony's right. The pasta is excellent. And tell him you'll want to order the special bread that goes with it. And I'd like a cup of black coffee, please."

As I turned to tell Anthony, he said, "I have it all here— in my head. Is that all, sir?"

Actress Jean Eagels

Actress Ethel Barrymore

"Yes, for now, thank you."

I shifted in my chair and turned my attention back to Ellen.

"What exactly do you do for the government?" she asked.

"I, er, file reports," I hedged.

"What kind of reports?"

"Well, I work for these government inspectors, and I make sure their reports are correctly written and understandable."

"Don't you ever get out of the office?"

"Oh, no, I'm pretty much behind a desk all day."

Singer/actor Eddie Cantor

I hated myself for lying to Ellen. It simply wasn't the way to start a relationship. And I already found myself drawn to her. There was something magical about her looks, the sound of her voice, her smooth skin, her beautiful hair.

Love, ever the opiate of male sensibilities. God shouldn't have given women so much power over men with just their looks. Of course there's no explaining it. No one has ever been able to define what it is that draws one person to another: looks, manner of dress, power, a way with words, personality, voice, or even certain physical traits such as an hourglass figure in a woman or a cleft chin in a male. With me it was her incredible eyes and smile.

I was getting ready to reveal a tiny bit more of the truth when several waiters swooped down on us and deftly placed our steaming Italian cuisine on the table. The other one left, but Anthony stood there looking at me.

I gave Ellen a questioning look.

She smiled. "I think he wants you to taste it."

"Oh, okay. Yours or mine?"

"Yours."

My fork dipped into a small portion of steaming noodles. I let it cool for a few seconds, and then slowly chewed it, savoring its rich taste. "A-okay, Anthony," I said, forming an O with my thumb and forefinger. "My compliments to the chef."

"My pleasure, sir." He bowed and left the two of us to be alone.

We had just about finished the meal when Ellen stunned me with a question. She leaned forward, her eyes boring holes through me. "You haven't been very forthcoming about what you do for a living, have you?"

She had a look on her face that was a mixture of hurt and anger. I wasn't sure how to answer. I didn't know how much she knew, so I responded lamely with, "What do you mean?"

"You purposely misled me."

"In what way?" (I tried acting dumb.)

"You do a lot more than just work behind a desk as a public servant."

"Er, perhaps I should apologize for not giving you more details?" I was still stalling, figuring she didn't know the whole truth.

"You're with Eliot Ness and the prohibition agents who've been making those raids that are all over the newspapers."

I was speechless. "I, uh—" was all that I could stammer.

"You might as well admit it; I know everything."

She threw me a sharp reproving look.

"But how could you? What did you do, hire a private detective to follow me?"

She bit her lip. Her eyelids were closed. "No, my family checked you out."

All of a sudden it hit me. "Your uncle and aunt, they own this place, don't they?"

She nodded. "They screen my dates. They even told me about the confrontation you and Mr. Ness had with Giardelli."

I stared at her in shock as my chest heaved. "What did your aunt and uncle do, tell you to keep seeing me so they could get the lowdown and pass it on to Capone? Do him a favor so that he, in turn, would be indebted to them?"

Ellen fidgeted with her fingers. "You've got it all wrong. They ordered me to break the date, but I refused. I told them they had no right to interfere in my social life."

Flapper girl by John Suckling

I felt used. I had been naïve. And I was steamed.

"I can't believe I was all pie-eyed over a dame like you. I'm probably lucky one of your uncle's friends didn't show up to 'take me for a ride.' "

"He's not like that. He's a respectable businessman. And don't tell me you didn't come here just to check things out. You can't work for that Ness fellow and be that clueless."

"Well, I didn't, and I don't care whether you believe it or not." I pushed my chair back and rose from my seat. I took out my wallet and threw down a ten-dollar bill. "Anthony probably gets a much bigger tip from Capone, but tell him that will have to do."

She had a stunned look on her face.

"Excuse me. I need some fresh air."

I wheeled and stormed out of the Green Mill, vowing to forget Ellen Esposito . . . forever.

CHAPTER 10

MARCH 30, 1930

Gangster nicknames

Willie "the Squealer" Bioff
Charles "Cherry Nose" Gioe
Claude "Screwy" Maddox
James "the Monk" Allegritti

O'Banion/Schofield Flower Shop (awning) – scene of Hymie Weiss "rented ambush" murder near Holy Name Cathedral

Louis "Two Gun" Alterie
Tony "the Greek" Anton
Eddie "the Eagle" Baldelli
James "the Bomber" Belcastro
Jake "the Barber" Factor
"Slippery" Frank Rio
Louie "Little New York" Campagna
Arnold "the Fixer" Rothstein
William "Klondike" O'Donnell
Edward "Spike" O'Donnell
George "Sport" Bucher
"Chicken Harry" Gullet
Joe "Jew Kid" Grabiner
Charlie "Cherry Nose" Gioe
Mike "Mooney" Giancana
Joe "Machine Gun" Granata
Rocco "Money Bags" Fischetti
Mike "de Pike" Heitler
Julian "Potatoes" Kaufman
Paul "Needle-Nose" Labriola
Jim "Toots" Mondi
John "Dingbat" O'Berta
Paul "the Waiter" Ricca
"Polack" Joe Saltis
"Mugsy" Spanier
Roger "the Terrible" Touhy
Tony "Mops" Volpe
Frank "the Enforcer" Nitti
Joe "Hop Toad" Guinta
Willie "Potatoes" Daddano
Max "Boo Hoo" Hoff
Mike "Golf Bag" Hunt
Al "Snorkey" Capone
Murray "the Camel" Humphreys
Mike "Googy Eyes" Marcello
Jake "Greasy Thumb" Guzik
George "Devil Driver" Moore
Antonio "Joe Batters" Accardo
William "Three-fingered Jack" White
"Samoots" Amatuna
Orazio "the Scourge" Tropea

"Bummy" Goldstein
Ralph "Bottles" Capone

* * * *

"What's the matter, buddy?" Eliot said as he put his arm around me. "You've been looking a bit morose lately."

I tried a bit of false bravado. "Oh, nothing. I think perhaps I've got a bit of a cold coming on."

Having just arrived at the office, I was rubbing my hands together in a futile effort to thaw them. Less than a week before, when I had first met Ellen, it had been unseasonably warm. Typically Midwest, today's weather was just the opposite. It was one of those cold blustery days that saw Chicago trying to live up to its reputation as the windy city. The howling wind outside came at people like a pack of yelping dogs.

Eliot motioned for me to have a seat near his desk.

"Sure, sure," he said, giving me one of those knowing looks of his.

"Girl trouble, eh?"

I gave him a sour smile. "I didn't think it showed. What about your steady girl?"

"Oh, yes. I've been going with Betty Andersen for over two years now."

"Is it serious?"

"Yep. I knew she was the one for me when we met for the first time."

"Right off the bat?"

He nodded. "From the very first."

"How did you know?"

He had a puzzled expression. "I can't explain it, I just knew."

"So when do we get to hear wedding bells?"

"As soon as this little vendetta with Capone is finished."

"Where does she live?"

"With her parents in the Jackson Park area, over near South Shore Country Club."

"How does she feel about your job?"

He shrugged. "She hates it. Worries about me all the time. But she understands it's something I have to do."

"You're a lucky man."

"What about your girl, this female creature that has you all in a dither? If you don't snap out of it, you're not going to be much good to me."

A very dead "Paddy" Murray (author collection)

199

"Well, I'm afraid it ended before we got started. As Walter Winchell would say, phfft – it's over, finished. Instead of humming snatches of 'When My Sugar Walks Down The Street,' I find myself dwelling on melancholic songs of lament, folly, and heartbreak."

"Who is she?"

"Ellen Esposito. Her dad and uncle run the Green Mill Restaurant and nightclub."

Eliot nearly fell out of his chair. He came out of a

Douglas Park Auditorium in **Chicago** – Dan Oberle Collection

stunned silence and regained his composure and leaned forward. "I don't know of anything specific on them, but you know they're connected in some way to the Capone organization.

"I know, I figured as much," I said dejectedly.

He waggled a scolding finger. "It's worse than what you think."

"What do you mean?"

His voice was strangled, as though speaking through a gag. "She's Murray Humphreys' girlfriend."

I was totally shocked. "The Camel?"

Ness nodded silently.

"I can't believe it," I said in incredulous tones.

He reached over and touched my arm sympathetically, "I don't know what happened between you two, but believe me, it's for the

Murray "the Camel" Humphreys

best. You don't want to get mixed up with anything that might give the appearance of impropriety and hurt the team."

I let out a long sigh. "Yeah, I suppose you're right. Well, you don't have to worry. Whatever might have been is over now."

"Cheer up, pal. There are millions of fish out there in the big ocean of romance. Keep trolling, something else will come along, you'll see."

The next day Eliot and I were driving along State Street when we spotted Jake Guzik being chauffeured around by what looked to be George Moore, the "Devil Driver."

"Did they make us?" Ness asked.

"I don't think so," I said.

"Just for curiosity's sake, let's follow them and see what they're up to."

"I'm game."

Eliot made a sharp turn to circle the block and come up behind them.

"What do you think Guzik's driver gets paid?" I queried.

"Five hundred a week," he responded.

Jake Guzik

I shook my head. "No way. That's over twenty-five Gs a year."

"Believe me, that's peanuts for these guys."

When we got back on State Street and headed the opposite direction, we couldn't find the two-tone cream and brown Marmon that Moore was driving.

"We've lost them," Ness said dejectedly.

I gingerly opened my door and maneuvered my body out on the Cadillac's running board. I held on for my life while I craned my head. Then I ducked back inside. "No we didn't. They're about six cars ahead of us."

"Eliot looked over with a horrified look on his face. "Are you trying to kill yourself? We're not the Keystone Kops! Get back in here."

I climbed back inside. "I've heard Guzik is Capone's business manager and paymaster. Where do you think they're headed?"

"Beats me," Ness replied.

We were both shocked beyond belief to discover that Guzik was making the rounds. He went from station house to station house, dropping big brown envelopes on the seat of a police car parked next to the main door.

"How much, Eliot?"

"How much what?"

"How much money do you think is in each envelope?"

Eliot looked at me with a sad, dejected expression. "I have no idea." (We later learned it was six to ten thousand dollars in each envelope.)

"Hey, Eliot," I said as we were on our way back to the office. "That ugly Marmon George Moore was driving was sitting pretty low on its springs. What do you think that was all about?"

"It's probably armor plated with bullet proof windows," he said. Ever since Hymie Weiss and his men tried to ambush Capone in his car back in 1925, all of Capone's tin Lizzies have been armored."

CHAPTER 11

PROGRESSIVE CHILD REARING – The theories of a psychologist named John B. Watson became wildly popular during the Twenties. He promulgated the motto: "Man is a machine." Watson was a behavioralist and stressed the importance of the environment when it came to bringing up children. Some of his rules were:

1. **Children can be trained to become doctors or lawyers**
2. **Parents should avoid smothering their children with affection**
3. **Parents should avoid hugging or kissing their children**
4. **Children who cry for attention should be ignored**
5. **Children should be fed according to a rigid schedule**
6. **Children should not be held on their mother's lap**

George "Devil Driver" Moore – after doing time and becoming a Christian

March 26, 1930

I had just walked into Eliot's office and saw that he was talking on the phone. Grabbing a newspaper, I caught up on world events. Another Hatfield had shot one of the McCoys in that famous feud between two Appalachian families. A fellow named William Beebe had fabricated a round structure called a bathysphere that was able to withstand tremendous pressures under water and had descended to an incredible depth of 2,200 feet, a new record.

Then there was a story about a Frenchman named August Picard, who built an aluminum globe and filled it with hydrogen, enabling him to soar 54,000 feet into the stratosphere, also a record. I found myself in awe of men like these and Colonel Charles Lindbergh whose daring exploits were pushing the frontiers of science and ushering the world into a new era that would be ruled by technology.

I shook my head in amazement as I read the details of a story about Izzy Einstein and Moe Smith, two New York prohibition agents who had raided 3,000 speak-easies and arrested 4,900 people. It made us look like we were running at slack speed. They were so famous that Douglas

Tony Accardo

Fairbanks and Mary Pickford had gone out of their way to meet them when the couple was in New York.

I turned to the sports section of the *Daily News* to see how the baseball Cardinals and Cubs were doing. I caught enough of Eliot's conversation to tell that his tone was serious and the subject was of extreme importance.

I set the newspaper aside and found my thoughts drifting to Ellen Esposito. She was in my head all the time. She haunted my dreams. It was as if life was imitating art – the standard formula for writers who pen love stories. Boy meets girl, boy loses girl, boy wins girl. Unfortunately, the part missing for me was the fairytale ending.

"We'll be there in an hour," I heard him say before he hung up.

"Where are we going, Eliot?" I asked, wondering what was in the wind.

"You'd better steel your nerves. Capone was released from prison a few days ago. After I make a few phone calls, we're going to meet with him."

I was too stunned to say anything, but I could feel a weakness creeping into my knees.

It was late-March, but it might just as well have been mid-January. In blustery Chicago, winter is nature's way of weeding out the faint of heart. A strong wind ripped in frigidly from Lake Michigan driving against the windowpanes and sending its icy breath howling around the eaves of buildings. Jack Frost, that playful sprite who paints windows with crystalline spirals and snowflake geometrics, was nipping at my nose. As we exited the car, I turned up my coat collar in a fruitless effort to keep warm.

The doorman at the Lexington, dressed in dark green livery, with shiny brass buttons and fancy gold braid, politely tipped his hat and opened the door for us. Our footsteps clattered on highly polished marble floors. A magnificent crystal chandelier hung about forty feet high in the hotel lobby. We walked over to an elevator where two members of Capone's Praetorian Guard were standing with watchful eyes. They obviously knew who we were. A colored man, dressed in a smart maroon outfit with black piping, greeted us. He flashed a broad smile showing big, even white teeth.

"Where can I take you gentlemen?"

"Fourth floor, please," Ness courteously replied.

The elevator glided to a smooth stop with its floor only about an eighth of an inch above that of the hallway.

"Watch your step, please," he said, pulling on the lever that opened the door.

Two doors to our right we saw a couple of menacing looking, heavy-set men with bulges under their coats. I had

some butterflies in my stomach, and the thought flashed through my mind that now I knew how Daniel felt when he was in the lair of the lion.

"We're here to see Mr. Capone," Ness announced.
Capone, through good behavior, had secured an early parole from the Pennsylvania prison and was back. The news had swept through town like a cyclone.

They patted us down. "He's expecting ya, go on in."
The heavy six-paneled door had the word PRIVATE in large gold lettering. We were about to enter 407 - the throne room, the heart of Capone's gangland empire.

Capone was sitting behind a huge desk, dressed in blue silk pajamas and a monogrammed red silk robe with velvet ties. To his left was a private bathroom, which rumor said was constructed with costly Nile-green tile. A glance at my chronometer said it was 10:30 a.m. We had heard that Capone stayed out until the wee hours and was a late riser.

He was smoking the fattest cigar I had ever seen. There were three other men in the large room. One of them I recognized as Phil D'Andrea. Facing us on either side of the desk were two hulking bodyguards. From my research I knew they were Frank Rio and Frank Diamond.

I glanced around the lavish room and was a little surprised. The deep, wide corner room was furnished fit for royalty. There was enough Italian marble and accessories to decorate St. Mark's in Venice. The paintings and statuary were similar to the ones that adorned the library at the University of Chicago (only these were originals, not copies). Over in one

corner was a large Saratoga trunk. In another was a coat rack that displayed an expensive-looking vicuña overcoat.

In the middle of the room was a massive gleaming mahogany conference table surrounded by twelve leather armchairs. Steel plates were affixed to the high backs and each place had a silver ashtray, notepad, and a gold Eversharp pencil.

I was surprised to see baggy-eyed Jake Guzik hunched over at a far end seat. I had heard that the Wabash Hotel is where Guzik had his headquarters. A black leather briefcase was parked next to his feet. Capone's accountant, he was busy entering figures in a green ledger. His coat was off and he wore a green eyeshade and straw sleeve protectors on his arms. There was a pile of slips and stacks of money on the desk. A metal strongbox was on the floor near his feet. I presumed the slips were I.O.U.s. He was so engrossed in his work he never once looked up.

The best word to describe the place was gaudy. The room, though lavish, was covered in unique parquet wood flooring; it lacked ascetic balance, and the garish Florida motif wallpaper seemed out of place. On one wall hung pictures of George Washington and Abe Lincoln. On another were autographed pictures from Jack Dempsey (in ring togs), Red Grange, and Big Bill Thompson. In a corner by the windows, framed by red damask curtains, one of his goons tended a crank Victrola that was softly playing themes from "Rigoletto."

Capone, his gray eyes warily fixed on his antagonists, motioned us to take a seat. He had just finished breakfast and was patting his lips with a monogrammed linen napkin.

"Have a smoke?" he asked, taking the wooden lid off his hand carved teakwood humidor.

"No, thanks," we both replied.

His face took on an odd look as though we had insulted him. "None finer— hand rolled in Cuba."

We shook our heads.

He leaned over, and one of his men relit his corona. "Okay, den let's get right to it. I hear youse guys are

causing me a lot of trouble. Whatta ya have ta say for yourselves?" he said grimly with his eyes hard on Ness.

His accent was more Bronx than Italian, which surprised me a little.

"We're merely enforcing the prohibition laws, Mr. Capone. The only reason you're suffering is that you seem to be the biggest violator of those laws," Ness answered.

Capone pulled reflectively at his lower lip. "But itsa bad law. Everybody knows that," he angrily retorted. "We're merely givin' people what they want. If they didn't want it, there wouldn't be any demand for what I have, and I'd be outta business."

"It isn't our job to pass judgment on which laws are good and which ones are bad. When you go into law enforcement you swear to enforce and uphold all the laws," I said.

Capone was self-absorbed, blowing big smoke rings at the ceiling. He brought his eyes back to Eliot, locking them on his tormentor.

"But why not be reasonable 'bout it? That way everybody wins. Just look the other way most of da time. That's what the cops do when it comes ta prostitution. We accept an occasional raid an some arrests as a necessary evil, a face-saving measure for da flatfoots."

"Respect and honor are a big part of your personal code, right?" Ness said.

Capone, nervously fingering a two-carat star sapphire ring on his left pinkie, looked a bit confused. "Yeah, so?"

"If you give your word to somebody, it's important to you that they think you are a man of your word, correct?"

"Uh, huh," he grunted.

"Well, how much respect do you have for those cops who accept money from you on a monthly basis?"

Capone just sat there, mulling over Eliot's words but not responding.

"You don't have any respect for them, we both know that."

The big guy rolled his eyes and threw up his hands. "Okay, so what!"

"Well, you're not the only person who believes in honor and respect. If I didn't do my job, I would lose all respect from my family— my father, mother, sister and brothers."

Capone pursed his thick lips, looked down at his desk and exhaled loudly. "So that's it, dat's the bottom line, a big fat No!" The tone was irritable now.

Capone pulled his six-foot porcine frame out of the chair and walked over and opened the Saratoga trunk. My eyes about popped out of my head. It was full of cash, some of it loose but much of it in large stacks with paper bands around them.

Money and power are his gods, I thought.

He took out several bundles and brought them back to his desk.

"How's about $4,000 a month for both of ya?" He pushed the stacks of money toward us. "No one would have ta know. Don't be a sucker. Nobody's on the legit. Enjoy life a little. That's more than I pay any judge or

Jake "Toad face" Guzik – Chicago Public Lib.

Frank Rio – Capone bodyguard

police official."

Eliot leaned over and pushed the money back. "With all due respect, Mr. Capone, the answer is NO! You do what you have to do, and we'll do what we've sworn to do. Your days are numbered. We're putting you out of business, period!"

I watched Capone in awe as he summoned his bulldog will and the fury rose within. The veins on his short neck popped out. All of the blood seemed to rush to his head, making those big white scars on the side of his face stand out in stark contrast. His eyes glittered – dark prisms reflecting a whole spectrum of ancient hurts and grudges. Capone slammed his fist on his desk as hard as he could. Then he jerked his right arm sideways, knocking a small herd of miniature ivory elephants to the floor.

"I gave you a chance to walk outta here alive. No lousy fed cops are gonna ruin my setup." He snapped his fingers and his sycophants rushed over and grabbed our shoulders, their muscular arms clamping us to our seats.

"Are you ready to go to jail, right now for the rest of your life, or possibly keep a date with the hot seat?" Eliot warned. "Do you really think we were stupid enough to come here alone? Tell your goons to look outside the window."

Capone frowned in disbelief and then motioned with his head for one of his men to walk over and look out.

"My entire unit is down there, fully armed and fully expecting us to walk out of this building in five minutes. If I don't give them a signal, they're coming in and taking you and your men out."

Capone laughed and waved him off. "My men can—"

Ness cut him short. "And if that isn't enough, there are a half a dozen journalists waiting to hear my version of what happened at this meeting. There are also two assistant district attorneys just itching for a chance to bring some serious charges."

Capone didn't say anything for about a full minute, which to me seemed more like an eternity. He just sat there and fumed, weighing his options. His nose was flared, like that of an angry bull.

"I could jus' make you guys disappear."

Eliot never flinched. "You wouldn't want to do that, Mr. Capone."

He arched his brows. "Oh, yeah?"

"Ness leaned closer and got in his face. "Yeah! When you mugs kill each other off, nobody cares. But when you go too far and kill cops, feds, or reporters, everyone gets up in arms. You take us out and Big Bill Thompson, your benefactor, will never win another election."

Capone's countenance went south.

"Remember how bad it was when Mayor Dever defeated Thompson a few years ago? The pressure got so intense, you were forced to flee Chicago and move your headquarters to Cicero."

There was another spell of brooding silence. Finally, Capone nodded his head and waved a hand at his two goons. "Let 'em go."

"But, boss . . ."

"I said, let 'em go. Not here, not now."

They relaxed their grip. I tried not to show it, but inside I breathed a huge sigh of relief. Ness straightened his tie and went over to the window and waved a hand.

As we started to walk out the door, Capone grumbled once again. His face was twisted.

"Youse guys have no idea what you're up against. I've got an army of 700 men on my payroll that's ready to do my bidding. The next time you decide to raid one of my breweries, we'll be waiting for ya. Then we'll see who has the last laugh."

"And we've got someone on the inside of your organization who tells us your every move," I boldly asserted.

Capone looked at me in shocked disbelief. Eliot could see that I was getting ready to make another wisecrack, a parting shot, and I saw him shake his head *no* at me, so I buttoned my lip.

As we left and closed the door behind us, there was a loud crash against the wall.

"You don't think Big Boy threw that expensive porcelain vase do you?"

Eliot turned with a boyish gleam in his eye. "I'd bet the Organization is about $1,000 bucks poorer."

When we stepped in the elevator, I took a swipe across my brow with my hand to wipe off a bead of nervous sweat.

"Wow, that was exciting, Eliot. Have any more fun lined up for us on today's agenda?"

He just looked at me and then started laughing hysterically. I stared at him like he was crazy.

I gave Eliot a wink. "We just missed an opportunity to become part of the *nouveau riche*."

Chicago reform mayor William Dever

He smiled. "Yeah, I could have bought my fiancée a $2,000 fur coat."

After we disembarked from the lift, he asked, "Just who is this mole that we have telling us the mob's every move?"

I grinned. "You know we don't have anyone. I just wanted to throw Big Boy off balance, make him sweat a little."

Ness shook his head and arched his eyebrows. "Very devious, Mike. Machiavelli would be proud of you."

"Do you think he'll send a couple of his torpedoes out gunning for us?"

Eliot squinted his eyes. "I don't think so. It all has to do with John Q Public. They're up in arms since the St. Valentine's Day Massacre. There is a lot of civic indignation right now."

"So Big Boy has seen this reform mood before and will wait for public apathy to set in and bring back normalcy?"

Eliot nodded. Then another one of his patented smirky grins. "But it'll be our job to keep gangsterism in the headlines and see to it that doesn't happen."

As soon as we exited the front door, a crush of reporters rushed over to us and fired off one question after another. It was pure mayhem.

"What was Big Al wearing?"
"Did you two really go in there unarmed?"
"What did Capone say? Did he offer you a bribe?"
"How much was it?"
"Did he get mad when you turned him down?"
"Did he threaten you?"

I noticed that one of the reporters was more sharply dressed than the others. He was brash and had a big cigar in his mouth. When he asked a question, he waved it at us with his right hand, as if using it to punctuate his sentences. I was astounded to see that he was wearing a big diamond encrusted belt buckle, the kind Capone handed out to his friends. The kind Jake Lingle was wearing when he got shot.

"The bottom line is we told Capone no matter how much money he offered us to lay off, the answer was no. We weren't interested in his money, period!" Eliot replied in a serious tone.

As we finished the interview and climbed back into the car, I heard one of the reporters say to the others: "THESE GUYS ARE DEAD DUCKS!"

Corrupt reporter Jake Lingle – author collection

The next day we were sitting in Eliot's office and Marillyn, his secretary, rushed in all excited, with copies of several newspapers.

"Look at these," she gushed. "We're famous."

NESS SAYS NO TO CAPONE read the *Star-Sentinel's* headline. **CAPONE BRIBE ATTEMPT FAILS** said the *Daily News*. But the one that caught our eye was the *Herald Examiner* that opened with the line, "Eliot Ness and his young agents have proved to Al Capone that they are untouchable." There was a picture of us with the story and the caption said in bold black letters:

"THE UNTOUCHABLES"

And so a legend was born!

CHAPTER 12

APRIL 12, 1930

The film *Scarface* was made in 1932, preceded by two other popular gangster movies, *Little Caesar* (Edward G. Robinson) and *Public Enemy* (James Cagney). *Caesar* was loosely based on Chicago's Cardinelli gang, and *Enemy* profiled Dion O'Banion.

Howard Hughes was told to make numerous changes in the film before it was approved by the Hays censorship committee. They thought it was too violent, and that it glorified the gangsters. Hughes was even forced to place a message at the beginning of the film outlining the state of deplorable affairs. It urged citizens to get involved in the fight against the effects of gangsterism. "It's your government – what are you going to do about it."

The film starts out by showing Capone being responsible for the murder of Big Jim Colosimo, making Johnny Torrio the new kingpin of the South Chicago Gang. Capone provides the muscle for Torrio, killing all competitors, including the Irish northsider Dion O'Banion. Torrio becomes disenchanted with Capone's violent ways, preferring instead to go the route of diplomacy. He also learns that Capone is making a play for his girl. Torrio puts out a contract on Capone but he outwits his assassins and learns that Torrio was behind the move. He then confronts and kills Torrio.

Dean (Dion) O'Banion

The movie comes to an exciting climax when Scarface discovers that his sister is having an affair with one of his men (George Raft).

Furious, he goes to the hotel room where they are staying and he shoots the man who has dishonored his sister. His sister, crushed by the turn of events and heartbroken, tells Capone that the two had secretly been married the day before.

A murder warrant for Capone's arrest is issued and Capone and his sister are killed by police in the ensuing gun battle.

Naturally, all of the gangsters in the film go by different names rather than their actual ones.

When Capone first heard that *Scarface* was being made he sent a couple of his thugs to Hollywood to check it out. Chicagoan Ben Hecht wrote the screenplay for Howard Hughes' studio. The torpedoes went to Hecht's hotel room in Los Angeles and demanded to know if the film was about Capone. Hecht assured them that the movie was really about other gangsters he had known from his reporting days, and the title was a showmanship gambit designed to attract the viewing public.

Chicago screenwriter Ben Hecht

Capone was appeased, but the city of Chicago was so upset about the explicit portrayal of municipal corruption, the movie was banned until 1942.

Ironically, Capone liked the movie and ordered a 16 millimeter copy of it for his personal use.

If you ever view the film, watch for Boris Karloff in a minor role. His next film, where he portrayed the Frankenstein monster, would make him a legend.

A few nights later Eliot came home with me after work. It had been nearly three months since he had last seen his aunt, Mrs. Griffin. She had invited him to eat supper with us, and he had accepted.

"What's on the menu tonight?" Ness asked.

I licked my lips. "Fried chicken, pickled beets, mashed potatoes and gravy and green beans."

Eliot grinned. "I've had her chicken at family gatherings. I know it'll be delicious. How about dessert?"

"Rhubarb pie, which you probably won't like," I kidded.

"Are you serious? It's my favorite. I'll probably want two pieces."

We parked our cars on the street and were walking toward the front porch when an automobile appeared and cruised down the street toward us. We had both spotted the car and were wary of its deliberate speed. It slowed as it neared our position, and when the light from a nearby streetlamp glittered on a gun barrel, we dove for cover.

Fortunately, there were two large concrete flowerboxes on each side of the sidewalk. As the gun began to chatter and spit fire, Ness dove for the one on the left, and I scrambled for the one on the right and hugged the ground.

We pulled our .38 caliber Colts from our shoulder holsters and retaliated. I remained behind the flowerbox and fired an errant round, but Eliot boldly stood up and squeezed off three shots into the would-be assassins' automobile. He was rewarded with the crash of glass in the rear window and the sound of one man cursing, as if he'd been hit.

That was enough for the mobsters. The car leaped forward and disappeared into the night.

I got up and brushed the leaves and grass from my slacks and jacket.

"Say," I said in a tone of faux irritation, "I thought you said Capone wouldn't come after us."

Eliot slipped his pistol back in his holster. His voice was subdued. "I didn't think he would."

We stood there silently for a minute, the night crowding in around us. The porch light came on, and Mrs. Griffin stepped out the door, clad in a print housedress with a full apron.

Courtesy Dell Comics/Desilu 1962

"What in the world was all that noise?" she demanded. Eliot was quick on his feet. "It appears as if that car needs some new sparkplugs. My Cadillac is in the shop being repaired. That was my old jalopy from home backfiring. Quite a bang, wasn't it?"

After supper Eliot quietly told me he wasn't worried that much about the incident. "At least it shows the rats are getting desperate and we've got them worried," he quipped. "Yeah, let's pay them back in spades for that cowardly assassination attempt," I said.

*   *   *

I was sitting in a small side room of the Chicago Public Library looking up information about the U.S. tax code, trying to find a way to get the goods on Capone for failure to report his income. I grew frustrated, not finding anything that I felt might be useful to Eliot or the IRS people. I rubbed my eyes, closed the book, and left the table to return the bulky volume to its original place on the shelf. As I started to slide it between the others, I noticed a slip of paper that seemed to have something written on it.

Meet me over in the biography section, it said.

Thinking it might be some kind of a trap, I slipped my hand inside my coat and placed it on the weapon in my shoulder holster. I cautiously moved past about twenty rows of books to the 920 part of the Dewey decimal classification system. I started with the A section and began carefully checking each aisle, one at a time.

Then I heard the hushed tones of a woman's voice. "Psst, Mike, over here."

I moved over one more aisle and was surprised to see Ellen Esposito standing there. "W-what on earth are you doing here?" I asked.

Ellen was her usual gorgeous self. Her hair was done in a Psyche knot, similar to that worn by Lillian Gish in *Hearts of the World*. She reached out and touched my arm. "I have to see you."

I recoiled slightly from her touch. "What do we possibly have to talk about? My boss said you're poison, and I should have nothing more to do with you."

"Yes, I know. My family pretty much feels the same way about you."

"So why are you here?" I said.

She fiddled with a fuchsia scarf. "Because I can't go on anymore like this. My uncle is breaking the law, and he excuses everything by simply claiming that he is running a business. But it's a vicious world where competitors end up dead. And my aunt is like all the other women who are married to gangsters. She doesn't ask questions about what goes on, and she doesn't believe anything in the newspapers. My uncle tells her that the stories are all a pack of lies – made up for the sole purpose of increasing circulation."

"I thought you had it made and were living the good life. Eliot also told me that you're Murray Humphrey's girl friend."

"That's right, I am his girlfriend, but I'm sick of this life and I'm sick of him."

I shook my head. "You sure fooled me. I could have sworn you were the one who was all upset at The Green Mill a few weeks ago when you found out I was working for the Untouchables."

She gave her head a slight toss. "Don't you see, that was just a ruse."

"A ruse?"

Murray "the Camel" Humphreys and Ellen Esposito (Dell Comics/Desilu1962)

"Yes – an act . . . all put on."
"Why would you do that?" I asked suspiciously.

"Because I really, really like you, and I don't want to go on anymore being part of a family that's connected to the Capone organization."

"What about Humphreys?"

"I've wanted to get away from him for months, but I didn't know how."

"Why didn't you just tell him that it was over?"

She looked at me, dumbfounded. "Are you kidding? You don't know him."

"I've always heard that Murray "the Camel" isn't like most of the other gangsters around Capone, that he's less prone to use gunplay and prefers to stay out of the headlines."

"Yes, yes, that's what everybody says . . . what everybody thinks. But he's a cold-blooded killer, and when it comes to women he's insanely jealous. The last girlfriend who walked out on him ended up in the hospital with a concussion, a bruised kidney, a broken arm, and a black eye."

My features rearranged. "How did you get mixed up with him in the first place?"

"Oh, he's smooth, very smooth. He hung around the Green Mill all the time and asked me out as soon as he spotted me. I said no, at first, but he was very persistent. He started sending me flowers, then jewelry. All my girl friends said I was nuts to turn him down. So I finally gave in and then it was more jewelry and soon expensive furs. I quickly became a showpiece – a possession he could drape on his arm and show off to others. Look here, world – take a gander at my trophy piece."

I placed both hands on her shoulders and looked her squarely in the eye. "You're smarter than that, Ellen. How could you fall for that kind of man – that kind of line?"

"Oh, Mike." Tears began welling up in her eyes. "Don't you think I've asked myself that a thousand times? Haven't you ever made a mistake in a relationship?"

I drew her to me and gave her comfort. She was right. I knew it was a strange alchemy that often drew men and women together. "Yes, yes I have."

I leaned back and threw her a questioning look. "Why did you wait so long to contact me after running me off that day at the restaurant?"

"Don't you see, I had to wait. They were watching me – my aunt and uncle . . . and the waiter. I wanted their suspicions to die down. I had to be sure it was safe."

"How did you explain all of this to Murray?"

"We had just had an argument because I caught Murray cheating on me. I told him I was foolishly trying to get back at him and when I met you by accident while I was running, I didn't know who you were. I told him that I had forgiven him for his indiscretion and I wanted him back if he promised not to ever do it again. He was angry, but at least he didn't hit me or slap me around."

I paused, wondering if the gulf between us was unbridgeable. There were some questions I wanted to ask Ellen: *How do I know this isn't just some elaborate scheme to get inside information from me to help your friends and relatives? How do I know you're not just using me to get away from Murray Humphreys?*

I couldn't bring myself to say any of those words. "Ellen, this is really getting complicated. What do you want me to do?"

She shrugged her shoulders. "Gosh, Mike, I don't have all the answers. All I know is that I can't go on living my old life. I can't make you any promises, but I do know I want to keep seeing you, and I hope you feel the same way about me."

"Oh, Ellen, Ellen. Yes, I do want to keep seeing you, but I don't know how this can possibly work."

I wanted to tell her that I missed her so much I was afraid it'd eat a hole right through me, but I was afraid it would come out sounding like something I'd cribbed from *Broken Blossoms*. "We're from two different worlds. You're still seeing Murray. You're living with a family that's breaking the law – laws I've sworn to defend."

She looked at me with a mischievous smile and gave a little laugh. "You forgot something else."

I stared at her with a puzzled look. "Don't tell me it's worse than what I've imagined."

"I'm afraid so. I'm Catholic and, let me guess, you're probably Protestant."

"You're right, I'm a Lutheran – the progeny of Martin Luther. But . . . everything else aside, how can we possibly have a relationship? How could we even see each other?"

"Murray does a lot of work keeping the Chicago mob in touch with their allies in Cleveland, Detroit, Atlanta, Kansas City and St. Louis. He goes out of town about every two weeks and is gone for four or five days or more at a time."

"So all we would have together are a few stolen hours. Even then it would have to be on the sneak. No one else could know," I said dejectedly.

"But if you feel the same way about me that I care about you, wouldn't it be worth it?"

I took her by the shoulders and looked deeply into her incredible eyes. "Ellen, do you realize that we've only been together for a grand total of one hour and forty-five minutes? I'm crazy about you and want to be with you every minute that I can, but there's no logic to it."

She made a helpless gesture. "I know. I feel the same way. I love you more deeply than I can figure out how to put into words."

"But . . . I've never felt this way before," I protested. "How do *I* know . . . how do *we* both know this isn't some kind of sophomoric crush, some mad fling straight out of an Edna Ferber novel?"

Her eyelashes fluttered. "I thought a lot about it the past few weeks. In fact, I've thought about nothing else. My grandmother once told me that when you find someone and you can't get him out of your head, and there's this knot in your chest and a tingly feeling when you're together – that's love. There's no explaining it, you can't make sense of it . . . it just takes over every fiber of your being."

I shook my head. "I know what you mean. I've seen some of my friends act that way, and I simply thought they were daft in the head. What is this strange alchemy that makes one person fall in love with another? I never thought it would happen to me."

I placed my hand on her cheek and she turned her head slightly and then gently kissed my fingertips. "I want to touch you, hold you, hear the sound of your voice, smell your intoxicating fragrance . . . "

My sentence was interrupted as she threw her arms around me, and we kissed in a passionate embrace.

Beauty cream with dangerous radioactive material to kill germs

"We'll have to keep our romance *au couvert* – secret," I said. "Eliot would probably kick me off the team if he found out about us."

She nodded. "There's just one more thing," Ellen said in a cautious tone. "I want to help."

I shook my head. "I don't understand. How can you help?"

"I can keep my eyes and ears open. Sometimes I'm with Murray when he gets phone calls. I usually block it out but from now on I'll soak everything up like a sponge while pretending to be disinterested as usual."

"No, it's too dangerous. I don't want you going Joan of Arc on me."

Ellen totally ignored my statement. "I'll be careful. Sometimes I hear them say things at the restaurant. They think nobody can touch them, so sometimes they don't watch what they say."

"But how can you hear what's going on if you're cooped up in a small room in the back?"

"I don't have an office as such. I tried that and hated the isolation. I spread my tally sheets out on a table at one end of the dining room so that I get to see other people and talk to the waiters."

"I've got an idea. I don't know if I can stand the thought of sharing you with that creep, Murray." I brought my hand to my forehead. "Oh, my gosh, I just thought of something. Has he . . . you haven't . . ?"

She placed her fingers on my lips. "No! He hasn't . . . we haven't. We don't know each other, biblically speaking. I still have my maidenhood. You don't understand the twisted code these men live by. They put their future wives and spouses on pedestals. Sex with them is mainly for having children. Prostitutes and mistresses take care of their other needs," she explained.

Sears metal head doll

$2⁹⁸

_Our Largest and Best

"So the wives are expected to put up with and ignore their husband's peccadilloes," I said.

"There's a little more to it than that. A lot of these women work very hard - cooking, cleaning, shopping, laundering, ironing and taking care of the children. By the end of the day they're exhausted and are glad not to have to fulfill other marital obligations.

"Yeah, I hear Capone's wife thinks he's practically a saint."

"He smothers her with furs and jewelry. I've only seen Mae a few times, but she seemed very supportive and devoted to her philandering husband," Ellen replied.

"It's all very difficult to comprehend."

"You can't imagine how bad it is. Jack McGurn once took his wife on a cruise and stashed his wife in Deck A and his mistress on a deck below. The only exception to this is at the annual Christmas party where it's wives only – no girl friends allowed."

208

"What if we got married? Then you'd be with me and I could protect you."

She shook her head dejectedly. "That won't work."

"Why not?" I shot back.

"Because Murray would come after you, and I couldn't handle the thought of being responsible for the consequences."

"I can take care of myself."

"Think about it. Can you imagine what it would look like if the papers printed all the lurid details of one of the Untouchables being involved with the fiancée of one of Capone's men? It would do irreparable harm to everything that you and Mr. Ness are trying to accomplish."

My shoulders slumped. "Yeah, I guess you're right," I said dejectedly. "Not a single member of the Untouchables is married. That was a condition Eliot imposed when selecting his team. We'll just have to maintain the status quo and see how it plays out."

"Once you and Ness put Capone and Murray behind bars, that will change everything."

"Yeah, but the way things are going right now, I don't see

McLean County Courthouse in **Bloomington** – Dan Oberle Route 66 collection

how it will happen. It's like trying to stick your thumb in a badly leaking dam. The government is trying to build a tax fraud case against Capone, but so far all the pieces haven't fallen into place."

Ellen and I parted with the understanding that we would have to be very careful with our secret romance.

*   *   *   *

Milles Park in **Bloomington** – Dan Oberle Route 66 collection

Our next raid was at night and took place at 3136 South Wabash Avenue. The brewery was masquerading as Midwest Trucking Company. But this time our lookout spotted a man on the roof sporting a Tommy gun.

"How are we going to deal with the man on the roof?" I asked Eliot.

He was sitting at his desk looking pensive. Pencil in hand, he was tapping the eraser end of it lightly on the desk. "We certainly will need to deal with him first," he said. "Any ideas?"

I stared at the ceiling and absentmindedly pushed my tongue against the side of my cheek as I racked my brain. "We need some kind of ruse," I said, bringing my eyes back to his gaze.

"Yeah, but what?" he said.

"How close is the next building?"

"Actually, the other place is a storage facility for a paper firm, and the buildings adjoin each other."

A bulb suddenly lit up in my brain. "We can send Steve Strohman up a ladder on the far side of the other building. From a hidden vantage point across the street, I can use a slingshot to shoot a pebble onto the roof of the brewery to distract the gunman. That will allow Strohman, already at the top of the ladder, to climb the rest of the way up and get the drop on him."

"That's good, but it's still risky for Strohman," Eliot said. "Let's add another man on the ground ready to shine a spot-light in his face when he looks over the side, you know— like a deer caught in the headlights."

I rubbed my hands together. "I like it. Now, what about gaining access to the brewery?"

Ness scratched his head. "I think I know what will work. We'll stop the regular delivery truck several blocks before they arrive at the facility. We can detain them and replace the driver and unloader with two of our men dressed in work clothes. They'll bring the truck to the entrance, signal with the horn, and gain access to the inside."

"We'll need more than just two men to go inside. How about hiding a couple of more men on the bed of the truck behind the barrels?"

He nodded. "Good idea."

The whole plan worked perfectly. Before the delivery truck arrived, the guard on the roof was distracted and disarmed with ease. Knowing that Capone was good for their bail, the men in the truck surrendered without any gunplay. We cuffed them to a streetlight that cast an opaline glow over the darkness.

Bokal and Tesson climbed over the tailgate in back and hid under a tarpaulin next to the barrels as we drove to the large overhead door. The men inside didn't expect anything when the truck tooted its horn four times because our previous busts were preceded by door smashing. Once we were inside, Eliot and I, guns drawn, jumped out of the truck as soon as he set the brake. The two men in the back of the truck vaulted over the sides. I fired a warning shot into the ceiling and the four men inside just sat there with stupefied expressions on their faces. I kept them covered while Eliot went to the back and let the rest of the crew, guarding the exits, inside. All in all it was probably the easiest bust we ever made.

It was also very profitable. We confiscated another truck, 275 barrels and 50 cases of beer and destroyed equipment valued at over $20,000. The equipment included an air compressor, fifteen 2,500-gallon tanks and five 1,800-gallon cooling tanks. There was even an electric blower to force fumes out through the roof. As Eliot and I were looking over the layout, Mizell came over with a big grin on his face and motioned to us to follow him.

Untouchables agent Dan Mizell

"Look at what I found if you want to see a new dodge," he said.

In a corner stood a huge barrel of naphthalene pellets, better known as mothballs. The mothballs had been spread next to every door and window to mask the fermenting beer odor.

Untouchables making an arrest – Dell Comics/Desilu

We also found a black book lying on a table that listed over 40 speak-easies served by the plant. When I saw that one of the places on the list was The Green Mill, my heart sank.

As we were preparing to leave another truck pulled up and blared its horn four times. Everyone was all smiles as we obligingly let it in. That made the score two trucks instead of one and added a pair of surprised prisoners to our scorecard.

One of the men we captured was Svoboda, the brew master taken in one

Bob Stack on the "candlestick" phone – courtesy Desilu Studios

of our other raids. He had speedily obtained his release by posting $5,000 bail and was back in business.

"You won't get out so quickly next time," Ness told him.

Tobacco-stained teeth showed in his reply. "That's what you think, copper."

Everything small enough was loaded on the trucks, and then we dumped out the beer. Before the raid Eliot had told us that he didn't want the brewing or cooling vats to be destroyed. As we pulled away from the plant with big fanfare, I asked him what he was thinking by leaving all that valuable equipment behind.

I could tell he had something up his sleeve with that sly smile he gave me. "I'm baiting a trap."

"How?"

"After we deliver our prisoners and drop off the trucks, I'll tell the men we're all going back, one at a time and conceal ourselves where we can't be spotted."

"Aha! You think that by leaving valuable equipment behind, some of Capone's other men might come back to collect the equipment."

"Brilliant deduction, Dr. Watson."

It was a long wait. We whiled away the hours of darkness, and when the sun came up, there was still nothing in sight. Around ten o'clock, three black sedans swept into the neighborhood and cruised about for nearly ten minutes to make sure there was no suspicious activity at the brewery. Then each car took up a strategic position so that a car approaching from any direction could be sighted immediately.

When the sentinel cars were posted, another car pulled up. Three men got out, looked around nervously, and then darted inside as the car pulled away.

A few minutes later a 7-ton truck appeared and pulled into the brewery. The sentinel cars blasted away on their horns when they saw us, but we raced in before the men could react. They had already loaded one of the big vats on the truck. They made no effort to escape, so we quickly patted them down for weapons. We were surprised to discover that one of the men captured was Charles Kamm, another one of Capone's master brewers.

CHAPTER 13

MAY 2, 1930

The term "speak-easy" probably came from old illegal Irish drinking pubs known as "speak softly shops," so as not to alert business establishments next door to what was going on. A typical speak-easy of the 1920s often masqueraded simply as a restaurant. But over in one corner of the room might be a wooden telephone booth with accordion doors. The telephone inside didn't work. After entering the booth and closing the door, the customer would knock three times on the side that adjoined the wall. A small panel would then slide back, and a bloodshot eye scanned the patron. If he passed scrutiny there would be a click, and the side of the booth would swing inward, allowing the person to enter a cramped, smoky, noisy atmosphere of free-flowing booze and bawdiness.

A pianist wearing a derby would be playing something like "I Wish I Could Shimmy Like My Sister Kate." He was part of a Dixieland band that included a banjo player, clarinetist and drummer, all wearing wide striped waistcoats and high-stiffed collars. Tables were supplied with small wooden mallets for beating time. Above the piano was the notice, WE PLAY REQUESTS. There was a wire washing line on which clothespins held dollar bill gratuities from pleased patrons.

Speak-easy – courtesy Dell Comics/Desilu 1962

Slender, youthful girls dressed in short, straight, fringed dresses and looping ropes of beads intermittently ceased serving at the tables to perform the Black Bottom, Turkey Trot and Charleston. The flowered wallpaper was spotted with satin-doll silhouettes and framed photos of dignitaries such as Al Smith, Rudolph Valentino, and Babe Ruth. The walls were also adorned with gilt-framed paintings of fleshy pink nude women, acquired when authorities closed down the Everleigh sisters' brothel on Dearborn Street.

Speak-easy peephole

A few days later I went to see Archie Martin, that walking crime encyclopedia Eliot had recommended to me. Actually, it was my third visit, and I found him to be even better than what I had expected. It was like he had been to the Chicago Public Library, the FBI file room, and the newspaper morgue of the *Tribune*, and had memorized everything there was on about seventy-five leading candidates for the Criminal of the Year award. He quickly filled me in on the information I was seeking.

I had some extra work at the office that was going to keep me late. I phoned my landlady, Mrs. Griffin, to tell her to go ahead and eat supper without me. I figured I could warm something up from the icebox when I got home. After I finished, while driving to my apartment, I remembered I had wanted to call home and wish my dad happy birthday before he went to bed.

After parking my car, I stepped into the Hotel Sherman lobby and went over to the Smoke Shop where there was a phone booth in back. The Sherman's Louis XIV Ballroom upstairs is where Big Bill Thompson, ten-gallon hat and all, had celebrated his return to City Hall for a third term when

he defeated reform Mayor William Dever's bid for re-election back in April of 1927.

It had been a fairly quiet election as Chicago elections go. Dever had taken the precaution of assigning 5,000 extra policemen to keep the peace that election day. The most notable event during the voting occurred when one of Capone's sluggers, Schemer Drucci, broke into a Dever supporter's office, beat him up and wrecked the place. The police were notified, and Drucci was picked up late in the afternoon. As they took Drucci to the station, Detective Dan Healy roughed Drucci up a bit in the car. Drucci became enraged and tried to grab the detective's gun. Healy pulled the gat free from Drucci's grasp and drilled him with four body shots.

Drucci was buried at Mt. Carmel Cemetery in unconsecrated ground. The Chicago Catholic hierarchy had made it clear that career criminals would not be given the blessing of the Church. Gounod's "Ave Maria" was sung at his funeral. A grieving Capone attended with quite a bit of stubble on his face, observing the Italian tradition of not shaving until after the burial.

Frank Nitti

The Sherman's Smoke Shop was on the ground floor to the right of the lobby. The place was a little over fifty feet deep and about thirty feet wide. One dapper man near the door was sitting at the front counter, smoking a cigar and reading the newspaper. Next to him were two men playing a game of Hooligan with a pair of dice and a leather cup. The proprietor was busy ringing up a sale for some cigarettes at the counter.

I made my way toward the back where the glass and wood-paneled phone booth was located. I had just finished my conversation with my dad when the corner of my eye caught a new figure coming through the doorway of the smoke shop. Dressed in a dark pin stripe suit and a color-splashed tie, I could see that he was carrying a Thompson submachine gun with its distinctive round drum. I heard him pull the action lever back, automatically chambering the first round. Like most victims, I was so transfixed by the weapon that I forgot to look at the man's face.

As soon as I saw him raise the weapon, I flung open the folding doors and dove to the floor. The gun began sputtering in its unique deep voice. In instantaneous fashion I grabbed the leg of a large metal table and flipped it over. I tried to curl into a fetal position behind the table to minimize my exposure.

I could hear the .45 slugs as they poured into the phone booth, gouged the walls and thudded against the table. Splinters flew from the groaning panels of the counter. The slugs shattered the glass in a deadly shower of fragments, blasted the metal phone unit, and riddled the dangling handset, severing the connecting cord in the process. The wooden oak panels were chewed into jagged splinters.

When the offending gun clicked on empty, there was a rush of noisy footsteps as the gunman turned and made his escape. I had protected my face by covering it with my arms and closing my eyes.

For about thirty seconds I stayed on the floor and carefully moved my body parts to see if everything still worked. I breathed a sigh of relief. Atropus, the Greek Fate who cuts the thread of life, apparently was not yet ready to snip my cord. My left ear was stinging, and I could see blood staining my suit jacket and shirt. Debris from the wreckage of the phone booth covered my body. I shakily stood up and shook most of it off, gingerly brushing my shoulders and sleeves. When I reached up to check my ear, I felt a glass shard embedded in the cartilage. I gingerly pulled it out and placed a handkerchief from my back pocket on the wound to stanch the bleeding.

I looked around to survey the scene. A couple of rubber plants were shredded, and a ruptured spittoon had disgorged its dark, liquid contents onto the floor. I figured that others in the shop dove for cover as soon as they saw the gunman walk in. I could tell by the look on their faces as they stared at me they couldn't believe I was still alive.

I removed my coat, flung off my tie and unbuttoned my shirt to determine the severity of my other wound. I seemed to be bleeding like a stuck hog, but the injury was in the fleshy part of my armpit and wasn't serious.

One of the men offered me his handkerchief. I thanked him and

1929 Stutz Versailles sedan

Jack "Machine Gun" McGurn

Cracker Jack and Bingo

applied it to the wound and rebuttoned my shirt. I kept my arm pressed to my side to hold the handkerchief in place.

"Did anybody see who it was?" I asked anxiously.

"I was afraid he might shoot *me* if I eyeballed him," one man replied.

"I was too busy ducking for cover," another one said.

The manager gave me a palms-up gesture as if to say, "Don't ask me."

A tightly packed knot of murmuring people formed in the doorway, looking at the carnage in astonishment with mouths wide open.

"All right, step back, everyone; let the police do their job."

A uniformed policeman, revolver in hand, elbowed his way through the wedge of people and into the store. The crowd slowly pulled back. The policeman's eyes were searching back and forth, his service revolver in a ready position as he looked suspiciously for perpetrators or places of concealment.

"What in blazes is going on here?" he demanded. He spied me holding a cloth to my ear and asked, "Are you hurt, buddy?"

I was in a lousy mood and gave him a sour look and a tart reply as I showed him a bloodstained hand. "No, it's only ketchup, officer."

"Call an ambulance," he said to the manager.

I waved him off. "No, it's okay, officer," I said. "It's a superficial flesh wound; I can drive myself to the hospital to have it cleaned and bandaged."

"Can someone tell me what happened here?" he asked.

"This gentleman was making a phone call, and some guy stepped through the doorway and shot up the place," the manager said.

The officer had a puzzled look on his face. "Anybody get a look at the shooter?"

Everyone shook his head.

He turned to me with a questioning look on his face. "The Capone mob doesn't kill people without a good reason. What motivated them to go after you?"

All of a sudden he did a double take. "Say, wait a minute. You look awfully familiar."

"I'm with Eliot Ness and his prohibition group," I said reluctantly.

His eyes grew round. "Oh, yeah. Your picture was in the paper a few weeks ago. I figured it was just a matter of time until this thing turned nasty. I bet it was an outsider they brought in . . . someone like Frankie Yale."

"Could be," I shrugged.

"You were darned lucky." He took out a pencil and notepad and wrote everyone's name down, plus other pertinent information such as place, time of day, etc.

A siren sounded in the distance, signaling the arrival of another squad car on the scene. One of the bystanders had apparently called the police station.

A fatally wounded Mayor Anton Cermak

The policeman turned and faced the crowd, waving them back. "All right everyone; get back to your business. Break it up. The big show is over."

I was getting ready to go to the hospital when the smoke shop manager slipped a note into my front coat pocket. After I got outside I unfolded it and looked at the message.

"Don't tell anyone I said so, but the shooter was Jack McGurn. He was wearing one of his patented light blue suits," it read.

I knew the man wasn't going to be willing to put his life on the line and testify to that in open court, but I appreciated his candor.

We'll meet again McGurn, and things will be different next time. That's a promise!

After our last brewery raid we continued backtracking the empty barrels being collected at the various speak-easies and this, in turn, led us to another scrubbing and cleaning plant. Although the mobsters now were very much on the alert, we were able to locate even more breweries, thanks to the footwork of Steve Strohman and Gary Tesson.

In rapid succession we knocked over a $120,000 brewery in a garage at 1712 North Kilbourn Avenue, on the North Side, and a $100,000 plant at 2024 South State Street. We had made a modification to our battering ram. A pointed bumper replaced the old one. The idea was to sweep debris off to the side in the same manner as the old cowcatchers on steam locomotives.

The first place was discovered through an anonymous telephone tip. As it developed, however, it wasn't a Capone brewery after all, but one operated by George "Red" Barker. Six men were taken into custody there, and we captured another truck, 135

Artist Thomas Hart Benton

barrels of beer, six 1250-gallon vats of mash and a 1500 gallon cooling vat filled with beer.

From one of Eliot's stoolies we learned that rival gangs were on the verge of a war of vengeance because they blamed one another for tip-offs that had led us to their breweries. These raids were quickly followed by another, but this time we ran into a different problem.

This brewery occupied the third and fourth floors of a building used by the Edelblute Warehouse Company. By moving their operations to a higher floor, we were unable to use our door-smashing dreadnaught.

"Look here, Mike," Eliot said. "They're using this freight elevator to bring raw materials in and to ship the finished product out."

I picked up an empty container. "Yeah, from the looks of things, they're using the name Alcorn Syrup and Products Company as a front."

Eliot pointed to Strohman and Bokal. "I want you two to guard the elevator shaft."

"Sure thing, Chief," Bokal replied.

"Bischoff and Kaufman, I want you two to go up to the top and guard the roof."

They nodded in compliance.

"How are we going in?" I asked.

"The rest of us will go up the outside fire escape and break in through the windows," Eliot said.

We synchronized our watches and gave everyone time to get in position. When we busted inside, we were amazed to find only two men on the premises. But it was still worthwhile. We took inventory, and I wrote up the complete list.

"Well, men, it looks like about 60,000 gallons of wort, 51 barrels of beer ready for shipment, icing equipment, five 3,000 gallon pressure tanks, fifteen 3,000 gallon aging tanks, special ventilating apparatus, and a mini-cooperage plant with 150 finished barrels."

"Quite a haul," Strohman beamed.

"What exactly are the aging tanks used for?" Mizell wanted to know.

"To complete the chemical process involved in brewing. If the beer isn't aged properly, you get what is known as green beer. The cheaper joints sometimes sell the stuff," Ness replied.

DeWitt furrowed his brow. "Don't the customers complain?"

"Most of them are so busy trying to have a good time, they'll drink almost anything."

"Yeah, I read in the paper the other day where a couple of guys went blind from drinking wood alcohol," I added.

Ness shook his head. "Amazing, simply amazing."

"Hey, Chief," DeWitt yelled. "Look at this piece of equipment. It's some kind of stamping machine that places the number 23 inside a diamond. What is that all about?"

"That's so Capone's muscle men can tell at a glance whether a particular establishment is using the syndicate's beer," I volunteered.

"What is special about the number 23?" Strohman asked.

"I don't know for sure, but I think that's how far down he was on the totem pole when he first started working for Johnny Torrio.," I replied.

Our operations widened as we latched on to a beer distributing plant at 222 East Twenty-Fifth Street. We found out about it in an interesting way. Eliot and I had tied on the feedbag at a greasy spoon on the North Side when a policeman strolled over to out booth.

"Ain't you guys some of those hot shots who work for that Ness character?"

I could hardly contain myself. "Sure," I said, "what can we do for you?"

He looked around suspiciously and then, seeing no one else, lowered his voice. "I'm gonna do you guys a favor and give you the address of a drop spot."

Curious, Eliot wanted to know how he knew this, yet

Politics and Prohibition

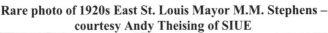
Rare photo of 1920s East St. Louis Mayor M.M. Stephens – courtesy Andy Theising of SIUE

Chicago restaurant – courtesy Dell Comics and Desilu

failed to do anything about it."

"Those lousy Capone creeps are only paying me $20 a month to keep my nose clean. I asked for a lot more, but they just laughed at me."

Eliot drew back with a surprised look.

"Look," he continued, "if you say anything about this I'll just deny it. Are you interested?"

"Sure," Ness said. "Why not?"

He gave us the name and address of a place where the mob dropped off booze for local delivery. "I'll tell you something else," he said in a huffy tone. "If they don't cough up more money, I'll be happy to name some more spots."

When we met with the others to plan the raid, Steve Strohman brilliantly came up with a new stratagem.

"Let's give this new idea of mine a try," he pleaded.

Ness looked over at me. "What do you think?"

"I think it just might be crazy enough to work."

"Explain it one more time," Ness said to Strohman.

"We'll place ourselves at the exact spot where their trucks have to slow down to turn into the plant. We'll pretend like we're fixing a flat tire. Then, as it goes by, we'll just jump into the back and ride on in."

It was such a simple idea, riding an empty beer truck that was returning to the plant for another load of deliveries. Eliot just couldn't resist it.

It worked perfectly.

Steve and Eliot parked a nondescript Model T Ford in the designated spot. Steve pretended he was tightening the lug nuts while Eliot, hands on hips, stood by and watched. As the truck came by, they swung over the tailgate and crouched low as it tooted its horn and the big double doors swung open. They waited until a man closed the doors and returned to a table where another man was sitting. The two men in the cab alighted and joined them at the table.

Eliot and Steve eased out of the truck, drew their weapons and practically were on top of the men before one of them looked up with a stupefied expression on his face. They patted the men down and relieved one of them of his gun.

DeWitt and I were assigned the role of scaling the building and closing off any avenue of escape from the roof. We took our ladder from the back of a pick-up truck we were using and darted into a back alley and approached the building from the rear.

"Up with it," I said softly to Paul as we approached the side of the building.

We hoisted the ladder, wordlessly thanking the garage man for padding it so ingeniously as it rested soundlessly against the building. Then we scrambled up the wooden rungs to the flat, tar-papered roof.

I put a finger to my lips. "Careful, so we don't make any noise and tip them off."

Looking about, I saw a skylight that had been painted over with black paint to protect from snoopers. Just beyond it loomed a rooftop doorway, standing at attention like a corner newsstand kiosk.

"You take one side and I'll take the other," I told Paul.

We didn't have to wait long. We didn't know it, but while the others were having an easy time of it downstairs, a couple of guys who had been in a second story loft when the raid was made, came scrambling toward us. We could hear the frenzied pounding of footsteps inside the doorway we guarded.

"Here they come," Paul whispered.

The door flung open. DeWitt tripped the man as he stumbled through the doorway. The fleeing man was of slim build and agile as a cheetah. He rolled to the roof but quickly was back on his feet with knife in hand. He lunged but Paul caught him by the wrist of his knife hand and they went down in a tumble.

Untouchables making an arrest – Dell/Desilu

Before I could come to Paul's aid another figure zoomed through the doorway.

"Hold it," I shouted. "This is a federal raid."

Instead of stopping, the man whipped out a pistol, fired a shot which I heard zing past my head, and began to sprint toward an adjoining rooftop. Meanwhile he let loose with another shot over his shoulder. Instinctively I snapped a shot at him with my .38. I winged him in the shoulder and he took a few tottering steps and plunged through the skylight. A horrifying scream slashed through the sound of the shattered glass.

Whirling to go to DeWitt's aid, I saw Paul rising with the thug in his grasp. He had disarmed the mobster, and as I started toward them, Paul drove his fist to the man's jaw; he wilted to the rooftop. I picked up the knife, and Paul,

incredibly strong for his size, threw the man over his shoulder and motioned me ahead of him down the stairs.

When we reached the main floor we lined everyone up, frisked them and held guns on them.

"Where's the other rat?" I said, "the guy who took a tumble through the skylight."

"Cripes, I don't know," Eliot responded. "We were too busy down here to notice."

Guggenheim Museum of Art in New York City by Chicago architect Frank Lloyd Wright

I looked up at the skylight and walked over to the spot where the man should have been. Directly beneath the skylight was the edge of a huge brewing vat. Paul joined me and we walked around the vat but our quarry was nowhere in sight. Paul started pointing his finger in jerky little motions at the vat.

I shook my head. "You don't think . . . "

Paul nodded and smiled crookedly. "Yeah, that's what I mean. The guy you winged has got to be in there taking a beer bath."

"Hey, somebody bring the ladder back in from the side of the building," I yelled.

Tesson brought the ladder in, and I ran it up against the side of the vat. I scrambled up and looked down into the foaming brew. DeWitt had been right. The hood's body was there, floating face down in the beer.

Leaning over the edge, I reached in, gripped his collar,

Sears outfit for boys

and dragged the motionless form over to the edge. It took all my strength, perched up on the ladder as I was, to hoist him gradually until his body draped over the edge.

Bischoff, the ex-football lineman, yelled up to me: "Let me up and I'll drag that monkey down from there."

I was more than happy to oblige. It was no task for him, with his enormous strength, to lift the thug under one arm and carry him back down. Then he laid the man on the floor.

"He's dead as a dodo bird. Somebody call a meat wagon."

All of a sudden it hit me. "Maybe not," I said. I went over and turned the man on his stomach and crooked his head sideways. I began pushing on his back with an occasional interval, hoping to somehow force the brew out of his lungs. I did this for about three minutes, and then, miraculously, the man coughed and beer flowed out of his mouth onto the floor.

Eliot called for an ambulance and the groggy, wounded man was taken to the hospital.

Paul DeWitt, Gary Tesson, and Steve Strohman were with me as I drove back to the office at the Transportation Building.

"Don't you think it was a waste of time, saving that hoodlum?" Tesson complained.

I thought about what he had said for a few seconds then replied: "Not at all. That's how I sleep well at night after I come home from the job." I later found out the man had a wife and five kids.

CHAPTER 14

MAY 10, 1930

THE MAHJONG CRAZE – Playing card and table games became more popular than ever, now that the working class had more leisure time, thanks to the 8-hour working day. Dominoes, checkers, bridge, Pedro, chess, and backgammon were standard fare. But the new craze that swept the nation was a game imported from China called mahjong. It has been described as a cross between dice, bridge, and dominoes. The game contained 144 tiles and required the use of such terms as "South Wind," "Pung," "Bamboo," "Chow," and "Red Dragon."

The rules were complex, compounded by the fact that several different variations were printed, depending on the maker of the set that was purchased. The upper classes hired private tutors to teach them the rules. The game was more popular with women than men, and they often immersed themselves in the culture by buying Chinese robes and tables.

Sears shoes for men

Shipping wt., 2 lbs.
Tan Calfskin   Black Calfskin

Merely Margy

When the communists took over China in 1949, they banned the game as a waste of time.

The Katzenjammer Kids

Capone and his men struck back. A few days later Eliot and I left the office to go to lunch, and when we went downstairs to get in his car, it was gone. My olfactory senses detected a faint, raw odor in the air. Apparently it was one of those days when the wind was blowing just right. Upton Sinclair wasn't far off when he described the sirocco coming from the Union Stockyards as "raw and crude." Chicagoans, of course, were accustomed to the odor and paid it no heed.

I took off my hat and scratched the top of my head. "Do you think one of the boys borrowed it?"

Eliot had a disgusted look on his face. "No way. They wouldn't do that without asking me. Someone must have stolen it."

"Yeah, and I'll bet we won't have any trouble figuring out who was responsible."

The next day the police found the car parked at the end of a dead-end street. The headlights and taillights were smashed, the wiring ripped out, and the upholstery slashed to ribbons.

The policeman who called Eliot about the car, Frank Cumberland, stopped by at the office the next day for a talk. It turned out that he and Eliot had attended the same high school and were old chums.

Eliot introduced us, and we sat in Eliot's office to listen to what he had to say.

"I just thought you'd like to know that our grapevine says you guys are the chief topic of conversation in the Capone mob."

216

"That's not surprising," Eliot said. "We figured as much."

"The word is they're mad—mad as h—"

"You can say that again," I interjected. One of Capone's men, I'm pretty sure it was Jack McGurn, tried to carve his initials on my body with his Tommy gun.

He shook his head. "Yeah, I heard about that little incident. You were very lucky. They say it's the first time McGurn ever messed up an assignment."

I got a little steamed. "Well, if I ever catch up with him he's going to be missing a few teeth, just like Fred "Killer" Burke."

He took on a serious tone. "Careful, McGurn's an ex-boxer."

"Well that should just about make us even. I was a football player for Amos Alonzo Stagg."

"Well, anyway," he said. "I just wanted to warn you guys. I'd be careful if I were you two. I certainly don't envy either one of you."

"We know how to take care of ourselves," Eliot said.

"One more thing. One of my informers told me that Capone called a meeting. All the top echelon men were on hand. It included Frank 'the Enforcer' Nitti, Ralph Capone, Jake Guzik, Murray 'the Camel' Humphreys, 'Three-fingered Jack' White, Jack McGurn, Tony (Mops) Volpe, 'Bomber' Belcastro . . ."

"The so-called "pineapple expert?" I asked.

"Yeah, if I were you guys, I wouldn't get into another car without first checking it for a bomb."

"We'll be careful," Ness assured him.

"And two of Capone's trigger men were there, 'Fur' Sammons and Phil D'Andrea."

"That's quite a line up," I said.

"Capone gave the okay to take you two out, but he said to make sure it either looked like an accident or an outside job."

Eliot thanked his friend for the information, and we shook his hand before he left. I didn't expect Big Boy to take our raids lying down, but now that his inner circle was discussing our future state of health, I knew we were skating on thin ice.

My troubled mind drifted to another topic. On the morrow, at McGurn's home turf, I was determined that the two of us would grapple in the manner of Ivanhoe and Front de Boeuf. Like two feudal knights of old selected to champion the cause of our armies, we would do battle – each of us in a struggle representing two diametrically opposed groups in the prohibition convulsion.

I was still plenty steamed about McGurn trying to send me to an early grave with his machine gun. It kept eating

Dagwood sandwich

away at me and I brooded about it. Rather than risk an ulcer, I foolishly decided instead to risk my life.

It had been an unusually hot day in northern Illinois – the kind of day when the heat shimmers off the concrete sidewalks and even the bobwhites seek shade in the backyard brush. Still upset about McGurn, I dialed the operator and asked for BRunswick 4070. I had a little chat with Archie Martin, my fact friend at the IRS.

"Do you know where Jack McGurn lives?" I asked.

"Just a minute. Let me look it up in my file."

Pause.

"All right, I think I have it here," he replied. "I know he drives a LaSalle, hates opera, and wasn't very successful in a brief boxing career. He had a glass jaw."

"Does he live alone?"

"Yes and no. He's married, but his wife is out of town for three weeks visiting relatives in Galesburg."

I could hear him thumbing through a sheaf of papers.

"It's got to be in this file . . . somewhere in Lincoln Park . . . yes. Here it is. It's room 304 at the Belden-Essex Apartments on Lincoln Park West. But he's registered under the name George Franklin."

"Thanks a million, Archie."

I waited until later in the evening, and then I drove over to the apartment complex with blood on my mind. I should have come up with some sort of ruse, but my muddled brain wasn't fully functioning. I looked at my watch. It said 10:05 p.m. After parking my car, I went inside and dashed up the stairs. My heart was thumping against my ribs, and my pulse was beating in my ears. I moved my shoulders up and down in an effort to loosen up and then took a deep breath.

I could barely hear a radio inside room 304 playing the tune, "Button Up Your Overcoat," by Fred Waring and the Pennsylvanians.

Keep away from bootleg hooch
When you're on the spree.
Take good care of yourself,
You belong to me.

I rapped three times hard on the door. A voice inside yelled, "Yeah, who is it?"

"It's Eliot Ness."

The door opened about six inches. McGurn stood there with a gun in his hand. "Say, you're not—"

I was in no mood for Marquis of Queensbury rules and didn't give him a chance to finish. I threw my weight against the door, and it knocked him backwards and he went down, banging his head on the hardwood parquet flooring. He was momentarily stunned, spread-eagled with his back on the floor, but the gun was still in his hand.

"You're gonna pay for that, punk." He started to move his gun hand from the floor and aim in my direction, but my jujitsu training paid off as I rushed over and kicked it out of his hand. It skittered away under a sofa.

"Say, I know you; you're Ness' right hand man."

I purposely let him get back on his feet.

"Yeah, it's Kriegan, Mike Kriegan, the man you tried to dry gulch last week."

He was good and mad. "I can't believe you . . . you, uh, walked away from that."

"Well it's payback time. I'm here to see if you're any good at anything besides shooting people in the back."

"You're about to find out. I'm pretty good with my fists," he sneered, shaking a clenched right hand.

I gave him an insulting chuckle. "That's not what I heard. People I talked to said you quit the ring because you had a yellow streak down your back."

"I'm gonna make you eat them words," he glowered as he barreled toward me in a blind rage.

I sidestepped him as he rushed at me and flung him headlong into the door. He crashed into it with a loud thump, fell to the floor, but quickly scrambled to his feet.

He threw me his best sneer as he wiped some blood from his nose. "Why you lousy . . . "

I rushed across the distance between us and rocked his head with two quick slaps that cracked loudly like pistol

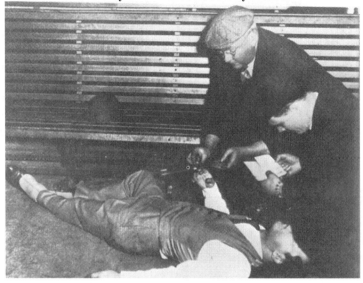

Jack "Machine Gun" McGurn – killed in a bowling alley on the anniversary of St. Valentine's Day Massacre

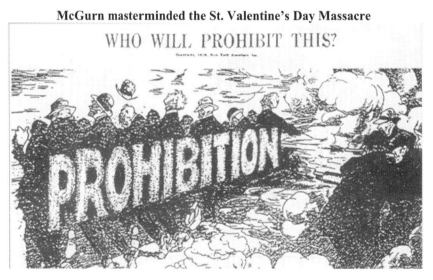

McGurn masterminded the St. Valentine's Day Massacre

shots. My objective was to make him so angry he couldn't think straight.

He staggered back, recovered himself, then came at me again with clinched fists in a Gene Tunney boxing stance.

McGurn took a roundhouse swing. I ducked and extended my foot, hooking his ankle. A quick jujitsu jerk caused him to take a header over a hassock, sprawling face first into an end table that broke off part of a front tooth. He pulled himself up and spat the shattered incisor on the floor, staring at it in disbelief. He was hemorrhaging blood from his mouth and nose.

McGurn was yelling obscenities as he picked up an ashtray and flung it at me. I sidestepped and it crashed against the wall.

He dove and tackled me around the waist and brought both of us to the floor. McGurn landed a few body punches and then brought his knee up into my groin. I rolled away from him and got back to my feet, clutching at the searing pain between my legs.

Then he grabbed an empty beer bottle by its neck and came running at me, the bottle held high, poised for a strike. I swiped a cushion from the couch and it absorbed most of the blow. Unfortunately, it struck enough of my left hand that I feared my little pinkie was broken. I grabbed the arm and hand that held the bottle and twisted it hard enough to cause him to drop it. I kicked it away to a corner of the room.

He backed away. We both stood there for a few seconds, breathing heavily, warily eyeing each other like injured lions, nursing our wounds and contemplating our next move.

"All right, McGurn. No tricks, no weapons, no jujitsu moves from me. Put up your dukes and let's slug it out, toe to toe. Let's see what you're made of."

He started to talk but let out a sputtering cough. Then he cleared his throat. "That's good enough for me. After I

218

mop up the floor with you, I'm gonna make you wish you'd never been born."

I clenched my fists and raised my hands in a Barney Ross defensive position. Then I motioned with my right hand for him to come and get it. I was gasping for air, totally exhausted, but somehow his threat on my life was just what I needed to get a second wind and prepare for his assault.

His upper lip curled back – like a rottweiler getting ready to attack. Then he came at me hard and *wham* landed a

Louise Rolfe – McGurn's "blonde alibi"

vicious kidney blow and another one square on my chest that felt like a sledgehammer. I thought my heart was going to stop beating. Next he unloaded a roundhouse right that was aimed at removing my head from my shoulders. I saw the move coming in time and ducked as a fist grazed the top of my head; I countered by driving a left hand into McGurn's midsection. He came back with a quick left jab, then a right cross and a left hook.

Stars of every hue danced before my reeling vision. I pushed him away and backed off, choked for breath and coughing from my depths, hoping for a brief respite to clear my head.

I lobbed a few desperate haymakers at him, but he backpedaled and managed to stay safely out of my reach.

I can't beat this goombah; he's too good.

He charged at me again, like a mad bull pricked by a picador's lance. This time I was able to ward off his thrusts so that he only landed a few glancing blows to the side of my head. My right ear stung like crazy. I backed him off with a few retaliatory blows of my own.

I was carefully watching his eyes. I could tell by his demeanor that he was moving in for the kill. All of a sudden, I remembered something from my conversation with Archie at the IRS.

Al Capone wearing a skimmer

McGurn's got a glass jaw. That's his Achilles heel.

McGurn got in several hard body blows with his concrete fists before I launched a rally purposely aimed at his nose, causing blood to gush forth from his left nostril. As he brought up his hands to protect his face, I called on my reserves and threw a hard right hook directly into his stomach where that mass of nerves are located in the solar plexus. He emitted a low moan and involuntarily dropped his hands just enough to let me follow through with a crushing right cross to his jaw. He groaned and went down on the floor in a heap.

I was so hurt and exhausted that I fell to one knee, gulping air in huge gasps, wincing from the burning sensation in my lungs, feeling that at any second I was going to pass out.

Out in the hall I could hear muffled voices. McGurn's doorbell was being buzzed insistently.

I stumbled back to my feet and caught my breath as I stood triumphantly over the prostrate McGurn. Huffing and puffing, it was as if I'd just run up the stairs to the top floor of the Wrigley Building. I jiggled some of my teeth and found a couple that wobbled. Reaching down, I hoisted McGurn to a wobbly upright position. He was unable to stand on his own two feet so I pulled his arm around my shoulder and together we stumbled toward the door.

I leaned McGurn against the wall and flung open the door. A gaggle of McGurn's apartment neighbors looked aghast at the two of us. There were loud gasps when I grabbed McGurn by the shirt collar and tossed him out into the hall where he crumpled into a heap.

"What happened to him?" a red haired, freckled man in a smoking jacket asked.

"He stepped on a banana peel," I wisecracked.

I turned and looked hard at the group. "Meet your neighbor, folks. This weasel's name isn't George Franklin. This is the great Machine Gun McGurn, Capone's ruthless killer."

There was another collective sucking of air. The men among the onlookers were shaking their heads in wonderment, and the women shrank back with white knuckles pressed to their open mouths.

"Only he doesn't look so tough now, does he?"

I reached down and pulled McGurn by his lapels toward my face. "Listen up, amoeba brain. I'm giving you a warning, so hear me good." I shaped my fingers into the figure of a gun. "You'd better steer clear of me because if I ever see you again on the streets, I'll figure you're gunning for me, and I'll get you (I snapped my fingers) just like that! From now on you're *persona non grata*. I'm keeping book on you. You know how you and your worthless kind are always getting away with killings by claiming self-defense? Well, I'm gonna ask for a bench trial. And I'll bet I can convince Judge Lyle, who hates your living guts, that it was self-defense."

McGurn's eyes fluttered and he emitted another low moan. I drew him even closer to my face. "Have you got that, tough guy?"

There were some people getting off the elevator at McGurn's floor. Some froze instantly when they saw what was happening, others scurried away, murmuring.

He nodded a weak *yes*. I drew back my fist to smash his face one more time. He threw up a hand and let out a pitiful whimper.

"No, no, don't hit me again . . . please."

I held my fist about a foot from his face, debating with myself whether to slug him again for good measure. Finally, I shoved him back to the floor. "You're not worth it, you guttersnipe."

I stood upright and gave the crowd a hard look. "Somebody better call an ambulance for this guy."

I turned and walked away, nursing a sore finger, a puffy eye that was going to turn into quite a shiner, and some bruised ribs. I hurt all over, like I had been run over by a Duesenberg.

Despite my battered condition, a satisfying warmth rushed through me. I tried to smile.

Couldn't.

Hawthorne Hotel in Cicero

CHAPTER 15

The music ♫ of the Prohibition Era was felt on many levels – political, economic, moral and, just as importantly, cultural. In response to the movement, the illegal became glamorous; rebellion became hip. The period gave rise to some of the most adventurous, high-spirited music ever made including: "Minnie the Moocher" by Cab Calloway, "Chicago Breakdown" performed by Louis Armstrong, "It Don't Mean A Thing (If It Ain't Got That Swing)" by Duke Ellington, and "I Got Rhythm" performed by Don Redman.

Musician "Fats" Waller

The next morning, when I awoke, the sun was streaming in through the sheer curtains on the east window of my bedroom. I was bathed in sunshine and pain. I got up and looked in the bathroom mirror. A bewhiskered mug with a nice shiner was staring back at me.

I dressed and thought about skipping my morning meal because I was running a bit late. Hunger won out. I cooked breakfast and then quickly gobbled up my bacon and eggs, scouring the plate clean with the last piece of toast. I washed it all down with a hot cup of Postum. Then I drove to the office.

Although still early in the morning, the late summer sun was already reflecting off Chicago streets and sidewalks with a shimmery air. At certain angles, the rays bounced off tall buildings and reflected back at me, and occasionally a blast of white light struck my eyes like hot needles.

I found Eliot back at work, feeling a little woozy from a three-day bout with a respiratory infection, but determined to forge ahead.

He gave me a stern glare as he appraised my cuts and bruises. "You look like you just went ten rounds with a Golden Gloves champion. Please tell me you didn't go after McGurn."

Slightly embarrassed, I nodded my head. "Dancing a few rounds with McGurn isn't all it's cracked up to be. But I remembered your comment that we would meet threats with action and violence with violence."

I made a feeble attempt at humor. "If you think my face looks bad, you should see McGurn's knuckles."

Eliot, that Manichaean who saw the world in black and white absolutes, stood with hands on hips and a faint scowl.

"I meant collectively. You must have macaroni for brains. Do you realize your cowboy actions will only complicate matters? McGurn will be three times more likely to come after us now."

"Yeah, you're probably right, Eliot. *Mea culpa* – my mistake. You know he's still married to Louise Rolfe, even though they only see each other on weekends. He knows the cops are still trying to pin the St. Valentine's Day rap on him. McGurn only married that 'blonde alibi' so she couldn't be forced to testify against him."

"I just hope Capone keeps him on a leash."

I nodded and ran a hand through my hair. "What's our next step?"

We were interrupted by a knock on the door. His secretary said there was a young man outside the office named Arleigh Jones who was anxious to meet Mr. Ness.

"Did he say what it was about, Marillyn?"

"No. He just said it was important."

"Well, okay, go ahead and send him in."

I gave the man a thorough frisking before he was allowed inside. He was a young chap, well dressed and wearing a bow tie and sporting shiny patent leather shoes.

"What can I do for you, Mr. Jones?" Eliot said as he shook his hand.

A nice looking kid with blonde hair, I guessed him to be around 22 years old. Eliot offered him a seat and then pointed over to me. "This is Mike Kriegan, my right hand man."

He stood up as I walked over and shook his limp hand.

"Well," he said in a high-pitched voice, "I want to join your Untouchables squad. I'm reliable, a fast learner, and I could contribute a lot," he said excitedly. "All I want is a chance."

Eliot gave me a quick look out of the corner of his eye and saw me shaking my head *no*.

"What are your qualifications?"

I almost laughed out loud. It turned out that the kid had absolutely no qualifications or training as an investigator.

"Can you use a gun?"

A terse no.

"Are you good with your fists?"

He had never been in a fight, so he didn't know.

"This is pretty tough work we do, Mr. Jones," Eliot said, trying to let him down gently. "All of our men are highly skilled and professionally trained."

The kid persisted. "I know I can help if you'll just give me a chance."

"Why would you want to do something like this?" Eliot asked.

"Look, Sir. There's nothing I'd rather do than be a gangbuster. My wife read about you fellas in the paper. She pointed to your pictures and said, 'Now those are *real* men.' "

"So you want to join us so you can impress your wife?"

He gave a nervous laugh. "Yeah, I guess you could say that. I'm married to 'Nanna Peel,' the exotic dancer. Maybe you've seen her in burlesque."

Ness shook his head no. "I've heard of her. She's very well known. Doesn't she have certain parts of her anatomy insured for something like $20,000 as a gimmick?"

"Yeah, but you should see her anatomy. She's worth all that, and more," he said excitedly.

"I'll take your word for it," Eliot said.

He had a sheepish look on his face. "Look, I don't know why she married a milquetoast like me, but I love her very much, and I want to do something to impress her."

I shook my head and rolled my eyes.

"Look, Arleigh. I wish I could help you, but I really have all the men that I need.

The only kind of an extra person I could use is one that could somehow get me some inside information on Capone and his outfit."

His eyes lit up.

"You mean like some kind of undercover man. I, I could do that. Capone and his men come to the burlesque shows all the time. Also, his men frequently hire Nanna to dance for parties at his speak-easies. I could keep my eyes and ears open and pass anything I hear along to you."

Ness was stroking his chin. "I don't know . . ."

"Plus," he said. "I already know Jake Guzik. I bet I could talk him into giving me a job with the Capone gang. And it just so happens I've done several favors for a real big judge. I can get a letter of recommendation from him to Jake Guzik and in that way land some sort of a job with the Capone mob."

Ness knew that under these circumstances he could probably succeed because "Greasy Thumb" Guzik was treasurer of the Organization, and he was always willing and anxious to keep his political connections happy.

"All right," Ness reluctantly decided. "If you can tie in with the gang, I'll have some assignments for you."

The kid, happy as a lark, shook our hands and strutted out the door. His whistle floated back as the door slammed behind him.

The next day, I was looking out the window of the office while Eliot was concluding a phone conversation. A big black sedan pulled up to the curb and a body was pushed out the rear door of the car onto the sidewalk.

Ohmygosh, it's the kid!

I raced out of the office and ran down a flight of stairs to the street level. Andy was a bloody mess and was moaning. I was horrified to see that he had been shot in the chest and his ears had been cut off.

"Where are your ears?" I shouted

He didn't speak but emitted a low groan and nodded to my left. I noticed a mongrel dog across the street sniffing at something. Thinking it might be bloody mass of human tissue and fearful that he would eat it, I drew my .38 and ran into the street screaming and waving my arms like a madman, with barely a glance in either direction. I reached the dog – but not before a taxi missed hitting me by a hair. I fired a shot that glanced off the sidewalk about five inches from his muzzle. He gave a

Arleigh Jones – the Kid

Capone's Palm Island estate in Florida

whelp and ran away. I retrieved the two ears, wrapped them in my handkerchief, and ran back to the kid.

"Let me help you up," I said

I leaned over and put his arm around my neck and brought him to his feet. We stumbled to my car and I leaned him up against it, opened the front door, and he fell inside.

Hamel Mother Road Pottery– Dan Oberle Route 66 collection

"Hold on, Arleigh. I'll get you to the hospital. How bad is it?"

"Pretty, bad," he coughed. "My lungs feel like they're on fire, and it hurts when I breathe.

"The bullet probably broke a rib," I said.

I drove as fast as I could to the nearest hospital. I was stopped by a patrol car when I ran a red light, but when I explained the emergency the policeman said to follow him. We drove at breakneck speed for about three miles with his distinctive gong ringing all the way.

The kid was seriously wounded and had lost a lot of blood as they took him in on a stretcher. Surgeons extracted the bullet and reattached his ears. They looked pretty bad for a few days, and I thought he was going to lose them, but circulation was finally established and they turned pink again.

"What happened?" Eliot and I asked him four days later when he was up to it.

"I got the letter, Mr. Ness," he said. "Then I went to see Mr. Guzik about the job. Several of Capone's thugs were in the room with him. You know what they said? They told me that they knew I was working for you and that I was to be a mole in their organization. Then they beat me up, cut off my ears, shot me, and dumped me in front of the Transportation Building."

"You are very lucky to have survived this," I said sympathetically.

He nodded in agreement. "Yes, I know."

"It's my fault," Eliot apologized. I shouldn't have let you proceed with the plan. It was much too dangerous and you were too young and inexperienced.

"I don't have any regrets, Mr. Ness," the kid said weakly. I'm more determined than ever to join your group, now that I've seen first hand how vicious they are."

"I'm sorry, Kid, but I don't want to be responsible for anything else happening to you. I just couldn't live with your murder on my conscience. It's not negotiable, and it's my final decision."

I felt sorry for the Kid. Despite what had happened to him, I could see that it nearly broke his heart to be turned down. But Ness was right. This kid was just too wet behind the ears.

*   *   *   *

A week later, Eliot and I were driving along Route 66 to the state capitol to give testimony to a group of legislators who were considering a new piece of legislation to supplement the existing prohibition laws.

I had been to the statehouse only once before in my life. It was a place where Illinois lawmakers gathered for only six months every other year. I had vague memories when I went there as part of a high school youth convention. My recollections were mostly of Lincoln statues, marble floors, and large oil paintings of important figures and expansive murals of important state events.

We left the night before we were due to testify, and it was cold, dark, and rain was falling, driving into the twin cones of light stabbing out from Eliot's Cadillac.

Firehouse Route 66 Museum at **Pontiac**– Dan Oberle Route 66 collection

I spotted a large flatbed truck rolling along in front of us with a heavy cargo secured under a tightly lashed tarp.

"I'll bet we have a truckload of illegal booze on that truck," I said to Eliot.

"You're probably right, but its out of our jurisdiction and I'm a little tired and don't feel like doing anything about this particular load."

"Yeah, I guess you're right."

Eliot mashed on the gas pedal, and we passed the truck and sped down the highway with the speedometer quivering uneasily on the 75 m.p.h. mark. A black and white road sign appeared briefly in the illumination of the headlights:

SPRINGFIELD, ILLINOIS - 22 Miles

I glanced in our side mirror and spotted small twin dots of white light. I jabbed a finger at Eliot's rear view mirror.

"There's a car behind us, and it's coming up pretty fast."

Eliot glanced at his mirror. "I see it. Grab your weapon."

I reached up and snatched my lever-action Winchester from the clips above the door. "I'm ready."

Eliot stripped off his gloves and dipped his hand inside his coat pocket and withdrew a .45 automatic. He kept a steady foot on the accelerator. "How are we doing?"

"Still gaining on us," I said apprehensively.

Eliot slowed for a curve in the road ahead, and I guessed that the following headlights were now less than fifty yards behind us. I dove into the back seat and moved over to the window and rolled it down, ready for action.

We hit a slick spot and the car skidded slightly. I could hear Eliot muttering under his breath as he fought to maintain control.

"They're coming up on our left in a flanking move," I shouted.

As Eliot regained control of the wheel, there was a blare of the other car's horn. We went into another curve and there was another horn blast as the car pulled along side. It was a 1928 Lincoln touring car.

I was just about ready to poke my Winchester out the window and let loose with a blast, when the other car accelerated and raced on ahead, its tail lights diminishing. Then the car was gone.

"Whew," Ness said as he wiped his brow with his overcoat sleeve.

"Well I'll be a son-of-a-gun. It must have been a bunch of revelers out joyriding," I said.

Eliot broke into hysterical laughter. "For crying out loud. Joyriders! A bunch of lousy joyriders. How do you like that?"

I took a deep relaxing breath and then placed the Winchester back on the brackets. I stayed in the back seat, leaned back into the plush upholstery and caught forty winks.

* * * *

Eliot was drumming his fingers on his desk. "We have had pretty good success at making raids on Capone's breweries. We'll keep up the pressure, but we also need to get more detailed information on his operations."

"Well, we know that his operation is big and well organized."

"Right. And from data collected by our operatives, we now know that they have a large sales office in the Liberty Hotel, over on the South Side, where orders are placed."

"And they have another office that handles distribution."

Eliot shoved a piece of paper toward me. "And this report from Wes Bokal shows another division takes care of production."

"Why don't we put a phone tap on their sales office so we can get a better overall picture and put the squeeze on them on all fronts?" I suggested.

"Eliot had a look of doubt on his face. "I know you're a good hand at wire tapping, but the building they are in is isolated, so I don't see how we can work it."

"So how do we gain access?" I mused.

I had a puzzled look on my face after Eliot said: "If Mohamed can't go to the mountain, maybe we can make the mountain come to Mohamed."

"Translation, please."

Adele and Fred Astaire – Library Congress

"Let's send a couple of our men over to the hotel and park in front and act as if they are recording data, comings and goings, etc. We want our men to be quite visible so they will realize that they are under constant observation. Then we'll put the word out on the street that we're planning a raid to get evidence."

"How does tipping them off help us?"

"Don't you see? I'm sure they're not going to want their operations disturbed. I'm betting that under cover of night, they'll move everything to a different location."

"I get it. Hopefully it'll be to a new spot where it's easier to tap their phones. Think it will work?"

"All we can do is hope."

The next morning Eliot called in DeWitt and Strohman and told them about the plan.

"Remember," he grinned, "I want you two guys to be seen every time they look out a window, walk into the hotel, or come out to get into their car."

"No problem," Strohman said cheerily. "They're going to think were customers they'll see so much of us."

The next day I got a bright idea. "Say, Eliot, let's do a little more than just keep an eye on these guys."

Eliot was reading a memo put out by George Q. Johnson, the U.S. District Attorney. He looked up. "What do you mean?"

"There's nothing that says we can't have a little fun on this job, is there?"

He eyed me suspiciously. "Meaning what?"

"Is it okay if I go over and join DeWitt and Strohman?"

"You're not thinking about doing something stupid, are you?"

"No. I just figure if two guys are making the mob nervous three might turn the heat up even more."

"Okay, but be careful."

"Great."

"And don't start any fireworks."

I drove over to the hotel and joined DeWitt and Strohman. I climbed into the back seat. "Hello, men . . . anything interesting?"

"It looks as if we have these guys walking on egg crates," Paul replied.

"Yeah, they're really scratching their heads, trying to figure out what we're up to," Steve added.

"Do you want to have some real fun?"

They both turned in their seats and looked at me. "Fun or danger?" DeWitt asked.

"Let's go right over to the lobby of the hotel and look around a bit."

"Are you nuts?" DeWitt shot back. "Count me out; I'm staying right here!"

"What about you, Steve? Are you up for some excitement?"

"Well, uh . . . maybe . . . yeah, that might be pretty interesting. I'm getting a little bored just sitting here all day."

Paul threw his hands up in the air. "You guys are both screwy. I'm staying put."

We walked into the lobby of the Liberty Hotel. The place was brimming with a swaggering pack of pearl-gray fedora hats, trademarks of Capone's men.

Steve shot me a big reckless smile. "I've wanted to look around in here for several days now. I'd like these goons to know that the time has come when we'll walk right into their parlor whenever we feel like it."

"You know, maybe barging in here like this was a lousy idea. These guys might think it's unsportsman-like to sully their turf."

To say that we caused a flurry of excitement is putting it mildly. There were a half-dozen hoodlums in evidence and, at a commanding nod from a sort of handsome man in his mid-forties, three of them sidled over to one of the elevators and parked themselves beside it in an alert, expectant manner which proclaimed that no unwelcome visitors were going to be permitted to enter that particular lift.

I nudged Steve. "Apparently that elevator with the

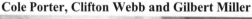

watchdogs is the one that leads directly to the rat's nest upstairs."

We sauntered toward the desk and, as we approached, two hoods lounging there moved slowly away. Behind the desk, the dapper, mousy clerk to whom they'd been talking in low tones drummed the counter with nervous fingers. He was white-faced and his tone disclosed an apprehension that trouble was about to explode around him.

"Yes, gentlemen," he squeaked, "what can I do for you?"

Steve, leaning on his elbows, grinned at him. "We just wanted to see what you charged for a suite by the month."

"I'm sorry, sir," the clerk gulped. "We are completely filled up."

"That's too bad," I interjected. "We're federal men and we've been considering the possibility of quartering all of our men here at the Liberty."

The little man looked as if he might faint at the very thought of it. His voice had a crackle as he spoke hastily.

"I'm sorry, gentlemen, but we are completely booked with permanent residents, and I have absolutely no idea when we might have a vacancy."

Steve just about gave the man apoplexy. "Well, maybe we'll take care of that situation sooner than anybody thinks."

One of the hoods with thick eyebrows and a Cro-Magnon skull was sitting at a small table with his gun and bullets on top of it. He was using a knife to make a cross on the nose so that it would be more deadly by making a bigger hole when it hit a human body. He picked up his gun and strolled over to us and said, "You guys have a lot of nerve coming in here and shooting off your mouths." His voice was thunderous.

"We're just doing our jobs— nothing personal. The only people who have anything to fear from us are those who are breaking the law. Steve gave him a sly look. "Now you wouldn't be doing anything illegal, would you, pal?"

The man was about to come back with a reply when I spotted one of the goons over in a far corner playing one of those newfangled electronic pin-ball type machines that were becoming increasingly popular.

"Hey, look what's over there."

Cole Porter, Clifton Webb and Gilbert Miller

Most of them had a steel ball that was batted around with flippers, but this one was sort of a shooting gallery.

I grabbed Steve and dragged him toward the machine. The game featured a pistol attached to a wire, and it was a marksmanship affair with an electronic beam making contact with each shot. The player was given 20 shots for a nickel.

"Why don't we have a little friendly competition? I'll go up against your best on this thing." I smugly looked around. "Who's the man?"

There was a murmur of voices. Then one of them with an oft-broken nose and large knuckles spoke up. "Joey Malucchi beats everyone else on this thing. Whadda ya say, Joey, ya think you can beat this loud-mouthed flatfoot?"

Joey stepped forward. He was a handsome young man of medium build I guessed to be in his late twenties. Eyes that shone like black olives glared at me. He was snappily dressed with pearl-gray spats covering his shoes. "I can take this guy anytime. The only time he'd have a chance is on the eighth day of the week."

"Since I'm not acquainted with this machine we need to play three games, total score wins. It might take a while for me to get a feel for this thing," I said timidly.

"One outta one, two outta three; makes no difference ta me, flatfoot."

"What are the stakes?"

"Stakes?" he asked with a puzzled look.

"Yeah, you know, something to make it more interesting."

One of them piped up, "How bout if Joey wins we drill you full of holes? If he loses, we just beat the living daylights outta ya."

"Or if I win, we march all of you down to the nearest police station to throw you in the jug," I countered pugnaciously.

"In your dreams, government man."

"Look, let's be serious about this. How about if I win, I get Joey's gold watch. If he wins, he gets my watch."

"One-sided bet. Your watch is a piece of junk," Joey said.

"Your not afraid you can't beat me, are you? Look at all the practice you've had. Besides, think how much fun it will be bragging to everyone how you took a chronometer from one of the Untouchables."

Road painting in 1927

Actor Harry Carey's Phaeton

Joey broke out into a big smile. "Yeah, Snorkey would get a big kick out of that, too. Okay, you're on."

I took off my watch. "Let the desk clerk hold the stakes. That way nobody welshes on the bet at the end."

Steve took my watch to the desk, and Joey's was delivered by a lantern-jawed thug named Monk Molgardo.

"You first," I said. "I need to know how hard I have to try to win."

"Just watch me," he countered with a tone of braggadocio.

Joey took off his suit coat and slipped a nickel into the coin box. Lights began brightly flashing, and all sorts of gongs and chimes went off each time he hit a moving target in the miniature shooting gallery. I watched carefully as he hit all the targets except numbers ten and twenty.

"Way to go, Joey!"

"That's showing 'em, kid!"

I looked over at Steve and he was shaking his head. I raised my hand. "Just a second, I need to confer with my partner." We walked over to a far corner.

"What's wrong?" I asked.

"What's wrong! We had these guys on the defensive, back on their heels. After Joey gets through pasting you, we'll be a laughing stock. You're the worst shot in our group." He gave me a look of disgust. "You and your stupid ego."

"You're exactly right about the ego. But you're forgetting one thing."

He furrowed his brow. "Yeah, what's that?"

I gave him a wink. "I've been spending a lot of time at the practice range, and I don't intend to lose."

Strolling over to the machine, I inserted my coin and squeezed off five shots. The first four were hits. The fifth missed. I squeezed off five more. It was the same thing, a miss on the fifth shot. After twenty shots I had sixteen hits and four misses.

"Joey's two ahead at the end of one round," Molgardo boasted.

I looked up at the machine. His score was on the left and mine was on the right.

Joey went through round two and again hit eighteen out of twenty, curiously missing on shots ten and twenty again.

"That's showing 'em, Joey!"

225

I looked over at Steve. He had one of those "I told you so" looks on his face.

On my second turn, I scored on my first four shots and aimed a little high on the fifth and scored another hit. Shots six through nine were hits, but when I aimed high on shot ten I missed. The exact same thing happened on the next ten shots, giving Joey a total of four misses after two rounds while I had six.

When Joey confidently stepped up to the machine for his final round, I decided on a gambit to try and unnerve him. "If you miss more than twice on this round, I'm going to beat you, Joey."

He flung me a contemptuous look. "Even if I miss three, you'll have to score a perfect twenty. Nobody has done that - ever."

Death of Roger Touhy

What I said must have worked because he missed exactly three shots on his final round.

I calmly stepped up to the machine and rattled off a perfect score. When I racked up twenty out of twenty, the machine's lights began blinking even more brightly and the bells and gongs got even louder. It also threw in an extra calliope-like sound no one had ever heard before.

Capone's men were stunned.

"Jeez, did youse see dat? A poifect score!"

"Unbelievable!"

"Nobody ever beat Joey before . . . not ever!"

"That fed is sure one lucky bum!"

An exhilaration of triumph surged through me, but I knew better than to gloat. I merely walked over to Joey and shook his limp hand.

"Good game. I guess I just got lucky."

He mumbled something unintelligible as he stood there crestfallen with a dazed look on his face. I took a quick survey. Joey's pals were standing around like a bunch of whipped schoolboys.

Steve was slack-jawed as we walked over to the desk and I collected the two watches.

"How did you manage to pull that off?" Steve asked as he calmly walked past a potted palm and joined me at the front desk.

"Wait until we get back to the car, and I'll explain everything to you and Paul."

When we turned there were five men with scowling faces blocking our path.

"Where do ya think you two bums are goin'?" a broad-chested one with a toothpick in his mug asked.

Woman's felt hat

$2 48
78R6500

I shook my head and looked over at Strohman. "I should have guessed it, pal. No honor among thieves."

Another thug with a pockmarked face rammed his chin near my face. "You big shot G-men are gonna pay . . ."

I didn't let him finish. I learned from playing football that the best defense is a good offense. I sucker punched him with a crashing wallop on his chin. As if he had been pole-axed, the big man fell straight forward on his face, out cold on his feet before he hit the floor. The lobby erupted into violent action. The other four surged forward and we found ourselves in the middle of a free-swinging mêlée, Steve's voice roaring happily above the confusion.

We had the advantage of surprise. As soon as my man went down, I quickly pivoted into a chunky mobster at my right, hooking a left hand to his stomach and laying him out with a follow up right to the chin - a hard and true punch after my first blow doubled him over. That left it four against two, and Steve momentarily reduced those odds by lifting a string-bean hood completely off the floor and hurling him into two others. All three of them went down to the floor in a trampled heap.

Meanwhile, another jackroller had leaped in close to me, and we wrestled our way along the front of the empty hotel desk. (The desk clerk quickly fled to the bathroom as soon as the fracas began.) While we were straining against each other, over his shoulder I saw that the door to the large steel hotel safe stood partially open and I caught a fragmentary glimpse of piles of ledgers and papers inside it.

My attention was painfully diverted at this point as the mobster wrapped me in a bear hug, cutting off my breath with what seemed to be abnormally powerful arms. Lunging forward, I drove his back up against a marble column and, grabbing him by both ears, banged his head lustily against the pillar. Once, twice, then a jujitsu chop to the throat, and he went completely limp and sagged to the floor.

Gasping for breath, I turned and leaped to Steve's assistance. He had one of the hoods in a headlock under one arm and was holding off a second with a fistful of the man's necktie near the throat. He kept twisting it until the gangster's face was turning blue while he desperately tore at Steve's iron grip. The little one Steve flung at them earlier had hurled himself onto Steve's back and wrapped both arms around his neck, trying to throttle him.

Reaching up I grabbed him by the hair, tore him off Steve's back, and swinging him around, put the thug out of action with two quick smacks on the chin. Freed of this encumbrance, Steve pulled down the head of the man he had by the necktie and simply smashed it into the skull of the goon protruding from under his other arm. Both men collapsed in a heap.

Panting, we surveyed the recumbent bodies, and Steve,

rubbing his hands together with wild-eyed enjoyment, looked at me and chuckled gustily.

"Your right eye is red and puffy."

"And you," I told him, "have got a cut lip and a bloody

The body of Jake Lingle

nose. But we'd better get things under control here because the safe over there behind the desk is open, and it's piled high with ledgers and other stuff that should be like money from home to the T-Men."

We started for the desk after a quick look assured us that all our opponents were disabled - *hors de combat* - but then, unfortunately, found we weren't out of the woods yet.

Our ruckus had made quite a bit of commotion, and from upstairs two more hoodlums came trotting down a back stairway into the lobby. Steve spun to face them, and I whirled to go behind the desk. Our new troubles were further complicated by a pair of toughs entering from the front door.

"Whatta you guys think you're doin'?" a thug with spatulate nose and thick lips demanded. He looked like he belonged in a cage at the Lincoln Park Zoo. Then, seeing me heading for the open safe, he and his companion leaped forward and he bulled me away from the door and tried to slam it shut.

By now, however, I had experienced enough of this foolishness.

Drawing my .38, I banged the fisted butt down on the top of his head, and his falling body effectively wedged open the door. I covered the other mobster with my gat.

Steve had pretty much the same idea, for I heard him bark at the two who had come down the stairway.

"We're federal officers. Just stand there nice and quiet and nobody will get hurt. But let me warn you; this .38 makes awfully big holes when it goes off."

I went into the safe and grabbed three ledgers. As I emerged, a new group of pistoleros stepped out of the elevator with weapons already drawn.

Pretty soon we're gonna have the whole Capone mob in

this place, I thought.

"Where do ya think you're goin' with them books?" a swarthy broad shouldered one demanded.

To make matters worse, all of the other bums that we had cold cocked were beginning to regain consciousness and stumble back on their feet.

"We're taking these in as evidence," I boldly asserted.

His mouth drew into a hard line and his eyes fixed on me like twin revolver barrels. "Oh yeah, sez you. You're not going anywhere 'cept maybe to the morgue." He had taken a large caliber gun from his shoulder holster and was lining up the barrel with my forehead.

Out of the corner of my eye I saw a figure rush through the door. I couldn't believe what I was seeing. It was young Arleigh Jones armed with, of all things, a *slingshot*. He let fly with an agate that struck my potential assailant just above the ear. The goon groaned and collapsed in a heap; as he went down his finger squeezed off a shot that smashed into the ceiling. The Kid quickly reloaded and let fly with other missiles that had the others ducking and trying to protect their skulls with their hands and arms.

The next thing I knew Paul DeWitt and a half-dozen Chicago police whirled in through the door with guns drawn. It was like the 7th Cavalry in the movies

Tony Genna shortly before death

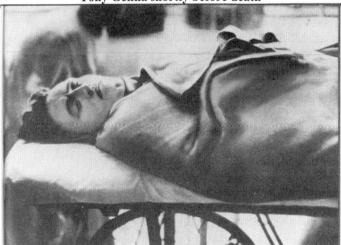

rushing to the rescue at the last second. Paul had seen what was going on from his vantage point and had called them.

"Only two of you feds inside here?" the captain asked incredulously. He was a burly, beefy man literally bursting his uniform.

"That's all we needed," Steve told him. "Just the two of us plus Dead-Eye Dick here with his trusty slingshot."

I reached over and gave Arleigh a congratulatory Dutch-rub on the top of his head. "Nice going young man. How did you just happen to be here?"

Arleigh gave me a sheepish grin. "I've been keeping tabs on the Untouchables. I've followed you guys on several occasions just waiting for the right moment."

Steve turned to the captain. "Are you sure you got

227

enough men to get these bums down to headquarters without losing any? We don't want one or two missing when we come down to file charges."

"Don't worry," the captain assured us while his men herded the prisoners outside and into a paddy wagon. "There are some of us wearing uniforms who don't hold with everything that goes on around these parts. I'm one of them. Your pigeons will be in the coop when you get there."

"Arleigh, can you come to our office tomorrow at 4:00 p.m.?" I asked.

"Sure, what's up?"

"I'll see you then. We need to talk about this situation."

"Sure thing. You're not mad at me are you?"

"No, it's nothing like that. We just need to talk. If you want, you can bring your wife with you."

Arleigh pivoted and went out the door and on his way.

"Darn," DeWitt grunted, "it looks like I missed out on all the fun."

"We'll tell you all about it in the car," I said as we walked across the street. Paul was clapping his hands with glee when Steve gave him all the details about the pin-ball showdown.

Planters Peanuts

"Okay," Steve said to me in high expectation, "how did you pull it off? You're the worst shot among the crew."

"Simple. For one, I've been practicing a lot on the firing range. Second, I paid very close attention to the exact point at which both of us were missing our shots."

Steve shrugged. "I don't understand."

"Like most games of chance, this machine is rigged by the manufacturer. If you hit a score of eighteen or better, you win a free game. The machine had an alternate wiring gimmick in a five shot sequence. After every fourth shot, I figured, you had to aim just a little high to hit the next target."

"I don't get it," Steve said. "Why did it take you until the last round to hit *all* the targets?"

"It took me two rounds to figure out the complete schematic. Shots five and fifteen needed to be just a little high. But shots ten and twenty needed to be slightly low."

"Well, I'll be John Brown," Steve said.

Steve shot me a questioning look. "So how did Joey get to be good, but not as good as you?"

"I'm not sure. But my guess is that he figured out the aim high part of it, but never did catch on to the aim low requirement. We're not up against geniuses, you know."

"Hey, let me get a gander at that gold watch you won," Paul said.

I proudly slipped it off my wrist and handed it to him. He let out a long, loud whistle in admiration. "It says *Swiss movement* on the back," he said admiringly.

"There's just one problem," Steve said.

"What's that?"

"When all the boys back at the office see this, they're all

going to think you're on the take."

We had a good laugh at that one.

After returning to the office in the Transportation Building, we showed the ledgers to Ness and he, in turn, handed them to Tesson, our genius for paperwork detail. He clucked his tongue and shook his head with repeated satisfaction while flipping through them.

"This is one of the best hauls we've ever made," he said approvingly. "The T-boys will bless you for this. Man-oh-man, there are lists of deliveries, speak-easies, breweries, profits and everything else in here. This is really a gold mine of information on the gang's income."

The next day Arleigh was given a surprise party and we gave him a plaque making him an honorary member of the Untouchables. He was so happy he almost broke down and cried. Nanna Peel was there, and you could tell by the look on her face that she was very proud of her husband. Arleigh was right about one thing. Nanna was concave and convex in all the right places!

When it was over Eliot took him aside and explained to him that his association with us had to be ended once and for all, and that under no circumstances was he to keep tabs on us.

Flit kills flies

"I understand, Mr. Ness," he said. "Don't worry. I won't bother you anymore. Just seeing the look on my wife's face when I got this award is something I'll never forget."

He left with a snappy military salute and his face wearing the biggest smile I'd ever seen.

* * * *

It was the end of a long day and I had walked a couple of blocks from my apartment to a nearby

228

confectionery to buy a carton of ice cream for dessert after supper. It was spumoni, Mrs. Griffin's favorite.

As I was paying the clerk the requisite thirty-nine cents for a hand-packed quart, I heard a muffled sound that reminded me of rolling thunder.

"Did you hear that booming sound?" I asked the young soda jerk.

"Yeah, I heard something, but no telling what," he said with a puzzled look.

"Is there any construction nearby?"

He had a blank expression. "None that I know. Thanks for your business," he said as he handed me the package.

"You're welcome," I said as I tipped my hat.

As I exited the store I saw a dark Buick sedan speeding toward me. Paul DeWitt called that particular model a "pregnant guppy" because of its bulging sides. There was a blonde-haired man in the rear with his head stuck out the window, as if to make sure no one was following them. I didn't recognize the driver or the blonde.

I continued walking toward Mrs. Griffin's house, wondering what that was all about. Now, as I drew near to her house, I was jolted to see a crowd gathered in front. As I broke into a run, I was startled to see that all of the windows were broken, the sashes hanging out grotesquely with bits of curtain dangling from their ragged edges.

"Federal man," I identified myself shortly to a policeman herding back the crowd of goggling onlookers. "What happened?"

"Somebody tossed a Dago football in the house," the policeman said.

"Ohmygosh," I groaned. "Anybody hurt?"

"I couldn't say, Mac. Maybe inside . . ."

I didn't hear the rest of it for I was running to the front entrance, the fear beating up in my throat that Mrs. Griffin might be lying there inside. I showed my badge again to a policeman at the door.

"The woman, Mrs. Griffin, is she all right?"

He shook his head sadly. "Sorry, she's dead."

Shock rippled through my body.

Actor John Barrymore

Actor Fatty Arbuckle

"You don't want to see it. She's a bloody mess. The sash weight from the window . . . it nearly took her head off. It's our guess that the bomb landed on the front porch while she was in the front room doing some knitting."

"No, no, it can't be," I moaned," tears welling up in my eyes. "She was a good person . . . wouldn't harm anyone. Why would anyone do this?"

"The bomb was probably meant for you. They had no motive to go after her."

That made it even worse. Poor Mrs. Griffin; killed because of me. I knew that the real person to blame was the one who threw the bomb, but that was small consolation. I looked around the room and saw it was a mess. The furniture, what was left of it, was good now only for kindling. There was dust all over the floor from shrapnel-bitten plaster walls. Broken glass fragments were all over the floor. The only thing that seemed undisturbed was a hand-made sampler on the wall that proclaimed, "God Bless Our Home."

I stood there in silence, thinking about fond memories of Mrs. Griffin. It seemed odd, but for a fleeting moment her death made me think of my Aunt Matilda who died six years previously from galloping consumption. Her husband had died two years earlier, from dyspepsia, the doctor said. But my mother always believed it was from Matilda's nagging tongue.

Thor, Mrs. Griffin's fiercely independent cat, wandered into the room. He looked dazed and scared. Somehow he had miraculously survived. I picked him up and cradled him against my shoulder, rubbing his ears.. "Looks like you'll be living with me now, old fellow."

All of a sudden it hit me. The blonde haired man in the Buick was the bomb thrower. I kicked myself mentally for not getting a gander at the license plate. "They're going to pay for this," I silently vowed.

*   *   *   *

That Friday night I met Ellen for another dinner, this time at the Club Rendezvous. I had suggested the ritzy Chez Paree at Fairbanks Court, but Ellen opted for Club Rendezvous. I ordered a steak but it wasn't the specialty of the restaurant. They were more into pasta and osso buco – veal.

While dining we became better acquainted, and my attachment to her grew stronger. We filled each other in on our childhoods, our tastes in music, favorite entertainers and authors.

One of the highlights of the evening was the music played by a group of jamming jazz musicians with a lot of improvisation – Johnny Dodd on the clarinet, Bix Beiderbecke on the horn, Kid Ory on the trombone, Sidney

Bechet on the saxophone, a large framed Negro with huge hands on the bass, and an energetic drummer named Bones. The music was a combination of African rhythm, Cuban, Creole, and Mardi Gras, with a lot of syncopation - tum, **ta**, ta . . . do **dah** dum - and counter rhythm.

I now knew what Columbus felt like when he discovered a new world. I just had to see her again, this time for another date. I suggested a Lillian Gish flick at the Bijou on Randolph Street and was floored when she insisted on going to a carnival instead.

Riverview Park: a thrill-a-minute carnival with an assortment of rides that promised plenty of "chills and spills" on Chicago's Northside. Located on Belmont Avenue with the Chicago River nudging its west side, it was the largest amusement park in the world. Eliot told me he came here quite often as a youth, riding the streetcar for two cents to get to his destination.

"How about some cotton candy, Ellen?"

"That sounds fine."

Ellen and I watched in fascination as the vendor took a long cone of paper and held it down in the spinning metal bowl. It magically converted sugar and food coloring into spider-like strands that were adeptly wound into a fluffy ball. Pink angel hair.

"Here, try some," I said, after paying the man a nickel.

"I haven't had one of these in a coon's age." She held the cone to her mouth and closed her lips around the sweet fleecy fibers. "Ummm . . . good stuff; it literally melts in your mouth."

"And, unfortunately, on your face. You have some in the left corner of your mouth."

She flicked her tongue sideways then frowned in puzzlement. "Your other left," I corrected. Because I was facing Ellen, I had told her the wrong side. "Here, it works better when you pick it off the cone with your fingers." I snatched a sticky morsel and playfully dangled it close to her mouth. She leaned her face forward and took it with her tongue.

"Over the lips and past the gums, look out stomach, here it comes!" she puckishly rhymed.

I smiled while licking my fingers. "Are you up to riding the Silver Flash?"

"What?"

"The roller coaster?"

"Oh, of course," she said. "I love exciting challenges. Why is it called the Silver Flash?"

Roller coaster at White City in Chicago

"Pure psychology. Silver is perceived as a sleek color and it seems as if you are going a hundred miles an hour."

"Let's do it," she said with an impish smile.

We finished the cotton candy then headed toward the ride, standing in line ten minutes next to the wooden scaffolding.

Every now and then the air would be pierced by the shrill horrified screams of plunging patrons being scared to death.

"I just love the clinking sound of the chain as it tows the string of cars to the top, dragging victims up the steep incline to their doom," I said.

It was our good fortune to get a seat in the lead car. A rush of adrenaline pulsed in our ears in fearful anticipation of plummeting down the back of an ancient writhing sea monster. The cars nearly came to a complete stop as they reached the apex of the wood and steel labyrinth, slowly negotiating the turn at the top.

Aragon Ballroom in **Chicago** at West Lawrence Ave.

"The brink of impending doom," Ellen said, placing her hands over her eyes.

Then we began to fall, like a car going over a cliff—headlong into the abyss with 25,000 pounds of thrust. Faster. Faster. Four white-knuckled hands moved quickly to the steel safety bar and maintained a vise-like grip as we held on for our lives, looking straight ahead, too terrorized to glance at each other. A gale force wind from the breakneck speed pulled Ellen's hair backwards. The harsh sounds of alloyed wheels, groaning on metal rails, and the whoosh of rushing air were nearly drowned out in a rising crescendo of screams and yells from passengers.

We hit bottom, caught our breaths, and zoomed up the next hill. As the train of cars careened around the first turn, passengers mouthed oohs and aahs of excitement. The centrifugal force threw Ellen's body against me; she squealed and clamped her hand on top of mine. The metal monster squirmed and thrashed as if it were trying to dislodge its offending tormentors. We trembled through the harrowing final stretch, our limp bodies slumping forward as the brake mechanism brought the ride to a screeching halt. The terror was over. We had survived.

"We're still alive. Thank God," she said.

Two exhausted bodies were gasping for air after the ninety-second exhilarating adventure. Ellen reached over and grasped my hand. I was surprised that the casual, connection of our bodies caused my nerve endings to jangle. Her touch left me feeling uneasy, as if my heart was wandering into uncharted territory.

"Let's go again," she said, with excitement in her eyes. "I felt like we were riding a blazing comet, zooming through the cosmos in frenzied search of a distant galaxy."

"That's very poetic," I chided. "But this time let's try the other one, the Jack Rabbit." She didn't have to ask me why it was called the Jack Rabbit.

We rode the roller coasters two more times before moving on to other pleasures.

"Have some hot roasted peanuts," I said, offering the newly purchased bag.

She daintily selected a few shell-covered morsels.

Next we rode on the Pair-O-Chutes. This was a tall latticework of steel originally called the Eye-Ful Tower because it had an observation deck on it. Inspectors didn't think that the deck was properly supported so it was shut down. Then someone got the idea of converting it into a parachute drop with the chutes and harnesses held in place by wires for safety's sake.

After that it was the Ferris wheel—a giant Erector set circle with swinging gondolas. It wasn't the one built for Chicago's 1893 Columbian Exposition. This was a scaled down version. The original had been dismantled and taken to the 1904 St. Louis World's Fair. After the fair closed it was dynamited, disassembled and sold for scrap.

Ellen surveyed the picture-perfect view below. "It's absolutely magnificent," she gasped, as the air rushed from her lungs. We could see the tracks of the miniature railroad train that encircled the park.

I loved everything about the amusement park—its carnival atmosphere, the happy sounds, the mixture of smells—Cracker Jack, popcorn, sawdust, crackling electricity—the revelry, the crowds, the energy of it all. We took in as much as we could.

We visited the midway, a three block long paradise of games of skill and chance. A derby-topped barker in a red-checkered vest was persuasive as he described fantastic human anomalies. Side shows—a man completely covered with tattoos, a female contortionist billed as Rubber Woman, a sword swallower, the alligator boy, a bearded lady, the petrified body of a male dredged from the Ohio River. I figured it must have been plaster of paris.

The bearded lady ad reminded me of a set of Burma Shave signs I had seen along Route 66 on a weekend trip to visit my parents in East St. Louis:

THE BEARDED LADY . . . . TRIED A JAR . . . . SHE'S

Chicago Board of Trade in 1925 – Harold Washington Library

NOW A FAMOUS . . . . MOVIE STAR. BURMA SHAVE

My improved marksmanship earned a Kewpie doll at the shooting gallery. Ellen jumped up and down and squealed with excitement whenever my small caliber bullet knocked down one of the moving animal targets. A brass casing plopped down on the counter each time I squeezed off a shot.

"Are those real bullets?" Ellen asked.

"Yes and no."

"Meaning?"

"It's what they call a .22 B-B. Twenty-two caliber bullets are made in regular, long, and short lengths. This shell fires a B-B pellet, similar to an air rifle. The pellets are strong enough to knock over the targets without damaging them. Most .22 rifles throw their shells off to the right, but the ejection port on these is on the bottom so they won't hit anyone standing nearby. The gun is mounted on a swivel for reasons of safety."

"Could I try it? I've never shot a gun before."

Chicago's new Paradise Theater

"Sure—there's practically no kick to these things. You know what Dashielle Hammet says?"

"What?"

"There's nothing more dangerous than a beautiful dame with a gun."

"Yeah, that's probably why they fasten them down."

Ellen gave me a sly smile and then cradled the weapon

231

against her right shoulder.

I leaned over from behind and showed her the proper grip. The intoxicating smell of her hair momentarily caused me to lose concentration.

"Don't squint like you see it done in western movies. When both eyes stay open you have better depth perception. Keep your breathing controlled. Line up the target in your sights and squeeze off a round."

Ellen excitedly began pulling the trigger. She let out little joyous squeals each time her B-B found its mark. She kept pulling until the gun made only a metallic clicking sound.

"You're a natural," I said. "One more bull's-eye and you would have won a prize. A regular Annie Oakley, that's what you are."

The Tilt-A-Whirl spun us dizzy; then we rode side-by-side on spirited merry-go-round horses while the machine's happy calliope cranked out several peppy tunes. Ellen won a teddy bear at a ring toss game. Then we gorged ourselves on plump roasted hot dogs smothered with mustard and pickle relish.

"You have a yellow glob on your chin," she teased.

I playfully thrust an angled feature toward her and she dabbed it with a paper napkin.

"There, that's better. You need someone to take care of you."

"Thank you, Miss," I playfully mocked. "That's exactly what my mother says."

We screamed and hollered on the Whip, an oblong-shaped seated ride that hurled its occupants around the ends with the same cracking motion made by the snap of a bull whip.

We scampered our way through Hades - a fun house featuring a winding maze of slanted floors. Distorting mirrors brought smiles of mirth. Goofy images—thin, fat, spindly legs, squished bodies, misshapen faces. Harmless obstacles mixed with unexpected sounds and noises. We recoiled at a horned devil face when it popped out. Suddenly the floor below began rocking as if the entire building were about to be consumed by a massive earthquake spawned by the New Madrid fault. Ellen grabbed my shoulder in a futile effort to maintain her balance. One final surprise at the exit—a sudden blast of air went up her dress, eliciting a startled, indignant yell.

I mildly protested when Ellen grabbed my arm and dragged me past a tall man wearing a painted sandwich board. The advertising promised bedazzlement from dark-eyed dancing beauties clad in veils and flimsy Turkish pantaloons.

We played Skee-Ball, and later we stood in amazement and listened in fascination as a mustachioed organ grinder, dressed like a gypsy in old-world clothes, turned the crank on his hurdy-gurdy. There was a patch on the sleeve of his shirt. His clothes were worn but clean. We were transfixed by the animated and playful antics of his small monkey, dressed in a red and yellow bellhop uniform, ceaselessly chattering. It darted back and forth on the wooden top of the music machine. A few coins were dropped in his tin cup at the end of the entertaining routine.

"*Hvala lijepo*" (Thank you nicely), the man said in perfect Croatian.

"Hey, there's a gypsy lady. Let's go in and have her read your fortune." I dragged Ellen into the small booth before she could answer.

"Have a seat and show me your hand," the old world woman said to her.

"But, this is silly – I don't believe in palmistry."

"Please, give me your hand—it's a spiritual roadmap."

Reluctantly, Ellen let the gypsy woman take her hand. She studied the lines. "You're a Cancer, aren't you?"

Ellen nodded.

Lucky guess.

"And you're an only child."

A soft *yes* escaped Ellen's lips.

Next she'll be telling her that she's going to inherit a very large sum of money.

"You should treasure that which you have recently found."

Hmm. That's interesting.

There is great danger ahead for you, but if you have the strength and will to survive, a long spell of much happiness will follow."

"I don't suppose you'd care to elaborate?"

The gypsy lady shrugged. "I'm sorry, that is all your hand tells me; I can say no more."

Ellen gave me a skeptical look as we left the fortune teller's booth. I smiled. "I thought the old woman's predictions were very interesting."

Ellen rolled her eyes.

Freddie The Sheik

DO YOU KNOW, FREDDIE, YOU'RE ALMOST A STRANGER, YOU HAVEN'T TAKEN ME OUT IN AN AGE.

SORRY, ANN, BUT I'VE BEEN AWFUL BUSY

Comic strip heroine Dumb Dora in the Windy City

I changed the subject. "Let's go through the Tunnel of Love." We neared the end of a perfect day and I saved the best for last.

We gingerly climbed into a boat in front of a darkened entrance that featured a big flashing red heart at the top. An attendant held the ride steady to keep it from wildly rocking. All of the couples in front were sitting close together. The guy directly ahead of us had a friendly arm around his girl. A hidden mechanism slowly pulled the

Fine suede leather jacket

boat through a meandering stream of shallow water, artificially colored by a blue dye. The murky interior was decorated in the style of a lush tropical paradise with soft Hawaiian music playing in the background. Electronically reproduced sounds of assorted exotic birds occasionally interrupted.

I put my arm around Ellen's waist and drew her to me. "That's a toucan calling to his mate," I whispered, hoping she would at least give me a peck on the cheek.

"Down, boy," she said, as if giving a command to an overly playful Labrador with a drooling tongue.

"Aw c'mon," I whined.

Suddenly, Ellen turned and grabbed me, giving me the most passionate kiss I had ever received, leaving me breathless. It was as if I had been kissed by one of Zeus's daughters – one of the nine muses.

To finish the day, Ellen begged me to take her up to an observation deck that was about 200 feet high.

"I'm not crazy about heights, okay?"

"Tough guy! Come on." She tugged on my arm.

The top of the tower could be accessed by a set of zig-zag metal stairs or by a newfangled car that Otis elevator had leased to the park on a trial basis. It was good publicity for the elevator company. We chose the elevator.

It took about twenty-five seconds to get to the top. The amusement park fairgrounds spread out below us in geometric shapes and color gone mad. The view was breathtaking. It wasn't very crowded on the platform. Some of the other people up there with us were taking snapshots with their box cameras.

Ellen wanted to go over to the railing, but I held back. She hugged one of my arms with both of hers. "Don't be a wet blanket." It's a beautiful day and there'll be a nice breeze."

Up here, on the deck, the wind off the lake was blowing a bit too much. We found a place around one side of the structure where the deck jutted out like a porch so you could get a better look at the park and the Chicago skyline.

We stood by the rail, having a gander, enjoying some privacy.

Seeing the amusement park stretched out before you, not through a window, but right before you, leaning against a rail and looking out at it, well, darned if it didn't take one's breath away.

I turned to Ellen to comment on this, to leave cynicism behind for a moment and be frankly impressed with everything. Ellen's eyes were wide and she was sucking in her breath, and not because of the view.

Somebody was coming up behind me.

Fast.

The outstretched hands hit me just as I was turning, my right hand reaching for my .38 snub nose under my coat, but not quite getting there. It was a guy in a panama hat and a wheat colored suit. Just as I was going over the rail, backward, I saw Ellen slapping at him with both hands and his hat flew off, got caught by the breeze, and went tumbling by me as I fell. I recognized him immediately. It was the man with the blonde hair I had seen in the car fleeing the scene the night Mrs. Griffin's house was bombed.

I hit a steel support beam, hard, on my back and it knocked the wind out of me. Somehow my preservation synapses kicked in and I grabbed at the beam, catching it in the crook of my arm. I clung to it, hugged it, wrapped both arms, both legs, around it. The support connected the platform to the tower structure at an angle and thank God I

Romper outfits for youngsters

hadn't got to my gun because I needed both hands. The support was about as big around as a man's leg, and had rough edges all around, digging into my flesh as I hung there in the breeze, my tie, my suit, flapping.

I was on the underside of the beam, like a sloth clinging to a tree limb. I stupidly glanced down and was hit by a spell of disordered vertigo. I quickly brought my line of sight back to the top rail of the observation deck. Ellen was gone. I assumed she was going for a security guard. At least she wouldn't be in harms way.

The blonde man leaned over the rail and started pounding my hands with his fist in an effort to dislodge me. I let go with one arm, clutching with the other, legs hooked 'round the slanted support, and somehow managed to get my .38 from under my arm. Just as I started to point it in his direction a sharp blow knocked it from my hand.

The man kept pounding at my grip as I rapidly let go with the hand he was aiming for and grabbed hold with the other. I knew it was just a matter of time before he dislodged me and I would fall to my death.

Think, Mike, think.

I braced myself good, and the next time he swung his fist

233

in my direction I grabbed hold of his wrist and with all the strength I could muster yanked him over the rail. I felt his fingers clutching at me in desperation as his body plummeted headlong in a death dive. He screamed a pitiful yowl all the way down until I heard a soft thud. All I could think of was that I was glad it was *he* instead of me and that some measure of justice had prevailed in the wake of Mrs. Griffin's cruel murder.

CHAPTER 16

SEPTEMBER 20, 1930

Drinking in 1760 – George Washington's era

The last half of the 18th century was a most intemperate time. It was common practice to take a break from hard work at 4 p.m. to imbibe and once again late at night, known as the Eleven O'clock Bitters. The bottles of babies were often laced with rum to keep them pacified. Alcohol was seen as a cure for common ailments such as sore throats or minor aches and pains. It was fashionable in the South to have a mint julep (whisky, flavored with mint) about an hour before noon. Rum, seasoned with cherries, was thought to protect from cold weather. It has been estimated that 30 percent of the clergy died drunkards. Liquor was seen as the indispensable lubricant for civilized and pleasurable social intercourse. In Massachusetts, habitual offenders were pilloried and made to wear shirts inscribed with the letters DRUNKARD.

The plan of focusing attention on the Outfit's activity at the Liberty Hotel to get them to relocate worked. They moved their base of operations to a nightclub called the Wellington.

Dan Mizell wore a disguise and went inside the place to help us get the necessary information needed to tap their phones. Fortunately, this place had a terminal box on a pole in a rear alley that would be accessible for phone tap purposes.

Mizell phoned Ness two days later from a public booth with the information,

"Ralph Capone is in the Wellington, and he seems to do most of his phoning from a telephone in an alcove just behind the bar. The joint is run by a guy named Percy Kilbride. Don't let the name fool you. He's a tough customer. The terminal box is on a pole in the alley. Unfortunately, there are always some plug-uglies hanging around it 24 hours a day."

"Anything else?" Ness said.

"No, I guess that's the gist of it."

"Okay. Keep up with the masquerade while I try to figure out a plan."

After Eliot hung up, we discussed our modus operandi for making the wiretap. The weather was stormy and the rain beating against the windows matched the drumming of his fingers on the desk.

"First, we need to get a room in the neighborhood from which to run our listening post," Eliot suggested.

Michigan Avenue in 1920 – Newberry Library

I nodded in agreement. "Then we have to figure out some way to lure the guards out of the alley while I rack the board on the terminal box and bridge the two terminals."

"I've got a friend at the phone company who can get you a pair of lineman's spikes," Eliot said. I'll also ask him to check the records of the area in which the Wellington is located so he can advise me of the boundaries of the master terminal.

Eliot called his friend at the phone office. He told him the tap would be a tough one because of the type of terminal box we were dealing with. We would need someone talking whose voice we'd recognize so we could join the exact two terminals. It would be quite a trick because there were over 75 terminals on that particular box.

"He's right, Eliot," I said after he gave me the details of his conversation. "I'll have to rack the entire board until I

Newly paved road in 1925 – Illinois State Historical Library

catch a familiar voice. Then it'll only take me a minute or two to join them."

The next time Dan Mizell called in with a report on his observations, Eliot instructed him to make regular phone calls from the private phone at the Wellington so that when the time came for the tap, no one would think much about it.

During the next few days we followed another lead which two of our men had uncovered. We raided a brewery that yielded two more five-ton trucks and equipment valued at more than one hundred thousand dollars. We followed our established pattern of trapping the men inside by blocking the exits and then crashing through the doors with our steel-bumpered truck.

The reports of our raid had hardly been filed when Mizell called in and told us that he was now accepted as a regular customer and that nobody said a word when he asked to "call a sheba" from the Capone alcove phone.

"We're going to try and run the tap tomorrow," Ness told him. "Kriegan has to get up that pole behind the Wellington, and when he racks the board he's going to need to hear your voice to know that he has the right plug."

"My part is easy," Mizell replied. "Just let me know what time you want my raspy voice on the air."

Eliot had a plan to lure the guards away from the alley behind the Wellington. He told Mizell to make the call at three o'clock the following afternoon.

"Here's the number of the telephone at the room we have rented," Eliot told Mizell. "Call that number at three o'clock tomorrow and just keep saying sweet nothings to Bischoff so that Kriegan can recognize your voice and pick out the proper terminals."

"I'll be on the line," Mizell promised. "But tell Kriegan not to take me too seriously when I start giving him love talk over the wire. Tell Bischoff he's the ugliest 'honey' I ever talked to on the phone."

The wheels started to grind quickly. Gathering the rest of the Untouchables in his office, Ness went over the plan in detail.

"We have to draw the mob's watchdogs off on a wild goose chase away from the alley where the terminal box is located," he told them.

One of the cars we often used on our raids was a Buick touring car.

"Paul," Eliot said to DeWitt. "I want you to put the top down so that you'll be recognized easily. Then at about two forty-five tomorrow afternoon, you, John and Gary

drive slowly past the Wellington a couple of times and then circle around the Western Hotel. You should pick up quite a convoy in no time at all, and when you do, just keep them busy a couple of blocks away from the Wellington as long as you can."

Sears mail-order home from their 1928 catalog

The Crescent. FIVE ROOMS AND BATH
$2,436 MONTHLY PAYMENTS $40

They nodded as Eliot turned to me. "Mike, you and I will be down that alley a ways at two forty-five. We should be able to watch the guards without being spotted ourselves, and if DeWitt and the others can manage to draw them off, we'll get to the pole and you'll go up and try to join those terminals. I'll stand watch for you at the bottom, because if they come back too soon, you'd be in big trouble."

"That's mighty comforting of you," I said with a sarcastic tone and a wink.

Then Ness turned to Bischoff: "Tom, you've got the toughest job of all – and my sympathies. You'll have to sit there in our new wiretap room and listen to Mizell make a

Copper boiler from 1928 Sears catalog

pitch for your affections as if you were a woman."

Bischoff laughed. "It should be hysterical. I'm anxious to hear what kind of a line Mizell hands out to the women."

Fortunately the next afternoon was crisp and clear. Otherwise, DeWitt and the rest of the gang might have looked a bit foolish riding around in a touring car with the top down.

At two-fifty Eliot and I parked my Terraplane a block from the alley behind the Wellington. We wore gum-soled shoes, and despite the debris cluttering the narrow alleyway, we made our way quietly to the intersection.

My watch read four minutes to three when Eliot peered around the corner and looked toward the rear of the Wellington, just a half a block away.

Eliot said there was only one man there, but he knew by the pearl gray hat that he was one of Ralph Capone's guards. His back was to us, and he stood beside a new Ford coupe facing in our direction.

Even as we watched, the back door of the Wellington flung open, and a second man ran out and spoke with great agitation and much arm-waving to the man who had been standing outside. Quickly they jumped into the car and roared down the alley toward us.

Jerking back, Eliot motioned to me and we ducked into a shallow entryway. Fortunately the alley was dark because of the high buildings on each side, and they didn't even catch a glimpse of us as they sped by.

Apparently the bait was working. DeWitt and the boys were attracting all the attention we hoped they would.

While Eliot scouted the alley, I had strapped on the climbing spikes and belted on the waist strap that would leave my hands free when I was on the pole.

"Let's go," I said, and we sprinted down the alley to the pole behind the Wellington.

The spikes dug into the wood as I climbed up the pole. Eliot stood guard while I opened the door of the square black terminal box and began to rack the board.

I opened the metal box and worked furiously on the board, my fingers literally flying over the terminals. I leaned sideways against the broad leather belt and looked down at Eliot and shook my head negatively.

"Run over it again," he called urgently through cupped hands.

I was beginning to get nervous, for there was no telling how long our luck was going to hold out. I was a sitting duck up there, and at any moment those goons might drive back into the alley or someone might come out the back door of the Wellington. Every passing second seemed like an hour with me outlined against the sky at the top of the pole.

I glanced down and saw Eliot slip his revolver from its shoulder holster and check it, no doubt gaining some comfort from its solid, familiar feel. I was about half way through checking the terminals a second time, searching for Mizell's familiar voice, when I finally found it. I didn't have the luxury of listening to what he was saying because I quickly bridged the two terminals and flashed an "okay" sign to Eliot with a circled thumb and forefinger. The sharp

Rudy Vallee and sports announcer Graham McNamee

Dan Mizell on the phone

click as I closed the door on the terminal box and the rasping sounds of my descending spikes were music to my ears.

"Okay, its all finished," I said as I hit the ground running. I pushed Eliot ahead of me toward the alley from which we had come.

"Let's get out of here," I said. "We've pressed our luck too much already." We paused briefly while I stripped off the spikes. "I had felt like the first prize at a turkey shoot while I was up there."

Driving back to the office, we were elated over our success. When DeWitt and the "bait detail" reported in, we were almost triumphant.

"Eliot, we had such a convoy it looked like a parade," he chuckled. "They couldn't figure out what we were up to and they must have had every hood in town on our tail."

"They certainly put the two most important ones on you, as far as Kriegan and I were concerned," Eliot told them.

"And thanks for keeping them out of our hair. Maybe now we'll be able to give them something else to think about."

With this new wiretap I felt confident that we were in a stronger position than ever. But goose pimples skated up and down my spine when I considered what might have happened if Eliot and I had been trapped in the alley behind the Wellington.

CHAPTER 17

THE FLORIDA LAND BOOM – Speculation in Florida land reflected the dizzying atmosphere of the Prosperity Decade. It happened, in part, because the automobile made it easier and more fun to travel long distances. The frenzy started around 1920 when American motorists became interested in Florida, traveling down the Dixie Highway to the land of sunshine and sandy beaches. Miami especially became a center of frenzied activity. Real estate offices sprang up overnight, and they sent thousands of agents into the streets hawking house lots or acreage. It became necessary to pass a city ordinance forbidding street selling and map showing due to the traffic congestion it caused.

Sinclair Lewis was historically sound when he selected George Babbitt as the real estate promoter of Zenith.

Fortunes were made overnight as the demand spiked prices upward. Henry Flagler made millions after he built a railroad along Florida's east coast. Fraud was rampant since there were no title investigations, no deeds recorded, and a mere ten percent binder or down payment was all that was necessary. Swindlers and unscrupulous salespeople sold lots that were underwater or completely inaccessible. One realtor promoted land in the Key Largo area by faking the discovery of buried pirate treasure there.

Even the Marx brothers got into the act. In *Going Cocoanuts*, Groucho Marx plays an unscrupulous hotel owner trying desperately to unload real estate on unsuspecting buyers.

By 1926 the "get rich quick" scheme began to tarnish as prices leveled off. Then disaster struck in the form of two quick hurricanes that ravaged the land, killing hundreds and injuring even more. Florida lost its sudden attraction and the speculative bubble collapsed. The razzle-dazzle boom had produced some millionaires, but it left thousands of others in debt or facing foreclosure and possible bankruptcy.

One of the people caught up in the Florida boom was Ray Kroc, a former salesman for the Lily-Tulip Cup Company that made paper drinking cups. When the boom collapsed, Kroc was so broke he had to play a piano in a nightclub to earn enough money to send his wife and daughter back to Chicago by train. He didn't have enough money to buy gloves or an overcoat and when he drove through Illinois and the icy streets of Chicago, he was frozen, disillusioned, and broke. He would later become a mixing machine salesman, buy out a couple of brothers in the hamburger business, and become a millionaire by starting the McDonald's hamburger franchise business.

Chicago's Maxwell Street during the Depression – Illinois State Historical Library

May 23, 1930

"There's some good news for us," I enthusiastically told Ellen over the telephone.

"What is it? – tell me," Ellen eagerly responded.

"We have a problem in southern Illinois that Eliot wants me to investigate."

"What kind of a problem?"

"Despite the success of our raids, the Capone organization's source of hooch isn't drying up as fast as it should. One of our informants told us that Big Al still has a good supply coming in from the Metropolis area down near Paducah, Kentucky. The Shelton gang and remnants of the Charlie Birger gang are bringing in supplies from Marion, Harrisburg, Herrin, Benton, and Fairfield, and shipping them up north to Capone where they get top dollar for the stuff," I explained.

"Wouldn't it be risky trying to ship it by truck over the miles and miles of highway necessary to get to Chicago? Illinois is a fairly long state, you know."

"Some of that problem is taken care of with payments under the table to certain members of the Illinois Highway Patrol. But it's harder to bribe state troopers than the city police."

"Why is that?" she asked.

"For some reason, they are not as reliable when it comes to staying bought. Perhaps it's because their pay is better and they have higher morale than most city policemen."

"Maybe it's because they patrol mostly rural areas and aren't as intimidated by the gangs that seem to dominate large cities."

"Yes," I replied. "That probably has something to do with it. Our stoolie tells us that much of the liquor is flown to Chicago from a landing strip northeast of Paducah, at a narrow area between the Tennessee and Cumberland rivers."

"What exactly is it that Eliot wants you to do?"

"He wants me to go down to southern Illinois and gather as much information as I can on the subject without arousing suspicions."

"What's your cover?"

"I'm supposed to be a telephone executive who is down there on a two-week fishing vacation."

"You're going away? I thought you had good news." Ellen sourly responded.

"I do . . . I think."

"What do you mean?"

"I was hoping by some stroke of luck that Murray Humphreys might be going out of town at the same time, and you could come with me."

"Wouldn't that be great? When are you going?"

"Eliot wants me to leave on Monday, May 27th."

Douglas Park in Chicago – Dan Oberle Route 66 collection

"We might have a problem," Ellen said with a note of dejection in her voice.

"Why is that?"

"Murray is going out of town, but he won't be leaving for Detroit until Friday the 2nd of June."

"That should work. Going to southern Illinois less than a week later will probably be okay with Eliot. He didn't have a specific date in mind."

"But where will we stay?"

"In a motel."

"But Mike, you know how I feel. I want a big church

Southern Illinois during the Charlie Birger and Shelton era – courtesy Southern Illinois University Press

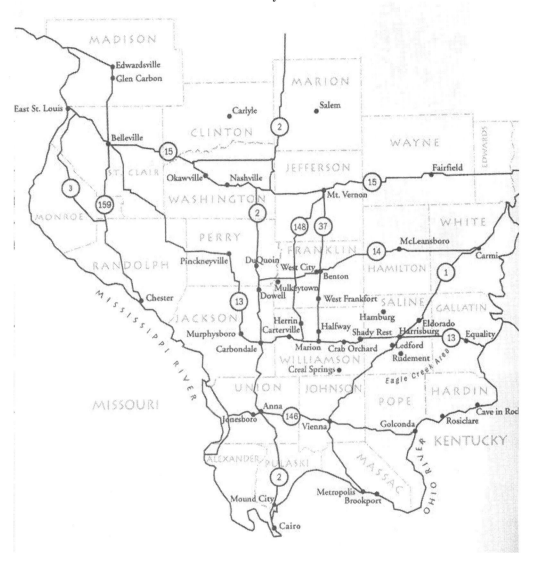

wedding, and I want to wear white. I want our wedding night to be the most romantic, wonderful evening ever. The Catholic Church says that's when you're supposed to claim my maidenhood. Call me old-fashioned–"

"I know, I know." I gave a little hand gesture. "We could register as husband and wife and then ask for twin beds. I'll tell the clerk that I have a snoring problem."

"Wait, I might have an even better solution."

I crooked my head. "Such as . . . "

"One of my best friends from high school - she and her husband have a cabin down at the Round Pond section of Mermet Lake. They go down there for quickie vacations about four times a year."

"Are there two bedrooms?"

"No, but the living room has a Murphy bed."

"What if they plan on going down there themselves that same week?"

"I just talked to her on the phone a few days ago. She said her husband was going to have hernia surgery in a few days. I don't think they are planning on going anywhere for a while. If I offer to rent it out for a week or ten days, I'm sure she'll say yes."

"That sounds just perfect. Do you know how to get there?"

"Yes. I've been there about a dozen times. Her family owned it when we were teenagers, and I was invited to go with her because we were inseparable."

"What about her parents?"

"They were both killed in a car accident two years ago."

"I'm sorry to hear that. You must have been fond of them."

"Yes. They were very good to me and were delighted that their daughter and I were such good friends."

We left Chicago early in the morning on June 3 and headed south on Route 1, which hugged the Indiana border and paralleled the New York Central Railroad tracks. Ellen was the "cat's meow," sporting a spiffy collegiate look with a white cotton shirtwaist accented by a long strand of faux pearls, a straight-cut beige skirt, and silk hose rolled down below a pretty set of rouged knees. Her saucy *avant garde* hat had the unmistakable flair that pertained to the creation of a millinery artist.

We passed through such quaint towns as Momence, Milford, and Rossville, farm country whizzing by us on either side. I was saddened by out-of-business signs in store windows and foreclosure signs posted on the farm property. I felt fortunate just to have a job.

We gassed up and ate lunch at a café in Danville. Then we continued on through Paris and Marshall, and suffered a flat just outside Lawrenceville. I put on the spare and stopped at a garage in town where a small nail was removed and a puncture in the inner tube was fixed with a hot patch.

Ellen pretty much knew the way to Mermet Lake in

238

Massac County, but we took along a map just to be sure. She was glancing through it and marveling at the names of towns she stumbled across at random.

"Do you wan to play town trivia, like when we first met

Flagpole sitting champ, Alvin "Shipwreck" Kelly

when we were running for exercise?"

"Sure."

"Do you know anything about the town of Olney?" she asked.

I gave her a quick glance and a smile. "A little. The place is crawling with white squirrels, brought there decades ago by naturalist Robert Ridgway."

"Ever been there?"

"Yep."

"White squirrels – I bet they're really cute."

"Yes, except squirrels and rats are two of the critters that can carry and spread the plague."

"The plague! You mean like the Black Death that wiped out about half of Europe in the Middle Ages?"

I nodded. "One and the same."

"Whew!"

Ellen continued scanning the map. "What about Herod? It's not far from Mermet Lake."

"I've never been there."

"It's the only town in Illinois sitting on top of an ancient volcano," she said.

"What town, the early financial capital of the state, refused a loan to Chicago developers, telling them that their city was too far north and would never amount to anything?"

She smiled. "That's easy – Shawneetown. What was the first town in Illinois settled by the French?"

"Cahokia."

"How about this one? What town had the first railroad bridge across the Mississippi?"

"Rockford - 1855," I said in an instant.

"Rock Island," she corrected saucily. "You're much too impulsive. But 1855 was right."

I smacked myself in the forehead. "Augghhh! That's the same type of mistake I made with the question you gave me about Davy Crockett's rifle."

"You mean the time you tried to trick me with that **two-headed coin**?"

I threw her an astonished look. "What? You, you . . .

knew?"

She threw her arms around my neck and kissed me on the cheek. "Of course. You're an easy read, my love."

I shook my head in amazement.

Ellen continued poring over the map but didn't ask me about any more towns.

At Patton, we got a glimpse of the beautiful Wabash River. We bought double-dip ice cream cones at a Mt. Carmel drug store soda fountain in tiny Wabash County. While we savored every lick, a newfangled machine called a jukebox was playing "When My Sugar Walks Down the Street."

Directly west of Mt. Carmel was Wayne County, home to the Shelton family that owned acreage on the eastern outskirts of the town of Fairfield. Three of the Shelton brothers, Carl, Earl and Bernie, were a formidable force in the bootlegging operations in southern Illinois. Fairfield was also in the heart of Illinois oil country and Carl was known to have invested in several oil wildcatting schemes trying to turn a dollar.

We picked up a lean and lanky hitchhiker outside Carmi. He looked like a scarecrow.

"Hop in," I cheerfully offered. "Where are you headed?"

The man, probably in his mid-thirties, had a day's growth of beard, was tieless, and wore a clean, but tattered and threadbare gray suit.

"I'm going to Vienna. I was laid off at the factory in Epworth. Been offered a job from my brother-in-law at a

Playwright Eugene O'Neill

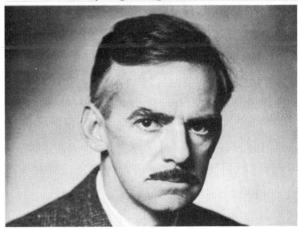

grocery store there."

Ellen turned in her seat. "You're lucky. A lot of people are unemployed right now, and jobs are scarce."

He nodded. "Don't I know it!"

After a few moments of silence, "I really appreciate you giving me a lift."

"Glad to help," I said. "I'm Mike . . . Mike Kriegan. This is Ellen, my fiancée. We're on our way to visit relatives down by Lake Mermet."

"Glad to know both of you. I just hope I'm not putting you out too much."

"Nonsense."

South of Norris City we hooked up with Route 45. Route 1 continued to hug the Illinois-Indiana border, ending at Cave-in-Rock. We crossed the north branch of the Saline

River and kept heading tangentially in a southwesterly course through Eldorado, Carrier Mills and Harrisburg and Ledford.

We dropped our passenger off when we reached Vienna.

"Much obliged," he said as he exited the vehicle and gave a wave with his hand.

"You're very welcome."

Our highway now doglegged southeast toward Massac County and the lake. Ellen looked at a map and noted that just to our west was the sluggish and serpentine Cache River which led to a swamp of cypress trees where outsiders feared to venture and locals did so with trepidation. She informed me that Mermet Lake was cast from a similar mold.

"What is this fiancée business you gave that hitch hiker?" Ellen said with a look of mock indignation.

I looked at her with a grin. "I figured it was the easiest explanation. Besides, it's just a matter of time."

She reached over and kissed me on the cheek.

The orange-wafered sun was getting close to the rim of the horizon. It was nearly dusk when we finally traveled down that bone-jarring side road that led to the cabin. The surrounding trees were thick-trunked and hypertrophied; a profusion of chestnut, hawthorn, swamp hickory, and buttonbush behind them were seemingly impenetrable.

The farther south you go in Illinois, the higher the average annual rainfall and the longer the growing season. Chicago gets about thirty-two inches, but Cairo has close to forty. Willows, sycamores, oak, paw paw, sweet gum and maples arched over a road spread with creek gravel. Splotches of twilight filtered through the dense canopy overhead. I gazed in fascination at a broad-leafed plant that looked like some kind of giant lily.

"Let's get out and stretch our legs," I said as we pulled into the driveway next to the cabin. I hopped out, flexed my shoulders, swatted a fly away, and went to the other side to help Ellen from the car. I couldn't keep from admiring her photogenic face with its perfectly aligned features.

"You're staring again," she said in a slightly embarrassed tone.

"I'm sorry. Sometimes I just can't help it." I drew her close to me and kissed her forehead, taking in the wonderful fragrance of her scented hair. Then I grabbed the suitcases from the trunk and slammed it shut.

Summer arrives early in southern Illinois, like a Latin rumba dancer: frilly ruffles and bright cotton. The countryside was tumescent with heat and humidity. Everything in the landscape around us spoke of the coming summer solstice. A quick look at the placid lake and lush

surroundings caused me to let out a loud whistle of admiration. God's handiwork was spectacular. The dense foliage made it seem like we were in a dark green primeval forest. Straight out of *Last of the Mohicans*. This place had magic.

"The woods were God's first temples," I mumbled reflectively.

Southern Illinois in its colonial years grew to be a bone of contention between the British and the French. It was occupied first by one, then the other, emerging from each occupation with the scar of nations branded on it.

"Southern Illinois is completely different from Chicago, isn't it?"

She nodded in agreement. "Most of the state is pancake flat, leveled by glaciers eons ago, but they didn't reach this far south, leaving beautiful lakes, valleys, and the rugged Illinois Ozark hills."

"My hometown of East St. Louis is flat, like Chicago, because it's situated on the Mississippi floodplain." I spotted an interesting looking plant and pointed. "Do you know what that is?"

"Hmm . . . yes, it's called a bloodroot because of the reddish color. It produces a white bloom in the spring that looks like a poppy."

"And that one?"

State champion bald cypress tree near Cache River -1,000 years old – Illinois Department of Conservation

"A mayapple plant. It only grows to about a foot and a half tall."

"It's beautiful."

I placed the suitcases on the ground and began picking a spray of flowers.

Illinois Route 13 in the early 1920s

"Careful," she warned. "The plant about a foot to your left is poison ivy."

I cringed. "How do you know?"

"Simple – leaves of three, let it be. The green leaves have urushiol in them, and the infected area spreads by contact. I learned the hard way when I was twelve."

Ellen placed both hands on her hips and arched her back to relieve the stiffness from the long ride. Then she reached for the sky, stood on her toes and wiggled her fingers. I followed the upward thrust of her hands with my eyes and noticed that the sky was beginning to cloud over. A portent of an approaching storm.

I handed the flowers to her. "You can place these in a jar or glass when we get inside. It'll spruce the place up a bit."

Masonic Lodge in **Plainsfield**, Illinois – Dan Oberle Route 66 collection

She held the flowers under her nose and inhaled their scented fragrance. "I just knew you were a walnut." She ended her sentence with a laugh and a sigh commingled.

"Walnut?"

"Yes. Tough as a rock on the outside, but soft on the inside."

I shook my head and rolled my eyes. Ellen's slender delicacy made me think of an Iris.

The rustic log cabin, on stilts to protect from flooding, sat about a hundred feet back from the road. The roof was green asphalt shingle. I could faintly hear the high note of a nearby trickling stream. The sound seemed to be coming from behind the cabin. Another hundred feet or so to the left was a small wooden boat dock on the edge of the lake. Several green heron and white egrets were fishing for supper. Some other colorful avian species that I couldn't identify were warbling cheerful songs. A tri-colored woodpecker was battering a dead log in a determined quest for a meal.

I was stunned by the visual beauty of this replica of a Louisiana bayou, right here in southern Illinois. I had once read that some of the bald cypress trees in the lake, reportedly 800 years old, were the oldest living things east of the Mississippi. The ebb and flow of this serene place made me fall in love with it immediately, despite the fact that I wasn't much of an outdoorsy person.

A set of wooden steps led to a front porch that had a mildewed swing on one end. A "bent willow" chair was on the other end. As a squirrel scampered up on the roof via a honeysuckle trellis, I swung open the screen and Ellen unlocked the door with her skeleton key. We trudged inside. The windowsills were gray with dust. The light in the room was sallow, the sun already racing to meet the horizon.

She pointed. "My bedroom is upstairs."

I left my grip next to a tweed couch and carried hers up to the bedroom.

"Okay if I set your grip on the bed?" I yelled.

"That's fine."

I clambered back down the stairs and looked the place

over. Ellen was wiping things off with a damp kitchen cloth.

I checked out back and, much to my surprise, found a wooden shower stall next to the small porch. I stared in wonder at the pioneer marvel. Rainwater coming off the roof was collected in a large metal cistern that sat on top of the stall. A small pipe ran from the tank to the showerhead. A simple pull on a chain opened a valve and cleansing water came cascading down. A pit filled with rocks to soak up the drain water was directly below the slats on the floor of the stall.

I went back inside and plopped into a rocking chair and continued my visual inspection.

Large, rough-hewn ceiling beams supported the roof. "It's roomier inside than what I thought when we first drove up," I commented.

The plank floor was covered with several large and colorful, but worn, hand-braided, oval throw rugs. A small section of the floor in front of the sink was covered with asphalt tile. The cabinets were varnished knotty pine. The side wall had a beautiful

Stoneyford Woods Forest Preserve near **McCook**, Illinois – Dan Oberle Route 66 collection

fieldstone fireplace with a cypress mantle.

I threw some kindling in the kitchen woodstove and made a fire. Our supper consisted of canned Vienna sausage with pork and beans. Desert was a shared apple and a couple of store-bought Moon Pies. I helped clear the dishes from the checkered oilcloth on the table, taking them over to the sink. Several workings of the handle on the pump left me frustrated and without water.

"Do we have to prime this thing?" I asked.

241

"No, the water table is high down here. Just work the handle a little faster to maintain suction," she answered.

"Where does the water go?" I asked as I pulled the drain plug when we had finished.

"To a French well directly underneath."

"You mean a big pit filled with gravel?"

"Uh-huh."

"It's probably the same one used by the shower drain."

Golfing sensation Glenna Collette – Library of Congress

After finishing the dishes, we relaxed on the living room couch.

"What did you do to get a fire going, rub two sticks together like a Boy Scout?"

I grinned and pulled a cigarette lighter out of my pocket. "I borrowed this from Paul DeWitt before we left."

"Too bad it's way too warm for getting the fireplace going," I said. "That would be very romantic."

She leaned over and gave me a kiss. "I don't need a fire to get romantic with you," she said with a flirtatious voice.

We went outside and sat on the porch swing, smooched and cuddled, and listened to crickets and bullfrogs serenading potential mates.

"How far are we from the Ohio River?" I inquired.

She pointed south. "Joppa is just a stone's throw from here, and the river's water laps its shore."

I didn't know it at the time but Joppa was the southern terminus of the Chicago & Eastern Illinois Railroad. It went through such towns as Chicago Heights, Villa Grove, Findlay, Salem, Mount Vernon, Benton, West Frankfort, Marion, Cypress, and ended at Joppa, which was across from Paducah, Kentucky.

When those ubiquitous mosquitoes, thirsting for human blood, began to bother us, we headed back inside and made ready for bed.

"I'll take a shower in the morning," Ellen said as she popped her head out of her bedroom door. "I'm too exhausted from the trip to worry about it tonight." She looked quite fetching in a yellow chenille robe with cold cream slathered all over her face.

"I'll wait until tomorrow too," I chirped.

The morning air the next day was cheerfully filled with the melody of birds. After finishing breakfast we decided to shower. I took mine first, just to make sure everything worked properly. Ellen went next. Looking through an open window, I couldn't resist taking a peek at her beautiful body in the stall, damp with droplets of water. I could only see bits and pieces of glistening silky flesh through the slats, but her lithesome, pleasingly curved form was enough to make my heart start pounding. After my eyes briefly roved her features I gave Ellen a loud wolf whistle and a hubba hubba.

"Sally Rand doesn't have anything on you," I said admiringly.

She shooed me away from the window with a "tsk, tsk" and a wag of her finger, her eyes doing an Eddie Cantor with a mock look of disgust. "Careful, don't forget it was Artemis, in Greek mythology, who turned some Peeping Tom into a stag because he'd seen her naked."

I threw my hand up. "Whoa, I'll try to curb my voyeuristic tendencies."

After she toweled off and finished dressing, I asked Ellen if she knew of any local places where I might go to start poking around about local liquor supplies.

Fan dancer Sally Rand - author's collection

"There's a popular roadhouse several miles down the way on the other side of the lake. You might give it a try."

"I'll make a trip there this evening, but first, you promised to take me fishing."

"I think you're really going to love it," she said, stroking my hair.

"I've never been fishing before. I probably won't be very good at it," I sighed.

"Hah, from what I've seen, you're pretty good at everything you set your mind to."

"Don't you think it will be a little dangerous, what with all those alligators lurking about?"

"I don't think there have ever been alligators in Mermet Lake," she reassured me.

Ellen was right about the alligators but wrong about my ability to succeed at anything I put an effort into. We were out on the lake for four hours. She had a long string of fish – mainly bluegill and large mouth bass – while all I caught was a snapping turtle and two small crappie.

Ellen cleaned the fish and cooked them for our supper. They were delicious.

After the dishes were put away, I made preparations to leave. "You'd better stay here," I said. Ellen was reading the latest issue of *Vanity Fair*. "I'll be on official business and no telling what kind of unsavory characters I might encounter."

She nodded. "I understand. I brought along an F. Scott Fitzgerald novel to read, *Tales of the Jazz Age*."

"I don't care for all that symbolism he throws into his stories," I said. "I thought *The Great Gatsby* was a bit of a bore."

"I'll let you know what I think when you get back." She stretched her fingers up into my hair and laced through it as she gave me a long and romantic kiss. "Please be careful, Mike."

I traced the outline of her chin with my thumb. "Don't worry, I will."

"Promise?"

I crossed my heart, gave her a wink, and went outside to the car.

It was a Friday night and the roadhouse, a big brown rambling structure, had a parking lot full of cars. The razzmataz strains of syncopated music poured from the place. It sounded like *Tiger Rag*. Inside it was noisy and full of smoke. I went over to the bar and ordered a drink. I could tell that the men standing on either side were regarding me with eyes that were either cautious or cold.

The bartender was a stout fellow with a butch haircut and thick forearms. He must have been six-foot-two with shoulders three axe handles across and hands like shovels. The din of conversation was occasionally punctuated by a raucous laugh or an explosive curse.

"Ain't seen you around before," he bellowed.

"I'm from Chicago."

A set of woolly eyebrows that meandered across his face arched in mild surprise.

All of a sudden I felt a little out of place in this inverted triangle of land where some folks referred to the Civil War as the War of Northern Aggression. I was acutely aware of a deep-rooted need to soak up some local color, to rub elbows with the locals, to learn the pattern and texture of their thought, to hear them speak and capture the intonation of their distinct voices.

"Name your poison."

I looked around. "Most of the people here seem to be

Frank Lloyd Wright – originator of "prairie-style" architecture

Technocracy advocate – Howard Scott

drinking something from fruit jars. What is it?"

"We call it Egyptian Mule – it's got a little bit of this, and a little bit of that, and a heckuva kick."

"What's the *this* and what's the *that*?"

He smiled. "It's a secret recipe. Don't worry, it ain't killed nobody . . . yet." His voice was tinged with a slight twang, typical of those who lived on the northern fringe of Dixie.

"Okay, I'll try one."

For some strange reason my thoughts briefly took me back to an English Lit class at the University of Chicago. There was this Shakespeare line uttered by King Henry VI. "I will make it a felony to drink small beer."

He poured some amber colored liquid into a Ball jar and shoved it in front of me. Its malodorous smell nearly made me gag.

I took a sip under his watchful eye and nodded in approval. My eyes started to water. "It's strong . . . but good," I gasped. I wasn't sure what it was, but I knew it wasn't pre-war, one hundred proof, bonded Kentucky bourbon.

The bartender waited on another customer while I sipped away at the concoction that burned like acid as it slid down my throat. When he came back I asked to see the manager.

"He's in back, but he's busy."

I slipped him a sawbuck. "Tell him Murray 'the Camel' Humphreys sent me, and I'll be sure to make it worth his while."

His fingers closed on it, savoring the feel of the paper. "Just go on back and knock on his door." He rapped his knuckles on the bar. Two quick knocks, then pause, followed by three more.

"Thanks."

I left my poison on the bar and wended my way through a thicket of patrons. When I got to the door I knocked in the manner that I had been instructed.

"Yeah, what is it?" came a raspy voice from inside.

"It's Mike, Mike Kriegan. Murray Humphreys from Chicago sent me."

The door pulled open slightly, and a man with a suspicious demeanor eyeballed me. "Who'd you say sent ya?"

"Murray . . . 'the Camel,' with the Capone Syndicate."

He scowled. "Nobody told me nothing about a visit from the Outfit." His hair was dark and long, and he had a beard that made him look like a Bolshevik.

"It's on the QT – didn't want the Shelton brothers to know about it."

"I'm not interested."

Not a Bolshevik, I thought. His intense eyes made him look more like Rasputin, that mad monk who advised the Romanov tsar.

He started to close the door, but I wedged my foot in it. "We're talking big money. Bigger than anything you've got going on here."

He eyed me warily. "Well . . . come on in, but you'd better not be wastin' my time."

He went over and sat behind a small desk and gestured for me to have a seat in the chair next to it.

He separated a cigarette paper with a practiced flip of the thumb and tapped out some Mail Pouch tobacco onto it. "Whad ya say your handle was?"

"Kriegan, Mike Kriegan." I offered my hand, but he ignored it.

"I know lotsa people up north, but I ain't never heard of ya." He slid his tongue along the edge of the paper to seal it.

"You know Frankie Rio?"

"Sure." He found a match and struck it with his thumbnail. The flare of the phosphor-tipped match dit its work.

"We're buddies."

"So?" he said between puffs on his cigarette.
It became clear that I had to gain his confidence before he was going to tell me anything.

"Look, I've even been in Capone's office at the Lexington Hotel. Jake Guzik works at a table over in one corner and Capone keeps his stash in a Saratoga trunk over in the other."

He fanned out the match and dropped it into an ashtray. After thoughtfully looking up toward the ceiling for a moment, he lowered his gaze to me.

"A friend of mine told me Big Al keeps something on his desk – a kind of good luck charm."

I smiled. "You must mean that herd of miniature ivory elephants. But some of them got broken. When I was in there one day he blew his top over a big raid Eliot Ness and his Untouchables made on one of his breweries. He knocked them off on the floor."

A slight smile. "Okay, so you work for Big Al. Where ya'll from?"

"East St. Louis, originally."

"Ya talk like a Chicago Yankee."

"Anything south of the B&O Railroad is southern Illinois – part of Egypt. And those tracks go right through East St. Louis."

He made an unintelligible har-rumphing sound. "Our definition down here is anything south of Mount Vernon."

"Why don't you ask me something about the place if you don't believe I'm from East St. Louis?"

"Where did you live?"

"Washington Park."

"That's *not* East St. Louis." His voice dripped with suspicion.

"It's a suburb on the north side."

"Yeah. What's the name of the Catholic school?"

"Central High."

"What hospital did Glenn Young go to after he was ambushed at the Okaw Bottoms?"

Shooting of Mayor Joe Adams of **West City** – the murder that sent Charlie Birger to the gallows (Harvey Dungey drawing)

"St. Elizabeth's, but that's in nearby Belleville."

He took another puff and blew a smoke ring ceilingward. "What was Charlie Birger's favorite hangout in East St. Louis?"

"The Monkey Cage on South Main."

"What hotel there was run by Art and Bess Neuman?"

"The Deluxe, right across the street from City Hall."

"Okay, that part of your story checks out. But how do I know you're a Capone man and not a local cop?"

I took the driver's license from my wallet. "See, a Chicago address."

"That still doesn't prove anything. Anyone can get a fake license."

I was racking my brain, trying to come up with something to prove I had connections. Then it hit me. I stuck out my left arm. "Take a gander at this."

I showed him my gleaming gold watch that I had won from Joey Malucchi in that amusement game shooting contest back at the hotel.

"That's an expensive watch. Snorky gave it to me as a Christmas present."

"Take it off so I can get a closer look."

Jazz great Miles Davis, born at **Alton** in 1928 and reared in **East St. Louis** (courtesy *Belleville News-Democrat*)

244

He looked at the watch in admiration. "Wow! This thing must be worth at least a thousand bucks. I don't know any copper who can afford one of these on a regular salary. Okay, what's your game?"

"Murray Humphreys sent me down here to see about making a connection with a source of liquor. Ness and his Untouchables are closing down so many breweries that we're beginning to run short."

"Why didn't you go straight to Carl or Bernie Shelton?"

"We've tried dealing with those two before, but they haven't been very cooperative. That Bernie has a temper you wouldn't believe, and he gets very unreasonable at times. I wouldn't be surprised if Capone doesn't put out a contract on those guys one of these days. You can buy heat from St. Louis for five thousand dollars a pop."

"What about Earl Shelton?"

"I hear he's just a big, dumb ox – does whatever his

Dion O'Banion's "handshake murder" drawing

brothers tell him to do. Carl is supposed to be the brains of the outfit and Bernie supplies the muscle."

"Yeah. Earl is dumber than concrete. Let's go out back, and I'll show ya what I've got out in the barn."

I followed as he moved with ursine tread to a big red building. Just inside a large set of double doors was a big flatbed truck. I helped him strip off a tarp.

"There's more than one hundred wooden crates on this rig, each of them large enough to hold 12 quart-bottles."

The words "Old Panther" were stenciled on each box. I picked up a crowbar that he pointed to and we clambered up on the truck. I selected a case at random, pried open a board, and he reached down, removed a bottle and handed it to me. I wrenched out the cork, took a whiff, then poured a little of the amber liquid into my hand and touched my tongue to it.

After stifling an impulse to squinch my face, I nodded. "Good stuff. Let's try one more."

I replaced the cork and handed him the bottle. We shifted several cases to get at one deeper in the load. Nails squeaked as he pried open another board. I reached down and sampled a different bottle.

"Okay, it checks out. You've got a pretty good thing going down here."

He grunted an acknowledgment.

"How much of this could you send to Chicago?"

He shrugged. "Probably about one hundred cases a week."

"At what price?"

"Fifty-six dollars a case."

"Isn't that a little high?"

He slid me a long look. "Just because we talk a little slow down here don't mean we're stupid yokels. My operating costs keep going up. It takes a lot of money to pay off the right people. I hear it's the same in Chicago."

I nodded. "Pretty much. Cash on the barrelhead?"

He threw down the stub of his cigarette and mashed it into the ground. "C.O.D. – that's the only way I do business."

"Where do you get this stuff?"

"Most of it comes from Kentucky, just across the border near the Mayfield area."

"I'll have to check everything out when I get back to Chicago, but I think we can do business. I'll give you a call when I know for sure."

"Fine."

I handed him a pen and a slip of paper. Write your name and phone number on this."

He jotted it down, we shook hands, and I headed back to the cabin to be with Ellen.

CHAPTER 18

JUNE 11, 1931

1920s poem about the Stock Market

Oh hush thee, my babe, granny's bought some more shares;
Daddy's gone out to play with the bulls and the bears,
Mother's buying on tips and she simply can't lose,
And baby shall have some expensive new shoes.

Ellen and I had been at Mermet Lake for six days.

Walking billboards - Depression want ads

During the sunlight hours we fished and relaxed. One day we went barefoot in the grass and deep-kissed under the lilacs. Another day we drove over to see the Creator's handiwork at a place near Herod called Garden of the Gods in the Shawnee National Forrest. It was fun identifying the unusual sandstone rock formations in the area. There was Anvil Rock, Camel Rock, the Devil's Smokestack, and the Great Stone Face whose lumpy profile reminded us of actor Wallace Beery.

In the evenings, I poked around local establishments at Herrin, Harrisburg, Benton, Marion, Carbondale, Cairo, and Metropolis.

It was a beautiful Saturday morning in southern Illinois, and Ellen and I were going on a picnic. Actually, it was a bit more than a picnic. I had heard that some barnstorming pilots were going to be in West Frankfort, so I decided that a picnic, combined with a ride in a vintage aircraft from the Great War, might be exhilarating.

Barnstorming – Library of Congress

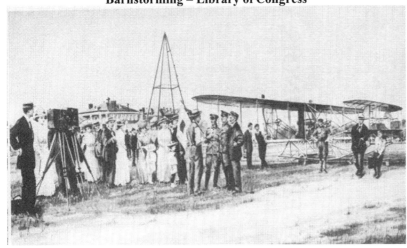

I was up early that morning, shaved, and put on a sporty outfit with two-tone wingtips, knee-length argyle socks, and spiffy plus-fours, better known as knickerbockers.

Ellen washed some clothes on a washboard with a dash of Oxydol while I fixed breakfast. We had coffee, toast, and jelly, and selections from a bowl of fruit. I made the toast by holding the bread with a pair of tongs over an open fire in the woodstove.

On our way there I couldn't resist telling Ellen a joke I had heard the night before in a roadhouse. "There was this man who had just moved into the area, and one day he decided that he wanted to go fishing at Horseshoe Lake," I explained. "He asked some of the locals what he should use for bait if he wanted to catch catfish. They told him that frogs had proven to be the best bait.

"The man decided that he could obtain his bait after he arrived. He selected a spot and waded out into the lake with his hip-boots and was stunned when he couldn't find any frogs. Why this is crazy, he thought. There must be plenty of frogs in a place like this.

Finally, he spied a cottonmouth moccasin with a frog in its mouth. He waded over and grabbed the snake by the throat in a determined effort to pull the frog from its grasp. An intense tug of war ensued. Desperate, the man reached down in one of his boots and pulled out a flask of whiskey and poured some of it down the snake's throat. The snake released its prey and swam away.

With proper bait the man soon was landing one fish after another. About ten minutes went by, and then he felt something bump against his leg. He looked down and couldn't believe his eyes. There was that same snake with another frog in his mouth!"

Ellen laughed so hard I thought she was going to fall out of her seat.

It was a perfect day for barnstormers and there was a crowd of about a thousand people who gathered under a cobalt sky, free of clouds, at a large open field that had a small runway. A slight breeze from the west subdued the warm summer temperatures.

The property belonged to Alex Felts, a flying enthusiast with a plane of his own. He had invited a friend who owned a vintage aircraft to participate in the festivities. Alex was a member of the local Jaycees, and money raised by the event was going to be used to help a local orphanage. That explained a twenty-five cent admission charge.

For fifty cents, one was allowed to sit in the cockpits while the pilots explained the history behind the airplanes. For five dollars they would take you up and give you a thrilling ten-minute ride.

Alex's plane was a British deHaviland DH-4, but the tail section was emblazoned with the emblem of Eddie Rickenbacker's old "Hat-in-the-Ring" squadron. Rickenbacker actually flew a French Spad, but nobody seemed to care. I smiled, thinking of the time my father had taken me to the

German Fokker D VII with Mercedes engine – Walter Boyne collection

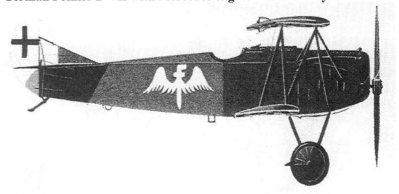

"Brickyard" at Indianapolis to watch Rickenbacker race sleek speedsters.

A small aircraft hangar with large doors and rounded roof was over to one side. The corrugated metal walls and roof were brightly painted. The roof was sun-reflective silver while the building was trimmed in a festive red, white, and blue. My eyes were drawn to a windsock at one front corner of the roof that was drooping languidly in a slight breeze.

Ellen was stylishly groomed and fashionably dressed in a cotton tweed outfit. Her autumn-leafed blond hair was mostly tucked under a sage green cloche hat, inspired by novelist Michael Arlen and a Rodgers and Hart song, worn

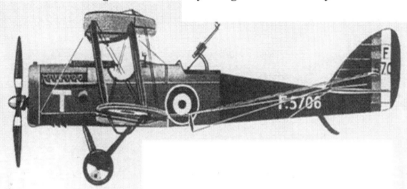

DeHaviland 4 Eagle with Rolls Royce engine – Walter Boyne collection

pour le sport. As usual, her *maquillage* (makeup) was understated. Pale green eyes looked at the world with a self-assurance that accented her high cheekbones and perfectly tapered chin. Her alluring scent and shapely body plagued me with an array of bewitching sensations. She was about to say something when suddenly she shaded her eyes with one hand and pointed to the sky.

"What's that flying in from the south?"

I followed her gaze. "It looks like an old German war plane, maybe an Albatros or a Pfalz D-3," I said.

Murmurs rippled through the crowd as the unusual old aircraft lumbered across the sky, only a few hundred feet above the trees surrounding the field. It came down slowly at no more than about eighty miles an hour. There was an awkward sort of grace in her flight across the sky. Everyone continued looking upward as the plane banked and lined up the runway. Its wooden propeller whipped the air with a distinctive buzzing sound. The ageless machine seemed to hover motionless for a moment, then very slowly she settled to the ground and bounced to a stop on her solid rubber wheels at the far end of the field.

The dashing pilot turned the plane around, taxied toward the crowd and raised his goggles before shutting down the engine. The twin-bladed propeller ended up in the horizontal position.

"I was wrong. It's a Fokker," I said.

The Fokker D VII had been freshly painted a bright red with black Maltese cross markings on the wings, rear fuselage, and tail.

I turned to Ellen. "That's the newer version of the type of plane flown by Baron Von Richthofen for the Germans."

"What is the difference?"

"The Baron's was a Fokker tri-plane – three wings."

"Was he their top war ace?"

"I think so. I believe he shot down about eighty allied planes before he was downed by a Canadian pilot."

Wooden chocks were placed under the wheels. Two lines were formed – one for the deHaviland and the other for the Fokker. Children and adults alike took turns sitting in the cockpits. Ellen went for the two-seat deHaviland, while I sought out the German plane.

My fingers played over the instrument console. I was amazed at the simplicity of the panel. Shaped like a horizontal half-moon, it featured a gas gauge, oil pressure gauge, oil temperature gauge and a tachometer. To the right of the no-nonsense panel were several obligatory on-off toggle switches for fuel supply and engine start, along with a choke and throttle.

"What do the pedals on the floor do?"

"They work the rudder," he answered.

"What kind of engine?"

"A Mercedes – top speed 190 kilo-

Swashbuckling Douglas Fairbanks in the *Thief of Baghdad*

meters per hour."

"That looks like a car radiator in front of the engine."

"It is. This bird was the scourge of the Allied Air Services," the owner, dressed in dusty flying togs, explained.

"Didn't Herman Göring take over the Flying Circus after the Red Baron was killed?"

"Yes," he replied. "The great ace Werner Voss was also killed before the D-VII came out."

The gun mounted on the cowling fascinated me. I gave a whistle of admiration. "That baby looks real."

"It is. Original Spandau 7.92 millimeter. The ammunition belts are loaded with blanks. After we give people rides, we plan to stage a mock aerial dogfight, and we like for it to look as realistic as possible."

"That should be exciting."

For the next hour the British-made deHaviland, with its Rolls Royce engine, circled the field, giving people brief rides. Ellen was one of the early passengers.

Later, I spread a blanket on the grass under the shade of a white oak tree as Ellen and I prepared to watch the aerial acrobatics. We were on the other side of the field, away from the rest of the crowd.

I looked at her and took in her natural beauty. "Are you having fun?"

She squeezed my hand and gave me a school-girl smile. "This is much more interesting than what I thought it was going to be. And the ride was simply fantastic."

The two planes took off and flew in opposite directions and then banked in wide circles that would bring them face-to-face in mock aerial combat.

"This should be interesting. The deHaviland has twin Lewis machine guns but is slower and less maneuverable than the Fokker," I said to Ellen.

"I know this is just an exhibition, but isn't it dangerous for the pilots?" Ellen queried. "Those planes are just sticks of wood and painted fabric."

"Some, I shrugged, "but they do this all the time, and everything is well rehearsed."

She shook her head. "If you say so."

"Flying machines were originally unarmed and were merely used to observe troop movements."

Tennis on the wing of a Curtiss "Jenny"

"Really? When did they start arming them?" she asked.

"Pilots thought of themselves as knights of the sky until one pilot's best friend was killed in ground fighting. He was so angry that he took a pistol with him on the next reconnaissance flight and took some pot shots at enemy pilots he encountered.

"How did that lead to the planes themselves being armed?" she inquired.

"It was a perplexing problem at first. A gun mounted on the cowling had to shoot through a whirling propeller. That was disastrous until Tony Fokker, a Dutchman working for the Germans, came up with an ingenious idea."

Ellen leaned back on her elbows. "Namely?"

"He synchronized the firing mechanism of the gun with the propeller by placing a cam on the propeller shaft."

"How on earth did he think of that?"

"According to the story, the idea

War ace Eddie Rickenbacker in his Spad

came to him when he remembered that as a youth he used to throw rocks through the blades of turning windmills in Holland."

Her face grew a frown. "You're just making this up to impress me."

I held up a hand with open palm. "It's the truth, so help me."

"I'll bet the Wright brothers didn't like the idea of their invention being turned into a killing machine."

"They were devastated."

"I hear talk that several companies are being formed to fly passengers commercially from place to place."

"Yes. Douglas Aircraft is planning the DC-3, and Ford has a tri-motor with corrugated aluminum wings and body. It's been dubbed the 'Tin Goose.'"

She knitted her brows. "Ford, Henry Ford, the same skinflint who produces automobiles and hates Jews?"

"Yes. Tom Bischoff told me the old tightwad is using mass-produced flivver steering wheels in the planes to save money."

"Look," Ellen pointed. "The dogfight is beginning."

The two planes, flying lower than normal for the benefit of the crowd, came at each other like caricatures of jousting knights, guns blazing.

They peeled off at the last minute to avoid a collision. The deHaviland performed a loop and circled around for another pass, while the Fokker did an impressive Immelmann roll and climbed to a higher altitude.

"How close do they have to be before they can fire their guns?" Ellen asked.

"I think it's something like a hundred yards. Anything farther and they'd just be wasting ammunition."

The Fokker pilot pulled his nose up in a steep climb, nearly hanging on its propeller before dipping downward on a shallow dive out of the sun. At about 80 yards he opened up on his opponent and the crowd gasped as smoke began to pour out of the exhaust stacks of the deHaviland.

"They must be using real bullets!" someone yelled from the crowd.

"Are they crazy?" Ellen said with a

look of bewilderment. Her face was flushed with confusion.

"Relax, dear," I reassured her. "That's just a device they've rigged to make it more realistic – like skywriting."

Suddenly it dawned on me that the smoke was black and not white.

The deHaviland made a sharp bank in a seemingly desperate attempt to elude its attacker, but the Fokker doggedly pursued with occasional orange bursts from the muzzle of its gun.

The deHaviland was low enough for the crowd to see the pilot angrily shake his fist at the Fokker.

"I think he just said something like 'Curse you, Red Baron.' "

Ellen rolled her eyes.

Suddenly, the deHaviland catapulted crazily in an out-of-control spin and crashed near us in a grove of trees at the end of the runway. The triumphant Fokker fluttered to earth and made a perfect three point landing.

Ellen and I ran to the scene of the crash, expecting the worse. The wooden propeller had splintered into a dozen pieces as it struck the base of a large sycamore. The cloth-

1920s cartoon cover - author's collection

Ziegfield Follies – Library of Congress

covered fuselage and wings were crumpled like a boy's model airplane made from balsa wood, tissue paper, and glue.

We held our breaths and crossed our fingers, dreading what our eyes were about to see.

I stood on my toes and craned my neck to gaze up at the crash scene. The deHaviland looked like a battered kite as it lay nestled ten feet off the ground in the branches of the huge tree. I momentarily glanced down at the engine that had been torn from its mountings and was lying partially embedded in the earth, emitting dying wisps of smoke.

I climbed the branches and miraculously found the pilot to be dazed, but alive and breathing. It seemed impossible that the pilot could have escaped without serious harm.

"You okay? Any broken bones?"

His face was cut, and there was blood on his goggles. He seemed groggy as he moved his fingers and arms and checked to see if everything worked. "I think my ankle is broken."

I called down to Ellen. "See if you can get an ambulance. He might have some broken bones."

The pilot yelled down to her. "There's a phone in the hangar."

"Why was that other pilot trying to kill you?"

He shook his head. "You don't understand. He wasn't *trying* to kill me."

I looked at him in abject disbelief. "He sure fooled me."

"We've done this so often. Each time, when it's over, we argue over who is the best pilot and who won the dogfight."

"That's crazy."

"So this time we decided to do it for real."

"You almost got yourself killed."

"Yeah, but it was a great feeling experiencing real combat. Neither of us was old enough to serve in the war."

"But you didn't have parachutes."

He shook his head. "Most pilots back then didn't use them. They were afraid the extra 20 pounds of weight would cost them speed, fuel, and maneuverability."

I shook my head. "Of all the nutty–"

The other pilot came running up. "Alex, Alex. Are you all right?"

He gave a weak smile. "I almost got you Brad Klaus, you Teutonic devil. When I saw my bullets rip through your plane, I was hoping they would damage your rudder or strike a control wire pulley so you couldn't climb."

Brad gave a whistle. "Boy, am I glad you're okay. What we did was really stupid."

"Yeah, but we put on a great show, didn't we?"

"Brad momentarily closed his eyes and then nodded with a broad smile. "Yeah . . . yeah, we gave 'em a show!"

CHAPTER 19

JUNE 13, 1931

Edna St. Vincent Millay's poem: "The Fig" 1922 (describing the self-destructiveness of the Jazz Age generation)

My candle burns at both ends;
It will not last the night;
But ah, my foes, and oh, my friends –
It gives a lovely light.

The deep resonant boom of thunder awakened me as it rattled the cabin with reverberations. It sounded as though a cannon had gone off outside. The Murphy bed I was sleeping on actually shook. I smiled, remembering those halcyon days as a youth when I thought that thunder was caused by God bowling up in heaven.

I rose up and turned my head to the window. It was dark as India ink outside. Thunder rumbled and thunderbolt flashes forked across the stygian blackness. My cousin, Marilyn Kinsella, taught me how to figure out how close a storm was. You just counted how many times you could say "Mississippi" between the flash of light and the clap of thunder. So, if I saw a flash of blue-white light, I started counting. "One Mississippi, two Mississippi, three Mississippi." Boom! The storm was about a half mile away because sound travels a mile in about five seconds. I restarted counting again and again until "One" and boom! The storm was now overhead. A summer storm was about to rage. I smiled again when I remembered what my grandfather had once told me: "In the Midwest, the weather does the one hundred and thirty-six things Mark Twain had given it credit for."

I tried to go back to sleep, but it was too hot and muggy. I looked over at the luminous green numbers on the ticking alarm clock. The glowing radium on the hands said it was three in the morning. I wondered whether the crashing sounds had disturbed Ellen's sleep, so I slipped into my clothes and tiptoed up the stairs to her bedroom to check on her. She stirred, and then sat up in bed, sleepily rubbing her eyes.

"Wow, that's some storm out there," Ellen said as she reached over and slipped a fashionable Oriental robe over her nightgown.

"Yeah, some of those dueling Greek titans must be running all over the heavens hurling lightning bolts at one another." I went over and sat on the edge of the bed and gave her a hug.

"I feel safe and secure when I'm in your arms," she cooed.

I nodded. "Don't worry, I'll never let anything happen to you."

She nuzzled my cheek. "I know."

"You'd better shut the window or else the coming rain will soak everything on the floor," she warned.

I looked over at the window. It was wide open, and the stiff breezes of the approaching storm front were whipping at the curtains. "I'll take care of it."

The Fates and Furies are loose tonight, I thought, borne on the winds of the gathering storm.

While ambling toward the window I cracked my knee into a maple nightstand, the corner striking that oh-so-tender spot just below the kneecap where I was sure every nerve in my body converged. It burned like crazy. "Ooh, ow, ow, ow, ouch," I muttered as I hobbled back and sat on the edge of the bed.

"Did you hurt yourself?" Ellen tenderly inquired.

I let loose with a soft moan. "Not really, but it stings like the dickens . . . something like when you crack your crazy

Edna St. Vincent Millet – Library of Congress

bone on the tip of your elbow."

"I'm so sorry," she sympathized.

"I'll be okay," I said as I rubbed the sting out of my knee, then got back up and limped over to the window. Ellen sighed as she sank back into the comfort of the bed. The rain was coming down in buckets now. I was shoving the window all the way closed when another streak of lightning lit up the sky. I was stunned to see the ethereal figure of a man darting from a copse of trees, across the road into the front yard.

What the heck? Had I seen what I thought I'd seen, or was it the wind and the shadows playing tricks on my eyes?

Thunder grumbled, and another flash of lightning lit up the yard, and through the storm-swept darkness I saw the man again, crouching by a cypress tree.

There was a gun in his hand. I was already drawing back when a shot rang out. The bullet shattered the glass as I turned and dove for cover. Pain cut through my upper arm, and I thought I might have been shot. I landed on the bed, grabbed Ellen as she bolted upright, and rolled with her in my arms to the floor, protecting her head from striking the wood. Pain zipped through my arm again as I rolled off her and sprang to my feet, sending the bedside lamp crashing to the floor in my haste.

"Mike, what–"

"Stay down," I ordered. "And

Cover of Judge Magazine – author's collection

250

don't light the kerosene lamp."

"Did lightning strike the house?" She apparently was

Route 66 at **Edwardsville, Granite City, Mitchell, Madison and Venice** - circa 1929

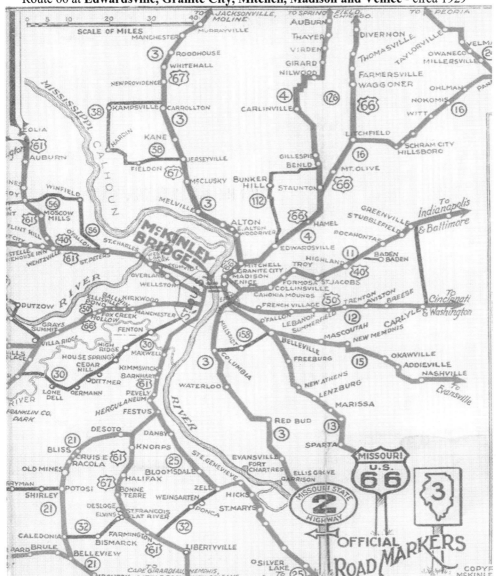

trying to comprehend what was happening.

"That was a gunshot. Someone just took a shot at me through the window." A macabre thought flashed through my mind. Eliot once told me that since the speed of a bullet is faster than the speed of sound, you never hear the bullet that kills you. My blood pressure ratcheted up.

It occurred to me that if Ellen had gone to the window, she might have been killed. And it was just a bit of luck that I happened to be looking down when the lightning struck.

Sprinting toward the hall, I shouted, "Get dressed! We've got to get out of here."

Ellen quickly grabbed her dress and shoes and ran into the hall.

"Mike, what's happening?"

"Get dressed," I repeated. "Hurry!"

I ran down the stairs, grabbed my gun, raced back up and went inside the bedroom. Pressed against the wall, I inched toward the window. I sure as heck wasn't going to give the

guy an easy target. Edging the drapes back with the nose of the gun, I squinted into the murky darkness. Another shot rang out just as the sky opened and it began to rain. There was a burst of flame as the bullet left the muzzle. It struck the window casing with a dull thud. I pulled back and stood there, straining to hear every little sound, praying that the lightning would flash again so I could see if there were any others lurking outside.

Was there just one man? Gosh, I hoped so. If I could get one clear shot, maybe I could nail the bum.

I edged to the corner of the window and took measure. Ten seconds passed, then about five more. Breath suspended, I listened to the shadows outside the house. Lightning split the sky open, and for a heartbeat everything was flooded with light. The flash cut through the room's darkness like the searching strokes of a knife.

"Man-oh-man," I mumbled as I saw another figure dart across the road.

I heard Ellen in the bathroom, fumbling around in the dark trying to get dressed. I went to her: "Are you decent?"

"Yes." She opened the door to a linen closet and reached up to the top shelf.

"What are you looking for?"

"A flashlight I saw when I changed the sheets on the bed." She knocked over a bottle and it landed hard on her instep. Ellen groaned and then nudged it into the closet with her foot to get it out of the way. I could hear her fumbling around with her hand searching for the flashlight.

"I found it!" She announced. "Mike, what's going on?"

I drew a deep, steadying breath. "There are two men out in front. One's crouched down by the cypress tree. We've got to skedaddle before we're trapped."

I told her not to turn the flashlight on because the drapes were open, and whoever was outside might see the light. She felt around on the dresser. "Where are my earrings?"

We heard the sound of a motor humming in the distance. She moved over to the side window facing the lake as the sound of the motor came closer and closer to the boat dock.

"Can you see how many men are in the boat?"

"I can't tell," she said.

I again noticed a stinging pain in my arm, and that my

skin was wet and sticky with blood. I touched the injury and felt a jagged shard of glass. I was relieved it wasn't a bullet hole. I plucked the piece of glass out. It burned as if a hot iron were stuck to my skin.

Ellen sneaked another look outside. "Those men in the boat," she said. "They're with the two out front, aren't they?"

"Yes."

"Do you think it's Humphreys or some of his men?"

"I wouldn't be surprised," I said. I fastened my shoulder holster and shoved the gun into its leather pouch. I had already thought of an escape plan. We'd have to go out the side window, drop down onto the small porch roof on a side en-trance, and hit the ground running. With any luck, we could get to the car.

I slammed the bedroom door shut and made a makeshift barricade by shoving the dresser in front of it in hopes of slowing the intruders down.

Ellen was pressed against the wall by the side window. "One man just got out of the boat, and he's using a flashlight. He's headed for the backyard . . . no, he's going around to the front. I can't tell if there's another one."

"Open the side window," I said. "We're going out that way. Let me go first so I can catch you."

I carefully climbed out the window, swung down, and tried to be as quiet as possible as I dropped to the porch roof. The asphalt shingles were slick from the rain, and I almost lost my footing on the sharp pitch as I landed. Widening my stance and bracing my legs, I prepared for Ellen to jump, all the while praying that lightning wouldn't strike and give us away. If there were others in the yard or boat, they might see us and sound an alarm.

I reached for Ellen just as I heard glass breaking downstairs. The noise was immediately followed by an earsplitting sound of gunfire coming from the front and rear of the house. They were simultaneously rushing both entrances, hoping to trap us inside.

There were ponderous noises as they knocked things over downstairs. How many were there?

Ellen tossed the flashlight to me, and I tucked it in the waistband of my trousers as she climbed out on the ledge.

"Let's go." My voice was a low, urgent whisper.

Ellen hesitated for a second or two, trying to focus, but when we heard the heavy pounding of footsteps on the stairs, she let go.

I caught Ellen around the waist. She slipped, but I held fast until she recovered her balance. Staying close to me, she scrambled on all fours across the roof. The rain was really coming down hard now. She reached the edge, tested the drainpipe, hoping she could hang on as she swung her legs over, but the drainpipe was loose.

"It'll make a racket if it falls," I warned. There were overgrown lilac bushes all along the side of the house. "This way."

She put her hand over her eyes as she jumped into the center of the thicket. Ellen scurried to get out of my way as I followed her.

"I'll check out front and see if we can make it to the car."

"Okay, just be careful," she said.

I handed her the flashlight. "Wait here."

"They must be outside!" a booming voice rang out from the house.

I swallowed hard, pulled my gun out and edged my way

U.S. Route 40 in Illinois, circa 1929

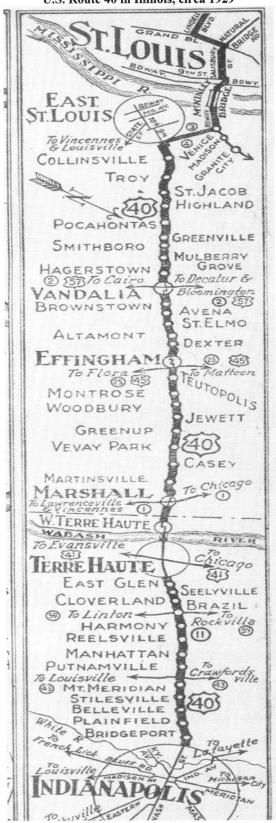

to the corner of the house, then ducked down and leaned out. I gave a disheartened sigh. The hood of the car was up, which meant they had put it out of commission. I looked to my right across the road, judging the distance to the lake. I didn't relish getting trapped and hunted in the dense maze of swamp and vegetation, but if we could run across without being seen, then we could eventually make our way to the crossroads.

I went back to Ellen. "We have to try to get to your boat. It's the only way to get out of here."

"Let's go!"

Our shoes made splashing and squishy sounds as we slogged toward the lake with haste. Things slithered and scampered to get out of our way. We made it to the edge of the dock before being spotted. Caught in the glare of a light shining down from the bedroom window, I pushed Ellen down as I turned and fired. I didn't know if I hit anything or not, but I wanted to give them something to think about while we made a dash to the boat.

"Give me your flashlight," I panted.

Pushing her down again for safety's sake, I turned again and flipped the light on. The beam caught one of the men running towards us from the house. I saw him clearly and gasped in surprise. I fired once and the bullet hit the man in the shoulder, knocking him to the ground.

One of the attackers let loose with a string of blasphemous curse words. I was forced to turn the light off as bullets whizzed past us.

I wheeled and turned the flashlight on again, letting it play on the boat that had just arrived. I saw another man waiting for us. The gunman was crouched down low, raising the barrel of a mean-looking rifle in our direction. I fired twice.

Ping. Zing. The first bullet hit the motor and ricocheted off into the darkness. The second found its mark, and the man let out a moan as he lunged over the side of the boat into the black water.

Flipping the light off again, I pulled Ellen to her feet and shouted, "Go," as a volley of gunshots sizzled and cracked in the air around us, splattering into the tree and the dock. Ellen slid across the dock, grabbed hold of the post to keep from falling into the water, and then frantically worked to untie our assailant's boat. I had already untied ours, jumped in, and was pulling on the starter cord. The engine coughed. I tried it again.

Nothing but sputter.

"See if something is hanging up the propeller," she shouted.

I frantically reached down and pulled off weeds that were tangled in the propeller and then yanked on the cord again. This time the motor responded.

Ellen finally got the rope undone, and she pushed the boat as far away from the dock as possible. I shouted for her to hurry. She jumped into the boat and fell back against me as I gunned the engine. Another hail of bullets splashed the water around us.

I hunched over Ellen, trying to

Sears khaki jeans with crepe blouse

3IL2835 Hills Khaki Jean with Crepe Blouse 3 Piece Outfit $2.79

protect her and keep my head down at the same time. Turning the boat north, I shoved the lever down. The front end of the boat came out of the water, bounced back, and then lurched forward. One bullet sizzled so close to my ear, I thought I felt the heat.

Looking back, I saw two men with flashlights running along the yard. Then one dove into the water. I figured we had maybe a thirty-second lead to get away. I sat back on the bench seat and let Ellen up.

As soon as she lifted her head, she realized we were headed away from civilization. "You have to turn around," she told me.

"Ixnay," I answered. "It's too late to turn back. They're going to come after us. Shine the light ahead."

Ellen sat between my knees and directed the Ray-O-Vac beam straight ahead. The light saved us from disaster. Another five seconds and we would have

Sears all wool tweed suit

ALL WOOL TWEED

crashed into a dead tree stump sticking out of the water. I veered sharply to the left, and then straightened the boat into a true course, zigzagging among the numerous tupelo trees and bald cypress with their distinctive bulging lower trunks.

"Thank God you grabbed the flashlight," I whispered.

"There's a sharp bend straight ahead," she instructed. "Slow down and turn right. Left is another dead end."

Clasping my knee for balance, she turned and lifted up to look behind us. "I don't see any lights yet," she said. "Maybe they won't follow us. Maybe they'll leave us alone now that we've gotten away."

When she turned around, I pulled her back against me. "My intuition tells me they're not going to give up."

"Freud says men don't have intuition; it's a woman thing."

"Okay, I have this hunch . . . . I think they've just gotten started. Did you see that rifle? They're armed to the hilt. They came to hunt, and they aren't going to give up without a fight. We've got to get to a phone and get help. Show me the quickest way to get back to a main road."

"Mermet Lake is complex with numerous inlets that are dead ends. There's a bait and tackle shop about two miles away. The roadhouse is up ahead and on the other side of the lake. We might find a phone there. Or we could backtrack."

"At the moment, that isn't an option for us. We'll run into them if we do," I said.

"I know," she whispered hoarsely. "There are at least twenty inlets that loop in and around. Some of them are dead ends," she warned. "And some circle back. If they know about them, they could get ahead of us and cut us off."

"Then we'll slow down, and if we see their lights, we'll take one of the side channels and hide until daylight." We were approaching another bend. "Which way?" I asked.

She looked past a grove of vine-covered trees. "I'm not sure. Everything looks different at night. I think this one circles back."

"Okay, we'll go left," I said and steered the boat in that direction.

"Mike, I could be wrong."

I heard the sound of a boat motor roaring in the distance. The sound was getting closer even as we steered around another tree trunk.

I could tell by Ellen's reaction she'd also heard the noise. I spotted a narrow channel, slowed the engine, and turned the boat once again. There were numerous branches hanging down, most covered with some kind of growth, similar to kudzu. I pushed them out of the way as we passed. As I inhaled deeply to relax, my nose was tweaked with the smell of ozone, lichen and fern. Once we had made another turn and I saw how narrow the channel had become, I shut down the engine.

Ellen turned the flashlight off. We huddled together for warmth and turned toward the sound. It was nearly as black as the inside of a coffin. Fortunately, the downpour had subsided and was reduced to a soft drizzle.

The swamp, covered with a pea-colored coating of duckweed, pulsated with nocturnal denizens. I twitched as something splashed in the water behind us. I figured the thrashing sound that followed was merely another of those Darwinian struggles for survival that played out on a regular basis in this watery world. The hunter and the hunted.

The bullfrogs suddenly stopped croaking, and the crickets fell silent. Something out there was moving. What in the world was it? The boat struck something. I thought it might be another tree trunk, but I couldn't be sure. The boat bobbed back, then stopped.

Ellen reached behind me, pushed a lever, and told me in a whisper to help her swing the motor up out of the water. "If we have to keep going in this channel, the propeller could get caught in the mud. The lake is flooded right now and it gets shallow in some of these inlets." The boat bumped against the obstacle once again.

"There they are," Ellen whispered.

We could see the light from the other boat scanning the thicket like a lighthouse beacon, swinging back and forth in a wide arc, searching for prey.

Camisole-style corset cover from Sears

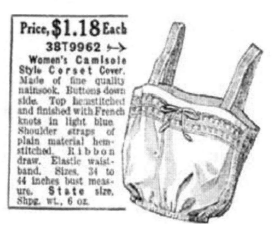

The light didn't find us. Ellen drew in a deep breath of rain-moistened air and slowly exhaled. We had just gotten over another hurdle, and I took a few seconds to thank God for that blessing. We weren't out of danger yet, but I had been right when I'd told her we could hide out until daylight and then get help. Soon there would be an end to this nightmare.

Our pursuers had gone on. The noise from their boat fading now. I guessed that they would continue on for several more minutes before they'd turn around and backtrack, searching more thoroughly.

My mind was racing. Were they professional hitters? If so, was it the Camel who had sent them? McGurn? Were they Capone's gunsels? Could the Chicago mob have tracked us to that part of Illinois called Little Egypt?

Lady's serge suit - all wool - from Sears

Ellen reacted to a branch that snapped above her. She glanced up at the foliage a scant second before a weight dropped on her left foot with a *whump!* Her fist flew to her mouth as if it took every ounce of willpower she possessed not to scream.

"Something is slithering up my leg." She froze, her hand gripping the flashlight in her lap.

"Mike, grab the oar," she whispered. "When I turn the light on, you've got to flip it out of the boat. Okay?"

I didn't understand. What was *it*? What was she talking about? I didn't question her though. I simply picked up the oar, held it like a baseball bat and waited.

"I'm ready."

She flipped the switch on. I felt my heart lurch in my chest. I almost dropped the oar when I saw the hideous black snake. The monster's forked tongue was darting in and out, as though he were anticipating the morsel he was going to bite, his triangular flat head poised above Ellen's kneecap. It seemed to be looking into her eyes.

Time seemed to be suspended as I deftly moved the oar to the middle of the snake's body and flipped it back into the water. "Holy moley!" I roared. "Holy moley!"

Ellen scrambled to her knees. She kept her flashlight beam trained on the snake, watching as it skimmed across the water into the bushes on the other side of the muddy bank.

"That was a close call."

I was examining her leg. "Did he get you?" I asked frantically.

"No, he didn't. He was probably more afraid than we were."

"What in tarnation was it?" I felt like my heart was clocking at a hundred and ten.

"It might have been a water snake, but I think it was a cottonmouth," she answered.

"A water moccasin – aren't they poisonous?"

"Yes," she agreed.

"Let's get out of here!"

I put my hand in the water to see if I could push the boat away from the bank. My fingers felt as if they were being sucked into the mud.

Ellen grabbed my arm and pulled it back. "You don't want to put your hand in the water, not around here."

I didn't need to ask why. Grabbing the oar, I used it to push off. "Do you think this way cuts through?"

"I've visited here many times and I know these waters, but in the dark I'm still second-guessing myself. I think this one dead-ends about a quarter mile from here. If we keep going, we could get trapped, and I don't want to walk through the swamp. It isn't safe, not at night, anyway. I think we should turn around and go back."

"That gets my vote."

"When we cross back over, let's use the oars and row across. If they're out there, they won't hear us."

Ellen picked up the other oar and helped me get the boat turned.

"If another lousy snake lands in the boat, they'll hear me, all right."

I traded places with Ellen and used the oars to get us to the opening of the channel. I stopped, and then turned to look. "What do you think? Can we make it to the road-house? If I could–"

"We went too far downstream," she interrupted. "We'll have to backtrack, and that's pushing our luck."

"Okay. We'll head straight across and hope there's a dock close by."

I couldn't see more than ten feet ahead, but I knew it was too risky to turn the flashlight on. Ellen climbed over the bench seat so she could get to the motor. She put her hand on the pull cord.

"What if we reach the middle and then the spotlight finds us?"

"Let's pray that doesn't happen," I said. We were gliding across the water now. My arms strained, working the oars. On my

Plaid lumberjack blouse

Ladies motor scarf outfit from Sears

next stroke, I kept one oar out of the water and used the other as an impromptu rudder to steer us in the right direction.

The light from the other boat was scanning the water.

"They're looking for us in the channels," she whispered.

I kept rowing but stole quick glances behind us. The beam of light was crisscrossing the water, but the boat wasn't moving. It was about two hundred yards away.

"They haven't seen us yet."

"Should I turn the motor–"

"No," I said in an urgent voice. "Hang in there. We might make it."

A minute later, the beam turned back in our direction. Ellen didn't wait for me to tell her to start the motor. She pulled hard. It didn't catch the first time. I swung the oars in and shoved Ellen down as a bullet whizzed past my head. She yanked on the rope and shouted *yes* when the engine sputtered to life.

I pulled my gun from the holster and shouted for Ellen to keep her head down, just as another bullet struck the water next to us. I propped my elbow on the bench and fired my weapon.

Whoever it was, they were coming fast now. I was trying to shoot out the spotlight. The first shot missed, but I heard someone cry out, and I hoped that meant I'd hit one of them. I squeezed off another round and was on the mark this time. The bullet shattered the light, giving us five, maybe ten seconds max before one of the thugs turned his flashlight on us.

Ellen couldn't judge how close we were to the bank. She tried to reach the throttle to slow the boat down, but it was too late. The boat suddenly lurched up out of the water and slammed into a thicket. It slowed down but didn't stop until hitting one of those bald cypress trees. The impact threw me into the front of the boat. I landed hard on my left side, slamming my knee on the floor. My upper arm, still throbbing from the cut of the window glass, hit the metal trim, tearing my skin and sending a jolt of pain down to my elbow.

Ellen's forehead struck the bench, and she cried out as she threw her arms up to protect herself.

The outboard motor died with a smoky gasp. I leaped out of the boat, holstered my gun, and pulled on Ellen. Dazed from the impact, she shook her head, trying to clear it as she felt around the boat for the flashlight.

"Come on," I shouted over the roar of the motor coming closer and closer.

My heart was slamming against my sternum. I was lifting her when she found the flashlight. Jerking her arm free, she snatched it. I wrapped my arm around Ellen, hauled her into my side and, half carrying her, ran into the dense brush. I didn't have the faintest idea where we were headed. Completely disoriented, we ran headlong into spiny branches. I grimaced and pushed through them with

1920s Barnstorming – note metal bumpers under bottom wing

my right arm. I could still hear the motor roaring in the distance and was desperate to get Ellen as far away as possible before the men came ashore.

We continued fighting our way through the brush and the soggy undergrowth, stopping twice to listen for signs that we were being followed. Something brushed against my leg and I slapped it away.

"Darn, I just snagged my dress on a briar."

"In all likelihood it was already ruined," I said.

Finally, breaking out of the bramble, we stumbled forward into the open.

Ellen stopped to get her second wind. She said she wasn't sure where we were.

"Should I risk it?" she asked as she lifted the flashlight and made ready to flick the switch. "I don't think they'll see the light if I only have it on for a second."

I calculated the consequences. "Do it," I said, huffing.

She flipped the switch, and then breathed a sigh of relief. "I think I know where we are." Turning the light off, she whispered, "It's about a mile to the roadhouse."

We were standing on the edge of a dirt road.

"You're sure?"

"Um, uh, yes."

I clasped her hand and started swiftly down the road. Ellen's conditioning from exercise running allowed her to easily keep pace. If we could get around the bend up ahead before our pursuers reached the road, we'd be in the clear. I kept glancing over my shoulder looking for lights. The only sounds were some stirrings by night creatures, our heavy breathing, and the pounding of our feet against the road.

Ellen turned on the light again, just in the nick of time because we would have run off the road where it curved. She tripped as she turned, but I caught her and kept her upright without slowing down. I looked behind us again but saw nothing following us. I was positive our pursuers hadn't seen us.

"My head is clear now," she panted.

I took hold of her hand, and we continued on. I could see

a light twinkling like a star in the distance and headed in that direction.

The road was gravel and mud. As we ran, I constantly scanned the brush on either side, figuring which way we would dive if I heard someone coming.

"You doing okay?" I whispered.

"I'm good," she answered.

I was greatly relieved when I saw the dark building ahead of us. The feeling of euphoria was short-lived, for a scant few seconds later I heard the sound of a car screeching around the curve behind us.

Reacting quickly, I felt sorry for Ellen. One second she was glancing over her shoulder to look for headlights, and the next she was being jerked off the road into a gully with me. I tried to help break her fall but she landed hard on her backside. I crouched beside her and pulled out my gun, my eyes scanning the road. Fortunately, we were concealed by scrub and thick bushes.

The car groaned to a stop next to us. I fought the urge to recoil as I heard a thrashing noise in the nearby bushes. I realized I was holding my breath when my chest began to ache. I heard Ellen slowly, quietly exhale. Her hand had a tight grip on my knee.

There was more thrashing in the underbrush, then muttering as the man walked back to the car, crunching gravel under his shoes.

"The damp air is getting to me," Ellen whispered. Her eyes suddenly began to tear, and her head rose up with eyes closed as if she were going to sneeze.

Please, God, not now. She can't make any noise . . . not

Prohibition cartoon – Cure for tonsillitis

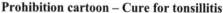

yet. Ellen squelched the sneeze by clamping her fingers over her nose and breathing through her mouth.

A door slammed, and then the car moved on. I wasn't going to take any chances though. I strained to hear every little sound. How many were there? I knew for certain four men had tried to ambush us. I'd seen two in front of the house and then two who'd driven the boat to the dock. Their goal had obviously been to trap us inside the house.

I changed my position to take the weight off my knees. Putting my arm around Ellen, I bent down and whispered, "They're looking for us at the roadhouse, and we're going to sit tight until they're gone. You still doing okay?"

She nodded. As soon as I turned back to watch the road, she rested her cheek against my back. I wanted to take advantage of the temporary breather in case we had to start running again.

I shifted my weight from one knee to the other. The smell of wet, rotten, decomposing leaves was thick and musty. Ellen complained she was waterlogged and felt as though we were sitting in compost.

Meanwhile it had stopped raining and the skies had cleared. I could see that Orion had arisen and stood at the eastern horizon. A crescent moon threw just enough light to cause the trees to cast shadows. The vague shapes looked like hunched gargoyles.

Gosh, how long had we been waiting? It seemed as though an hour had passed since we'd dived into the brush, but then time had pretty much stopped from the moment the first gunshot was fired.

"What do you think happened to the man in the boat who fell into the water?"

"If my bullet didn't kill him, he probably drowned," I said.

"I can't imagine dying in such a manner."

"It's worse than you think."

"What do you mean?"

"A medical examiner once told me that when you drown, your head feels like a hundred firecrackers are going off inside. Your eyes bug out of your head and your eardrums burst like they were punctured with ice picks."

"How awful."

"It gets worse. Your throat feels like its being ripped out and your lungs feel like they're filling with hydrochloric acid."

Leopold and Loeb – killers of Bobby Franks

14 year-old Bobby Franks

I heard the car before I saw the headlights through the branches. It came roaring down the road, passed us without slowing, and sped on.

I chanced it and leaned out to see which way the car was headed. It slowed at the crossroad, and then went straight ahead, which meant the men hadn't given up yet and were searching another back road. I strained, but couldn't see the license plate.

"They'll have to give up looking for us soon," she whispered. "It will be light, and they won't want to risk being seen by early morning fishermen. Don't you think they'll give up?"

"Maybe," I allowed. "We'll stay here for about a half hour to make sure."

I shuddered, thinking about the snake that fell into the boat. For some strange reason, it made me think of Cerberus, the three-headed dog of Greek myth that guarded Hades to insure no one escaped from there.

"Cerberus had a snake for a tail," I said absentmindedly.

"What?"

"Cerberus, the three headed dog. He had a snake-like tail."

"Didn't Hercules kill that monster?"

"He wrestled and subdued him, despite being bitten, but he didn't kill him."

"Trivia: Why did Cerberus have three heads?"

I knew this one. "The three heads represented the past, present, and future."

"Didn't Cerberus have a sister named Medusa – that hussy with snakes for hair?"

I nodded. Ellen was very good at historical trivia.

We waited about twenty more minutes. "Let's go," I said as I stood. I pulled Ellen to her feet. "Let's stay close to the side of the road and keep the flashlight off."

"Okay," she agreed. "But if you hear them coming, don't throw me into a ditch again. Just tell me. My backside's going to be bruised. And try not to get hung up on thistle bushes and briars."

Ellen finally let loose – "Aaa . . . choo!!!"

"Gesundheit!"

"Gee, that felt good."

I couldn't help wondering how many ticks or leeches we'd picked up out there in the lake. As we approached the roadhouse, I decided not to take any chances, so we went back into the brush and edged our way around to the back door. I peeked in a window to see if anything was moving inside. It was difficult to see, but the place looked empty. We backtracked to the front, and I began looking on the ground for a sturdy rock.

"I'll have to go in through a window," I said, picking up a jagged boulder.

"What are you doing?"

"I intend to break the glass."

Ellen moved over to the front door.

"The door is solid wood. You'll never get in that way."

"Maybe we should just say *open sesame*." Ellen said.

I folded my arms and uttered the mystical

command from *Ali Baba and the Forty Thieves.*

"Know any more magical words?" she asked after nothing happened.

Ellen reached up, slid her hand across the sill. "Aha!"

I shook my head in amazement as she inserted the key and twisted the knob.

I pushed ahead of her, squinting into the darkness. "We can hide out here until daylight. Let's see if we can find a candle."

I froze as I thought I heard a sound – perhaps a squeaky floorboard.

"Stay put," I whispered as I pulled out my gun and cautiously walked toward the noise.

Would they have left a man behind? I nearly fell as my foot tripped against what I surmised was a barstool. I regained my balance as my left hand caught the edge of the bar and gave me something solid to hold on to. I was turning away from the counter when I felt the tiniest brush of air against the hairs on the nape of my neck. I knew without turning around or hearing a sound that someone was coming up behind me.

CHAPTER 20

JUNE 14, 1931

MODEL -T FORDS: In 1921 Americans bought a grand total of 1.5 million cars, and most of those sold were the affordable Model-T. Henry Ford was rather eccentric and thought that colors were impractical and costly, so every car he mass-produced was black. Cars quickly became known as a "jalopy," Tin Lizzie, or "flivver."

Most of the Fords had no heater, no defroster, no speedometer, no radio, and no self-starter. One man joked: "I don't need a speedometer. When my Model-T goes five miles and hour the fenders rattle. At twelve miles an hour my teeth rattle; if it goes fifteen miles per hour the transmission falls out."

The Model-T was hard to start in the cold as the oil in the crankcase turned to the consistency of molasses. If the car backfired while being cranked, this led to numerous people being knocked unconscious or suffering broken hands or arms.

Due to an odd mechanical quirk, the car went up steep hills better in reverse than in forward gear.

Conversely, the car was affordable, reliable (except for overheating) and was easy to repair. One owner claimed breakdowns could be fixed with baling wire, hatpins, electrical tape and chewing gum.

Some farmers were known to replace the back tires with tractor tires and use the car to plow their fields.

"Ellen, run," I shouted. I wheeled to face the intruder. I couldn't see his face; it was too dark. The huge shadow struck a blow at my wrist, knocking the gun from my hand. It clattered to the floor. Then the hulking shadow grabbed my arm and twisted it back with one hand as the other came up fast to nail me under the chin.

I ducked, but not fast enough. His knuckles landed on my chin, snapping my head back. Searing pain shot through my jaw. I mustered every ounce of power I had in my left fist and punched the attacker in the gut. "Ooof!"

Where had this guy come from? Was he left behind by the others? Had he already gotten to Ellen? Enraged, I struck again. With the speed of a jackhammer, the man parried my blow and then swung his foot up to kick my knee. I twisted, and it was only a glancing blow to my thigh. But a crunching uppercut landed flush on my chin, and I sank to the floor unconscious.

When I awoke, my eyes fluttered for a few seconds. I was flat on my back. I tried to get my bearings. Trees of all kinds were everywhere, an untidy colonnade rising through the undergrowth. It was just past the break of dawn, and the sun, already a fireball in the early morning sky, was dancing through holes in the canopy. A lone dragonfly darted back and forth like a devil's darning needle.

"Welcome back, Mr. Kriegan," a harsh voice rang out.

I turned my head toward the sound. It was Murray Humphreys, and he had one arm around Ellen's waist. His other hand held a pistol to her head.

"How did we get here?" I asked, rubbing a lump on my head.

"My car, it's over by the road behind those bushes."

"Where are the rest of your goons?"

Typewriter used by Leopold and Loeb to compose the ransom note

Henry and son Edsel Ford (at the wheel) – 1926

The Fifteen Millionth Ford

"They drove back to our cabin to get into some dry clothes. One of them is wounded. I said I'd meet up with them after I finished with the two of you."

I stumbled to my feet. "You'd better think about what you're doing, Humphreys," I said. "Bootlegging or racketeering is one thing; they'll give you the chair for murder."

His gun arm snapped, as if he were throwing the weapon. The shot knocked loose a chunk of dirt inches away from my left foot.

"Stay right where you are. Don't move." He gave a split-second smile. "This is going to be sweet revenge. You'll get a bullet between the eyes, and I've got something very special in mind to repay Ellen for her betrayal."

"Let her go," I pleaded. "What happened between us was my fault. I was the one who pursued her."

A hard scowl stiffened his features. "The last time I checked, Buddy Boy, it takes two to tango. Nobody two-times me and gets away with it. She's going to regret the day she was born before I'm through with her."

"Eliot Ness will hunt you down for this," I countered, trying to stall for time.

Bob LaFollette and labor leader Samuel Gompers of the AF of L

He shook his head. "There isn't any way he'll be able to pin anything on me because no one is going to find any bodies. I'm going to bury both of you here in this God-forsaken swamp. With the heat and the moisture, your bodies will decompose rapidly. You'll be skeletal in three months. Ness and the feds will figure some local moonshiners did away with you."

I could see by the look on Ellen's face that she was terrified. "You're wrong. I told Eliot. He knows exactly where we are and what we're doing down here."

He kicked a long-handled spade that was on the ground toward me. "Quit stalling, an' start diggin'." I picked up the shovel and reluctantly set to work.

"Please, let us go," Ellen begged.

His lips drew back, and he did something with his free hand that made Ellen cry out. I made a threatening gesture

Dancer "Bojangles" Robinson

with the shovel, and he fired another warning shot that whizzed past my ear. Then he smartly backed out of swinging range.

"Keep digging, or so help me I'll kill both of you right now and dig the grave myself."

I jammed the shovel into the moist earth and shoved it deeper with my right foot. I rocked the handle and tossed the dirt to the left.

"There, that's better," he said. "Just keep at it. The hole only needs to be about three feet deep."

I tried to stall for time by pretending to dig deep, but then drew the spade back before tossing out a less than full load of dirt.

Think, Kriegan, think!

I dug for about fifteen minutes, but I couldn't come up with a plan for rushing him without getting Ellen killed. He held her tight in his grasp, and the gun barrel at her head made red circles on her temple.

Another five minutes or so passed. The hole was about two feet deep, and I wondered how much time we had before Humphreys decided it was deep enough. I stroked rapidly and grunted a lot, hoping that would throw him off.

After several more minutes, he grew impatient. "Come, come, faster, faster or I'll finish you off right now."

Time was running out.

"The deeper I go the wetter the soil. It's tougher digging through this muck and mire," I complained.

He shoved down on Ellen's shoulder, forcing her to her knees, then prone, her face in the dirt. Some got in her mouth. She gagged and finally managed to turn her head to the side.

"Don't hurt her," I said, momentarily stopping.

He ignored me and put his foot on her spine. "This is taking too long," he said impatiently. He waved the gun at me. "Don't slack off."

I knew that Humphreys was fastidious about being clean and neatly dressed. I doubted if he was anxious to get in the hole. Just throwing the dirt back in on top of our bodies was going to be distasteful to him.

Ellen gave out a soft moan, and Humphreys lost his patience with her. He kicked at her with his foot. "Get up and get in the hole and throw out the loose clods with your hands."

Ellen obeyed his command and slid into the hole. I gave her a hug. "You okay?"

She nodded, gave me a weak smile, and began grubbing out handfuls of moist dirt.

"When Eliot finds out something has happened to me, he's going to crack down even harder on your boss. Capone is finished. It's just a matter of time."

"Keep digging. We've got a plan to take care of that lousy Ness. Did you guys really think you were going to win this fight?"

I tossed another shovel of dirt on the growing mound. "Eliot's tougher than you think."

"Too bad you're not gonna be around to see how it plays out."

Ellen's hair was caked with mud and hung down in tendrils as she tossed clump after clump onto the pile. The growing mound was beginning to interfere with Murray's line of sight, so he moved several feet closer to us. Then he looked down into the pit.

"What in blazes? Playing games, eh? I'll finish the both of you right now!"

He fixed his gaze on me, trained his gun on my forehead and started to squeeze the trigger.

Ellen screamed like a banshee and threw a clump of dirt at him. Direct hit on his shoulder. The gun fired somewhere up in the air. With his attention diverted, I drew the long handled spade back like a javelin and threw it at his legs, blade first, as hard as my weary arms could muster.

The tip slammed into his left shin and he yelled in pain and surprise. I quickly vaulted out of the hole and threw myself on him. As we went down together, I felt the gun pinned between our chests, digging into my sternum. The arm holding it was twisted in an unnatural way. I slammed the other down as he tried to bite my nose.

I figured he was probably out of shape but would still be powered initially by adrenaline. He pitched and rolled, managing to slide the gun arm out.

Then something came from the side in a brown-white blur, striking him hard in the temple, quick as a snake bite.

Stock market crash cartoon

Greta Garbo – author's collection

His head whiplashed. Another blow, and he relaxed his grip long enough for me to land a hard right to his chin. His eyes rolled and his body went limp. I twisted the gun from his fingers.

Ellen's muddy shoe kicked him again. I extended my open hand to let her know that was enough. Humphreys was unconscious. He was breathing, but not moving. The side of his head was starting to balloon from edema.

I was panting. So was Ellen.

She reached down toward Murray, and then stopped herself.

I put my arm around her. "Are you sure you're okay?" She nodded and reached up, kissing me on the cheek.

I needed something for binding.

Thought of something.

I gave the gun to Ellen. The way she took it told me she had held one before.

"He probably won't stir, but don't get any closer. If he awakes and makes any effort to get up, shoot him in the kneecap. If that isn't enough, shoot him in the other knee. Keep the gun aimed at his head and watch him. I'll be back in a few minutes.

Taking the shovel, I moved away from the clearing and went deeper into the woods, running hard until I came upon a viny plant. Chopping off several long shoots, I ran back and trussed Murray in a tight hogtie, his hands behind his back and his feet bent backward and tied to his hands. He was breathing fine, and his neck pulse was strong and regular. He'd probably have a badly bruised shin, a monster headache, maybe a concussion, but he'd survive to stand trial for attempted murder.

I took the car keys from his pocket, picked him up and tossed him over my shoulders like a sack of potatoes.

"Let's go find the car. I'll shove him in the trunk and we'll take him to the nearest police station."

"We were very lucky to get out of this alive," she said.

"Yeah, I know. But it'll make a great story to tell our children and grandchildren."

I reached over and plucked a leaf fragment from Ellen's hair. She smiled slyly and gave me another hug.

We were at the police station in Mermet for a couple of hours while the police captain interviewed us and took our statements. The town of Mermet was small, and it had an equally small police station and lock up facility – two cells. Murray Humphreys was incarcerated in one. The other was occupied by a haggard-looking man who looked as if he'd gone on a drinking binge.

"We'll transfer this Humphreys character to the county jail this afternoon, after we've had a chance to interrogate him."

After removing a myriad of beggar's lice from my slacks I glanced up at a ceiling fan whose paddles were sluggishly turning, its movement slowed by the heat.

"He'll probably be calling some fancy Chicago lawyer to assist at his arraignment," I said.

The captain pulled out a handkerchief and mopped his forehead. "It won't do him any good. If the charge is attempted murder, there won't be any bail. Is he really one of Capone's top men?"

I nodded. "You don't think Capone will try and bust him out, do you?"

He extended his open

260

hand and waved it back and forth. "No way. They worried about the same thing at the Benton jail after Charlie Birger was found guilty of murder. Birger didn't get away, and he was as tough as they come."

Curious, I asked: "Were you at his hanging?"

"Sure was. Wouldn't have missed it for the world."

"What was it like?" Ellen interjected.

"A real circus. There was this huge crowd. Little kids were sittin' on their daddy's shoulders. Older kids were perched in the forks of nearby trees. Adults were on roof-tops.

"Everybody was waiting for the big moment. Several law enforcement officers and Phil Hanna, the hangman from Carmi, were waiting for him on the specially-built platform.

"A murmur went through the crowd as the east door of the building opened up, and out came Birger, smartly dressed in a light gray suit, accommodated by a Jewish rabbi from St. Louis."

"I didn't know he was Jewish."

"Yeah. They buried him in a consecrated family plot next to his father in St. Louis."

"Was he nervous? Did he say he was sorry?"

"He was a little shaky, but the darnedest thing happened before they put the noose and hood on him."

"How so?"

"Before he went to meet the devil, he just looked up and said, 'It's a beautiful world.'"

"That's it? That's all he said?" I asked, incredulous.

He held up his right hand. "So help me."

"Wow! That's some story."

"I'll never forget it, even if I live to be a hundred an' ten."

I drew in a long breath, slowly exhaled and looked over at Ellen. I could tell she was exhausted from the ordeal. "If there isn't anything else, I guess we'd better be going."

"We're finished."

"Thanks for everything," I said as I rose to shake his hand.

When we opened the door to leave, he

"No way. They worried

American Gothic by Grant Wood – 1930

Actress Lois Wilson

Western star Buck Jones

said, "Just one more thing."

What's that?" I replied as I glanced back over my shoulder.

He had kind of a sheepish grin on his face and was pointing to my wrist. "I know the two of you went through a terrible ordeal, but do you really think it's right to keep his expensive gold watch."

Ellen and I both laughed uncontrollably as we waved dismissively and closed the door behind us.

After stopping at the local hardware to buy some new door locks and screen cloth, we headed back to the cabin. The first thing we did was take a shower. Then we rubbed some Unguentine on our scrapes and cuts.

Fortunately, things weren't as bad inside as they might have been. There were some bullet holes in the knotty pine paneling, broken glass on the floor, busted locks, and a shattered ceramic rooster cookie jar on the kitchen floor. Ellen cleaned up the broken glass and tacked screens over the windows (upstairs and down) while I fixed and repositioned the locks. They were the type that fitted flush with the frame of the door and were not part of the doorknob.

By nightfall, we were exhausted, both mentally and physically.

I gave Ellen a kiss as she fluffed a pillow on her bed and slipped under a light cotton sheet.

"I'll see you in the morning," I said, getting ready to close her door.

"Wait. I, I think I would like it if you stayed with me tonight."

"Are you sure?"

"I just don't want to be alone. Can I trust you just to cuddle – nothing more?"

I gave her a reassuring smile. "Sure."

I walked over to the other side of her bed and sat on the edge while I removed my shoes. I turned and lay on my side, facing her. I leaned forward and gave her a kiss on her forehead. Incredibly, given the pleasure of it, we weren't even touching when we fell asleep.

I opened my eyes at dawn and looked over at Ellen. She was still in dreamland. Her head was on my arm, her cheek on my shirt just above my elbow. Her hair was touching my face, a feathery, tantalizing sensation. She lay on her side with her eyes closed, pale lashes resting not far from a bruise and scratch on her face, results of the previous night's ordeal. I reached up to touch it, but stopped just shy and drew back my hand. Holding it tucked to my throat, I looked more.

Her strawberry blonde hair spilled onto her forehead and was slightly mussed. The sunlight streaming through the windows fell on her hair, making it look lighter than it actually was. I marveled at her peaches and cream complexion. The bridge of a slightly upturned nose had a few freckles on it. Her ears were nicely shaped with small lobes. I noticed another small scratch on her cheek.

Radio inventor Lee De Forest

I reached up and ran a hand over my face, checking for cuts and bruises. There were several scratches that had lightly scabbed over, and my jaw was sore. That knot on the back of my head was still giving me a slight ache.

There was a cocklebur still tangled in her hair that I gently removed. I fondly remembered that Frank Cumberland, my best friend as a teen, referred to them as porcupine eggs. I began to smooth her hair and touch her face, my fingertips brushing lightly over her nose, lips, ears. Her hair smelled of jasmine. It was as if I was mapping her out, memorizing every nook and cranny. I reached over and kissed her on the mouth. Her incredible eyes fluttered open.

"I love every inch of you, Ellen." The words came easily.

"Are you enjoying yourself?" she asked.

"Why, er . . . uh, yes," I stammered. "I want you now . . . and tomorrow . . . forever."

She looked at me with an impish smile. "Mind if I join in?" She wrapped her arms around my neck, drew close, and gave me a passionate kiss. I responded in kind, feeling an absurd happiness steal through me.

"I think I'm going to enjoy being Mrs. Michael Kriegan," she said, softly rubbing the stubble on my chin with her thumbs.

"How many kids do you think we should have?"

"Most Catholic families have three or four," she said, shaking her head to toss a curl away from her eye.

"Most Protestant families have one or two," I countered.

"She lowered her voice and narrowed her eyes like a seductress. "I think we can find a way to compromise on that."

"What about church?"

"We can compromise on that, too."

"What do you mean?" she said, brushing a forelock on my temple.

"We'll alternate churches every other week.

"Won't that be confusing?"

"I think both of our families will like that compromise."

"No, I mean confusing to our children."

"Both churches practice infant baptism. Both are Christ-centered. I think that is the most important thing. We can explain the differences as doctrinal interpretations."

"What if they like one church more than the other?"

I shrugged. "That's natural. I prefer Dick Tracy to Moon Mullins, but I still read both comic strips in the newspaper."

She nodded in silent thought.

"Besides, do you have a better idea? I certainly wouldn't ask you to give up your religious beliefs for mine."

"Yes, and it certainly wouldn't be fair for me to expect you to give up Lutheranism."

I nodded. "Do you think your priest will accept the idea? After all, in most cases the Church of Rome insists that the children of a mixed marriage be reared Catholic."

"We won't give them any choice. This is America. This is a new era of liberated thinking. We have religious freedom in our country."

"Yes, we can certainly be thankful for that."

Her face grew worried.

"What's wrong?"

"You're not going to do this cops and robbers thing for the rest of your life, are you?"

I shook my head. Once this ordeal with Capone is finished, I go back to being a boring telephone executive."

A look of relief spread across her face.

"I want to spend the rest of my life playing with the kids and pleasing you."

"I can just imagine our little boys," she said. "They'll be a miniature version of you, all bright and alert."

"And our daughter will be a tintype of her mother, sweet, loving and warm."

"Our children most likely will be a mix of both of us." She tossed me a winsome smile. "But you probably mean daughters, not daughter."

"What?"

"Twin girls run in the family."

I took a deep breath. "When we get back to Chicago, I'm buying you a diamond ring. You and I have a destiny with love forever true."

A couple of days later, we drove back to rat-a-tat-a-tat city.

(Flora and fauna information on Southern Illinois in the previous chapters courtesy of **Chris Mc-Ginness**)

Robert Goddard & first liquid fueled rocket

John Philip Sousa – Library of Congress

CHAPTER 21

JUNE 20, 1931

On my first day back to work after the southern Illinois assignment, I noticed Eliot seemed a little morose. I placed a sympathetic hand on his shoulder. "What's bothering you, Eliot?"

He leaned over and placed both hands over his face. Then he looked up. "I just found out that a friend of mine who went into the investment business committed suicide."

"I'm so sorry. Did he use a gun?"

"No, he took a dive out of a twelfth story window in the Banker's Building, over near the Rookery."

I walked over to a chair, sat down, and hung my head. "This Depression is really hitting a lot of families hard. It doesn't seem right does it? We have people down by the lakefront railroad tracks living in Hoovervilles while the Gold Coast crowd is living it up."

"I know," he said. "It really bothers me to see people on the streets lined up at soup kitchens and men trying to support their families selling apples for a nickel on the street corners."

"It seems like the old homilies our parents taught us – honesty, integrity and hard work aren't holding up very well in the real world."

"Not here in Chicago," he said bitingly.

"Not anywhere," I grumbled.

"It's hard to believe – men who've been at their job for thirty years – out of work; businesses that have been around forever – gone."

I swallowed. "Let's hope that this New Deal thing Roosevelt has cooked up can make a difference."

"Yeah," he answered dryly. "A lot of people are beginning to lose faith in the system and we could have anarchy."

I nodded. We sat there silently for a few minutes, each lost in his thoughts. Finally, I spoke up and filled Eliot in, chapter and verse, on the details on the Mermet Lake trip.

"Southern Illinois and the Paducah area of Kentucky are supplying Chicago with contraband booze, but it's not what you think," I explained.

"We've assumed all along that the Shelton brothers are in charge of this operation," Eliot responded.

"But it isn't true. I discovered through several sources down there that the Sheltons have a big

Where the blame lies – anti-immigration cartoon

Vanity Fair Depression cartoon

House Speaker Joe Cannon of Illinois

dislike for the Capone mob and won't have anything to do with them. They seem to be content with taking care of business in southern Illinois. After Charlie Birger was executed they moved their base of operations to East St. Louis, and they let their associates run things south of Mount Vernon."

Eliot scratched his head. "So who is sending the alcohol up to Chicago?"

"Several independents. But the good news is that everything seems to be coordinated through phone calls placed at the Wellington. If we listen long enough with our wiretap, we can find out when and where the drop is to be made and intercept it."

"That was good work, Mike."

"Thanks. You'll also be pleased to know that I helped put Murray Humphreys in the Mermet pokey."

He arched an eyebrow. What was Humphreys doing down there?"

"He followed Ellen and me."

"Ellen – not that Esposito woman?"

"Yes, I didn't tell you that we got back together several weeks ago."

Eliot slumped in disappointment. "You know how I feel about your seeing her."

"It's more than that, Eliot. We love each other and plan to get married once we put Capone out of business."

Eliot shook his head. "What a fine kettle of fish. You know if this thing between the two of you gets our office involved in controversy I'll have to dismiss you from the team."

I nodded. "Yeah . . . I know. Let's hope it doesn't come to that."

"I need to go shopping for a new car," Ellen said. "My '28 Nash needs a ring job."

I tossed her a skeptical look. "Wouldn't it be cheaper to

Hoot Gibson and his Cadillac

take it to a local garage and have it serviced?"

"Cheaper, yes – more exciting, no," she saucily replied.

Ellen looked fetching in another one of her *haute couture* outfits, accented by a sealskin purse and a matching cloche hat.

"You look great in that getup. Is it a Molyneux?"

She made Barney Google goo goo googly eyes at me. "No, it's a Louise-boulanger."

"If you really insist, we can go to several places and shop for a new car."

"Marvelous!"

While in my car I couldn't help but notice Ellen extending her left had to admire the engagement ring I'd given her a few days

1929 Essex coupe with rumble seat

earlier. It was nearly a full carat in weight and had taken a big chunk out of my savings. I bought it over the phone from Harry Liberstein, the "busy jeweler" back in my hometown of East St. Louis. We were classmates in high school and he assured me the gem was of the highest

quality when it came to clarity and cut. I could tell by the look in Ellen's eyes that he had kept his word.

We drove to a variety of car dealerships and apprized their offerings.

A boattailed Stutz Bearcat – "Too popular and too common among the young sheiks and shebas. Everybody trying to be 'in' has one."

A Dodge touring car – "Too boxy and high axled."

A Lincoln phaeton – "It looks like a mob hit car."

A twelve-cylinder Oldsmobile – "The type of car that one might expect to be leading a funeral procession."

A Plymouth coupe – "I might as well be buying a black Model-A Ford."

A Chevrolet – "I'm not ready for anything that quiet."

"I don't think there's anything left," I exasperatingly said with elevated shoulders and open palms.

"Tut, Tut. There's got to be a flivver out there with character, style, speed . . . emotion."

"Surely there's something . . . perhaps continental."

"European?"

"Why not?"

1929 Stutz 2 passenger torpedo

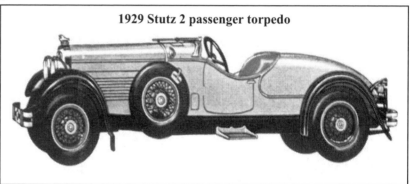

I took her to a place I knew on the edge of Chicago, where the old livery stables had been converted to streetcar barns. The garage was large and newly painted and an attentive, if grease-stained, young man stood up suddenly as we entered. The interior of the ex-stable was gleaming with brass lamps and lovingly polished paintwork. It had the distinct oily smell of ozone flavored burned-dust scent. The young man wiped his hands hastily on a piece of cotton waste and hurried toward us.

I extended my hand. "This is Ellen Esposito, and I'm Mike Kriegan."

He nodded. "Glad to meet you, ma'am." We shook hands. "Mr. Kriegan, what can I do for you?"

"We're looking for a car – something eclectic, different, exotic—"

"Powerful," Ellen interjected.

The man looked around and gestured toward a sober looking Duchesse.

"Excessively staid."

I threw her a quick wink and a smile. "Definitely too stuffy," I added, trying my best to be supportive.

"What about this one?" Ellen inquired, patting the bright red enamel of a long, low sports car that shone like a battle chariot. It was built rakishly low and wide bodied to hold up an engine of fiendish power. The young man looked Ellen up and down, as if trying to gauge her nerve.

"Is it a Lagonda?"

"No, Hispano-Suiza. French made. First one was built for King Alfonso of Spain. See the eagle on the radiator cap?" He ran his hand over the hood – what the Brits call a bonnet. "Eight liter engine, overhead cam, multiple-disc clutch, live-axle drive. This is the 46CV model."

I kicked one of the tires. "How many horses?"

"One hundred horse power at 1600 revs per minute," he boasted.

Ellen was running her fingers over the chrome mascot. She turned to me. "Is that good?"

"That's fantastic."

"Didn't this car win the Paris to Dakar Road Race last year?" I asked.

"He nodded. Yes, this make and model, but not this specific car."

Ellen's eyes were glinting with seeming reverence, as if she were touching a masterwork of engineering art.

"Can we take it out for a spin? I'm sure I can drive her all right. I need a fast car."

"Ellen, don't you think it might be a bit much and too impractical?"

Street scene on Route 66 in **Atlanta** – Dan Oberle collection

"Oh, Mike, you'll love me in this car – you'll see."

I reluctantly relented and the man fetched a set of keys. "Please, be careful."

I nodded.

The man tossed the cotton rag and gingerly climbed into a rear one-seat compartment barely large enough to hold him. Ellen slid behind the wheel as I held the door open for her. She pulled out the choke and turned on the key. The cylinders cut in with a mighty roar. I joined her on the passenger side with my knees tucked under my chin.

Ellen released the brake, and the car zoomed out into Heywood Street, scattering pedestrians. Luckily there were no policemen around. She achieved a neat screeching turn to the left and headed out for the open road. I pulled down on the brim of my slouch hat to tighten it on my head. A quick backward glance revealed a garage man who was tight-lipped and white as a sheet.

I cast an admiring look at Ellen. She was so alive and full of energy. I realized she was my polar opposite – a risk taker. It was a side of her I'd never seen before . . . as if she were the personification of the New Woman, gleefully throwing off the old Victorian constraints and basking in the glow of her newly found freedom.

Some men were threatened by this brash assertiveness

1930 Mercedes

that demanded women be treated as equals. I remembered the words of Carol Kennicott, the heroine of Sinclair Lewis' *Main Street*. "We're going to chuck it. . . . We're going to . . . come out and play with you men in the offices and clubs and politics you've cleverly kept for yourselves."

I was astonished by this new emancipated woman, but not threatened.

After about a mile, Ellen opened the throttle and allowed the full power of the engine to surge forward. My eyes closed tightly as I commended my soul to God. I risked a peek and saw the speedometer flick up past eighty and into the red. The mechanic leaned forward and bellowed, "That's fast enough, ma'am! I'm convinced! You can handle her!"

Ellen allowed the car to slacken speed and, for the first time, took her eyes off the road. She seemed a little disappointed.

"Oh, very well," she grumbled. My feet nearly went through the floorboard as she deftly completed a screaming U-turn on two wheels, and proceeded to whisk us back to the garage with more expedition and skill than on the way out.

We swept into the garage, came to an abrupt halt, and Ellen switched off the throaty growl of the engine.

Gillette shaving stand

I swallowed to regain my hearing. The engine of the Hispano-Suiza had been roaring like a lion. *She's really going to buy this motorcar*.

"Where did you learn to drive like that?" the mechanic gulped.

She tossed her head. "Alonzo Rivera, winner of the 1924 Lisbon road race, taught me. He said I had the makings of a race driver."

Ellen looked at me in pleading fashion. "What do you think, Mike?"

I took in a deep breath and pushed a comma of

hair back into place. "Darling, I think you've already made up your mind."

Her bright eyes danced. "You're right, I have."

She turned to the mechanic. "How much?"

"I uh, I really wasn't planning to sell it. I just rebuilt the engine . . . thinking about racing it myself."

"I don't mind what it costs."

He shoved his hands into his pockets and stared at the ground. "I really hate giving her up."

"Six months."

"What?"

"Let me have it for six months, and then I'll sell it back to you."

"I couldn't let it go for less than $7,000."

"And will you buy it back in six months for $6,000?"

"Uh, yeah, if it's still in good shape."

"Done!"

* * * *

Our wiretap on the Wellington Café proved vastly informative and highly interesting at times. Ralph Capone, we learned, usually went there in the late afternoon or evening. Since there would now be a lull in our raiding activities as various teams tracked down new leads, I decided to help man the listening post in Cicero.

A telephone headset was perched on a small table with a large yellow pad and several sharpened pencils beside it. John Kaufman had been manning the station. I took in the rest of the room with a glance. DeWitt was dozing with his mouth open in a stuffed chair and Mizell was resting on a couch.

"Has there been any action on the Alexander Graham Bell?"

"Nothing important," he answered.

I told Kaufman that I would take over now and that I had arranged for Tom Bischoff to relieve me later. Kaufman left and I sat down in the chair, waiting for the buzzer that would indicate a phone call to the Wellington. I watched it like a man waiting for a time bomb to explode. I gave up after half

an hour and started reading the newspaper. No sooner had I finished the front page when the sharp buzzing of the phone brought me up out of my chair.

I snatched up the headset and clamped it to my head. It was a woman's voice, far off and syrupy.

"New Orleans calling for Mr. Ralph Capone."

"Just a minute," came a harsh, grating voice that pounded against my eardrums. Then a firm business-like voice.

"This is Ralph Capone."

"Yeah, this is Angelo."

"Uh, Angelo, what's on your mind?"

"I just wanted to let you know that it's all fixed in the third race down here tomorrow. It'll be Black Bart at 20-1."

"Are you sure it's all set?" asked Capone.

"Absolutely. I'm betting five G's myself. I'm absolutely positive.

"Well, you better be. I'll put fifteen G's on it. Black Bart in the third. Right?"

"Right," said the faraway voice.

"Okay, thanks for calling."

Hanging up the headset, I turned to DeWitt and Mizell with a grin: "I can give you gentlemen a solid gold, bona fide, guaranteed, for sure genuine tip on a horse that can't lose tomorrow in the third race at New Orleans."

"You're kidding," Mizell answered.

"Not a bit," I replied. "Some gent named Angelo just called Ralph Capone all the way from New Orleans to tip him that the race is a sure fix. So sure that this Angelo is betting five thousand dollars on it and Capone is wagering fifteen thousand dollars."

DeWitt quickly sat upright. "Do you think Eliot would mind if we all put a little of our money on it? It's not very often we get a chance that's too good to pass."

"Let me call Eliot and see if it's

okay. I wouldn't want us to get our tit in the wringer over this."

I rang Eliot at the office and popped the question.

"You're not gonna believe his response," I said as I hung up the receiver.

"Really?"

"Uh, oh - was he mad?"

I stared at them with a disbelieving expression. Then I slowly allowed a broad grin to creep across my face. "He said to put in a ten dollar bet for him, too."

We were a day away from payday and didn't have much money. Between the three of us, we managed to scrape together the magnificent sum of twenty dollars.

"So we'll be filthy rich tomorrow night," I quipped. "This horse is a twenty-to-one shot, which means we'll have four hundred dollars to split three ways."

Paul took the money and left to place the bet, whistling *Ain't We Got Fun.*

When Friday came around, I became so engrossed in paperwork that I had forgotten all about our wager at the track. It was late in the day when I picked up the phone and heard Paul DeWitt grumbling at the other end.

"I just called one of my friends at the sports department at the *Tribune* and guess what happened?"

I figured he was putting on the dog just to throw me. "Did the odds change before the race? How much did we win?"

"Black Bart placed fifth – out of the money."

"You're kidding?"

His voice was morbidly emphatic. "No, sir. That's the straight dope."

"Well, I guess that taught all of us a lesson. While you're at it, you might whisper a brief prayer for Angelo."

I can't say for sure whether there was a direct connection, but two days later there was an article in the paper. The story said that a small-time gangster was found in a ditch on the outskirts of New Orleans, his body riddled with bullets.

Our tap on the phone paid dividends the next day. We overheard a conversation between Ralph Capone and Joe Fusco about the plant we had raided earlier on South Wabash. The Capone group was planning to reopen it, thinking that we would be too busy planning raids on other establishments.

We had Wes Bokal keep an eye on the place, and he called Eliot a few days later to let him know that they had moved new equipment into

Man O' War – Library of Congress

Film censor Will Hays

Body of Frank Capone

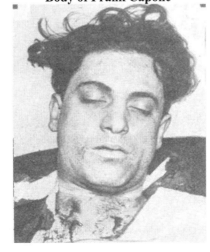

the building.

A couple of days later, Eliot led us on a raid that was a repeat of the first one. We smashed the doors with the truck and covered all the exits. The place was closed down again, costing Capone a huge amount of money and liquor supplies in the process.

A few days later, the storm broke. Arriving at the office even earlier than usual to go over some reports, I was hard at work and hadn't noticed the passage of time until Eliot walked in and asked if I was ready to go to lunch.

Looking at my watch, I saw that it was nearly eleven-thirty and I suggested a restaurant on Michigan Boulevard that had a blue plate special.

"Tell Kaufman to pull the car around while I make a quick phone call to Betty," he said.

"He wasn't at his desk when I came in, but I'll look again," I replied.

Going to the door, I scanned the outer office and called over my shoulder, "John's not here."

"That's peculiar," Eliot remarked. "Now that you mention it, I haven't seen him all morning. Give him a call at his home."

I walked back to my desk and reached for the telephone and called his home. His wife Diane answered almost immediately.

"John?" she asked.

"No, this is Mike Kriegan. I was hoping I would find John there."

Worry tinged her voice as she answered.

"He isn't here, Mr. Kriegan. He hasn't been home all night. I thought probably he was out with you somewhere. Don't you know where he is?"

"Now don't get all upset," I told her. "He's probably around checking up on something. I'll get in touch with him and have him call you as soon as possible."

"Please do," she said with a trace of panic.

I lamely tried to comfort her. "Everything will be all right. Don't worry."

But Eliot and I did. It wasn't like Kaufman to disappear without a word. A pencil snapped between my fingers as I put in a call to Detective Captain Michael Anderson, one of Chicago's honest cops.

After what seemed like ages, I heard this strong, sure voice at the other end.

"Captain Anderson speaking."

"Mike," I said. "This is Mike Kriegan from Eliot Ness' office."

"Greetings," he replied. "How are things in the liquor patrol business?"

"Eliot and I are fine. How are things with you?"

He chuckled. "Not too good. I must be getting old. I hit a hoodlum with my fist this morning and he didn't stay down."

I grinned at what probably was the truth, although I would have laid a bet that the old fire-eater's opponent didn't get up.

"John Kaufman, Eliot's driver didn't show up today, and his wife tells me he wasn't home last night. Things have been getting a little hot around here, and I wondered whether you'd check around and see if you can get any word on him."

"I'll see what I can find out," he promised briskly and rang off.

Eliot called the garage and was informed that Kaufman hadn't been in to pick up the car. Now we were really getting worried. Eliot and I waited by my phone for Captain Anderson to call back.

Shortly after noon the phone rang. It was the captain, and he sounded concerned.

He told Eliot that he might have some bad news, but he

Pierce Arrow

didn't want him to get all heated up because it might not be our man. He said that they found a body in a ditch outside Chicago Heights, but it was all shot up and there wasn't any identification.

"Where's the body now?" Eliot asked.

He said they took it over to Hannigan's Funeral Home near the Kensington Police Station.

"Thanks," Eliot told him heavily. "I hope it isn't our man Kaufman, but I've got a terrible feeling. Let's go," Eliot said sharply after he hung up.

The ride to the South Side was one of the longest of my life, although Eliot drove with reckless urgency. I thought

Judge Landis and Babe Ruth – author's collection

about what it would be like for Ellen if someone had to tell her the news that something had happened to me.

Actors Gabby Hayes and William Boyd

We pulled up in front of Hannigan's Funeral Home, and looking at the near brick building with the wide glass window in the front, I had to steel myself to make the journey with Eliot up the flower-bordered walk leading to the large white door.

Fear had a relentless grip on my throat, making it difficult to breathe. From the depths of the quiet flower-scented rooms inside, I heard a melodious chime in answer to the jab of my finger on the button. The wait seemed interminable before the door swung open and we were facing a bland unctuous man peering birdlike through a pince-nez from which trailed a black ribbon that looped around his neck.

"Yes, gentlemen?"

"We're from the United States District Attorney's office," Ness said, flipping out his credentials. "I understand the state police brought a body here a little while ago that was found out in the Heights. We'd like to take a look at it."

"Oh, yes," he nodded, dropping his welcome customer look. "You mean the unfortunate gentleman who had the, er, accident."

"That's the one," Ness told him.

"Follow me, please."

Standing aside to usher us in, he shut the door with the typical gentleness of his trade, and the musty odor of weeping flowers and astringent formaldehyde closed in around us. I always flinched at the smell of these places, and I breathed shallowly as he led us along a thickly carpeted hallway and through the rear into a bare, chilly room in which the only furnishings were two white surgical cabinets such as you see in hospitals, a straight-backed white metal chair, and a large enameled waste bucket with a foot-pedal top.

There also were two flat, rubber-wheeled carts which hospitals use for stretcher patients. Both of them bore bodies, their rigid mounds draped with white rubber sheets.

Ernest Hemingway – Brown Bros.

I moved toward one of them, barely conscious that Eliot was alongside me, and the mortician leaned over and drew back the sheet. A gusty breath rushed from my throat. It wasn't Kaufman but a grizzled

THE LASS WHO LOVED A SAILOR

ancient with hollow cheeks and a marble, vein-marked forehead.

My relief was short duration.

"Sorry, gentlemen," the mortician intoned regretfully, his voice filled with self-reproach. "This is not the one. This gentleman died, uh, a natural death."

We turned to walk across the room to the other slab. My throat tightened when he reached down to draw back the sheet, and as the rubber peeled away, I felt hot tears stinging the corner of my eyes, a roaring in my ears.

Lying there was a lifeless husk that had been John Kaufman. I stood there, eyes riveted on the strong, bold face. And my stare was drawn irresistibly to the gaping hole just above the left ear.

"Dumdum," I heard Eliot whisper.

"Bas- -rds," I mumbled, somewhat surprised at my use of profanity.

Carefully, Eliot drew the clammy rubber sheet up over the immobile face.

"We owe him a lot. He watched our backs on numerous raids," I said.

Eliot nodded.

I remembered the night in Pete Falcone's saloon when the killer in the silk shirt stood behind Ness with a poised stiletto and John's warning saved his life. I pictured him in my mind's eye behind the wheel of the steel-bumpered truck as he fearlessly drove it through the brewery doors.

I glanced at Eliot who had a blank expression on his face. I figured he was probably reminiscing along the same lines.

"So help me, God," he vowed. "Whoever did this is going to pay with his life."

* * * *

October 1930

Eliot and I were in his office one Friday morning when the phone rang. We were in a particularly bad mood because our latest series of raids hadn't been very successful. It was as if somebody was tipping the Capone mob off. We felt like we weren't making much headway. Eliot was busy wiping some spilled coffee off his tie, and he motioned for me to pick up. It was Bill Hunt, a stoolie we nicknamed "Willie the Canary." His words were nervous and hurried.

"If ya can meet me in the men's room at the Sears store on State Street at eleven-thirty, I got some dope ya might be interested in."

His wanting to meet us via a department store washroom indicated that it wasn't very healthy these days to be talking to Eliot Ness. I clamped my hand over the mouthpiece and informed Eliot of Willie's request. Eliot hesitated, and then gave me a thoughtful nod.

"All right," I told him. "We'll be there at eleven-thirty sharp."

"This could be a trap," I warned Eliot.

"I know. We'll get there twenty minutes early to check the place out. We'll bring Paul DeWitt and Gillespie along with us to be close by, acting like typical shoppers. That way there'll be safety in numbers, and they can keep an eye on anyone who goes in the washroom."

Charlie Chaplin

We drove two cars to the Sears store. Eliot and I cautiously went into the men's facility. One man who was washing his hands, left a few seconds after we entered. We proceeded to check out all the stalls to make sure they were empty. I stayed in one stall and hopped up on the toilet seat, feeling pretty much like a

269

hunched over toad. There was enough of a crack where the stall door was hinged for me to see Eliot.

Another man came into the room and used the urinal. Eliot was at one of the basins meticulously washing his hands. He took his time as he dried them off on the pull down dispenser cloth. Then he went back to the bank of basins and started combing his hair. The other man quickly washed and dried his hands without paying much attention to Eliot. Then he briskly vacated the room.

Five minutes later Willie came inside. His adam's apple bobbed nervously in his skinny neck as he spoke, all the while making nervous glances toward the door.

"Just thought ya might want to know the Big Fella threw a fit yesterday. The way I got it from a guy who was there, Capone carried on like a raving maniac. He was pacing back and forth, the veins popping out on the sides of his face. He kept yellin,' "I'll kill 'em, I'll kill 'em with my bare hands." He even took a couple of chairs and busted 'em good on a table. The guy told me . . . "

Willie broke it off as three men entered the restroom. One of them was laughing at a punch line the other had delivered to finish a joke. They wouldn't be laughing, I thought, if they knew the third man was Paul DeWitt and had them covered with his .38.

Willie disappeared into a stall and Eliot went into his hair combing routine while the three men used the urinals. After all of them left, Willie came out from his stall.

"This guy tells me," Willie hurriedly picked up where he had left off, "that they had a heckuva time calming Capone down."

I smiled as I pictured Capone going berserk, with his white scars outlined against a crimson face that was filled with rage.

"They were all there: Jake Guzik, Machine Gun McGurn, Mops Volpe, Bomber Belcastro, brother Ralph and Three-fingered Jack White. They jus sat there till the Big Fella wears hisself out. Then he starts all over again, and Ralph tries to calm him down by telling him that they got enough trouble without trying to knock off some feds."

"Finally, they chase everybody outta the room 'cept Al and Ralph, and the last thing this guy hears is the Big Fella saying 'I want Ness dead, even if it's on the front steps of City Hall.' And thatsa 'bout it," Willie gulped nervously.

Willie headed for the door, but after he grabbed the handle he turned around, came back, and handed a note to Eliot.

"I almost forgot. I jotted down something else for ya on this slip of paper."

*   *   *   *

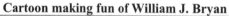
Cartoon making fun of William J. Bryan

Albert Einstein

"Mike, pull up a seat. There's something we need to talk about."

My stomach tightened into a ball of anxiety. Eliot had a look on his face I'd never seen before. He wasn't merely crestfallen or dejected. He looked crushed.

I pulled up a chair. "Sure, Eliot. You look worried. What's up?"

He rose from his desk and began pacing the floor, his thumbs hooked in the armholes of his vest. "Last night I sent some of the boys out on a reconnaissance mission to check out a possible brewery. They were ambushed and Gary Tesson got killed."

"Oh, no, no!" I shook my head in sorrow. Tears welled up in my eyes when I thought about what a good man Tesson had been. I remembered the conversations I'd had with Gary and some of the jokes we had shared. "I can't believe it. First John, and now Gary. Have you told his parents yet?"

Eliot was dabbing at the wetness in his eyes with a handkerchief. "No, I was going to do that this afternoon when I got my composure back."

I shook my head. "What a shame. Gary was an asset to the team – lots of guts and integrity."

"Are you going to try and find a replacement?"

"No, I just received a call from the boys at IRS. They say in a month or two they'll be ready with their tax evasion case against Capone. I also checked with the Treasury Department and they said they're ready to go with their charges of prohibition law violations."

"That's great. At least John and Gary's deaths won't be in vain. They were an important part of our work."

Eliot nodded. "You can say that again."

It took a few moments before either one of us said anything. Then Eliot dropped his head and stared at the floor. "There's something else, Mike."

"Not more bad news?"

"I'm afraid so. I think someone is leaking information to Capone and his men. I think that's how Gary ended up getting killed last night." That slip of paper Willie the Canary handed me yesterday said that Capone was getting information about our operations."

His words hit me in the sternum like a sledgehammer. "But, who? How?"

"I've done some checking. I don't think it's a member of the team."

I shook my head in disbelief. "Then . . . who?"

"I hate to tell you this, Mike, but I think it's Ellen Esposito."

I nearly fell out of my chair. "Ellen? But she isn't privy to what's going on. We don't discuss my work."

"Think hard, Mike. It probably wasn't anything overt. She undoubtedly was too smart for that. Think subtle. Some insignificant comment, a minor slip on your part."

"You're wrong, Eliot. It wasn't Ellen. I know her."

Cub and Cardinal great Rogers Hornsby

Eliot's eyes had a hard look to them. "That's what Sampson said about Delilah before she cut his hair."

"She was with me all that time at Mermet Lake. I wouldn't have made it back without her. You're wrong."

"Remember when Arleigh Jones, The Kid, was battered and had his ears cut off?"

"Of course."

Eliot leaned forward with his elbows on the desk. "Did you ever mention Arleigh to Ellen?"

"Absolutely not! No, I . . . uh." My thoughts took me back in time. I tried to think of all my conversations with Ellen. Then it hit me. There was this one brief comment . . . . an inadvertent slip of the tongue.

"Okay, I did mention him to her one time. Once! But it was harmless. She didn't pry for more information. She wouldn't betray us. You're talking about the girl I'm going to marry."

"I know, Mike. But think about it. You've been with her a few months. You don't really know her. She grew up with a family connected to Capone. The first twenty-two years of her life have left a lasting impression on her. Zebras can't change their stripes."

"I don't know, Eliot. What you're saying is logical, but I can't believe it's true. Surely it's not possible."

"There were probably other times when little things that you said, comments you made, were a tip off. Perhaps it was something innocuous like, 'I won't be able to see you until seven o'clock tonight,' or 'we've got something big planned for tomorrow.' "

I leaned forward and buried my face in my hands. There was no use denying it. Eliot was probably right. It was the

William Randolph Hearst

only logical explanation. My work had recently become more and more a part of our conversation. Ellen explained it away by saying that she was worried sick about something happening to me.

"I know you didn't mean for any of this to happen, Mike. But it still doesn't change anything. You're off the team. If the press ever gets hold of this the Untouchables will be subject to ridicule. I hate to do it, Mike. We're so close to the end and you were an important part of it. I don't know if I could have made it without you."

Off the team. Those words . . . like a shotgun blast in the chest.

I rose to my feet, unable to look Eliot in the eye. "I'm sorry, Eliot. So sorry things turned out this way. It's going to be hard for me to live with myself knowing that my actions might have been responsible for the death of one of our group."

"We don't know that for sure, Mike," Eliot said consolingly.

"I'm so sorry." My tongue was thick and my words seemed to stick in my throat.

Eliot came over and gave me a hug. "Don't be too hard on yourself, pal. You did a lot of good under tremendous pressure. Lesser men would have fallen apart."

Stan Laurel and Oliver Hardy

"Thanks, I appreciate that, Eliot" I offered weakly. I gave him a limp handshake. "So long, buddy. Be sure and send me an invitation to your wedding."

Eliot stepped back with a perplexed frown. "Are you crazy? This doesn't change anything about our relationship. I still want you to be my best man."

"I dunno Eliot. Uh, I guess so, that is if you still want me."

"Of course I do. Hey, Mike, it's me . . . Eliot. Why don't you take a week off before you go back home. You've been under a terrible strain."

"Sure, Eliot. That's what I need. Well, I'll be seeing you."

We shook hands again and I turned and walked out the door. I was too embarrassed to say anything to Marillyn Watts as I stumbled past her desk.

Artist Georgia O'Keefe

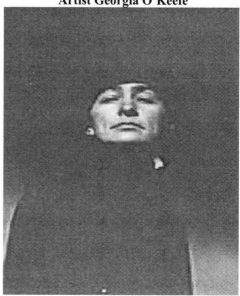

* * * *

"How could you do it Ellen? Betray my love, my trust?"

A frown appeared on the bridge of her nose. "Mike, I don't have the slightest idea what you're talking about."

I had gone to her apartment to confront her. She had moved there after our trip to Mermet Lake and Murray Humphreys had tried to kill us.

I was furious and it showed. "You can go back to your old life now. There's no use pretending anymore."

"Mike, what on earth do you mean? You're talking crazy."

I slammed my fist on her kitchen table where we were seated. "It's over, Ellen. Eliot finally figured out that you've been giving information to the Capone mob."

She shook her head. "That's insane."

"We don't have absolute proof, but you're the only one who knew details about our operations. Your treachery probably got one of our men killed."

Typical tourist park of the 1920s

272

"Oh, Mike, Mike my darling; you've got it all wrong." She stood up and came over to me. Standing behind my chair, she put her arms around me and kissed my cheek.

I pushed her away and bolted to my feet, turning to face her so she would feel the full brunt of my wrath. "Don't give me any of that. We're through, finished. I just can't believe I was stupid enough to believe your lies."

She was sobbing now, but those crocodile tears weren't fooling me.

"Mike, I swear it wasn't me. I love you with all my heart. I could never do anything like that."

I was unmoved. "Save it, they sure gave out the Academy Award for "Best Actress" to the wrong person this year. You've got all the others beat by a mile."

She took my hands and with tears streaming down her cheeks tried to plead her case. I shoved them down and turned toward the front door. "I'm leaving now. Your sob act isn't going to do you any good. It's a real shame Ellen because I thought we were a perfect match for each other."

I walked out the door and slammed it behind me, closing a sorry chapter in my life.

CHAPTER 22

JULY 17, 1931

MAYHEM MENU OFFERED BY FIVE POINTS GANG

Punching	$2
Both eyes blacked	$4
Nose and jaw broke	$10
Knocked out with black jack	$15
Ear chawed off	$19
Shot in leg	$25
Stab	$25
Doing the big job	$100

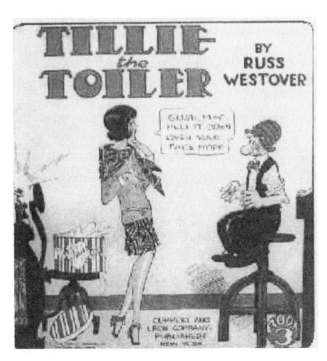

Sexy Betty Boop

During the next few months Eliot and the team continued making raids on Capone's breweries and collecting ledgers and receipts to tie Capone to the enormous profits of his illicit enterprises and help build a case against him. Someone once said that the wheels of justice grind exceedingly slow. With the records and ledgers we had seized in raids providing much of the evidence, both Ralph Capone and Jake "Greasy Thumb" Guzik were nailed on income tax evasion charges which netted them three and five year prison sentences respectively. Cousin Frank Nitti went to the slammer for eighteen months.

I was still in Chicago, moping around my apartment feeling sorry for myself. I wanted to stay long enough to see if the Untouchables could put Capone away. I bought a newspaper every day to read about their exploits and stay abreast of new developments. Most of the time I stayed inside still dressed in my pajamas. My only consolation was Thor, Mrs. Griffin's unusually affectionate cat that was now living with me.

I thought a lot about Ellen. I couldn't help myself. Her memory tortured my soul. Over and over I replayed the happy times we'd shared together. I knew it wasn't good for my mental health, but I couldn't help it.

One day the postman rang my doorbell and delivered a package. I had to sign for it because it was insured. I peeled away the tape and packing material, wondering what could be inside such a small box. There was no note or message inside, just a ring with a solitary diamond – the one I'd given to Ellen.

Life without Ellen was unbearable, but I also longed for my old job. I ached to once again be a part of the Untouchables – to feel the adrenaline rush just before we went crashing through a set of brewery doors – to share in

the camaraderie with the group as we rehashed events after the raid was over.

Eliot was scheduled to appear before a grand jury to give testimony about Al Capone. Chicago was abuzz with excitement when the newspapers reported on June 12, 1931, that indictments were handed down against Al Capone and sixty-eight others, charging them with hundreds of violations of the prohibition laws and tax evasion.

Everyone wondered if Al Capone and his Jewish lawyers were going to find some way to beat the rap. Capone was freed after posting $50,000 bail on an income tax charge that said he failed to pay $215,000 in federal taxes on his income.

The day before his testimony, I got a call from Eliot. I was surprised because it was the first time he'd contacted me since my dismissal from the team.

His voice bubbled with enthusiasm. "Hello, pal. I've got good news for you."

I stroked my three day growth of facial whiskers. "I know, Eliot. I've been following your progress in the newspaper."

"Yes, it looks like we're finally going to put Capone away, but that isn't why I called."

"Don't tell me you've set a wedding date."

"No, not that either, although it probably won't be long."

"Well, what is it?"

"You're back on the team."

The hairs on the back of my neck prickled. "How, why?"

"It wasn't Ellen. She wasn't the source of the leak. I had it all wrong?"

I couldn't believe my ears. "How did you find out?"

"It really bothered me that you weren't on the team anymore. Yesterday I was in reverie, thinking about the good times, reminiscing about our adventures, and then it hit me."

My heart was pounding in my chest. "What was it, what

came to mind?"

"I was thinking about the time you went up that telephone pole and tapped Capone's phone."

"Okay, I remember, what about it." My hand flew to my forehead. All of a sudden I figured it out. "Wait, let me guess. If we had the ability to tap Capone's phones, why couldn't he do the same thing to us? He tapped our phones at the office."

"Exactly. You got it right, Mike."

"Oh, Eliot. Why didn't I think of that. It could have saved us so much grief."

"That's water under the bridge now, Mike. I want you to be there with me when I testify tomorrow."

"Sure thing, boss. Right now I'm on my way to see Ellen. I'm going to get down on my knees and beg her forgiveness."

"We're human, old buddy. We all make mistakes. Please give her my apologies also."

"I will. Bye, Eliot, I'm on my way with wings on my feet."

I excitedly drove over to Ellen's apartment, hoping she'd be there. She answered the doorbell, looking just as beautiful as ever.

"Mike, what . . . what on earth are you doing here?"

"Oh, Ellen. Can you ever forgive me? I just found out from Eliot that you weren't the source of our leak."

"What do you mean?"

"Eliot discovered that Capone was finding out about our operations because he tapped our phones at the office."

"Oh, Mike, that's wonderful news." She stepped back and gave me a stern look. "I tried to tell you I wasn't the one. How could you have doubted me?"

"I'm so sorry, Ellen. I'll never doubt you again. Please say you forgive me." I kissed the back of her hands.

"She tenderly placed her arms around my neck. "I was so hurt by what you said – those horrible accusations – I thought I'd never be able to forgive you." She paused.

"Yes, go on."

"But then I thought about it. I've been miserable ever since we've been apart."

"Me too, honey."

"If I had been in your shoes and Eliot Ness had told me what he told you, I probably would have reacted the same way. After all, we hadn't really known each other that long."

"By the way, Eliot sends his regrets and offers his sincerest apology."

"Tell him I accept." Ellen gave me a passionate kiss and then drew back, tossing me a mischievous look. "Did you remember to bring anything with you?"

I stood there a few seconds in puzzlement. "Oh, yeah!" I reached inside my suit coat and pulled out a diamond ring and slipped on her finger.

George Eastman

She extended her hand and admired the bauble. "Nice rock! I think I'm going to like being Mrs. Mike Kriegan."

We kissed again and promised to love each other till the end of time.

After Eliot testified, we went back to his office. I was scanning the front page of a newspaper I had bought in the courthouse lobby.

"Hey, Eliot. The paper says that Baby Face Nelson was caught robbing a jewelry store and they're sending him away."

"Where to?"

"Joliet."

"Good. One less bum to worry about. Any other criminal news?" he asked.

"Yeah, it says that Fred and Doc Barker – Ma Barker's boys - just got out of prison and they're already suspected of killing a sheriff in Missouri."

"Rehabilitation doesn't seem to be working very well in our prison system," he said somberly.

"Not when it comes to hardened criminals." I changed the subject. "I bet Capone and his mouthpiece try to claim that since his income came from illegal sources, it would be illegal to try and make him pay taxes on the money."

He smiled. "It would mean that prostitutes and professional gamblers should also be exempt. That's an interesting concept – the IRS trying to collect legal taxes on illegal money."

"Yeah," I replied, "it might somehow be construed as a violation of the 5th Amendment – like forcing someone to testify against himself."

"The government might win if the IRS keeps this information to itself and doesn't tell other law enforcement agencies."

Famous cough drops logo

Ness nodded. "The courts might go along with that."

"If Capone goes to prison, we break the back of this whole rotten mess. Then you'd be free to marry Betty, your sweetheart."

He laughed. "Betty is already trying to get me to agree to a tentative wedding date." He took out a newspaper clipping from his desk drawer and handed it to me. "An acquaintance of Betty's from Quincy sent her this."

The clipping was from the *Whig-Herald*. It was an editorial with the heading THE BIG GUY ON THE HOT SEAT.

"I've even heard rumors that Cleveland, Ohio, wants to hire me to clean up a similar mess in that town."

I glanced over the article and saw that it gave much of the credit to Eliot. A slightly fatuous grin bent my lips. "Big man, huh?"

Eliot lowered his head, slightly embarrassed. "Hey, congratulations, you deserve every bit of praise you get," I said.

"Are you still planning to marry Ellen Esposito?"

"Yeah, she's still under my skin. I'm happy as a

Theda Bara – "The Vamp Girl"

275

lark when I'm with her."

Four days after the indictments were handed down, Big Al walked into court with his lawyer and pleaded guilty to the charges. Eliot and I were sitting in court at the time of the arraignment on July 30, 1931. I jabbed him in the ribs with my elbow.

"If Capone gets the max he could be fined $90,000 and be given thirty-four years in prison for failure to pay taxes from 1924-1929."

Eliot shook his head. "No way. Capone and his lawyer have some kind of deal cooked up where he'll pay about $50,000 in fines and get about nine months in jail."

I studied Capone and saw that he had a smirk on his face. "I'm afraid you're right. That won't be much of a victory for us – all that hard work and bullet dodging for a measly fine and a few months in jail."

Eliot's face wore a frown. "Unfortunately, that's just about par for tax violations. The judge would have to set a huge precedent to give Capone what he deserves."

"What would make you happy?"

Eliot bit on his lower lip as the wheels turned in his brain. "He would have to get about six years to make it all worth it." He paused a few seconds. "Wouldn't it be great if they sent him to that new prison the feds are building in San Francisco."

"Yeah, I read about that place. It's supposed to be on an island in the bay near the Golden Gate Bridge."

"It's called Alcatraz," Ness said. "You don't get sent there directly, they cull prisoners from all over the country and pick the 'worst of the worst' to go there."

"That would be great if he ended up there. Otherwise, I fear he might go to someplace like Atlanta and bribe the warden into giving him a cushy job at the prison library."

Our discussion was cut short as U.S. District Attorney George Q. Johnson began to explain the terms of the deal Capone's lawyer had worked out with the attorney general, the IRS, and an assistant secretary of the treasury.

I glanced over at Capone. He was dressed in a outlandish lavender colored suit, matching accessories and black and

Lincoln statue at **Divernon/New Salem** – Oberle Route 66 collection

Shea's Service at **Springfield** – Dan Oberle Route 66 collection

white spectator shoes. He was chewing furiously on a stick

House in **Lincoln** – Dan Oberle Route 66 collection

of gum. His usual entourage of well-heeled gunmen sat behind him. His eyes shuttled back and forth between the judge and his attorney. Capone's countenance went south as he glanced our way and caught a glimpse of Eliot and me.

Capone's jaw dropped a foot when he heard grave remarks from the jurist. "Mr. Capone must understand that a plea of guilty is a full admission of guilt. The court must assume, on the defendant's plea, that the defendant committed the offenses as stated in the indictment. The defendant must realize that this court alone will determine the punishment."

Capone's attorney replied that it was his understanding when he made the agreements that the court would accept them.

Capone nearly fell out of his chair at what he heard next. "The defendant must understand that the punishment has not been decided before the close of the hearing. There can be no bargaining in the federal court."

Capone and his lawyer briefly conferred and then the judge was informed that the guilty plea would be withdrawn, and that a jury trial would determine Capone's guilt or innocence.

The trial was held for eleven days, starting on October 6. Capone was represented by the firm of Nash and Ahern. Squad cars carrying a bevy of detectives escorted Capone from the Lexington to the Federal Court Building on Dearborn, between Adams and Jackson. The eight-story structure was of massive Roman Corinthian design, apropos for such an important trial. It would later be the site of the famed Kefauver Crime Commission hearings.

Eliot and I were again on hand for the Big Show. As the Big Fella was escorted into the hall next to the

276

courtroom, he was besieged by a mass of reporters. His dress was once again outlandish, a pea colored pinchback suit with shiny brown and white Florsheims. One of the reporters used the word racketeer in connection with the charges against Al. He smiled and then upbraided the reporter for using the word.

"Racketeer! Why, the real racketeers are the banks." You could always depend on Capone for a good quote. Chicagoans counted it a dull day when there was not at least one story in the papers about Capone.

Everyone stood in respect for the judge when the traditional "Oyez, oyez, all rise – court is now in session . . ." was mouthed by the bailiff. Then they took their seats and waited for the jury selection process to begin.

I nudged Eliot. "I wonder how many jurors he has in his pocket?"

"It only takes one," came a terse reply.

"Capone looks way too cheerful," I said.

Eliot didn't respond. He seemed tight as a drum. He probably felt as if the weight of the world was on his shoulders. Nearly three years of work might go down the drain. I could tell he was wondering whether the fix was in.

When the name of the first venireman was called, Capone

Marlene Dietrich in The Blue Angel

quickly lost his composure. "What's going on?" I quietly asked Eliot.

"I'm not sure. My guess is that Judge Wilkerson switched jurors at the last minute with another judge to prevent jury tampering and subornation of perjury."

I was surprised to see that the judge wasn't wearing any judicial robes. The man with tousled gray hair simply wore a dark blue business suit. It took him until 4 p.m. to empanel the jury – all men. The members swore that they harbored no ill will toward Capone, nor did they have a desire to see him imprisoned.

The next day the government paraded witnesses who testified that Capone had filed no tax returns for the years 1924 to 1929 and others who swore to Capone's ownership

of certain businesses such as a Smoke Shop that profited over $500,000 during a two-year period.

Motel at **Mitchell** – Dan Oberle Route 66 collection

On the third day the witness parade continued. "Who are the government's assistant district attorneys?" I asked Eliot.

"The only one I recognize is Dwight Green."

Eliot glanced over at the prosecution team. "The others are Bill Froelich, Mike Clawson and Jacob Grossman. I hear Green has ambitions of running for governor."

I nodded. "A case like this will certainly give him name recognition."

"Have you heard the latest?"

What's that?" I replied.

"Capone had a tailor fitting him for a new suit at the Lexington last night."

I shrugged. "Where's the story in that?"

His pal, Frankie Rio was with him. Frankie told Capone that he didn't need any fancy new duds where he was going. He suggested instead that he order a suit with stripes on it."

I had to smile at that one.

On Friday we were on our way to the 6th floor courtroom when I slightly bumped against a man in a gray suit on the elevator. I felt the hard contours of a revolver as a result of the encounter. The man was Phil D'Andrea, Capone's bodyguard who had been sitting

Walt Disney's Mickey Mouse

behind him all during the trial. After we were seated, I leaned over and told Eliot about the incident.

"No wonder some of the witnesses seemed a little nervous

Al Capone – Chicago Historical Society

when they testified. I'll say something about it to the prosecution."

Eliot went over to the prosecution team and relayed what I had told him. Dwight Green then asked permission to approach the judge. Wilkerson motioned him forward and the two engaged in a whispered session. Wilkerson told Green that after about ten minutes into the trial he would signal the bailiff to notify D'Andrea that a messenger outside had a Western Union telegram for him.

True to his word, the signal was given shortly after the trial reconvened. When D'Andrea went outside he was hustled off by agents to a side room and separated from his revolver. Then he was brought back into the courtroom. Ahern, Capone's lawyer, tried to intercede on behalf of D'Andrea telling the judge that the man had a good record of taking care of his mother and that he meant no affront to the court. Wilkerson would have none of it and dispatched D'Andrea with a contempt citation and a six months jail sentence.

The trial continued and other prosecution witnesses

Modish Mitzi

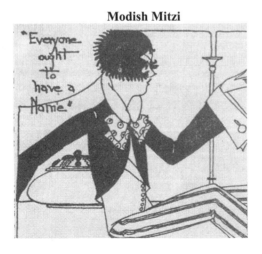

included waitresses who testified about Capone's large tips, tellers who took large bets from Capone at the racetrack, and contractors from Miami who had remodeled Capone's estate at Palm Island.

"Well, this is the prosecution's last witness," Eliot whispered as he leaned in my direction.

"Who is it?"

"Edward O'Hare."

"O'Hare . . . isn't he the man who got rich by marketing the mechanical rabbit to dog tracks," I asked.

"Yes."

"What in the world made him brave enough to testify against Capone?"

Eliot threw me a perplexed look. "George Johnson told me he's doing it in exchange for his son getting an appointment to the Naval Academy in Annapolis."

"You mean "Butch" O'Hare?"

"That's right."

O'Hare was associated with several tracks and testified to some big spending and big winnings by Capone.

The next day the prosecution rested its case, and the defense staged its dog and pony show. In spite of the recent Supreme Court decision about paying taxes on illegal income in the *Sullivan* case, enough "ifs" were still floating around to leave room for legal hedging. Capone's team put a Hialeah bookie on the stand who testified that Capone had

Dodge sedan

lost as much as $10,000 numerous times betting the ponies. Under cross-examination, the bookie was asked to name some of the horses, but he said that he couldn't recall their exact names off the top of his head.

My own research lit a bulb in my brain. I quickly scribbled a note and took it over to the defense table. After he read it, Dwight Green smiled and gave me an A-OK signal with his hand.

"Isn't the horse betting losses thing a moot point?" Green asked the judge.

"How so?" countered the judge.

"I believe that this is a specious argument – grasping at straws. According to the IRS code, it's my understanding that bettors may only deduct *losses* from *winnings* at the racetrack. So far, the defendant hasn't admitted to anything but being a loser at the track."

The judge nodded in affirmation. "I believe that is correct Mr. Green."

As one might expect, there were a variety of interesting spectators who showed up and a few oddball events that enlivened the proceedings. A Union Civil War veteran, whom I judged to be in his nineties, brought a bouquet of flowers into the courtroom and handed it to the judge. Then he took a seat and proceeded to sleep through the rest of the trial.

The noted author Rafael Sabatini sat in on the proceedings for one day. He was in town to promote his latest swashbuckling romance/adventure novel. Reporters asked him if he was going to write a novel about Capone. He told them that he probably wouldn't because Capone seemed to be a man who lacked ideals. Sabatini stated that Benito Mussolini would probably be a more fitting subject for a work of fiction.

A shapely brunette witness from the Miami Western Union office said she thought Chicago was boring. "What do y'all do for excitement up here?" she asked.

On another occasion Beatrice Lillie, the star of *The Third Little Show* that was playing at the Great Northern Theater, showed up. Her husband, Lord Peel, was with her. There was a slight delay in the proceedings that day as other spectators rushed over for her autograph.

Dick Tracy by Chester Gould

Perhaps the most damning evidence against Capone were the ledgers and receipts recovered after our tussle with the mobsters at the Liberty Hotel. Prosecutors introduced receipts for $7,000 worth of suits; $1,500 per week hotel bills; $39,000 worth of phone calls, and $20,000 for silverware.

Also, thanks to information we supplied, Capone was shown to have committed 5,000 violations of the Volstead Act since 1920.

On the ninth day of the trial Capone showed up in another one of his flamboyant pastel-colored outfits.

I leaned over toward Eliot. "What color would you call that?"

"I don't know – maybe flamingo."

After the tenth day of the trial, the defense rested. Ahern gave his summation, pointing out that much of what the public had read in the newspapers was pure exaggeration. He noted that Capone lived in a rather unassuming house at 7244 Prairie Avenue – hardly the residence of a wealthy man. He asked the jury to find Capone innocent of the "intent to defraud" charge, claiming that it was his honest belief that he owed no taxes on his income. "Mr. Capone is a persecuted man. The evidence in this case shows only one thing – that he's a spendthrift."

The prosecution then gave its final arguments in the case. Johnson, arms flapping with the vehemence of his emotion, hit hard on the piles and piles of evidence

collected by the Untouchables in our raids. He showed the jury a picture of Capone's expensive Cadillac. He handed

Cartoon - couple necking

them other pictures of his ostentatious Palm Island estate in Florida. And he surprised everyone by showing the jury another picture of a Capone retreat, this time in Cuba.

Dwight Green got up and assailed the Robin Hood image painted by the defense as he reminded jurors about how Capone gave $8,000 diamond encrusted belt buckles to his hoodlum friends, not to the homeless or the hungry.

The jury retired for deliberations at 2:40 p.m.

"How long do you think it will take?" I asked Eliot.

He shrugged. "It could be a few hours or a few days."

Reporters and officials stood around in the hallway for hours, as did Capone, in case of a quick verdict. "Don't guilty verdicts come in quicker than not guilty ones?" I asked Eliot.

"Usually, but you can never say for sure."

Paul DeWitt arrived and asked if we had heard anything yet. I pointed to the jurors, most of whom were in their shirtsleeves. They were in another part of the building but you could see them through the windows. "They're still locked in debate," I answered.

American Flyer trains - made in Chicago

When night fell Capone left the building, deciding to sweat it out at the Lexington. We went to get a bite to eat at

279

a local restaurant. When we finished, we came back to the courthouse. Around 11 p.m. there was a burst of applause from the 6th floor corridor of the courthouse. The last holdout had apparently given in to the majority.

A half-hour later, Capone and Judge Wilkerson returned to the courtroom. Wilkerson asked the jury foreman if they had reached a decision. "Yes, we have, Your Honor," came the reply. The foreman handed a note to the bailiff, who in turn delivered it to the clerk of the court who read it. It was a puzzling, muddled verdict, leaving me to wonder whether ordinary citizens were up to the task of handling complex legal issues. On the first indictment for 1924 they voted *not guilty*. On three of the twenty-two counts charging tax evasion for 1925, 1926 and 1927, they voted *guilty*. It was guilty also on counts 13 and 18, which charged failure to file a return for 1928 and 1929. On all the remaining counts, the vote was *not guilty*.

The defense immediately announced that they would file an appeal with the U.S. Court for the Seventh District. Judge Wilkerson said that sentencing would be on Saturday, October 24, one week later.

Capone showed up at his sentencing in a purplish suit.

Racketeering cartoon

Eliot said he thought it was periwinkle. Capone had a nervous look as he stood to hear the sentence. A bead of sweat popped out on his forehead. His hands were locked in an awkward manner behind his back.

Different sentences were handed down on the various counts, but when it all added up, he was sentenced to eleven years in prison, fined $50,000, and ordered to pay court costs amounting to $30,000. Wilkerson denied bail and ordered Capone to be taken to the Cook County Jail. From there he was to be whisked away the next day to the federal penitentiary in Atlanta.

There was bedlam as reporters snapped pictures and then rushed to file their stories for an extra edition that was sure

to come. Some stayed to shout questions at Capone before he was led away.

1920s couple at a speak-easy

"Do you think you got a fair trial?"
"Are you going to write your memoirs in prison?"
"Who's taking over the Outfit while you're gone?"
"What do you think of Judge Wilkerson?"
Capone's only reply: "It was a blow below the belt, but what else can you expect when the whole community is prejudiced against you."

Then he softened a little.

"Please don't take my picture after they lock me up. Think of my family."

The next day, Eliot arranged for a five-car caravan to escort Capone from the Cook County Jail to the old Dearborn train station. Everyone was armed, thinking of the possibility of a last-minute rescue attempt. Capone was escorted from his jail cell by U.S. marshals.

Shouts of encouragement from other prisoners echoed down the corridor.

"Keep your chin up, Al."
"Ya got a bum break, Big Fella."

Capone goes to jail

"This city owes ya a lot, Al."

"You'll own the joint in a few months, Snorkey."

TO BE OR NOT TO BE? THAT IS THE QUESTION

The comments seemed to buoy Capone's spirits. "Jeez," he said with a tinge of pride. "You'd think Mussolini was passin' through."

We forced a path through the photographers and helped Capone into the second car in the caravan. It was about 10:30 when the gates were opened and we began to move out. There was a crowd of roughly 400 people near the gates, straining to get one last glimpse of Al Capone.

"Keep your eyes open," I told DeWitt and Kaufman. "There's no telling what Capone's goons might try to pull." As it turned out, our trip was uneventful. We drove on California Boulevard to Ogden Avenue, then onto Jackson Boulevard and on over to Clark Street. Soon we pulled up in front of the Dearborn Station. There was another large crowd and scads of photographers on hand. Capone got out

Josephine Sinard – Wife of Hymie Weiss - Courtesy Sarah Sinard

of his car and we trailblazed a path through the unyielding mob in flying wedge fashion, much like the old football formation that was outlawed.

Many of Capone's friends were in the crowd and they yelled encouragements to him. I spotted two of his younger brothers, and they said their farewells to Al with a nod and a special look in their eye. Nobody lifted a finger to impede our progress.

That evening we took Capone to the train station for his trip to that grim prison in Atlanta. We boarded the *Dixie Flyer*, the pride of the Chicago & Eastern Illinois Railroad. The train consisted of eight coaches and the second from the last was reserved for Capone and his entourage of lawmen and U.S. marshals.

When Eliot and I checked Capone for the last time, he was already seated and had lit up one of his big fat cigars. He looked at us with those famous cold gray eyes.

"Well, thanks to you two I'm on my way to do eleven long years on a tax rap."

"I think the judge probably tossed in a few years for other things you've gotten away with over the years," Eliot replied.

He nodded. "I'm not sore at anybody, but I might not be here in this fix if I'da listened to my boys and rubbed you two out that day at the Lexington."

"No, you'd be facing the chair if you would have had us

Shall Chicago Stand for This?

killed. Try to think of this as a long vacation. You'll probably get out early for good behavior the way you did in Pennsylvania," I said.

"Yeah, maybe I'm better off. There's too much hassle and too much killing in this business. They ought to make it legit."

It was obvious Capone still thought of himself as a buccaneer capitalist rather than a gangster. The American dream gone sour.

"You wouldn't have been interested if it had been legitimate," Ness said dryly.

Capone was still watching us as we backed out into the corridor, seeing him for the last time.

Our entire crew was on the platform as the doors of the train clanged shut and the engine began to pull away. None of us said a word until the red lights on the tail end winked out in the distance.

I turned to Eliot. "Hey, boss. How about you and I have a double wedding?"

He remained silent a few seconds. Then he smiled big and put his arm around me. "Sure, why not old buddy – that might be fun."

We stood there in a quiet state of euphoria, basking in self-satisfaction. The miasma of evil that had hung over Chicago for over a decade had finally been lifted. Justice had been served. *All's right with the world.*

It had been a difficult struggle, like Roland with his sword *Durendal* holding off the Saracens at Roncesvalles. I reconsidered. No, I thought, this was more modern. I took a deep breath and smiled, wondering if this was what Wyatt Earp felt like after cleaning up Dodge City.

POSTSCRIPT

Al Capone was taken to Atlanta Prison on May 4, 1932. His mother retained renowned lawyer William Leahy in an effort to get her son's conviction overturned. The main focus of the appeal was based on the Statute of Limitations. Capone lost the appeal.

In August of 1934, a high security train transferred

Frank Nitti commits suicide

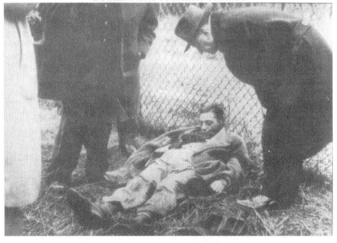

Capone from Atlanta to a place known as The Rock – Alcatraz.

By 1938 Capone was exhibiting advanced stages of his syphilitic disorder. He had moments of dementia, loss of motor control, and fell prey to occasional babbling.

Due to his illness, he was released early from prison in November of 1939, less than two months after this author was born. He lived out the rest of his life, his brain pulped by paresis, on his Palm Island estate on Biscayne Bay in Florida. He died of a cerebral hemorrhage on January 25, 1947. Ironically, Capone died penniless.

Capone in retirement at Palm Island, Florida

After Capone was sent away, Eliot Ness spent time as a "revenooer," chasing moonshiners around the hills of Kentucky and Tennessee. Then he was offered a job in Cleveland to take on what was known as the Mayfield Road Mob. In many respects, what he accomplished in Cleveland was more noteworthy and brave than his Chicago crusade. His actions against a corrupt Cleveland police force resulted in the resignation of 200 police and police officials.

Eliot died from a heart attack shortly after approving the final proof galleys on his Untouchables book that was made into a television series by Desilu Studios.

Murray "the Camel" Humphreys was convicted at his trial for attempted murder but got off on a procedural error when the state Supreme Court reversed the decision. He went on to become one of the top men in the Capone syndicate after Big Al was sent to prison.

Jack "Machine Gun" McGurn was gunned down in a bowling alley at 805 North Milwaukee on February 14th, 1934, the anniversary of the St. Valentine's Day Massacre. A comic valentine was left near the body. Claude Maddox and Tony Accardo are thought to have been the shooters. Maddox was also known as John "Screwy" Moore.

Mike Kriegan married Ellen Esposito and they moved back to his hometown of East St. Louis. He went into the real estate business and did quite well for himself. They had four children – twin girls and two boys. The oldest was named Eliot and the other was christened John, honoring his Untouchables friend John Kaufman who was ruthlessly killed by the Capone mob.

MORE CRAZY QUOTES, INCREDIBLE TRIVIA AND AMAZING FACTS

What other nickname was attributed to Chicago besides Second City and Garden City? **A.** The "Gangster Capital of the World"

What phrase was used to describe the St. Valentine's Day Massacre? **A.** The "crime of the century"

How much were most daily newspapers in 1927? **A.** Three cents

Whose money personally financed the creation of the nation's first crime lab (run by Northwestern University) that introduced ballistics as a new tool for law enforcement? **A.** Affluent members of the Chicago Crime Commission

More gangster nicknames: Jimmy "the Swede" Morand, Anthony "Tough Tony" Capezio, Maurice "Mossy" Enright, Joe "Jew-Kid" Grabiner, Charles "Limpy" Cleaver, John "Mitters" Foley, Joe "Ragtime" Howard, Richard "Peg-Leg" Lonergan, Jimmy "Hot Stove" Quinn, James "Bozo" Shupe, Ray "Crane-Neck" Nugent, "Dapper Dan" McCarthy, Margaret "Kiss of Death" Collins, Ecola "the Eagle" Baldelli, John "Jew" Bates, "Dago Mike" Carrozzo, William "Shorty" Egan, Louis "the Farmer" Friedman, Julian "Potatoes" Kaufman, Hugh "Stubby" McGovern, James "Pluck" Mulcahey, Jimmy "Hot Stove" Quinn

What was the temperature in Chicago the day of the St. Valentine's Day Massacre? **A.** Eighteen degrees Fahrenheit – typical bone-chilling Chicago weather

Who accidentally ran into the Cadillac of the St. Valentine's Day assassins just minutes before they committed the foul deed? **A.** A delivery man named Elmer Lewis. The Cadillac's driver briefly looked at the dent in the car and waved him on, indicating that it was a minor repair job.

Who was the first person to discover the seven bodies at the massacre scene? **A.** Clair McAllister, a self-employed painter. He went there at the urging of Jeanette Landesman, a housewife who was ironing clothes when she heard the shots.

From what St. Louis gang did Capone recruit many of the men involved in the massacre? **A.** The Egan's Rats gang

What was the *Herald-Examiner's* lead sentence about the killings? **A.** "Chicago gangsters yesterday graduated from murder to massacre!"

Who did many newspapers prematurely blame for the shootings? **A.** Rogue cops

Why is New Yorker Frankie Yale the most likely suspect in Jim Colosimo's murder? **A.** He was in the murder-for-hire business and just happened to be "visiting" Chicago the day of the shooting.

Jack Zuta

What was Dean (Dion) O'Banion's favorite nickname for his Southside Italian rivals? **A.** Greaseballs

What kind of bullets were fired by a Thompson sub-machine gun? **A.** .45 caliber pistol bullets at a rate of eight hundred rounds a minute. Larger bullets that the manufacturer experimented with produced too much of a kick.

Ann Shivers of **Peotone**, Illinois, was one of three finalists in the 2004-05 Teen Jeopardy contest. Her third place finish earned her $18,000.

When was the Tommygun invented? **A.** In 1917 by John Thompson, a retired military ordinance officer

Who first brought the Thompson gun to Chicago? **A.** Dion O'Banion, born in **Maroa**, Illinois (near **Decatur**), brought three of the guns back to Chicago in 1924 after a trip to Colorado.

Why was Chicago's Little Sicily also known as "Little Hell?" **A.** The burn-off fires at the city's nearby gas works (next to the Chicago River) gave that area a reddish glow in the sky.

What was the big difference between Irish gangsters and Italian gangsters? **A.** Both were Catholic but Irish gangsters disdained wine and objected to prostitution, promiscuity and abortion. Italians generally had no objection to any of the aforementioned.

  Lonely Irish girls often went with Italian boys because Irish men usually married in their late twenties, preferring to establish themselves financially before committing to marriage.

What was a "peteman?" **A.** This was slang for a safecracker, one of Dion O'Banion's specialties. O'Banion often used nitroglycerine to blow the doors off safes. Rose Keefe in *Guns and Roses*, the definitive biography of O'Banion, describes the process thusly: "An air pump was used to scatter a wispy line of gunpowder around the door crack, placed the pump at the bottom and a funnel of powder at the top, and sealed the rest of the crack with putty. When applied, the pump sucked the air from the safe's interior, creating a vacuum that drew the powder inside. After being set off by a cap, the powder exploded, shaking the steel box open with a whoosh of acrid, eye-burning smoke."

Who was the first victim of a Tommygun killing? **A.** Charles Kelly, a member of the Ralph Sheldon gang, was gunned down on October 3, 1925, in front of the Ragen Athletic Club at 5142 South Halstead.

Why was James Murray serving time at Leavenworth in 1925? **A**. James, brother to Paddy Murray who was gunned down with Hymie Weiss in the famous "rented room ambush," was the mastermind of the great train robbery at **Roundout**, Illinois, some thirty miles north of Chicago. This was the **largest train robbery in U.S. history** with a take of nearly $3 million. An accidental shooting of Dock (Vincent D'Onofrio of *Law and Order* fame) led to the arrest of Murray and the Newton brothers of Texas, who had previously robbed some 80 banks.

The Newton boys generally robbed banks at night where there was less chance that someone might be killed. When vault makers switched over from rectangular doors to round Cannonball doors, blowing them open became much more difficult.

Willis Newton (Matthew McConaughey), the leader of this gang of four brothers, was taken to **Rockford** and kept in isolation until he made a deal with authorities to help them recover most of the money in exchange for relatively light sentences of about four years in prison.

The biggest mistake made in filming *The Newton Boys* 1998 movie was in a scene where Willis Newton tries to rationalize their robberies by claiming that farmers and ranchers weren't losing any money because it was all insured by the government. The FDIC – Federal Deposit Insurance Corporation - didn't come into existence until the New Deal during the 1930s.

"Chicago is unique. It's the only completely corrupt city in America." - Alderman Robert Merriam. When a reporter remarked that **East St. Louis** was equally corrupt, he replied, "Yes, but it isn't nearly so big."

Old 1920s saying – "This job will be easy. It's a **lead pipe cinch**!"

What was Jamaican Ginger? **A**. It was a concoction that contained enough wood alcohol to damage one's eyesight and affect the nervous system, producing a peculiar gait called "jake leg."

"Hooch hounds" – a nickname for federal prohibition agents

Why did Capone bring 5,000 turtles to Chicago? **A**. He thought racing turtles would provide gambling entertainment at nightclubs, cabarets and speak-easies. They proved to be largely unreliable and recalcitrant and were released into the city's ponds and lagoons.

"Bullet widow" – A woman whose gangster husband was slain by shots from a gun

Joe Saltis

"We only stole from the bankers what the bankers stole from the people." – John Dillinger

What was newly elected Mayor Anton Cermak's plan for eliminating the Capone gang? **A**. He offered suburban bootlegger Roger Touhy assistance from the Chicago police force (using quasi-legal measures) to put the Chicago syndicate out of business. Touhy turned him down.

What was Joe Zangara's motive for trying to kill President-elect Franklin D. Roosevelt in 1933? **A**. He claimed that voices in his aching stomach had ordered him to kill all kings and presidents. His shots missed, killing the Chicago mayor instead.

Midnight bullfight – After an evening of saloon-hopping, young sheiks of the Twenties era often drove their cars to the corner of Michigan Avenue and Randolph Street in Chicago. Then they would press the pedal all the way to the floor and speed down the sidewalk, yelling and screaming for pedestrians to get out of the way.

What astounding conclusion about the Mafia was made by FBI Chief, J. Edgar Hoover? **A**. He said that the Mafia was non-existent, and that it was made up by reporters to sell newspapers.

What term do natives of central and northern Illinois sometimes use to derisively describe Southern Illinois and its hayseed inhabitants? **A**. Appalachia

What hot entertainment spot in **Taylorville** is home to a constant parade of Country and Western singing stars? **A**. Nashville North

What is the **only building in Illinois with a phone booth on the roof**? **A**. No, it's not the *Planet* building in **Metropolis** for Superman's use. The phone booth is atop City Hall in **Lincoln**, Illinois, because that is the Midwest reporting site for the National Weather Service. (from **Heather Pounds** of **Taylorville** and the Central Illinois Tourism Office)

By the late 1920s **it was still legal** for a boat departing from Canada to declare that it was headed for an American port with a cargo of liquor.

Why was the O.P. Inn in **Melrose Park** notorious? **A**. It was a known hangout for gangsters of every stripe and sin. Its walls were decorated with autographed photos of hoodlums such as Dillinger and Pretty Boy Floyd.

What happened to the building at 2122 North Clark Street, site of the St. Valentine's Day Massacre? **A**. It was torn down in 1967 and is now merely a side lot next to a retirement home.

This author relied heavily on *The St. Valentine's Day*

Massacre by William Helmer and Arthur Bilek for the previous segments about that event.

Dutch uncle – a close friend of the family who seems like a relative

"Mac" – a generic term used as a substitute for a person's real name

Apple Pan Dowdy – Popular dessert in the 1920's. According to the song, it "Makes your eyes bug out and your tummy say howdy!"

Cub second baseman Rhyne Sandburg, stolen from the Phillies in a trade, was inducted into baseball's Hall of Fame in the summer of 2005.

The most famous stagecoach robber in history, **Black Bart**, once lived in **Decatur**, Illinois. Astoundingly, our state has claim to notable Wild West figures such as Joe Glidden (barbed wire), Ned Buntline (dime novel), Wyatt Earp, (gunfight at the OK Corral) Pawnee Bill, Jack Slade (notorious outlaw), Wild Bill Hickok and Bat Masterson.

Decatur, also known as Soy City (the Soybean Capital of the USA), claims the **oldest continuous municipal band in America**, and it was home to the company that made Hi Flyer kites from 1921-1981.

Plans are afoot in 2005 to build the largest skyscraper in the world in Chicago near the shore of Lake Michigan. Developers say it will be nearly a half-mile tall.

Famous Illinoisan – **Dave Butz** of **Belleville** was a defensive tackle in the NFL. After playing one year for the St. Louis Cardinals, they foolishly traded him to the Washington Redskins where he became a star and recorded 59 & 1/2 sacks from 1975-1988.

Christine Brewer – courtesy
Belleville News-Democrat

Western Electric of **Cicero**, Illinois, first began to manufacture "candlestick" telephones with a rotary dial in 1919. They were made of brass and required frequent polishing. When harried housewives complained, the company began painting them over with black lacquer.

Eliot Ness in the *Untouchables* program was always seen using a black phone. Restored phones of this type can be bought on E-bay for around $350.

What world class singer travels the globe for performances, but resides in **Lebanon**, Illinois? **A.** Christine Brewer

Fox Television in fall of 2005 launched a new dramatic series called *Prison Break*. It is the story of a man who has an innocent brother in prison on death row. He decides that

the only way to save his brother's life is to help him break out. The best way to do this, he figures, is to get himself incarcerated in the same prison.

In order to fully convey the harshness and stark reality of prison life, the producers decided to film the program at the old rock pile known as **Joliet Prison** which was abandoned as a correctional institution several years ago.

In the movie *The Pride of St. Louis*, starring Dan Dailey and Joanne Dru, former star Cardinal and **Cub** pitcher Dizzy Dean gets a job as an announcer for St. Louis baseball games. Lacking a formal education because he quit school to chop cotton after the third grade, Dean butchers the King's English. "He slud hard into second base" was a typical Deanism. A teacher at **East St. Louis High** spearheaded complaints that Dean was undermining efforts to teach English students proper grammar. Backed by the National Council of English Teachers, Dean gave in to pressure and announced his retirement at the end of a broadcast. Local fans were so downhearted that the teachers reconsidered their position and finally relented. The compromise: "Dean can continue teaching the youngsters about baseball and we'll teach them proper English."

MORE HIGH SCHOOL PREP NICKNAMES

Aledo – Green Dragons, Antioch Sequiots, Arcola Purple Riders, Astoria Rebels, Bunker Hill Minutemen, Bureau Valley Storm, Cairo Pilots, Century Centurians, Christopher Bearcats, Coal City Coalers, Cobden Appleknockers, Crystal Lake Gators, Darnall Maple Leafs, Dekalb Barbs, LaSalle Meteors, Dongola Demons, East Aurora Tomcats, Wood River Oilers, Elk Grove Grenadiers, Egyptian Pharaohs, Effingham Flaming Hearts, Evanston Wildkits, Fairfield Mules, Fenwick Friars, Fisher Bunnies, Franklin Flashes, Freeburg Midgets, Freeport Pretzels, Genoa-Kingston Cogs, Goreville Blackcats, Grayville Bison, Havana Ducks, Hoopeston Cornjerkers, Illiopolis Pirates, Joliet Steelmen, Julian Jaguars, Kankakee Kays, Knoxville Blue Bullets, Lake Forest Caxys, Lebanon Greyhounds, Lemont Injuns, Lincoln Railsplitters, Lockport Porters, Loyola Academy Ramblers, Marian Hurricanes, Marquette Explorers, Mattoon Green Wave, Monmouth Zippers, Monticello Sages, Morton Potters, Mt. Carmel Caravan, Normal Ironmen, Palestine Pioneers, Pittsfield Saukees, Plano Reapers, Polo Marcos, Red Bud Musketeers, Rochelle Hubs, Rockford East E-Rabs, Roxana Shells, St. Patrick Shamrocks, Schaumburg Saxons, Serena Huskers, Simeon Wolverines, South Beloit Sobos, South Shore Tars, Southwestern Piasa Birds, Streamwood Sabres, Taylorville Tornadoes, Union Yankees, Waldorf Thunder, Westmont Sentinels, Wethersfield Flying Geese, Young Dolphins. (Taken from *Why Mascots Have Tales* by Fred Willman.)

285

Promoter Tex Ricard's greatest nightmare by artist Steve Kamka